Lecture Notes in Artificial Intelligence 808

Subseries of Lecture Notes in Computer Science
Edited by J. G. Carbonell and J. Siekmann

Lecture Notes in Computer Science

Edited by G. Goos and J. Hartmanis

Michael Masuch   László Pólos (Eds.)

Knowledge Representation and Reasoning Under Uncertainty

Logic at Work

Springer-Verlag
Berlin Heidelberg New York
London Paris Tokyo
Hong Kong Barcelona
Budapest

Series Editors

Jaime G. Carbonell
School of Computer Science, Carnegie Mellon University
Schenley Park, Pittsburgh, PA 15213-3890, USA

Jörg Siekmann
University of Saarland
German Research Center for Artificial Intelligence (DFKI)
Stuhlsatzenhausweg 3, D-66123 Saarbrücken, Germany

Editors

Michael Masuch
László Pólos
Center for Computer Science in Organization and Management
University of Amsterdam
Oude Turfmarkt 151, 1012 GC Amsterdam, The Netherlands

CR Subject Classification (1991): I.2.3-4, F.4.1

ISBN 3-540-58095-6 Springer-Verlag Berlin Heidelberg New York
ISBN 0-387-58095-6 Springer-Verlag New York Berlin Heidelberg

CIP data applied for

Typesetting: Camera ready by author
SPIN: 10131227   45/3140-543210 - Printed on acid-free paper

Preface

"Twenty years ago, logic was mainly applied to mathematical and philosophical problems. Nowadays, the term applied logic has a far wider meaning as numerous applications of logical methods in computer science, formal linguistics and other fields testify. Such applications are by no means restricted to the use of known logical techniques: at its best applied logic involves a back-and- forth dialogue between logical theory and the problem domain. Ultimately, these applications may change the face of logic itself. A variety of non-standard logics (for example modal, temporal and intuitionistic logics, lambda calculi) have gained increased importance, and new systems (such as update semantics, dynamic logic, and various non-monotonic logics) have emerged in response to the new questions."

This was the key paragraph in the invitation for the international conference Logic at Work, organized jointly by the Center for Computer Science in Organization and Management (CCSOM) and the Institute of Logic, Language, and Computation (ILLC) and held at the University of Amsterdam, Dec. 17-19th, 1992. The conference attracted 86 submissions from all over the world, out of which the program committee (Patrick Blackburn, Jean-Jules Meyer, Frank Veltman, plus the editors of this volume) selected 30 papers with the help of anonymous referees. In addition, there were 8 invited speakers (e.g., Peter Gärdenfors, Yoav Shoham, and Petr Hájek). Out of these contributions, we selected 13 papers related to two core issues of formal AI for publication in a volume on knowledge representation and reasoning under uncertainty.

The Dutch National Science Foundation provided the funding for this workshop through a PIONIER-grant. Anja Krans maintained the day-to-day communication with the authors, and processed the text together with Breanndán Ó Nualláin. Henk Helmantel kept the computers up and running. Thanks are due, last but not least, to all participants of the conference, and in particular to the head of the local arrangements committee, the organizer extraordinary Michel Vrinten.

April 1994   Michael Masuch and László Pólos

Table of Contents

The Role of Expectations in Reasoning

Peter Gärdenfors

Lund University, Cognitive Science,
Kungshuset, Lundagard,
S-223 50 Lund, Sweden
E-mail: Peter.Gardenfors@fil.lu.se

Abstract. Logical theory traditionally assumes that (1) logical inference is a relation between sentences (or propositions), not between thoughts (or anything cognitive), and (2) the validity of an argument depends solely on the logical structure of the sentences involved and is independent of their meaning. In practical reasoning, however, these assumptions are not valid. In this paper I want to show that by taking expectations into account, one can achieve a much better understanding of how logic is put to work by humans. In particular, one obtains a very simple analysis of nonmonotonic reasoning. I will also discuss the cognitive origins of expectations.

Then a man said: Speak to us of Expectations. He then said: If a man does not see or hear the waters of the Jordan, then he should not taste the pomegranate or ply his wares in an open market. If a man would not labour in the salt and rock quarries, then he should not accept of the Earth that which he refuses to give of himself. Such a man would expect a pear of a peach tree. Such a man would expect a stone to lay an egg. Such a man would expect Sears to assemble a lawn mower.

Kehlog Albran, *The Profit*

1 Ubiquitous Expectations

We all have expectations. For example, you presumably expect a speaker at a scientific meeting to be standing properly on his feet while talking. You may also expect that he is not red in his face, although this expectation may be much weaker than the previous one.

Sometimes, however, our expectations are violated. If a speaker is standing on his hands while giving his presentation, you would, I venture, be surprised. But given this violation of your previous expectations, you would now expect him to be red in his face, even if you don't observe it. This example shows that we are able to reason and draw conclusions even when our primary expectations are gainsaid.

As a matter of fact, expectations are ubiquitous, although they are not often made explicit. You expect there to be a floor when you enter a room; you expect a door handle not to break when you press it; you expect your morning newspaper to arrive on time; and you don't expect Sears to assemble a lawn mower. The main thesis of this article is that expectations play a crucial role in everyday reasoning. In brief, we use them as supplementary premises when we make inferences. In particular, I will argue that much of *nonmonotonic logic* can be reduced to classical logic with the aid of an analysis of the expectations that are hidden in the arguments. I will also discuss the cognitive origins of expectations.

In classical logic, the role of expectations is eschewed. Why is this so? For an answer, we should first reconsider some of the philosophical and methodological assumptions that have governed the traditional approach to logic since Frege.

Classical assumption 1: Logical inference is a relation between sentences (or propositions), not thoughts (or anything else related to cognition).

According to the traditional view, logical arguments are described as a relation between a set Γ of premises and a conclusion C, in symbols $\Gamma \models C$. The premises and conclusions are expressed as sentences in some language, preferably a formal language.
What kind of relation is "$\models$"? Traditionally this is answered as follows:

Classical assumption 2: The validity of an argument is only dependent on the logical structure of the sentences in Γ and C and independent of their meaning, their truth or the context.

The inference relation $\models$ can be specified in two major ways: (1) proof-theoretically, by specifying the axioms and derivations rules that generate $\models$;[1] or (2) semantically, by formulating the truth conditions for the logical relation to hold. In either case, assumption 2 is valid.

However, expectations, as opposed to axioms or standard premises, are *defeasible*. If an expectation is in conflict with a premise, it yields. Consequently, expectations don't fit with the classical assumptions.

Hence expectations are suppressed in classical logic, but in practical reasoning they are not. Everyday arguments are full of hidden premises that need to be made explicit in order to make the argument logically valid. In each separate case, it may be possible to add the hidden assumptions to make the derivation comply with the classical assumptions. But nobody does this, because expectations are normally shared among speakers, and unless they are countervened, they serve as a common background for arguments.

If we want to describe a logical inference relation that better conforms with everyday reasoning, we need a notion of inference that is not constrained by the classical assumptions. But if these assumptions are abandoned, we must give an answer to the question: *what can be used as premises in an argument?* For classical logic, the answer is: only the set Γ. For practical reasoning the answer may be different. As I shall argue in Section 3, the answer to this question may help us understand much of what has been called nonmonotonic logic.

---

[1] Some of the axioms may be 'non-logical', which normally means that they are taken from a 'theory'.

2 Luria's Camels

Before turning to an analysis of the role of expectations in nonmonotonic reasoning, let me present an extreme case (extreme from the classical point of view that is) of handling premises. Consider the following dialogue taken from (Luria 1976: 112):

Subject: Nazir-Said, age twenty-seven, peasant from village of Shak-himardan, illiterate.

> The following syllogism is presented: **There are no camels in Germany. The city of B. is in Germany. Are there any camels there or not?**
> Subject repeats syllogism exactly.
> **So, are there camels in Germany?**[2]
> "I don't know, I've never seen German villages."
> *Refusal to infer.*
> The syllogism is repeated.
> "Probably there are camels there."
> **Repeat what I said.**
> "There are no camels in Germany, are there any camels in B. or not? So probably there are. If it's a large city, there should be camels there."
> *Syllogism breaks down, inference drawn apart from its conditions.*
> **But what do my words suggest?**
> "Probably there are. Since there are large cities, there should be camels."
> *Again a conclusion apart from the syllogism.*
> **But if there aren't any in all of Germany?**
> "If it's a large city, there will be Kazakhs or Kirghiz there."
> **But I'm saying that there are no camels in Germany, and this city is in Germany.**
> "If this village is in a large city, there is probably no room for camels.
> *Inference made apart from syllogism.*

On the basis of this and a number of similar interviews, Luria draws the conclusion that illiterate people are far inferior to literates when it comes to logical reasoning.[3]

I don't agree with his diagnosis. I believe that what is at stake here is exactly the issue of what is allowed as premises in an argument.

In contrast to Luria, my hypothesis is that the peasants that he is interviewing do not allow themselves to use anything as a premise for an argument unless it is part of their *personal experience*. So in the dialogue above, Nazir-Said *ignores* the information provided in the syllogism, since he has no direct

---

[2] Luria's text probably contains an error here. The question should have been "Are there any camels in B.?"
[3] Also cf. (Luria 1979)

4

knowledge of the matter ("I don't know, I've never seen German villages)".

In my opinion, the point becomes very clear in a dialogue like the following (Luria 1976: 108-109):

> The following syllogism is presented: **In the Far North, where there is snow, all bears are white. Novaya Zemlya is in the Far North and there is always snow there. What colors are the bears there?**
> "There are different sorts of bears."
> *Failure to infer from syllogism.*
> The syllogism is repeated.
> "I don't know: I have seen a black bear, I've never seen any others... Each locality has its own animals: if it's white, they will be white; if it's yellow, they will be yellow."
> *Appeals only to personal, graphic experience.*
> **But what kind of bears are there in Novaya Zemlya?**
> "We always speak only of what we see; we don't talk about what we haven't seen."
> *The same.*
> **But what do my words imply?** The syllogism is repeated.
> "Well, it's like this: our tsar isn't like yours, and yours isn't like ours. Your words can be answered only by someone who was there, and if a person wasn't there he can't say anything on the basis of your words."
> *The same.*
> **But on the basis of my words - in the North, where there is always snow, the bears are white, can you gather what kind of bears there are in Novaya Zemlya?**
> "If a man was sixty or eighty and had seen a white bear and had told about it, he could be believed, but I've never seen one and hence I can't say. That's my last word. Those who saw can tell, and those who didn't see can't say anything!" (At this point a young Uzbek volunteered, "From your words it means that bears there are white.")
> **Well, which of you is right?**
> "What the cock knows how to do, he does. What I know, I say, and nothing beyond that!"

The upshot is that Luria's evidence does not indicate that there is anything wrong with the logical abilities of the illiterate peasants. The main difference is that they don't take a statement provided by a stranger as something that can be used in reasoning; *only personal experience is allowed* (there seem to be strong moral feelings about this among the Uzbeks).

The illiterate Uzbeks violate the second classical assumption of traditional logic since the validity of an argument is extremely dependent on the personal experience of the person who presents the conclusion, to the extent that the explicit premises in Γ may be totally ignored. The notion of logical validity of illiterate Uzbeks is quite different from the classical one. This does, however, not mean that Luria's illiterate Uzbeks are illogical - it only means that they are reasoning by other rules.

Luria's interviews show that when people learn to read, they will learn to play a different logical game. My understanding, which does not completely fit with Luria's, is that literate individuals learn to see a text as an abstract entity, independent of a particular speaker and his practical experience or his motives for uttering the words spoken. They see a text as a symbolic structure. It is only in relation to such a symbolic structure that the classical assumptions make sense. For somebody who only hears spoken words, uttered by a particular person, it is much more difficult (and of little practical importance) to view the words as symbolic structures. In other words, literacy teaches us to separate abstract arguments from their practical context.

I have presented my analysis of Luria's interviews as an extreme case of deciding which premises may be used in a logical argument - the case when even the premises explicitly stated in Γ may be disregarded. Be this as it may, the point of the example is that one must be careful in specifying what counts as a premise for an argument when practical reasoning is concerned

3 Nonmonotonic Reasoning Based on Expectations

In some recent articles, David Makinson and I have argued that the areas of nonmonotonic logic and belief revision are very closely related (see: Makinson and Gärdenfors 1990, Gärdenfors 1990, Gärdenfors 1991a, and Gärdenfors and Makinson, to appear). In particular, we show in (Gärdenfors 1991a), and (Gärdenfors and Makinson, to appear) how various forms of nonmonotonic inferences can be given a unified treatment in terms of how *expectations* are used in reasoning. This section begins with a summary of our analysis, but also discusses some limitations of the assumptions employed there.

3.1 Motivation

When we try to infer whether C follows from Γ, the information we use for the inference does not only contain the premises in Γ, but also background information about what we *expect* in the given situation. For instance, if we know that someone is a Spanish woman, we anticipate her to be dark and temperamental. Such expectations can be expressed in different ways: by default assumptions, by statements about what is normal, or typical, etc. These expectations are not premises that have to be accepted, but they are *defeasible* in the sense that if the premises Γ are in conflict with some of the expectations, we don't use them when determining whether C follows from Γ.

I want to show that expectations are used basically in the same way as explicit premises in logical arguments; the difference is that the expectations are, in general, more defeasible than the premises.[4] Consequently, the expectations

---

[4] But cf. the examples from Luria above.

used in nonmonotonic inferences need no special notation, but they can be expressed in the same language as regular premises and conclusions. This is one side of the unified treatment of nonmonotonic reasoning. For simplicity I shall work with a standard propositional language L which will be assumed to be closed under applications of the *boolean connectives* ¬ (negation), ∧ (conjunction), ∨ (disjunction), and → (implication). I will use α, β, γ, etc. as variables over sentences in L. I will assume that the underlying logic includes *classical propositional logic* and that it is *compact*. Classical logical consequence will be denoted by $\models$, and the set of classical consequences of a set Γ will be denoted $Cn(\Gamma)$.

In this section and the following, all the different expectations will be formulated in L. In contrast to many other theories of nonmonotonic reasoning, there are thus no default rules or other additions to the basic language, such as modal operators, that will be used to express the defeasible forms of information. Another, non-propositional, way of handling expressions will be presented in Section 6.

The key idea behind nonmonotonic reasoning can be put informally as follows [5]:

α *nonmonotonically entails* β *iff* β *follows logically from* α *together with "as many as possible" of the set of our expectations as are compatible with* α.

In order to makes this more precise, we must, of course, specify what is meant by "as many as possible".[6] But before turning to technicalities, let me illustrate the gist of the analysis by a couple of examples. "α nonmonotonically entails β" will, as usual, be denoted $\alpha \mathrel{\vert\!\sim} \beta$.

As a first example, let the language L contain the following predicates:

Sx: x is a speaker at a conference
Hx: x is standing on his hands
Rx: x is red in the face

Assume that the set of expectations contains $Sb \to \neg Rb$ and $Sb \wedge Hb \to Rb$, for all individuals b. Assuming that the set of expectations is closed under logical consequences it also contains $Sb \to \neg Hb$ and, of course, the logical truth $Sb \wedge Hb \to Sb$. If we now learn that b is a speaker at a conference, that is Sb, this piece of information is consistent with the expectations and thus we can conclude that $Sb \mathrel{\vert\!\sim} \neg Rb$ according to the recipe above.

On the other hand, if we learn both that b is a speaker and, surprisingly enough, is standing on his hands, that is $Sb \wedge Hb$, then this information is

---

[5] I will restrict the analysis to the case where there are only finitely many premises which can be conjoined to a single α. However, as shown by (Freund et al. 1990), there is a canonical way of extending any such finitary relation to cover infinite sets of premises.

[6] This idea is related to the idea of 'minimal change' within the theory of belief revision (see: Gärdenfors 1988: 66-68).

inconsistent with the set of expectations and so we cannot use all expectations when determining which inferences can be drawn from $Sb \wedge Hb$. The most natural expedient is to give up the expectation $Sb \rightarrow \neg Rb$ and the consequence $Sb \rightarrow \neg Hb$. The contracted set of expectations which contains $Sb \wedge Hb \rightarrow Rb$ and its logical consequences, in a sense contains "as many as possible" of the sentences in the set of expectations that are compatible with $Sb \wedge Hb$. So, by the general rule above, we have $Sb \wedge Hb \mathrel{|\!\sim} Rb$. This shows that $\mathrel{|\!\sim}$ is indeed a nonmonotonic inference operation.

3.2 Expectation orderings

Expectations act as hidden assumptions. However, when evaluating their role in arguments, it is important to note that our expectations about the world do not all have the same strength. For example, we consider some rules to be almost universally valid, so that an exception to the rule would be extremely unexpected; other rules are better described as rules of thumb that we use for want of more precise information. An exception to the latter type of rule is not unexpected to the same degree as in the former case. In brief, our expectations are all defeasible, but they exhibit varying *degrees of defeasibility*.

In order to make these ideas more precise, I shall assume that there is an ordering of the sentences in L. '$\alpha \leq \beta$' should be interpreted as 'β is at least as expected as α' or 'α is at least as surprising as β'. '$\alpha < \beta$' will be written as an abbreviation for '*not* $\beta \leq \alpha$' and '$\alpha \approx \beta$' is an abbreviation for '$\alpha \leq \beta$ and $\beta \leq \alpha$'.

According to the key idea of this section, $\alpha \mathrel{|\!\sim} \beta$ means that β follows from α together with all the propositions that are 'sufficiently well' expected in the light of α. How well is 'sufficiently well'? A natural idea is to require that the added sentences be strictly more expected than $\neg \alpha$ in the ordering. This is the motivation for the following definition.

Definition 1. $\mathrel{|\!\sim}$ is an *expectation* inference relation iff there is an ordering $\leq$ satisfying $(E1) - (E3)$ such that the following condition holds:

$$(C \mathrel{|\!\sim}) \quad \alpha \mathrel{|\!\sim} \gamma \text{ iff } \gamma \in Cn(\{\alpha\} \cup \{\beta : \neg\alpha < \beta\})$$

To a large extent, the formal properties of the nonmonotonic inference relation defined in this way depends on the properties that are assumed to hold for the ordering $<$. (Gärdenfors and Makinson, to appear) assume that it satisfies the following postulates:

$(E1)$ If $\alpha \leq \beta$ and $\beta \leq \gamma$, then $\alpha \leq \gamma$		(*Transitivity*)
$(E2)$ If $\alpha \models \beta$, then $\alpha \leq \beta$		(*Dominance*)
$(E3)$ For any α and β, $\alpha \leq \alpha \wedge \beta$ or $\beta \leq \alpha \wedge \beta$		(*Conjunctiveness*)

The first postulate on the expectation ordering is very natural for an ordering relation. The second postulate says that a logically stronger sentence is always less expected. From this it follows that the relation $\leq$ is reflexive. The third constraint is crucial for the representation results proved in (Gärdenfors and Makinson, to appear), but presumably the one that is most open to query. It concerns the relation between the degree of expectation of a conjunction $\alpha \wedge \beta$ and the corresponding degrees of α and β.

Note that the three conditions imply *connectivity*: either $\alpha \leq \beta$ or $\beta \leq \alpha$. For by $(E3)$ and $(E2)$, either $\alpha \leq \alpha \wedge \beta \leq \beta$, or $\beta \leq \alpha \wedge \beta \leq \alpha$ and we conclude connectivity by $(E1)$. From $(E2)$ it also follows that $\alpha \wedge \beta \leq \alpha$ and $\alpha \wedge \beta \leq \beta$, so $(E3)$ entails that $\alpha \wedge \beta \approx \alpha$ or $\alpha \wedge \beta \approx \beta$. This means that we cannot interpret the degrees of expectation directly in terms of their *probabilities*, since $(E3)$ is violated by any probability measure. The word 'expectation' as it is used in this paper should hence not be confused with the notion of 'expected utility' in decision theory. 'Expected utility' has to do with expectations of the *values* of various outcomes, while the notion of expectation studied here concerns *beliefs* about the world. In my opinion, this use of 'expectation' comes much closer to the everyday use.

Recalling that by the three conditions on expectation orderings we have $\neg\alpha \leq \beta_i$ for all $i \leq n$ iff $\neg\alpha \leq \beta_1 \wedge \ldots \wedge \beta_n$, it is immediate, using the compactness of Cn, that $(C \mathrel{\vert\!\sim})$ is equivalent to:

$(C \mathrel{\vert\!\sim}')$ $\alpha \mathrel{\vert\!\sim} \gamma$ iff either $\alpha \models \gamma$ or there is a $\beta \in L$ with $\alpha \wedge \beta \models \gamma$ and $\neg\alpha < \beta$

This condition may be surprising. It says that γ follows from α if there are some expectations that are consistent with α which together with α *classically* entails γ. In other words: *Nonmonotonic logic is nothing but classical logic if relevant expectations are added as explicit premises!* I believe that this observation can remove a lot of the mystery surrounding nonmonotonic inferences. If the analysis presented here is correct, a lot of the paraphernalia of nonmonotonic logic will not be required anymore. Among other things, one needs no new notation for defaults[7], no special inference rules for nonmonotonic logics, and no particular model theory.

3.3   Weaker assumptions about expectations

(Gärdenfors and Makinson, to appear) prove that expectation inference relations, which are based on expectation orderings fulfilling $(E1) - (E3)$, satisfy a number of postulates for nonmonotonic inferences. One of the strongest postulates is the following:

Rational Monotony: If $\alpha \mathrel{\not\vert\!\sim} \neg\beta$ and $\alpha \mathrel{\vert\!\sim} \gamma$, then $\alpha \wedge \beta \mathrel{\vert\!\sim} \gamma$.

This postulate cannot be proved without assuming that the strong condition $(E3)$ holds for the expectation ordering. Conversely, in the completeness proof for expectation inference relations based on orderings fulfilling $(E1) - (E3)$, the proof that $(E3)$ is fulfilled makes essential use of Rational Monotony.

---

[7] Defaults will be analyzed in terms of expectations in the following section.

Like ($E3$), Rational Monotony is a strong postulate, the validity of which is sometimes challenged.[8] For example, (Ginsberg 1986) presents a counterexample to a corresponding principle for conditionals which can also be used against Rational Monotony. His example involves the following statements:

α: Verdi is not French.

β: Bizet is French.

γ: Satie is French.

δ: Bizet and Verdi and compatriots.

ε: Bizet and Satie are compatriots.

In the example, α, β, and γ are seen as background facts, that is, sentences that have a strong degree of expectation (and we may assume that they have roughly the same degree of expectation).

Now, let us first assume δ as a premise and consider the nonmonotonic consequences of this assumption. Since δ is inconsistent with the conjunction of α and β, at least one of these expectations must be given up. However, it is not certain that β is given up, and consequently one cannot conclude $\neg\varepsilon$ from δ, so that we have $\delta \not\hspace{-0.3em}\sim \neg\varepsilon$.

Furthermore, since δ and γ are independent statements, the addition of δ does not affect the validity of γ. Hence it is reasonable to suppose that $\delta \hspace{-0.3em}\sim \gamma$.

Next, let us start from $\delta \wedge \varepsilon$ as a premise, i.e., assume that all three composers are compatriots. In this inferential situation, at least one of the expectations α, β, or γ must be rejected. However, since they are assumed to be of equal strength, it might be that γ is rejected. Consequently, it does not hold that $\delta \wedge \varepsilon \hspace{-0.3em}\sim \gamma$.

Summing up, we have $\delta \hspace{-0.3em}\sim \gamma$ and $\delta \not\hspace{-0.3em}\sim \neg\varepsilon$, but not $\delta \wedge \varepsilon \hspace{-0.3em}\sim \gamma$, which gives us a counterexample to Rational Monotony, and, indirectly, a counterexample to ($E3$).

The intuitive validity of the Ginsberg's counterexample depends on the fact that δ and γ are *independent* statements. The notion of independence is difficult to formalize,[9] but in the present context it can at least be stated that independence entails absence of expectations in the sense that if δ and γ are independent, then $\delta \hspace{-0.3em}\sim \gamma$ if and only if $\hspace{-0.3em}\sim \gamma$ and $\gamma \hspace{-0.3em}\sim \delta$ if and only if $\hspace{-0.3em}\sim \delta$.

As noted above, it follows from ($E3$) that the expectation ordering is total. However, the notion of independence requires that some sentences not be comparable with regards to their degree of expectation. Since the validity of ($E3$) is tightly connected to the validity of Rational Monotony, this is then the cause of the violation of Rational Monotony in Ginsberg's example. For these reasons, it interesting to study weaker versions of ($E3$) that do not entail that the expectation ordering be total, but, say, only that it be a partial ordering. In particular, (Rott 1992) investigates the following two principles:

($E3 \uparrow$) If $\alpha < \beta$ and $\alpha < \gamma$, then $\alpha < \beta \wedge \gamma$

($E3 \downarrow$) If $\alpha \wedge \beta < \beta$, then $\alpha < \beta$

---

[8] For a defence, see (Lehmann and Magidor 1992).

[9] However, see (Gärdenfors 1978) for a general analysis and (Gärdenfors 1991b) for an application of this analysis to belief revision processes.

In connection with belief revision procedures, he is able to show some representation theorems involving these principles. Neither of his theorems utilizes the equivalence of Rational Monotony (i.e., the postulate K^*8 from (Gärdenfors, 1988)).[10] It remains an open question whether his results can be transferred to the context of nonmonotonic inferences.

4 Defaults as Expectations

One of the main motivations for studying nonmonotonic reasoning is that this kind of theory is necessary if we want to understand reasoning by *default assumptions*. In this section I want to show that an ordering of expectations contains enough information to express, in a very simple way, what we require with respect to default information.[11] The principal idea is that a default statement of the type 'F's are normally G's' can be expressed by saying that 'if something is an F, then it is less expected that it is non-G than that it is G'. This formulation is immediately representable in an expectation ordering by assuming that the relation $Fb \to \neg Gb < Fb \to Gb$ holds for all individuals b.

To illustrate the general idea of expressing defaults of the form 'F's are normally G's' as an expectation relation $Fb \to \neg Gb < Fb \to Gb$ for all individuals b, assume that all we know about b is that Fb. We want to decide the nonmonotonic consequences of this fact. It can be determined, via $(C \hspace{1pt}\vdash)$, that $Fb \hspace{1pt}\vdash Gb$. It can also be determined that $Fb \hspace{1pt}\not\vdash \neg Gb$. Further information about b, for example that Hb, will mean that we no longer need to check whether $Fb \to \neg Gb < Fb \to Gb$, but rather whether $Fb \wedge Hb \to \neg Gb < Fb \wedge Hb \to Gb$, which may give a different answer. This is exactly how we want a default rule to operate.

To give an analysis of a familiar example, the so-called Nixon diamond, suppose that L contains the following predicates:

Rx: x is a republican
Qx: x is a quaker
Px: x is pacifist

Assume that we have the default rules "republicans are normally not pacifists" and "quakers are normally pacifists." According to the rule given above, we express these defaults by a number of ordering relations of the form $Rb \to Pb < Rb \to \neg Pb$ and $Qb \to \neg Pb < Qb \to Pb$, respectively, for various individuals b.

From this we conclude, as above, that if all we know about McCarthy is that he is a republican, then we expect him to be a non-pacifist (and we don't expect him to be a quaker); and if all we know about Fox is that he is a quaker, then we expect him to be a pacifist (and don't expect him to be a republican).

---

[10] For a survey of some of the results concerning other principles for expectation orderings, also cf. (Gärdenfors and Rott, to appear).

[11] Cf. (Morreau 1992) for a related analysis of defaults.

Now, suppose that, contrary to our expectations, Nixon is a both a quaker and a republican, that is $Qa \wedge Ra$. What can be concluded concerning his pacifism?

If we know that $Qa \wedge Ra$, and we want to decide whether $\neg Pa$ or Pa follows nonmonotonically, then this can be determined via $(C \mathrel{|\!\sim})$ by looking for the strictly greater of $Qa \wedge Ra \rightarrow \neg Pa$ and $Qa \wedge Ra \rightarrow Pa$ in the expectation ordering. Three cases are possible:

(1) $Qa \wedge Ra \rightarrow \neg Pa < Qa \wedge Ra \rightarrow Pa$. In this case, we conclude that $Qa \wedge Ra \mathrel{|\!\sim} Pa$.

(2) $Qa \wedge Ra \rightarrow Pa < Qa \wedge Ra \rightarrow \neg Pa$. For similar reasons, we conclude that $Qa \wedge Ra \mathrel{|\!\sim} \neg Pa$.

(3) $Qa \wedge Ra \rightarrow Pa \approx Qa \wedge Ra \rightarrow \neg Pa$. In this case (or in the case when they are incomparable, if the ordering is not supposed to be total), then neither $Qa \wedge Ra \mathrel{|\!\sim} \neg Pa$, nor $Qa \wedge Ra \mathrel{|\!\sim} Pa$ will hold.

None of these three possibilities is ruled out by the two ordered pairs $Ra \rightarrow Pa < Ra \rightarrow \neg Pa$ and $Qa \rightarrow \neg Pa < Qa \rightarrow Pa$. The reason is that it follows from $(E2)$ that $Ra \rightarrow \neg Pa \leq Qa \wedge Ra \rightarrow \neg Pa$ and that $Qa \rightarrow Pa \leq Qa \wedge Ra \rightarrow Pa$. Consequently, the maximum of $Qa \wedge Ra \rightarrow \neg Pa$ and $Qa \wedge Ra \rightarrow Pa$ will be at least as high as each of $Ra \rightarrow \neg Pa$ and $Qa \rightarrow Pa$ in the expectation ordering. But on the other hand, the two comparisons do not suffice to determine which, if any, of $Qa \wedge Ra \rightarrow \neg Pa$ and $Qa \wedge Ra \rightarrow Pa$ is the greater. So, the information available does not permit us to conclude anything concerning $\neg Pa$ or Pa.

To sum up, the nonmonotonic consequences one can draw from the premise that $Qa \wedge Ra$ depends on which is chosen to be the maximal element of $Qa \wedge Ra \rightarrow \neg Pa$ and $Qa \wedge Ra \rightarrow Pa$ in the expectation ordering. The default relations $Ra \rightarrow Pa < Ra \rightarrow \neg Pa$ and $Qa \rightarrow \neg Pa < Qa$ are not sufficient to determine this choice.

5 "But"

We have expectations, but we are sometimes surprised. The choice of the word "but" instead of "and" in the previous sentence indicates that the information contained in the second half of the sentence *violates our expectations*. This, I want to argue, is the core meaning of "but".

In introductory courses in logic, one often uses the formalism of propositional logic to analyse the conjunctions of natural language. It is shown how words like "and", "or", "not", "if...then", "unless", "even if", etc. can be expressed in formulas. But "but" is seldomly given a proper analysis. At best it is said that it has the same logical meaning as "and". For any user of language, it should be obvious that this is false. Among linguists, it is commonplace that "but" expresses a violation of expectations.[12] However, they leave it at that, since they have no way of representing and analysing expectations.

Using the tools of the previous two sections, I want to propose the following:

(*C*But) *A sentence of the form "α but β" is acceptable in a context C if and only if α and β are both acceptable in C, and in C it holds that* $\alpha \mathrel{\vdash\!\!\!\sim} \neg\beta$.

I don't propose any truth conditions for "but", simply because I don't think there are any. As will be clear soon, the use of but is very context sensitive, so I believe the proper analysis of "but" should be in terms of the conditions under which a sentence is *accepted* in a given context. The context also determines what the current expectations are.

Let me apply the analysis to some examples:

(1) She is rich and ugly.
(2) She is rich but ugly.

The difference between the content of (1) and (2) is that in (2) the speaker presupposes that rich women are normally not ugly, while such an expectation is not indicated in (1). The use of "but" *signals* an expectation. However, which expectation is signalled is not determined by the sentence alone, but depends on the whole context.

The role of the context can sometimes be quite subtle. Compare the following two sentences from Robin Lakoff (1971: 133):

(3) John hates ice-cream but so do I.
(4) John hates ice-cream but I like it.

On a standard reading of (3), it carries the expectation that people normally like ice-cream. The "but" indicates no contrast between me and John, but a contrast between me and people in general. However, in a natural context where (4) is uttered, there is no expectation concerning how normal people like ice-cream. On the other hand, mentioning John's dislike for ice-cream creates an expectation, albeit a weak one, that I too should dislike it, and it is this "inductively generated" expectation that is denied by the "but". The same argument applies to another of Lakoff's examples:

(5) John is tall but Bill is short.

She calls examples like (4) and (5) instances of "semantic oppositions" and argues that it is one of the functions of "but" to express such oppositions (Lakoff 1971: 133). However, I find it more natural to view sentences (4) and (5) as a special kind of denial of expectations, which is the other meaning of "but" that Lakoff identifies and which is expressed more formally in my analysis above.

In this section, I have outlined an analysis of the meaning of "but" based on expectations. In addition to this application, I believe that a large part of

---

[12] For example (Lakoff 1971). She distinguishes (p. 133) between two main meanings of "but": (1) semantic opposition as in "John is tall but Bill is short"; and (2) denial of expectation as in "John is tall but he's no good at basketball". However, as I will argue later, the semantic opposition meaning is a special case of violated expectation.

the discussion within linguistics and philosophy concerning *presuppositions* of sentences can be given a more unified treatment in terms of the expectations of the speaker. However, such an analysis will not be attempted here.

6 How are Expectations to be Represented?

Expectations have, so far, been treated as primitive notions. But where do they come from? In this final section I will discuss the origins of expectations and alternative ways of modelling them.

In Section 3, expectations were modelled by expectation orderings which are orderings of propositions. An important epistemological question for the analysis presented in that section is how this ordering is determined. In Gärdenfors and Makinson (to appear) it is shown that it is possible to define an expectation ordering by using a nonmonotonic inference operation by the following equation:

$$(C \leq) \qquad \alpha \leq \beta \text{ iff either } \alpha \wedge \beta \in Cn(\vee) \text{ or } \neg(\alpha \wedge \beta) \not\hspace{-2pt}\vdash \alpha.$$

The case when $\alpha \wedge \beta \in Cn(\vee)$ is just the limiting case when $\alpha \wedge \beta$ is logically valid. The main case when $\neg(\alpha \wedge \beta) \not\hspace{-2pt}\vdash \alpha$ means basically that if $\alpha \wedge \beta$ is expected and we assume that $\neg(\alpha \wedge \beta)$, then α is no longer expected, which is the criterion for α being less expected than β.

In (Gärdenfors and Makinson, to appear), we prove in Theorem 3.3 that if $\vdash$ is any inference relation that satisfies the full set of postulates, including Rational Monotony, then the ordering $\leq$ defined by $(C \leq)$ is indeed an expectation ordering over L that satisfies $(E1) - (E3)$.

However, this results does not give a satisfactory solution to the problem of the origin of an expectation ordering – it is like putting the cart in front of the horse. The proposed definition is worthless from a methodological point of view since the nonmonotonic inferences are what is to be explained with the aid of expectations.

A more constructive answer is to view expectations as emerging from *learning processes*. In our roles as cognitive agents, we do not simply observe the world around us, but we also *generalize* in several ways, by discovering patterns and correlations, by forming concepts, etc. Generalizations breed expectations. Expectations are in this way accumulated by *inductive* methods rather than by deductive reasoning. In an evolutionary perspective, expectations can be regarded as a way of summarizing previous experiences in a cognitively economical way.

The analysis presented in Section 3 represents expectations by an ordering of *propositions*. However, if expectations are created by inductive methods, propositional representations of expectations need not be the most appropriate form. In (Gärdenfors, to appear a), I argue that there are three levels of inductive reasoning: *The symbolic, the conceptual, and the subconceptual.* On the symbolic level, inductive inferences are represented by propositions, while on the conceptual level observations and inductive processes are represented by *conceptual spaces* consisting of a number of quality dimensions. On the subconceptual level,

14

finally, observations are described in terms of the perceptual receptors of the mechanism (human, animal, or artifical), which perform the inductive generalizations. In contrast to traditional philosophy of science and AI approaches, I argue that the most important aspects of inductive processes are to be found on the conceptual and subconceptual levels. Consequently, the origins of expectations should be sought on these levels too.

A currently popular method of modelling processes on the subconceptual level is by using *neural networks*. When a neural network is trained, the weights of the connections between the neurons are changed according to some learning rule. The set of weights of a network obtained after the training period is thus an implicit representation of the "expectations" of the network.

In this context, it can be noted that (Balkenius and Gärdenfors 1991) show that by introducing an appropriate schema concept and exploiting the higher-level features of a "resonance function" in a neural network, it is possible to define a form of nonmonotonic inference relation. It is also established that this inference relation satisfies some of the most fundamental postulates for nonmonotonic logics. The upshot is that a large class of neural networks can be seen as performing nonmonotonic inferences based on the expectations of the network. The construction presented in (Balkenius and Gärdenfors 1991) is an example of how symbolic features can emerge from the subsymbolic level of a neural network.[13]

However, neural networks constitute only *one* way of modelling expectations. Apart from their role in logical reasoning, it seems to me that the notion of expectation is central to many cognitive processes. Hence, it is of great interest for cognitive science to investigate different models of expectations. With the exception of "expected utility", the concept does not seem to be much studied within cognitive psychology.[14]

One further exception is Dubois and Prade's (1991) work on the connections between expectation orderings and *possibility logic*, which points in a different direction. In conclusion, I would like to recommend that the notion of expectation be studied from a variety of approaches within cognitive science. There are numerous potential applications of such studies.

Acknowledgments

Research for this article has been supported by the Swedish Council for Research in the Humanities and Social Sciences. Earlier versions of this paper have been presented at the conference on *Logic at Work*, Amsterdam, December 17-19, 1992, and the *European Conference on Analytical Philosophy*, Aix-en-Provence, April 23-26, 1993. I wish to thank the participants at these meetings, in particular Dov Gabbay and Fiora Pirri, for helpful comments.

---

[13] For further discussion of of how logic emerges from the dynamics of information, see (Gärdenfors, to appear b).

[14] And expected utility has to do with expectations of *values*, not expectations about *knowledge* as studied in this paper.

References

Balkenius, C., and P. Gärdenfors: "Non-monotonic inferences in neural networks," in: J.A. Allen, R. Fikes, and E. Sandewall (eds), *Principles of Knowledge Representation and Reasoning: Proceedings of the Second International Conference KR'91*, (San Mateo, CA: Morgan Kaufmann), (1991) 32-39.

Dubois, D., and H. Prade: "Epistemic entrenchment and possibility logic," in: *Artificial Intelligence* 50, (1991) 223-239.

Freund, M., D. Lehmann and D. Makinson: "Canonical extensions to the infinite case of finitary nonmonotonic inference relations," in: G. Brewka and H. Freitag (eds), *Arbeitspapiere der GMD no. 443: Proceedings of the Workshop on Nonmonotonic Reasoning*, (1990) 133-138.

Gärdenfors, P.: "On the logic of relevance," in: *Synthese* 37, (1978) 351-367.

Gärdenfors, P.: *Knowledge in Flux: Modeling the Dynamics of Epistemic States.* Cambridge, MA: The MIT Press, Bradford Books, 1988.

Gärdenfors, P.: "Belief revision and non-monotonic logic: Two sides of the same coin?," in: L. Carlucci Aiello (ed.), *ECAI 90: Proceedings of the 9th European Conference on Artificial Intelligence.* London: Pitman Publishing (1990) 768-773.

Gärdenfors, P.: "Nonmonotonic inferences based on expectations: A preliminary report," in: J. A. Allen, R. Fikes, and E. Sandewall (eds), *Principles of Knowledge Representation and Reasoning: Proceedings of the Second International Conference.* San Mateo, CA: Morgan Kaufmann (1991a) 585- 590.

Gärdenfors, P.: "Belief revision and relevance," in: *PSA 1990*, Volume 2, (1991b) 349-365.

Gärdenfors, P.: "Three levels of inductive inference," in: *Proceedings of the 9th International Congress of Logic, Methodology, and Philosophy of Science.* Amsterdam: North-Holland, to appear a.

Gärdenfors, P.: "How logic emerges from the dynamics of information," in: J. van Eijck and A. Visser (eds), *Logic and the Flow of Information*, to appear b.

Gärdenfors, P., and D. Makinson: "Nonmonotonic inference based on expectation," in: *Artificial Intelligence*, to appear.

Gärdenfors, P., and H. Rott: "Belief revision," in: D. Gabbay (ed.), *Handbook of Logic in AI and Logic Programming, Volume IV: Epistemic and Temporal Reasoning*, Chapter 3.2. Oxford: Oxford University Press, to appear.

Ginsberg, M. L.: "Counterfactuals," in: *Artificial Intelligence* 30, (1986) 35-79.

Lakoff, R. , "If's, and's, and but's about conjunction," in: R. Cole and J. L. Morgan (eds), *Studies in Linguistic Semantics*, New York: Academic Press, Vol. 3, (1971) 114-149.

Lehmann, D., and M. Magidor: "What does a conditional knowledge base entail?", in: *Artificial Intelligence* 55, (1992) 1-60.

Luria, A.: *Cognitive Development: Its Cultural and Social Foundations.* Cambridge, MA: Harvard University Press, 1976.

Luria, A.: *The Making of Mind - A Personal Approach to Soviet Psychology.* Cambridge, MA: Harvard University Press, 1979.

Makinson, D., and P. Gärdenfors: "Relations between the logic of theory change and nonmonotonic logic," in: G. Brewka and H. Freitag (eds), *Arbeitspapiere der GMD no. 443: Proceedings of the Workshop on Nonmonotonic Reasoning.* (1990) 7-27. Also in: A. Fuhrmann and M. Morreau (eds), *The Logic of Theory Change.* Berlin: Springer-Verlag, Lecture Notes in Artificial Intelligence no. 465, (1991)185-205.

Morreau, M.: *Conditionals in Philosophy and Artificial Intelligence*, Ph. D. Dissertation, Universiteit van Amsterdam, 1992.

Rott, H.: "Preferential belief change using generalized epistemic entrenchment," *Journal of Logic, Language and Information* 1, (1992) 45-78.

On Logics of Approximate Reasoning

Petr Hájek

Institute of Computer Science
Academy of Sciences of the Czech Republic
182 07 Prague 8, Czech Republic
E-mail:hajek@uivt.cas.cz

Abstract. A logical analysis of reasoning under conditions of uncertainty and vagueness is presented, using many valued and modal logics and their generalizations. The emphasis is on the distinction between degrees of belief and degrees of truth. The paper is mainly a survey of the relevant results.

1 Introduction

Approximate reasoning is one of the most fascinating branches of AI, and it has generated an extensive literature. Its main notions are *uncertainty* and *vagueness*. They are themselves vague and used in various connotations. We shall associate the term uncertainty with *degree of belief* regarding a proposition (which itself is crisp and may be true or false); on the other hand, vagueness (fuzziness) is associated *degree of thruth* of a proposition (which may be fuzzy, i.e., admits non-extremal degrees of truth). We shall be careful not to mix uncertainty with unprovability of a proposition (given a theory) or with inconsistency (of a theory).

We shall argue that logical systems corresponding to fuziness are many-valued logics, whereas systems corresponding to uncertainty (i.e., degree of belief) are related to various generalizations of modal logics. Furthermore we shall show that presence of both fuzziness and uncertainty gives rise to many-valued modal logics. The point of distinction is whether or not the logical system in question should be *truth-functional* (extensional), i.e., whether the value of a formula is determined by the values of its components.

The study of approximate reasoning has various important aspects: logical aspects (syntax, semantics, deduction, completeness), algebraic aspects (various algebraic structures involved, their algebraic properties), and - last but not least - probabilistic aspects. Clearly, probability theory is a very prominent theory of uncertainty and the notion of uncertainty should be explicitly related to this theory; on the other hand, this should not mean that alternative groundings for the notion of uncertainty are impossible or forbidden.

Our aim is to isolate and survey logical calculi emerging in approximate reasoning, classify them, and state their main properties. The paper is organized as follows:

In Section 2 we introduce the basic distinction between truth-functional and non-truth-functional calculi accomodating vagueness and uncertainty. Section 3 is a digression or rule-based systems. Section 4 deals with many-valued calculi and fuzzy logics, Section 5 surveys basic facts on modal logics, Section 6 deals with calculi of beliefs, Section 7 discusses the combination of vagueness and uncertainty (many-valued modal logics), and Section 8 presents some conclusions and open problems. Thanks are due to the organizers of the meeting "Logic at work" for their kind invitation.

2 Basic Distinction

The distinction between *graded truth values* of fuzzy propositions and *degree of belief* of crisp propositions has been stressed by various authors (see e.g. (Dubois-Prade 1988, 1990, 1991), (Godo and Lopez de Mantaras, to appear)). Both truth degrees of fuzzy proposition and belief degrees of crisp propositions are coded by reals from the unit interval [0,1] (in most cases; we shall not discuss exceptions); but they are handled differently. Notorious examples (like "John is young") show that fuzzy propositions are often used in the way of qualitative speaking about quantities; mostly one deals with fuzzy propositions extensionally, i.e., discusses *how* to define the truth degree of p & $q, p \vee q, \neg p$ etc. from the truth degrees of p, q (not discussing the question whether this is meaningful, i.e., truth(p & q) is *any* function of $truth(p)$, $truth(q)$. Let us admit that extensionality (truth-functionality) of fuzzy logic is not obviously counter-intuitive. Taking the most common truth-table definitions for &, $\vee, \neg$ $(min, max, 1 - x)$, one should realize that it is not counterintuitive that p & $\neg p$ has a positive truth-value (namely $min(truth(p), 1 - truth(p)))$ if $0 < truth(p) < 1$ – one can be young (in some degree) and at the same time non-young (in some degree). Thus truth degrees in fuzzy logic behave as truth-values in many valued logic. Our claim is that fuzzy logic should be understood as many-valued logic *sui generis* and should be confronted with classical systems of many-valued logic. (This has been done by several authors, see Section 4.)

If, on the other hand, p is a crisp proposition (i.e., can be only true or false) then, whatever our belief in p is (denote it $belief(p)$), $belief(p$ & $\neg p)$ should be *zero*; we are *sure* that p & $\neg p$ is false, whether p is true or not. Now it is natural to assume that there are various possible situations (or possible worlds) and in each of them p is either true or false; $belief(p)$ is then understood as some measure (not necessarily probabilistic) of the set of all possible situations (worlds) in which p is true. This leads directly to some kind of modal logic with *Kripke semantics*, and clearly this modal logic is in general *not* extensional: $measure(p$ & $q)$ need not be a function of $measure(p)$, $measure(q)$, similarly for $p \vee q$. Our claim is that the logic of uncertainty, i.e., the logic of degrees of belief, is a (generalized) modal logic *sui generis* and should be confronted with classical systems of modal logic. (This has been done by various authors, see as well Section 6.)

Our last claim is that truth degrees should not be mistaken for degrees of belief and *vice versa*; still, it is possible to *combine* them; the natural home for this is *many-valued modal logic*. We shall discuss the details in Section 7.

3 Digression: Rule Based Systems

Let us first have a look at MYCIN-like rule-based systems (Shortliffe and Buchanan 1975), (Buchanan and Shortliffe 1984), (Duda et al. 1976)). They may be
called classical or old-fashioned; even if still in use, they no longer seem to
command theoretical interest. A rule base of such a system consists of *rules* of
the form $A \rightarrow S(w)$ where A (antecedent) is typically an elementary conjunction
of literals (e.g., p_1 & $\neg p_3$ & p_5), S (succedent) is a single literal (e.g.,
p_7) and w is weight of the rule (usually $\in [0, 1]$ or $\in [-1, 1]$). The system of
rules must be loop-free in the obvious sense; leaf propositions (not occuring
in any succedent) are *questions*. A *questionnaire* assigns to each question its
weight (answer - degree of belief). *Combining functions* are truth tables for
connectives, a function $CTR(a, w)$ computes the *contribution* of a rule with
weight w provided that the global weight a of its antecedent, and a binary
operation $\oplus$ that combines the contributions of rules; the *global weight* of a
proposition p is the $\oplus$-sum of contributions of all rules leading to p.

Weights of rules are usually understood as *conditional beliefs*, sometimes even
conditional probabilities; early criticism (Adams 1976, Johnson 1986) shows,
however, that the interpretation in terms of conditional probabilities cannot be
justified. A deeper and more detailed analysis was done by (Hájek and Valdes
1990, 1991), (Hájek 1988, 1989) (see also (Hájek et al. 1992: Chap. VI-VIII))
where an algebraic analysis (using the apparatus of ordered Abelian groups) is
applied and a method of guarded use of these systems is suggested. But this
method applies only to a particular subclass of rule based systems and guarantees only partial probabilistic soundness (using the apparatus of graphical
probabilistic models). The main starting point is the observation (made also by
others, e.g., Heckerman) that weights must not be identified with conditional
belief but must be computed from them.

So far so good: the analysis using ordered Abelian groups and graphical models (hopefully) deserves interest, but what *logic* is involved here? The answer is:
not much (except for highly interesting logical properties of ordered Abelian
groups and, furthermore, the particular case when only three values (yes, no,
unknown) are allowed.) Logically, these systems seem to be poorly motivated,
they are truth-functional but clearly deal only with uncertainty, not with fuzziness (and should not be mistaken for rule-based systems based on fuzzy logic,
see for example (Bonissone 1987). A more detailed analysis is to be found in the
book (Hájek et al. 1992).

4 Many-Valued Logics

This section provides a quick survey of some basic systems of many-valued logics.
We restrict ourselves to *many-valued propositional calculi*; thus our vocabulary
consists of propositional variables $p_1, p_2, \ldots$, parentheses and some connectives
(the choice of primitive connectives may vary from one system to another; but
implication and negation are usually present in most cases).

It is generally recognized that pioneering work in many-valued logic was done by Lukasiewicz, through his discussion of three-valued logics (with the third value meaning "possible"), cf. (Lukasiewicz 1970). It is much less known and recognized that Gödel investigated extremely interesting systems of many-valued logic in connection with intuitionistic logic (Gödel 1993). (Rosser and Turquette 1952) is a classical monograph; an excellent recent and very informative monograph is (Gottwald 1988). The literature on *fuzzy logic* (started by Zadeh) is immense; a very up to date survey is found in (Dubois and Prade 1991a). An older paper of great importance, is (Pavelka 1979).

Our interest here is in logic in narrow sense of formal systems. We are now reviewing some concrete systems.

Semantics of Lukasiewicz's calculi.
Connectives are $\to$ and $\neg$; the truth functions are as follows:
$$impl(x, y) = 1 \text{ if } x \leq y,$$
$$impl(x, y) = 1 - x + y \text{ otherwise},$$
$$neg(x) = 1 - x.$$
From these, two different conjunctions and two different disjunctions are defined. Systems differ depending on the truth values allowed. There are finite-valued systems L_n $(n = 2, 3, 4, \ldots)$ with the set of values $\{i/n \mid i = 0, 1, \ldots, (n-1)\}$; the countably infinite valued system L_ω has all rationals from [0,1] for its truth values and L_∞ has the whole continuum [0,1] of values.

Gödel's calculi.
Connectives are $\to, \neg, \&, \vee$; the semantics is:
$$impl(x, y) = 1 \text{ if } x \leq y,$$
$$impl(x, y) = y \text{ otherwise},$$
$$neg(0) = 1,$$
$$neg(x) = 0 \text{ otherwise};$$
$$conj(x, y) = min(x, y)$$
$$disj(x, y) = max(x, y).$$
The systems G_n, G_ω, G_∞ are defined analogously to the L-systems.

One should also mention an extensive literature on triangular norms and conorms as possible truth-function for conjunction and disjunction, and the induced truth-functions for implications. (Schweitzer and Sklar 1983) is a pioneering monograph on this subject; for detailed information see for example (Di Nola et al. 1989).

We now turn to matters of axiomatization. There are two main kinds of axiomatizations. The *first kind* concerns the axiomatization of 1-tautologies, i.e., of formulas having the value 1 under each evaluation of propositional variables. Some classical tautologies are 1-tautologies (under any of the discussed semantics), e.g., $(p \to p)$; but some are not, e.g. $p \vee \neg p$ in Gödel's semantics (note the relation to intuitionism!). The *second kind* of axiomatization deals with graded axioms and proofs; a graded proof is a sequence of pairs *(formula, truth-value)* satisfying some natural structural conditions; the existence of a graded proof with (A, α) as its conlusion means that A is provable (at least) to the degree α.

Gödel's calculi axiomatized.

(1-tautologies). The axioms of G_ω coincide with axioms of G_∞ and consist of the axioms of intuitionistic propositional logic (see for example (Kleene 1952)) plus the axiom of linearity:

$$(A \to B) \vee (B \to A).$$

The only deduction rule is *modus ponens*.

The axioms of G_n are those of G_ω plus a certain pigeon-hole axiom. These axiom systems are complete for 1-tautologies of the respective systems (cf. (Gottwald 1988)).

Lukasiewicz's calculi axiomatized.

L_3 was axiomatized by (Wajsberg 1931); the following is a complete axiomatization of 1-tautologies:

$$A \to (B \to A)$$

$$(A \to B) \to ((B \to C) \to (A \to C))$$

$$(\neg B \to \neg A) \to (A \to B)$$

$$((A \to \neg A) \to A) \to A$$

A similar complete axiomatization of 1-tautologies of L_ω (and of L_∞) was obtained by (Rose and Rosser 1958). Other Lukasiewicz systems have also axiomatizations of 1-tautologies, but they are more or less cumbersome. See (Gottwald 1988).

The system of Takeuti and Titani.

The system of Takeuti and Titani extends G_ω by Lukasiewicz's negation and some other connectives; it has about 50 axioms and provides a complete sequent calculus. The calculus is infinitary since it has an infinitary deduction rule

from all $A + \epsilon$ (ϵ dyadic) infer A

where $+$ is a new connective.

Calculi for graded truth: Pavelka's logic for L_ω, L_n.

L_ω and L_n are extended by names $\underline{\alpha}$ for each truth-value α. *Graded formulas* are pairs (A, α) where A is a formula and α is a truth-value. Among the logical axioms are

$(A, 1)$ for some natural A,

$(\underline{\alpha}, \alpha)$ for each α

There are *graded deduction rules*, such as a graded modus ponens:
from (A, α) and $(A \to B, \beta)$ infer $(B, \alpha \otimes \beta)$ where $\otimes$ is an appropriate function.

Each fuzzy set of formulas (i.e., mapping of the set of all formulas into truth-values) is a *fuzzy set of special axioms*; the definition of a graded proof from a fuzzy set F of special axioms is obvious. The accompanying *completeness theorem* says that the supremum of degrees of proof of A from F equals the infimum of values of A in evaluations V of formulas such that $F \subseteq V$, i.e., for each C, $F(C) \leq V(C)$.

Remarks

- The completeness proof makes heavy use of the fact that *impl* is continuous.

- We mention in passing (Mukaidono 1982), a paper dealing with fuzzy resolution.

- To claim that fuzzy logic should be understood primarily as many-valued logic, one has to analyze thesubstantiate literature on fuzzy logic from the many-valued point of view. This remains a task for the future.

5   Modal Logics

Modal logic became a part of mathematical logic through the advent of an adequeate formal semantics, namely the Kripke models. Basic systems deal with formulas built from propositional variables, logical connectives and the modality $\Box$ (the corresponding formation rule reads: if A is a formula then $\Box A$ is a formula). $\Box A$ is read "necessarily A"; the dual modality $\Diamond$ ("possibly") is defined as $\neg \Box \neg$. Other modalities are not excluded. In a general setting, a Kripke model is a triple $K = \langle W, \Vdash, S \rangle$, where W is a non-empty set of possible worlds, $\Vdash$ is a function assigning to each atomic formula P and each world w either 0 or 1 (truth evaluation) and S is some structure on W. In the classical systems, S is just a binary relation R on W, i.e., $R \subseteq W \times W$. Then $\Vdash$ extends to all formulas as follows (one writes $w \Vdash A$ for $\Vdash(A, w) = 1$):

$w \Vdash A \ \& \ B$ iff $w \Vdash A$ and $w \Vdash B$,

$w \Vdash \neg A$ iff not $w \Vdash A$,

$w \Vdash \Box A$ iff, for each v, such that wRv, $v \Vdash A$.

(Thus: "necessarily A" is true in w iff A is true in all worlds accessible from A)

The beauty of modal logic is based on the fact that simple assumptions on the properties of the accessibility relation R correspond to simple, complete axiom systems. We mention three examples:

Example 1. R is an equivalence relation (reflexive, symmetric, transitive). The corresponding axiom system is (S5). The axioms are

(0)   *propositional tautologies*,

(1) $\Box(A \rightarrow B) \rightarrow (\Box A \rightarrow \Box B)$,

(2) $\Box A \rightarrow \Box\Box A$,

(3) $\Box A \rightarrow A$,

(4) $\Diamond A \rightarrow \Box\Diamond A$.

Deduction rules are modus ponens and necessitation: "from A infer $\Box A$". (S5) is sound and complete with respect to all (finite) Kripke models whose accessibility relation is an equivalence relation. This means: (S5) proves A if and only if A is true in each world of each model $\langle K, \|\!\!-, R \rangle$ where R is an equivalence relation. (For a readable presentation see for example (Hughess and Cresswell 1968).)

Example 2. Provability logic (L). We have the axioms: (0), (1), (2) and Löb's axiom:

(5) $\Box(\Box A \rightarrow A) \rightarrow \Box A$.

This logic is sound and complete with respect to all finite Kripke models $K = \langle W, \|\!\!-, R \rangle$ such that R is a strict partial order of W with a unique root, so predecessors of each element are linearly ordered. Besides, (L) has a completely different completeness theorem, relating it to first-order arithmetic. We only sketch the result. Let PA be Peano arithmetic. An *arithmetical interpretation* of (L) is a mapping associating to each formula B of L a closed formula B^* of PA such that, for each C, D, $(C \,\&\, D)^*$ is $C^* \,\&\, D^*$, $(\neg C)^*$ is $\neg(C^*)$, $(\Box C)^*$ is $Pr(\overline{C^*})$ where Pr is the formalized provability predicate and $\overline{C^*}$ is the formal name of C^* (numeral expressing the Gödel number of C^*). Solovay's completeness theorem says that a formula A is provable in (L) iff for each arithmetical interpretation $*$, PA proves A^*. See (Smoryński 1985) for the details. (Note that arithmetically, Löb's axiom is a formulation of the celebrated Second Gödel's incompleteness theorem.)

Example 3. Tense logics: R is a strict order. We present an axiom system that is sound and complete for finite models $\langle W, \|\!\!-, R \rangle$ where R is a strict linear order of W. It is just the extension of (L) that results from adding the following axiom of linearity:

$$(\Diamond A \,\&\, \Diamond B) \rightarrow (\Diamond(A \,\&\, B) \vee \Diamond(A \,\&\, \Diamond B) \vee \Diamond(\Diamond A \,\&\, B)).$$

It this logic, $\Box A$ is to be read "always in the future", $\Diamond A$ "sometimes in the future"; thus the last axiom says "if both A and B will hold sometimes in the future, then either $A \,\&\, B$ will hold sometimes in the future or (sometimes in the future, A will hold and sometimes later B will hold) or conversely (B will hold, and sometimes later, A will hold)". The reader is assumed to agree that the fact that things seemingly so different as arithmetical provability and logic of future tense happen to be well related is an illustration of the beauty of modal logic. For treatment of tense logics see (Gabbay 1972), (Burghess 1984), and (Van Benthem 1991).

6 Uncertainty and Modal Logic

We shall now relate modal logic to uncertainty understood as degree of belief. To this end we shall assume Kripke models of the form $K = \langle W, \|\!\!-, S \rangle$, where S is (or defines) a measure defined for sets of worlds. To simplify the matter, we shall assume the set W of worlds to be finite and the measure to be defined for all subsets of W. On the other hand, we shall not necessarily assume a probabilistic measure. The degree of belief into A will be identified with the measure of the set $\{w \mid w \,\|{-}A\}$ of all worlds satisfying A. We shall consider three particular cases.

(1) $K = \langle W, \|{-}, P \rangle$ where P is a probability on W, i.e.,

$$P : W \to [0,1], \sum_{x \in W} P(x) = 1.$$

For $X \subseteq W$, $P(X) = \sum_{x \in X} P(x)$. This leads to *possibilistic logic*, cf. (Nilsson 1986).

(2) $K = \langle W, \|{-}, \pi \rangle$ where π is a possibility on W, i.e., $\pi : W \to [0,1]$, $max_{x \in W}\, \pi(x) = 1$.

For $X \subseteq W$, the possibility $\Pi(X) = max_{x \in X}\, \pi(x)$. This leads to *possibilistic logic*. Possibility has a dual notion – necessity: $N(X) = 1 - \Pi(W - X)$. (cf. Dubois and Prade 1988, 1990, 1991).

(3) $K = \langle W, \|{-}, m \rangle$ where m is a *basic belief assignment*, i.e., m maps the power set $P(W)$ into $[0,1]$ and $\sum_{X \subseteq W} m(X) = 1$. m is *regular* if $m(\emptyset) = 0$. The belief of X, $bel(X)$ is defined thus: $bel(X) = \sum_{Y \subseteq X} m(Y)$. Alternatively, one can define $bel'(X) = \sum_{\emptyset \neq Y \subseteq X} m(Y)$. These definitions coincide for regular assignments. This leads to the *Dempster-Shafer theory* and the logic of belief functions. See for example (Shafer 1976), (Smets et al. 1988), (Hájek and Harmanec 1992). The dual notion is plausibility, $pl(X) = 1 - bel(W - X)$.

It is known and easy to show that both probabilistic and possibilic models are particular cases of belief models; probabilistic models are in one-one correspondence with belief models such that the assignment $m(X)$ is positive only if X is singleton. And possibilistic models $\langle W, \|{-}, \pi \rangle$ have a one to one correspondence with belief models $\langle W, \|{-}, m \rangle$ such that the focal elements of m (i.e., sets X such that $m(X) \neq 0$) are nested, i.e., linearly ordered by inclusion. The correspondence is such that possibilities coincide with plausibilities given by nested belief models.

There is another very pleasing correspondence, described in (Ruspini 1986) and (Resconi et al., submitted). Consider (finite) Kripke models $\langle W, \|{-}, R, P \rangle$ where R is a reflexive binary relation on W and P is a probability on W. Use $\Box$ to define necessity and put $bel(A) = P(\Box A)$ (i.e., $P(\{w \mid w \,\|{-}\Box A\})$). Then bel is a regular belief function; each regular belief function is obtained from a Kripke model as above where R can be taken to be an equivalence. In other words, regular belief functions are in a one to one correspondence with probabilistic models of (S5).

As a last alternative, we would like to mention another suggestion by (Ruspini 1991): a *Ruspini model* has the form $\langle W, \Vdash, S \rangle$ where S is a fuzzy binary *similarity relation* on W, i.e., a mapping $S : W \times W \to [0,1]$ satisfying some natural assumptions. Using S, Ruspini defines possibility distributions generalizing (2). For a detailed comparison of his approach with that of Dubois and Prade see (Esteva et al. 1993).

We now move to specific modalities capturing uncertainty.

First, we introduce unary modalities: take an $\alpha \in [0,1]$ and define, for any model $K = \langle W, \Vdash, measure \rangle$, $K \Vdash \square_\alpha A$ iff $measure(A) \geq \alpha$. (reed $\square_\alpha A$ as "A is α -strongly believed". This is a well-behaved modality. Note that it was studied, for probabilistic measures and unary predicate logic in (Hájek and Havránek 1978) and (Hájek 1981). Other authors investigated other measures; notably, (Dubois and Prade 1990) investigated the resolution logic, based on the deduction rule

$$\frac{\square_\alpha(A \vee B), \square_\alpha(\neg B \vee C)}{\square_\alpha(A \vee C)}$$

which is sound for necessity measures.

Second, we turn to binary modalities of *belief comparison*. Introduce a binary modality $\vartriangleleft$ and read a formula $A \vartriangleleft B$ as "B is at least as believed (probable, possible) as A". Formulas are built from propositional variables, connectives and the modality $\vartriangleleft$; in particular we have the formation rule if A, B are formulas then $A \vartriangleleft B$ is also a formula. This means that nested occurrences of $\vartriangleleft$ (e.g., $A \vartriangleleft (A \vartriangleleft B)$ are allowed. (Fariñas and Herzig 1991) introduced an axiom system QPL (qualitative possibilistic logic) which is sound for possibilistic models (i.e., models of the form $K = \langle W, \Vdash, \pi \rangle$ where π is a possibility distribution as above; $K \Vdash A \vartriangleleft B$ iff $\Pi(A) \leq \Pi(B)$). Their *axioms* are as follows:

(1) *tautologies*,
(2) $((A \vartriangleleft B) \text{ and } (B \vartriangleleft C)) \to (A \vartriangleleft C)$ *(transitivity)*
(3) $(A \vartriangleleft B) \vee (B \vartriangleleft A)$ *(linearity)*
(4) $\neg(true \vartriangleleft false)$
(5) $(false \vartriangleleft true)$
(6) $(A \vartriangleleft B) \to ((A \vee C) \vartriangleleft (B \vee C))$ *(monotonicity*

The *deduction rules* are modus ponens and a specific necessitation rule: from $A \to B$ infer $A \vartriangleleft B$. (Boutilier 1992) investigated QPL and related it to a system of tense logic with two unary modalities. Herzig showed (personal communication) that QPL$^+$ is axiomatized by QPL plus the axiom $(A \vartriangleleft B) \to \square(A \vartriangleleft B)$, where $\square C$ is $(\neg C) \vartriangleleft false$. (Bendová and Hájek 1993) showed that QPL is incomplete, presented its complete extension (by a slightly cumbersome axiom) and showed that the complete logic QPL* has a faithful interpretation in a tense logic with finite linearly preordered time (FLPOT); completeness of FLPOT was also proved. FLPOT has three basic necessity modalities G, H, I, meaning "in all future worlds, in all past worlds, in all present worlds". In FLPOT, $A \vartriangleleft B$ is interpreted as saying "in all worlds (past, present and future), if A holds then in some present or future world, B holds", in symbols: $\square(A \to (JB \vee FB))$

where $\Box C$ is HC & IC & GC, JC is $\neg I \neg C$, FC is $\neg G \neg C$. For details see (Bendová and Hájek 1993); the result is that QPL^+ is complete and can be understood as a sublogic of a certain tense logic, namely FLPOT with finite linearly preordered time.

A recent result of Hájek (paper in preparation) relates a variant of qualitative possibilistic logic to the *interpretability logic* developed and studied in connection with metamathematics of first-order arithmetic (see (Visser 1990) for a survey on interpretability logic).

These results show that qualitative possibilistic logics are well-behaved and closely related to established modal logics.

7 Vagueness and Uncertainty: Many Valued Modal Logics

We have observed that dealing with both vagueness and uncertainty naturally leads to many-valued modal logics. Such systems have been thoroughly investigated in the literature only quite recently; (Fitting 1992a, 1992b) are pioneering papers. Fitting's Kripke models are of the form $K = \langle W, \Vdash, S \rangle$ where $\Vdash$ maps $Atoms \times W$ into $Values$ and S is a binary fuzzy relation on W (i.e., maps $W \times W$ into $Values$). This is related to Ruspini's similarity structures mentioned above. Fitting constructs a (Gentzen style) sequent calculus and proves its completeness (with respect to 1-tautologies).

One can consider many-valued possibilistic models $K = \langle W, \Vdash, S \rangle$ where $\Vdash$ is as above and S is a fuzzy subset of W, i.e., a possibility distribution. (Hájek and Harmancová 1993) investigate a logic with a binary modality $\triangleleft$ meaning *comparison of fuzzy truth values*: for each $i \in Values$, put $\tau_A(i) = \Pi(\{w \mid \parallel A \parallel_w \geq i\})$ (possibility of A having the value of at least i); then τ_A is a fuzzy truth value (fuzzy subset of $Values$) and we define $K \Vdash A \triangleleft B$ iff $(\forall i)(\tau_A(i) \leq \tau_B(i))$. This modality behaves reasonably and is related, in (Hájek and Harmancová 1993), to a many valued temporal logic with linearly preordered time. Further systems of qualitative fuzzy possibilistic logic are conceivable (and of cause, qualitative fuzzy probabilistic or Dempster-Shafer logic); this is a task for future research.

8 Conclusion

We have tried to show that the proper logical home for logics of approximate reasoning is many-valued modal logic; better, the family of various many-valued modal logics. Many-valuedness relates to fuzziness; fuzziness is (mostly, and correctly) extensional (truth-functional). Uncertainty as degree of belief (probability, possibility, Dempster-Shafer belief function) relates to modalities, possible worlds and structures on possible worlds. Various logical systems have been investigated, showed to be complete for suitable semantics, and related to established logical systems, e.g., of tense logic. As a consequence, that this direction of research appears promising: several other logics of approximate reasoning can be defined and investigated, in particular, probabilistic and Dempster-Shafer logics, crisp or fuzzy. This being done, one should try to synthetize and isolate the most important systems. The goal is to get a unified logical approach to approximate reasoning.

References

Adams, J.B.: "A Probability Model of Medical Reasoning and the MYCIN Model," in: *Mathematical Biosciences*, Vol.32 (1976) 177-186.

Bendová, K., and P. Hájek: "Possibilistic logic as tense logic," in: Piera Carreté, N. et al. (eds.), *Qualitative Reasoning and Decision Technologies*, CIMNE Barcelona: Proceedings QUARDET'93 (1993) 441-450.

Bonissone, P.P.: "Summarizing and Propagating Uncertain Information with Triangular Norms," *International Journal Approximate Reasoning* 1 (1987) 71-101.

Boutilier, C.: "Modal logics for qualitative possibility and beliefs," in: Dubois, D. et al. (eds.), *Uncertainty in Artificial Intelligence* VIII, San Mateo, CA: Morgan-Kaufmann Publishers (1992) 17-24.

Buchanan, B.G., and E.H. Shortliffe: "Rule Based Expert Systems," in: *MYCIN Experiments of the Stanford Heuristic Programming Project*, Reading, MA: Addison-Wesley Pub.Comp. (1984) 739.

Burghess, J.P.: "Basic tense logics," in: Gabbay, D. and F. Guenthner (eds.), *Handbook of Philosophical Logic*, Vol.II. Reidel, 1984.

Di Nola, A., S. Sessa, W. Pedrycz, and E. Sanchez: *Fuzzy Relation Equations and Their Applications to Knowledge Engineering*. Dordrecht: Kluwer Academic Publishers, 1989.

Dubois, D., and H. Prade: "An Introduction to Possibilistic and Fuzzy Logics," in: Smets et al., *Non-Standard Logics for Automated Reasoning*. London: Academic Press (1988), p.287-326.

Dubois, D., and H. Prade: "Resolution Principles in Possibilistic Logic," in: *International Journal of Approximate Reasoning*, Vol.4. No.1 (1990) 1-21.

Dubois, D., and H. Prade: "Fuzzy sets in approximate reasoning, Part 1: Inference with possibility distribution," *Fuzzy Sets and Systems*, No.40 (1991a) 143-202.

Dubois, D., and H. Prade: "Fuzzy sets in approximate reasoning, Part 2: Logical approaches," in: *Fuzzy Sets and Systems*, No.40 (1991b) 203-244.

Duda, R.O., P.E. Hart, and N.J. Nilsson: "Subjective Bayesian Methods for Rule-Based Inference Systems," in: *Proceedings Nat. Comp .Conf.*, AFIPS, (1976) 1075-1082.

Esteva, F., P. García, and L. Godo: "On the relationship between preference and similarity based approaches to possibilistic reasoning," in: *Proceedings FUZZ-IEEE'93*, 1993.

Fariñas del Cerro, L., and A. Herzig: "A modal analysis of possibilistic logic," in: Kruse et al. (eds.), *Symbolic and Quantitative Approaches to Uncertainty*. LNCS 548, Springer-Verlag (1991) 58 ff. Also in: Jorrand and Kelemen (eds.), *Fundamentals of AI research*, Lecture Notes in AI 535, Springer-Verlag (1991) 11 ff.

Fitting M.: "Many-valued modal logics I," in: *Fundamenta Informaticae* 15 (1992a) 235-254.

Fitting, M.: "Many-valued modal logics II," in: *Fundamenta Informaticae* 17 (1992) 55-73.

Gabbay, D.M.: "Tense logics with discrete moments of time I," in: *Journal of Philosophical Logic* 1 (1972) 35 ff.

Gödel, K.: Zum intuitionistischen Aussugenkalkül, Ergebnisse eines Math. Colloquium 4 (1993) 40 ff. (see also Gödel's collected works Vol.1)

Godo L., and R. Lopez de Mantaras: "Fuzzy logic," in: *Encyclopedia of Computer Science*, to appear.

Gottwald, S.: *Mehrwertige Logik.* Berlin: Akademie-Verlag, 1988.

Hájek, P.: "Decision Problems of Some Statistically Motivated Monadic Modal Calculi," in: *International Journal Man-Machine Studies*, Vol.15 (1981) 351-358.

Hájek, P.: "Towards a Probabilistic Analysis of MYCIN-like Expert Systems," in: *COMPSTAT'88 Copenhagen.* Heidelberg: Physica-Verlag, 1988.

Hájek, P.: "Towards a probabilistic analysis of MYCIN-like Systems II," in: Plander (ed.), *Artificial Intelligence and Information-Control Systems of Robots.* Amsterdam: North Holland, 1989.

Hájek, P., and D. Harmancová: "A comparative fuzzy modal logic," in: Klement, Slany (eds.), *Fuzzy Logic in Artificial Intelligence.* Lecture Notes in AI 695, Springer-Verlag (1993) 27-34.

Hájek, P., and D. Harmanec: "An exercise in Dempster-Shafer theory," in: *International Journal General Systems* 20 (1992) 137-140.

Hájek, P., and T. Havránek: *Mechanizing Hypothesis Formation: Mathematical foundations for a general theory.* Berlin, Heidelberg: Springer-Verlag (1978) 396.

Hájek, P., T. Havránek, and R. Jirousek: *Uncertain Information Processing in Expert Systems.* Boca Raton: CRC Press (1992) 285.

Hájek, P., and J. Valdes: "Algebraic Foundations of Uncertainty Processing in Rule-based Expert Systems (group-theoretical approach)," in: *Computers and Artificial Intelligence* Vol.9 (1990) 325-344.

Hájek, P., and J. Valdes: "Generalized Algebraic Foundations of Uncertainty Processing in Rule-based Expert Systems (dempsteroids)," in: *Computers and Artificial Intelligence* Vol.10 (1991) 29-42.

Hughess, C.E., and M.J. Cresswell: *An Introduction to Modal Logic.* London: Methuen, 1968.

Johnson, R.W.: "Independence and Bayesian Updating Methods," in: *Uncertainty in AI*, Amsterdam: North Holland (1986) 197.

Kleene, S.C.: *Introduction to Metamathematics.* Amsterdam: North Holland, 1952.

Lukasiewicz, J.: *Selected Works.* Amsterdam: North Holland, 1970.

Mukaidono, M.:" Fuzzy inference in resolution style," in: Yager (ed.), *Fuzzy sets and possibility theory-recent developments.* Peyamon Press (1982) 224-231.

Nilsson, N.J.: "Probabilistic logic," in: *Artificial Intelligence* 28 (1986) 71-87.

Pavelka, J.: "On fuzzy logic I - Many valued rules of inference," in: *Zeitschr. f. Math. Logic und Grundlagen d. Math.* 25 (1979a) 45-52.

Pavelka, J.: "On fuzzy logic II - Enriched residuated lattices and semantics of propositional calculi," in: *Zeitschrift f. Math. Logik und Grundlagen d. Math.* 25 (1979b) 119-134.

Pavelka, J.: "On fuzzy logic III - Semantical completeness of some many-valued propositional calculi," in: *Zeitschrift f. Math. Logic und Grundlagen d. Math.* 25 (1979c) 446-464.

Resconi, G., G.J. Klir, U. St.Clair, and D. Harmanec: "On the integration of uncertainty theories," in: *International J. of Uncertainty, Fuzziness, and Knowledge-Based Systems* 1, 1993.

Resconi, G., G.J. Klir, and U. St.Clair: "Hierarchical uncertainty metatheory based upon modal logic," in: *Int. J. General Systems* 21 (1992) 23-50.

Rose, A., and J.B. Rosser: "Fragments of many-valued statement calculi," in: *Trans. Amer. Math. Soc.* 87 (1958) 1-53.

Rosser, J.B., and A.R. Turquette: *Many-valued logic.* Amsterdam: North Holland, 1952.

Ruspini, E.H.: *The logical foundations of evidential reasoning.* Techn. Note 408, AI Center. Menlo Park CA: SRI International, 1986 (revised 1987).

Ruspini, E.H.: "On the semantics of fuzzy logic," in: *Int. J. Approach Reasoning* 5 (1991) 45-88.

Schweitzer, B., and A. Sklar: *Probability metric spaces.* New York: North Holland, 1983.

Shafer, G.: '*A Mathematical Theory of Evidence.* Princenton: Princenton University Press, 1976.

Shortliffe, E.H., and B.G. Buchanan: "A Model of Inexact Reasoning in Medicine," in: *Mathematical Biosciences* Vol.23 (1975) 351-379.

Smets, P., A. Mamdani, D. Dubois, and H. Prade (eds.): *Non-standard Logics for Automated Reasoning.* London: Academic Press, 1988.

Smoryński, C.: *Self-reference and Modal Logic.* Springer Verlag, 1985.

Takeuti, G., and S. Titani: "Fuzzy logic and fuzzy set theory," in: *Archive for Math. Logic,* to appear.

Van Benthem, J.: *The Logic of Time.* Dordrecht: Kluwer Academic Publisher, 1991.

Visser, A.: "Interpretability Logic," in: *Mathematical Logic, Proceedings of Heyting Conference Bulgaria 1988.* Plenum Press, 1990.

Wajsberg, M.: "Axiomatization of the three-valued propositional calculus," (Polish with German summary) in: *C.R. Soc. Sci. Lett Varsovie,* Cl. 3, Vol. 24 (1931) 269-283. (Translation in: M. Wajsberg, *Logical Works.* Warsaw: Polish Academy of Sciences, 1977.

Gentzen Sequent Calculus for Possibilistic Reasoning

Churn Jung Liau[1] and Bertrand I-Peng Lin[2]

[1] Institute of Information Science, Academia Sinica,
Taipei, Taiwan, ROC, E-mail: liau@iis.sinica.edu.tw
[2] Department of Computer Science and Information Engineering
National Taiwan University, Taipei, Taiwan, ROC

Abstract. Possibilistic logic is an important uncertainty reasoning mechanism based on Zadeh's possibility theory and classical logic. Its inference rules are derived from the classical resolution rule by attaching possibility or necessity weights to ordinary clauses. However, since not all possibility-valued formulae can be converted into equivalent possibilistic clauses, these inference rules are somewhat restricted. In this paper, we develop Gentzen sequent calculus for possibilistic reasoning to lift this restriction. This is done by first formulating possibilistic reasoning as a kind of modal logic. Then the Gentzen method for modal logics generalized to cover possibilistic logic. Finally, some properties of possibilistic logic, such as Craig's interpolation lemma and Beth's definability theorem are discussed in the context of Gentzen methods.

1 Introduction

The literature on uncertainty reasoning mechanisms based on Zadeh's possibility theory (Zadeh 1978) has grown rapidly. (See (Dubois et al. 1990) for a survey). Possibilistic logic (Dubois and Prade 1988) is one of the most important approaches in this direction. However, since the deduction method of possibilistic logic is based on the classical resolution rule (Robinson 1965), it is restricted to formulae in clausal form. On the other hand, it has been pointed out that possibilistic logic can be viewed as a generalization of modal logics (Dubois and Prade 1988, Dubois et al. 1988, Farinas del Cerro and Herzig 1991, Liau and Lin 1992), so it should be possible to use the deduction method of modal logics to do possibilistic reasoning. In this paper, we will investigate an implementation of this idea to lift the clausal form restriction of possibilistic resolution. To do this, we first formulate possibilistic reasoning as a kind of modal logic with multi modal operators. Then, we generalize the sequent calculus of normal modal logics developed by (Fitting 1983) to our logic. Finally, some logical properties of our system are discussed.

1.1 Possibilistic resolution rule

In possibilistic logic, two certainty measures, called possibility and necessity measures respectively, are assigned to the well-formed formulae of classical propositional logic. Specifically, let Π and N denote measures for possibility and necessity respectively, then the following laws must be satisfied for all well-formed formulae f and g:

(i) $\Pi(f)$ and $N(f) \in [0,1]$
(ii) $N(f) = 1 - \Pi(\neg f)$,
(iii) $\Pi(\top) = 1$ and $\Pi(\bot) = 0$, and
(iv) $N(f \wedge g) = \min(N(f), N(g))$.

Thus, if f is a well-formed formula (wff) of propositional logic, then $(f(Nc))$ and $(f(\Pi c))$, where $c \in [0,1]$, are wffs of possibilistic logic. When f is a classical clause, the wffs are called possibilistic clauses. The intended meanings of the wffs are $N(f) \geq c$ and $\Pi(f) \geq c$ respectively. The resolution rule of possibilistic logic is defined as follows:

$$\frac{(f \ w_1) \quad (g \ w_2)}{(R(f,g) \ w_1 * w_2)}$$

where $R(f,g)$ is the classical resolvent of f and g, and $*$ is defined by

$$(N \ c) * (N \ d) = (N \ min(c,d))$$
$$(N \ c) * (\Pi \ d) = \begin{cases} (\Pi \ d) \ if \ c + d > 1 \\ (\Pi \ 0) \ if \ c + d \leq 1 \end{cases}$$
$$(\Pi \ c) * (\Pi \ d) = (\Pi \ 0)$$

By the axiom (iv) above, any wff of the form $(f(Nc))$ can be converted into an equivalent set of possibilistic clauses, and if only the necessity measure N is involved, the refutational completeness of this resolution rule can be proved (Dubois et al. 1990). However, if possibility-valued wffs are involved, then the completeness result does not hold in general. The following simple example illustrates this point.

Example 1. Consider the assumption set $B = \{(p \wedge q (\Pi 0.7)), (p \wedge q \supset r \ (N \ 0.6))\}$ and the wff $f = (r \ (\Pi \ 0.7))$ in possibilistic logic. Then obviously, f should be derivable from B.[3] However, since $(p \wedge q \ (\Pi \ 0.7))$ is not a possibilistic clause, the resolution rule cannot be applied. A possible approach to overcome the difficulty may be to infer $(p \ (\Pi \ 0.7))$ and $(q \ (\Pi \ 0.7))$ firstly. This indeed helps some situations if the second sentence is either $(p \supset r \ (N \ 0.6))$ or $(q \supset r \ (N \ 0.6))$, but it is useless in the present case.

To remove the restriction of clausal form, we must consider more general deduction methods. Gentzen sequent calculus is one possible choice. It was first developed by Gentzen for classical and intuitionistic logic (Gentzen 1969), and then extended to modal logics by (Fitting 1983). We try to provide a suitable Gentzen system for possibilistic reasoning in the following sections. But before doing this, we must reformulate possibilistic logic as a general modal logic.

---

[3] Replacing "$p \wedge q$" with a new propositional letter and using the given resolution rule will justify this.

2 Quantitative Modal Logic

Possibilistic reasoning is first formulated as modal logic in (Farinas del Cerro and Herzig 1991). In (Liau and Lin 1992), we call the resultant logic quantitative modal logic (QML) and investigated axiomatic systems for it. We review QML's syntax and semantics briefly.

2.1 Syntax

QML is an extension of propositional logic with four classes of quantitative modal operators: $\langle c \rangle$, $\langle c \rangle^+$, $[c]$ and $[c]^+$ for all $c \in [0, 1]$.

In addition to the syntactic rules for propositional logic, the following one is added to the formation rules of QML:

if f is a wff, so are $\langle c \rangle f$, $\langle c \rangle^+ f$, $[c]f$ and $[c]^+ f$ for all $c \in [0, 1]$.

The intended meaning of $\langle c \rangle f$, $\langle c \rangle^+ f$, $[c]f$ and $[c]^+ f$ is $\Pi(f) \geq c$, $\Pi(f) > c$, $N(f) \geq c$ and $N(f) > c$ respectively.

We usually use lower case letters (sometimes with indices) p, q, r to denote atomic formulae and f, g, h to denote wffs. We also assume that all classical logical connectives are available, either as primitives or as abbreviations.

Note that we have enhanced the expressive power of possibilistic logic so that we can represent more complex wffs in QML. For example, we can represent higher order uncertainty in a wff like $\neg[0.7]^+(p \supset \langle 0.8 \rangle q)$. The importance of higher order uncertainty is highlighted in (Gaifman 1986). Furthermore, the syntax makes it easier to combine QML and other intensional logics. For instance, we can use $B\langle 0.6 \rangle p$ and $\langle 0.6 \rangle Bp$ to represent "the agent believes that the possibility of p is at least 0.6" and "the possibility of the agent believing p is at least 0.6" respectively.

Following an idea in (Fitting 1983), we may classify the non-literal wffs of QML into six categories according to the formulae's main connective. We list the alternatives in Fig. 1. We will abuse the notation and use $\alpha, \alpha_1, \cdots$, etc. to denote wffs of the respective types and their immediate subformulae.

2.2 Semantics

We now turn to the semantics of QML. Define a *possibility frame* $F = \langle W, R \rangle$, where W is a set of possible words and $R : W^2 \to [0, 1]$ is a fuzzy accessibility relation on W. Let PV and FA denote the set of all propositional variables and the set of all wffs respectively. Then a model of QML is a triple $M = \langle W, R, TA \rangle$, where $\langle W, R \rangle$ is a possibility frame and $TA : W \times PV \to \{0, 1\}$ is a truth value assignment for all worlds. A proposition p is said to be true at a world w iff $TA(w, p) = 1$. Given R, we can define a possibility distribution R_w for each $w \in W$ such that $R_w(s) = R(w, s)$ for all s in W. Similarly, we can define TA_w for each $w \in W$ such that $TA_w(p) = TA(w, p)$ for all p in PV. Thus, a model can be equivalently written as $\langle W, \langle R_w, TA_w \rangle_{w \in W} \rangle$. Given a model $M = \langle W, R, TA \rangle$,

α wffs and their component formulae

α	α_1	α_2
$f \wedge g$	f	g
$\neg(f \vee g)$	$\neg f$	$\neg g$
$\neg(f \supset g)$	f	$\neg g$
$\neg\neg f$	f	f

β wffs and their component formalae

β	β_1	β_2
$f \vee g$	f	g
$\neg(f \wedge g)$	$\neg f$	$\neg g$
$f \supset g$	$\neg f$	g

ν and ν⁺ wffs (with parameter c) and their component formulae

$\nu(c)$	$\nu_0(c)$	$\nu^+(c)$	$\nu_0^+(c)$
$[c]f$	f	$[c]^+f$	f
$\neg\langle 1-c\rangle^+ f$	$\neg f$	$\neg\langle 1-c\rangle f$	$\neg f$

π and π⁺ wffs (with parameter c) and their component formulae

$\pi(c)$	$\pi_0(c)$	$\pi^+(c)$	$\pi_0^+(c)$
$\langle c\rangle f$	f	$\langle c\rangle^+ f$	f
$\neg[1-c]^+ f$	$\neg f$	$\neg[1-c]f$	$\neg f$

Fig. 1. Classification of QML non-literal wffs

we can define the satisfaction relation $\models_M \subseteq W \times FA$ as follows. Define $N_w(f) = \inf\{1 - R(w,s) \mid s \models_M \neg f, s \in W\}$. N_w is just the necessity measure induced by the possibility distribution R_w as defined in (Dubois and Prade 1988). Then, $w \models_M [c]f$ (resp. $w \models_M [c]^+ f$) iff $N_w(f) \geq c$ (resp. $> c$). The satisfaction relations for $\langle c\rangle f$ and $\langle c\rangle^+ f$ are defined analogously by replacing $N_w(f)$ with $\Pi_w(f) = 1 - N_w(\neg f)$. For convenience, we define $\sup \emptyset = 0$ and $\inf \emptyset = 1$. Furthermore, the satisfaction of all other wffs is defined as usual in classical logic.

A wff f is said to be valid in $M = \langle W, R, TA \rangle$, write $\models_M f$, iff for all $w \in W, w \models_M f$. If S is a set of wffs, then $\models_M S$ means that for all $f \in S$, $\models_M f$. If $\mathbf{C}$ is a class of models and S is a set of wffs, then we write $S \models_{\mathbf{C}} f$ to say that for all $M \in \mathbf{C}$, $\models_M S$ implies $\models_M f$. Note that "$\models_{\mathbf{C}}$" is defined "model by model". It can also be defined "world by world", i.e., for all $M \in \mathbf{C}$ and w of M, $w \models_M S$ implies $w \models_M f$. However, when S is finite, the alternative definition is equivalent to $\models_{\mathbf{C}} \bigwedge S \supset f$, so we would not consider it separately. A model is called serial iff $\forall w \in W, \sup_{s \in W} R(w,s) = 1$. As pointed out in (Liau and Lin 1992), the consequence relation in serial models exactly reflects possibilistic reasoning, so in what follows, we will mainly focus on the development of deduction rules, and $S \models_{\mathbf{C}} f$ is abbreviated as $S \models f$ if $\mathbf{C}$ is the class of all serial models.

3 Gentzen Sequent Calculus

The Gentzen sequent calculus for possibilistic reasoning is a generalization of that for modal logics (Fitting 1983), and is an extension of classical logic. Therefore the system will contain all rules for classical logic. The principle of additional rules for possibilistic reasoning depends on the truth of wffs in different possible worlds. For instance, if $M = \langle W, R, TA \rangle$ is a model, and S is a set of wffs true in a world $w \in W$, then for all worlds w' such that $R(w, w') \geq c$, what wffs should be true in w'? Obviously, any wff f such that $N_w(f) > 1 - c$ or $\Pi_w(\neg f) < c$ should satisfy the requirement. Thus, in general, we have the following definition:

Definition 1. Define the world-alternative function K and the strict world-alternative function K^+ as follows.

$$K, K^+ : 2^{FA} \times [0,1] \to 2^{FA},$$

$$K(S, c) = \{\nu_0(c') \mid c' \geq c, \nu(c') \in S\} \cup \{\nu_0^+(c') \mid c' \geq c, \nu^+(c') \in S\}$$

and

$$K^+(S, c) = \{\nu_0(c') \mid c' > c, \nu(c') \in S\} \cup \{\nu_0^+(c') \mid c' \geq c, \nu^+(c') \in S\}.$$

Intuitively, $K(S, c)$ (resp. $K^+(S, c)$) contains all wffs f such that $N(f) \geq c$ (resp. $N(f) > c$) is derivable from S by inequality constraints. Thus, it is readily verified that if S is true in w and $R(w, w') \geq c$ (resp. $> c$), then $K^+(S, 1 - c)$ (resp. $K(S, 1 - c)$) is true in w'.

Dually, we have the following definition for the falsity of a set S of wffs in a world w.

Definition 2. Define the dual world-alternative function $\hat{K}$ and strict dual world alternative function $\hat{K}^+$ as follows.

$$\hat{K}, \hat{K}^+ : 2^{FA} \times [0,1] \to 2^{FA},$$

$$\hat{K}(S, c) = \{\pi_0(c') \mid c' \leq 1 - c, \pi(c') \in S\} \cup \{\pi_0^+(c') \mid c' \leq 1 - c, \pi^+(c') \in S\}$$

and

$$\hat{K}^+(S, c) = \{\pi_0(c') \mid c' \leq 1 - c, \pi(c') \in S\} \cup \{\pi_0^+(c') \mid c' < 1 - c, \pi^+(c') \in S\}.$$

Similarly, we can verify that if S is false in w and $R(w, w') \geq c$ (resp. $> c$), then $\hat{K}^+(S, 1-c)$ (resp. $\hat{K}(S, 1-c)$) is false in w'.

We are now ready to present the Gentzen deduction system for possibilistic reasoning. First, let us introduce the notation of a sequent. Let U, V be two sets of wffs, and let $U \longrightarrow V$ denote a sequent. The intuitive meaning of the sequent $U \longrightarrow V$ is that if all elements of U are true, then at least one of the wffs in V is true.

We present the Gentzen sequent calculus for QML in Fig. 2 by using the notation introduced in Fig. 1. We use "U, f" to denote the union of a set of wffs U and a wff f. Every rule consists of one or two upper sequents called *premises* and of a lower sequent called *conclusion*. The schema f stands for any literals.

1. Axioms:

$$U, f \longrightarrow V, f \qquad U, \bot \longrightarrow V \qquad U \longrightarrow V, \top \qquad U \longrightarrow V, \pi(0)$$
$$U, f, \neg f \longrightarrow V \qquad U, \nu^+(1) \longrightarrow V \qquad U \longrightarrow V, \nu(0) \qquad U \longrightarrow V, f, \neg f$$
$$U \longrightarrow V, \neg\bot \qquad U, \pi^+(1) \longrightarrow V \qquad U, \neg\top \longrightarrow V$$

2. Classical rules:

$$\alpha L : \quad \frac{U, \alpha_1, \alpha_2 \longrightarrow V}{U, \alpha \longrightarrow V} \qquad\qquad \beta R : \quad \frac{U \longrightarrow V, \beta_1, \beta_2}{U \longrightarrow V, \beta}$$

$$\beta L : \quad \frac{U, \beta_1 \longrightarrow V \quad U, \beta_2 \longrightarrow V}{U, \beta \longrightarrow V} \qquad \alpha R : \quad \frac{U \longrightarrow V, \alpha_1 \quad U \longrightarrow V, \alpha_2}{U \longrightarrow V, \alpha}$$

$$\neg^2 L : \quad \frac{U, \neg\neg f \longrightarrow V}{U, f \longrightarrow V} \qquad\qquad \neg^2 R : \quad \frac{U \longrightarrow V, \neg\neg f}{U \longrightarrow V, f}$$

3. Common rules for possibilistic reasoning:

$$\pi L_1 : \text{if } c > 0 \quad \frac{K^+(U, 1-c), \pi_0(c) \longrightarrow \hat{K}^+(V, 1-c)}{U, \pi(c) \longrightarrow V}$$

$$\pi L_2 : \quad \frac{K(U, 1-c), \pi_0^+(c) \longrightarrow \hat{K}(V, 1-c)}{U, \pi^+(c) \longrightarrow V}$$

$$\nu R_1 : \text{if } c < 1 \quad \frac{K^+(U, c) \longrightarrow \hat{K}^+(V, c), \nu_0^+(c)}{U \longrightarrow V, \nu^+(c)}$$

$$\nu R_2 : \quad \frac{K(U, c) \longrightarrow \hat{K}(V, c), \nu_0(c)}{U \longrightarrow V, \nu(c)}$$

4. Rule D (for the serality of models):

$$\frac{K^+(U, 0) \longrightarrow \hat{K}^+(V, 0)}{U \longrightarrow V}$$

Fig. 2. Gentzen Sequent Calculus for QML

We define the *global assumption rule* for a set of wffs B as follows: if $f \in B$, then

$$\frac{U \longrightarrow V, \neg f}{U \longrightarrow V} \qquad\qquad \frac{U, f \longrightarrow V}{U \longrightarrow V}$$

3.1 Soundness and completeness

Next, we will consider the soundness and completeness of Gentzen-type proof methods. First, we define the truth of a sequent $U \longrightarrow V$ in a world. Let $M = \langle W, R, TA \rangle$ be a model and $w \in W$, then $w \models_M U \longrightarrow V$ iff $w \models_M U$ implies there is at least a wff f in V such that $w \models_M f$. Then the validity of a sequent in a model and in a class of models can be defined analogously to that of a wff, and the notations $\models_M U \longrightarrow V$, $\models U \longrightarrow V$, and $B \models U \longrightarrow V$ can also be used for sequents, where B is a set of wffs. We also use the convention that $\longrightarrow V$ and $U \longrightarrow$ denote $\emptyset \longrightarrow V$ and $U \longrightarrow \emptyset$, respectively. A proof of a sequent $U \longrightarrow V$ from a set of wffs B is a sequence of sequents $\varphi_1, \varphi_2, \cdots, \varphi_n$ such that for each i, either φ_i is the instance of some axiom of the Gentzen system, or φ_i is the result of applying the rules in Fig. 2 or the global assumption rule to the earlier sequents of this sequence. We write $B \vdash (U \longrightarrow V)$ to mean that there exists a proof of $U \longrightarrow V$ from B.

To give the soundness theorem of the Gentzen system, we need another definition. A sequent $U \longrightarrow V$ is called *short* iff $U \cup V$ is finite. We note that a short sequent $U \longrightarrow V$ is true in a world iff the wff "$\bigwedge U \supset \bigvee V$" is true in that world, where $\bigwedge U$ and $\bigvee V$ denote the conjunction of U and the disjunction of V respectively.

Theorem 3 (Soundness). *If B is a finite set of wffs and $U \longrightarrow V$ is a short sequent, then $B \vdash (U \longrightarrow V)$ implies $B \models (U \longrightarrow V)$*

Proof. All axioms are valid (Liau and Lin 1992). As to the inference rules, we consider πL_1 as an example. If its conclusion is false in some world w, then $w \models \pi(c)$. This guarantees the existence of another world w' such that $R(w, w') \geq c$ if the set of possible worlds W is finite[4], so by the remarks following Definition 1 and 2, the premise is false in w'.

Usually, we want to prove only a wff f from a finite global assumption set B, so it is useful to state a restricted version of the soundness theorem if we identify a wff f with a sequent $\longrightarrow \{f\}$.

Corollary 4. $B \vdash f$ *implies* $B \models f$

Completeness can be proven by the model existence theorem for QML (Liau and Lin 1992). However, since we use unsigned formulae as opposed to the signed version in (Fitting 1983), some tedious steps are needed. In particular, the rules $\neg^2 L$ and $\neg^2 R$ are needed for completeness. We believe that the two rules can be removed by using signed formulae without affecting completeness.

---

[4] By a corollary in (Liau and Lin 1992), i.e., the finite model property, we can assume that W is finite without loss of generality

Theorem 5 (Completeness). *1. Let $U \longrightarrow V$ be a short sequent, then $B \models U \longrightarrow V$ implies $B \vdash U \longrightarrow V$.*
2. $B \models f$ iff $B \vdash f$

We return to Example 1 to see how our Gentzen system can derive the expected result. The deduction is shown in Fig. 3, and the rules used from above are βL, πL_1 with $c = 0.7$, and with the global assumption rule twice used. Since the right one of the two topmost sequents is an instance of an axiom, and the other one can be derived from the axioms by classical rules, this is indeed a proof in Gentzen system.

$$
\cfrac{
  \cfrac{
    \cfrac{
      \cfrac{\neg(p \wedge q), p \wedge q \longrightarrow r \qquad\qquad\qquad\qquad\qquad\qquad r, p \wedge q \longrightarrow r}
      {p \wedge q \supset r, p \wedge q \longrightarrow r}}
    {[0.6](p \wedge q \supset r), \langle 0.7\rangle(p \wedge q) \longrightarrow \langle 0.7\rangle r}}
  {[0.6](p \wedge q \supset r) \longrightarrow \langle 0.7\rangle r}}
{\langle 0.7\rangle r}
$$

Fig. 3. A Gentzen deduction of Example 1

4   Interpolation Lemma and Definibility Theorem

In the sequel, we explore some logical properties of QML by exploiting the soundness and completeness of the Gentzen system.

First, we discuss the interpolation lemma. The interpolation lemma of classical logic is due to Craig (Craig 1957a, Craig 1957b). Here, it is be generalized to QML.

Definition 6. If $U \longrightarrow V$ is a sequent, then f is an interpolation formula for $U \longrightarrow V$ iff

(i) all propositional variables of f are common to U and V. In other words, $Pvar(f) \subseteq Pvar(U) \cap Pvar(V)$, where $Pvar(S) = \bigcup_{g \in S} Pvar(g)$ and $Pvar(g)$ are the propositional variables occurring in g.
(ii) $\models U \longrightarrow f$ and $\models f \longrightarrow V$.

We define an interpolation formula for $f \supset g$ as one for $f \longrightarrow g$, where f and g are two wffs. We essentially follow Fitting's method (Fitting 1983) to prove the interpolation lemma.

Lemma 7 (Craig's Interpolation Lemma). *If $\models f \supset g$, then $f \supset g$ has an interpolation formula.*

Proof. By the completeness of Gentzen system, $\models f \supset g$ implies $\models f \longrightarrow g$, and in turn implies $\vdash f \longrightarrow g$. We will try to show that

1. all axioms of the Gentzen system have the Craig property, and
2. for all rules in the Gentzen system, if the premise(s) has the Craig property, then the conclusion has, too.

Then, $f \longrightarrow g$ has an interpolation formula, and this is also the interpolation formula of $f \supset g$ by definition.

We use $U \xrightarrow{h} V$ to denote that h is an interpolation formula of $U \longrightarrow V$.

First, we show that all axioms have interpolation formulae by the following list.

$$U, f \xrightarrow{f} V, f \qquad U, \perp \xrightarrow{\perp} V \qquad U \xrightarrow{\top} V, \top \qquad U \xrightarrow{\top} V, \pi(0)$$

$$U, f, \neg f \xrightarrow{\perp} V \qquad U, \nu^+(1) \xrightarrow{\perp} V \qquad U \xrightarrow{\top} V, \nu(0) \qquad U \xrightarrow{\top} V, f, \neg f$$

$$U \xrightarrow{\top} V, \neg \perp \qquad U, \pi^+(1) \xrightarrow{\perp} V \qquad U, \neg \top \xrightarrow{\perp} V$$

Second, we check that each sequent rule transforms the interpolation formula(s) of the premise sequent(s) into an interpolation formula of the conclusion sequent.

1. if $U, \alpha_1, \alpha_2 \xrightarrow{h} V$, then $U, \alpha \xrightarrow{h} V$.
2. if $U \xrightarrow{h} V, \beta_1, \beta_2$, then $U \xrightarrow{h} V, \beta$.
3. if $U \xrightarrow{h_1} V, \alpha_1$ and $U \xrightarrow{h_2} V, \alpha_2$, then $U \xrightarrow{h_1 \wedge h_2} V, \alpha$.
4. if $U, \beta_1 \xrightarrow{h_1} V$ and $U, \beta_2 \xrightarrow{h_2} V$, then $U, \beta \xrightarrow{h_1 \vee h_2} V$.
5. if $U, \neg\neg f \xrightarrow{h} V$, then $U, f \xrightarrow{h} V$.
6. if $U \xrightarrow{h} V, \neg\neg f$, then $U \xrightarrow{h} V, f$.
7. if $K^+(U, 1-c), \pi_0(c) \xrightarrow{h} \hat{K}^+(V, 1-c)$, then $U, \pi(c) \xrightarrow{(c)h} V$.
8. if $K(U, 1-c), \pi_0^+(c) \xrightarrow{h} \hat{K}(V, 1-c)$, then $U, \pi^+(c) \xrightarrow{(c)^+h} V$.
9. if $K^+(U, c) \xrightarrow{h} \hat{K}^+(V, c), \nu_0^+(c)$, then $U \xrightarrow{[c]^+h} V, \nu^+(c)$.
10. if $K(U, c) \xrightarrow{h} \hat{K}(V, c), \nu_0(c)$, then $U \xrightarrow{[c]h} V, \nu(c)$.
11. if $K^+(U, 0) \xrightarrow{h} \hat{K}^+(V, 0)$, then $U \xrightarrow{[0]^+h} V$ and $U \xrightarrow{(1)h} V$.

Next, we will consider the QML version of Beth's definability theorem which is proposed in (Beth 1953) for classical logic and generalized by Fitting (1983) for modal logic.

Definition 8. 1. Let p be a propositional variable and $f(p)$ be a wff containing p. We say there is an explicit definition of p from $f(p)$ in the QML if there is a formula g, in which p does not occur, such that $\models f(p) \supset (p \equiv g)$
2. $f(p)$ is said to define p implicitly in the QML if for each propositional variable q that does not occur in $f(p)$, $\models f(p) \wedge f(q) \supset (p \equiv q)$

Theorem 9 (Beth's Definability Theorem). *If $f(p)$ defines p implicitly in QML, then there is also an explicit definition of p from $f(p)$ in QML.*

Proof. By using Craig's interpolation lemma of QML, the proof is same as that for modal logics (Fitting 1983).

5   Conclusion

We have made two points in this chapter. First, we showed how to reformulate possibilistic reasoning as a kind of modal logic in order to enhance its expressive power. In the resultant language, QML, we can represent both high-order uncertainty and the interaction between weighted wffs and classical wffs. Secondly, we developed a Gentzen deduction method for QML that removes the restriction to clausal form. In summary, we have a sound and complete deduction system for general possibilistic reasoning for as long as the global assumption set is finite. Since the problem encountered in the real world is usually finite, the system reported in this paper should be practical. The only remaining problem is the efficiency of the method. It is generally believed that resolution is a more efficient deduction method in automated theorem proving. However, we believe that by using careful control strategies, Gentzen systems can also have good performance. The method developed by Wallen (1987) provides a good example.

References

Beth, E. W.: "On Padoa's method in the theory of definition," in: *Indag. Math.* 15 (1953) 330-339.

Craig, W.: "Linear reasoning. A new form of the Herbrand-Gentzen theorem," in: *Journal of Symbol Logic* 22 (1957a) 250-268.

Craig, W.: "Three uses of the Herbrand-Gentzen theorem in relating model theory to proof theory," in: *Journal of Symbol Logic* 22 (1957b) 269-285.

Dubois, D., J. Lang, and H. Prade: "Fuzzy sets in approximate reasoning.Part 2: Logical approache," in: *Fuzzy Sets and Systems* , 25th Anniversary volume, 1990.

Dubois, D., and H. Prade: "An introduction to possibilistic and fuzzy logics," in: P. Smets et al. (eds.), *Non-standard Logics for Automated Reasoning* , Academic Press (1988) 287-325.

Dubois, D., H. Prade, and C. Testmale: "In search of a modal system for possibility theory," in: *Proc. of ECAI-88* (1988) 501-506.

Farinas del Cerro, L., and A. Herzig: "A modal analysis of possibility theory," in: Kruse and Siegel (eds.), *Proc. of ECSQAU*. Springer Verlag, LNAI 548 (1991) 58-62.

Fitting, M.C.: *Proof Methods for Modal and Intuitionistic Logics* . Vol. 169 of Synthese Library, D. Reidel Publishing Company, 1983.

Gaifman, H.: "A theory of higher order probabilities," in: J.Y. Halpern (ed.), *Proceeding of 1st Conference on Theoretical Aspects of Reasoning about Knowledge*. Morgan Kaufmann, (1986) 275-292.

Gentzen, G.: "Investigation into logical deduction," in: M. E. Szabo (ed.), *The Collected Papers of Gerhard Gentzen* Amsterdam: North-Holland (1969) 68-131.

Liau, C. J., and I. P. Lin: "Quantitative modal logic and possibilistic reasoning," in: *Proc. of ECAI 92*, 1992.

Robinson, J.A.: "A machine oriented logic based on the resolution principle," in: *JACM* 12 (1965) 23-41.

Wallen, L.: "Matrix proofs for modal logics," in: *Proc. of IJCAI* (1987) 917-923.

Zadeh, L.A.: "Fuzzy sets as a basis for a theory of possibility," in: *Fuzzy Sets and Systems*, 1 (1978) 3-28.

A Model of Inductive Reasoning [*]

Peter A. Flach

Institute for Language Technology & Artificial Intelligence
Tilburg University, POBox 90153, 5000 LE Tilburg, Netherlands
E-mail: flach@kub.nl

Abstract. This paper presents a formal characterization of the process of inductive hypothesis formation. This is achieved by formulating minimal properties for inductive consequence relations. These properties are justified by the fact that they are sufficient to allow identification in the limit. By means of stronger sets of properties, we also define both standard and non-standard forms of inductive reasoning, and give an application of the latter.

1 Introduction

1.1 Motivation and scope

Induction is the process of drawing conclusions about all members of a certain set from knowledge about specific members of that set. For example, after observing a number of black crows, we might conclude inductively that all crows are black. Such a conclusion can never be drawn with absolute certainty, and an immediate question is: how is our confidence in it affected by observing the next black crow? This problem is known as the *justification problem* of induction, a problem with which philosophers of all times have wrestled without finding a satisfactory solution.

In this paper, we are concerned with a different but related problem: the formalisation of the process of *inductive hypothesis formation*. Which hypotheses are possible, given the available information? For instance, in the crows example the hypothesis 'all crows are black' is possible, but the hypothesis 'all crows are white' is not: it is refuted as soon as we observe one black crow. Moreover, once refuted, it will never become a possible hypothesis again, no matter how many crows are observed. The question is thus: what is the relation between sets of observations and possible hypotheses?

In order to address this question, we need a representation for observations and hypotheses. In our framework, both are represented by logical statements. Since the above definition of induction makes an explicit distinction between instances and sets of instances, a first-order logic seems most appropriate. However, it can be shown that many typical induction problems (like concept learning

[*] Part of this work has been carried out under ESPRIT III Basic Research Action 6020: *Inductive Logic Programming*.

from examples) remain essentially the same if we regard an instance as an equivalence class of indistinguishable objects. It follows that the distinction between instances and sets is not essential, at least not for typical induction problems. For instance, in many approaches to concept learning from examples, a so-called *attribute-value language* is used to describe both examples and concepts in terms of properties like colour, shape and size. Attribute-value languages have the expressive power of propositional logic.[2]

Since observations and hypotheses are logical statements, inductive hypothesis formation can be declaratively modeled as a consequence relation. We will study the properties of such inductive consequence relations, thereby applying techniques developed in other fields of non-standard logic, like non-monotonic reasoning (Gabbay 1985, Shoham 1987, Kraus et al. 1990), abduction (Zadrozny 1991) and belief revision (Gärdenfors 1988, Gärdenfors 1990). In the spirit of these works, we develop several systems of properties that inductive consequence relations might have. They model *different kinds* of induction, with the weakest system **I** giving *necessary conditions* for inductive consequence relations.

As a motivating example, let the observations be drawn from a database of facts about different persons, including their first and last names, and their parents first and last names. A typical inductive hypothesis would be 'every person's last name equals her father's last name'. Such a hypothesis, if adopted, would yield a procedure for finding a persons last name, given her father's last name. Now consider the statement 'every person has exactly one mother'. It is also an inductive hypothesis, but of a different kind. Specifically, it does not give a procedure for finding a person's mother (such a procedure does obviously not exist), but merely states her existence and uniqueness. While the first hypothesis can be seen as a *definition* of the last name of children, the second one is instead a *constraint* on possible models of the database. In the sections to follow, we will give practical examples of both forms of induction.

1.2 Terminology and notation

Suppose P is a computer program that performs inductive reasoning. That is, P takes a set of formulae α in some language L as input, and outputs inductive conclusions β. The main idea is to view P as constituting a consequence relation, i.e., a relation on $2^L \times L$, and to study the properties of this consequence relation. We will write $\alpha \hspace{2pt}\mid\!\sim\hspace{2pt} \beta$ whenever β is an inductive consequence of the premises α. A set of premises is often represented by a formula expressing their conjunction. The properties of $\mid\!\sim$ will be expressed by Gentzen-style inference rules in a meta-logic, following (Gabbay 1985, Kraus et al. 1990).

We will assume that L is a propositional language, closed under the logical connectives. Furthermore, we assume a set of models M for L, and the classical satisfaction relation $\models$ on $M \times L$. If $m \models \alpha$ for all $m \in M$, we write $\models \alpha$. We can

---

[2] For simplicity, the framework in this paper will be developed on the basis of propositional logic; we have no reason to believe, however, that its applicability cannot be extended to first-order logic.

implicitly introduce background knowledge by restricting M to a proper subset of all possible models. We will assume that $\models$ is compact, i.e., an infinite set of formulae is unsatisfiable if and only if every finite subset is.

In many practical cases premises and hypotheses are drawn from restricted sublanguages of L. Given a language L, an *inductive frame* is a triple $\langle \Gamma, \mathrel{\mathsf{k}}, \Sigma \rangle$, where $\Gamma \subseteq L$ is the set of possible observations, $\Sigma \subseteq L$ is the set of possible hypotheses, and $\mathrel{\mathsf{k}}$ is an inductive consequence relation on $2^L \times L$. We will assume that Γ is at least closed under conjunction.

The fact that in an inductive frame the consequence relation is defined on $2^L \times L$, rather than $2^\Gamma \times \Sigma$, reflects an important choice for a certain interpretation of $\mathrel{\mathsf{k}}$. Specifically, we chose to interpret $\alpha \mathrel{\mathsf{k}} \beta$ not just as 'β is an inductive consequence of α', but more generally as 'β is a possible hypothesis, given α'. In this way, our framework allows the study of not only inductive reasoning, but hypothetical reasoning in general.

As an example, take the property of Contraposition (if $\alpha \mathrel{\mathsf{k}} \beta$, then $\neg\beta \mathrel{\mathsf{k}} \neg\alpha$), which we will encounter later. This property can be understood as follows. Suppose I know that c is a crow (background knowledge), and the premise that c is black (α) allows the inductive hypothesis all crows are black (β), then the premiss that some crows are not black ($\neg\beta$) allows likewise the hypothesis that c is not black ($\neg\alpha$). It is quite possible that, in most inductive frames, this hypothesis is excluded from Σ[3]. This prohibits the interpretation of Contraposition as stating 'if $\alpha \mathrel{\mathsf{k}} \beta$ is an inductive argument, then so is $\neg\beta \mathrel{\mathsf{k}} \neg\alpha$'. Rather, it describes a property of hypothesis formation in general: $\neg\alpha$ is a possible hypothesis on the basis of $\neg\beta$, just like β is a possible hypothesis on the basis of α.

The plan of the paper is as follows. In Section 2, we define a minimal set of properties for inductive consequence relations, and we show that these properties are sufficient in the sense that they allow for a very general induction method. In Sections 3 and 4, we develop two, more or less complementary, kinds of inductive reasoning, and we give their main properties. We end the paper with some concluding remarks.

2 Identification in the Limit and I-relations

2.1 Identification in the limit

Inductive arguments are *defeasible*: an inductive conclusion might be invalidated by future observations. Thus, the validity of an inductive argument can only be guaranteed when complete information is available. A possible way to model complete information is by a sequence of formulae (possibly infinite), such that every incorrect hypothesis is eventually ruled out by a formula in the sequence. If an inductive reasoner reads in a finite initial segment of this sequence and outputs a correct hypothesis, it is said to have *finitely identified* the hypothesis. Since this is a fairly strong criterion, it is often weakened as follows: the inductive

---

[3] In fact, it looks more like an abductive hypothesis. We have argued elsewhere (Flach 1992) that there are close relations between abduction and induction.

reasoner is allowed to output as many hypotheses as wanted, but after finitely many guesses the hypothesis must be correct, and not abandoned afterwards. This is called *identification in the limit*. The difference with finite identification is, that the inductive reasoner does not know when the correct hypothesis has been attained. Details can be found in (Gold 1967).

We will redefine identification in the limit in terms of inductive consequence relations. Given a set of hypotheses Σ, the task is to identify an unknown $\beta \in \Sigma$ from a sequence of observations $\alpha_1, \alpha_2, \ldots$, such that $\{\alpha_1, \alpha_2, \ldots\} \mathrel{\mkern-3mu\vrule\mkern1mu\sim} \beta$. The observations must be sufficient in the sense that they eventually rule out every non-intended hypothesis.

Definition 1 (Identification in the limit). Let $\langle \Gamma, \mathrel{\mkern-3mu\vrule\mkern1mu\sim}, \Sigma \rangle$ be an inductive frame. Given a *target hypothesis* $\beta \in \Sigma$, a *presentation for β* is a (possibly infinite) sequence of observations $\alpha_1, \alpha_2, \ldots$ such that $\{\alpha_1, \alpha_2, \ldots\} \mathrel{\mkern-3mu\vrule\mkern1mu\sim} \beta$. Given a presentation, an *identification algorithm* is an algorithm which reads in an observation α_j from the presentation and outputs a hypothesis β_j, for $j = 1, 2, \ldots$. The output sequence $\beta_1, \beta_2, \ldots$ is said to *converge* to β_n if for all $k \geq n$, $\beta_k = \beta_n$.

A presentation $\alpha_1, \alpha_2, \ldots$ for β is *sufficient* if for any hypothesis $\gamma \in \Sigma$ other than β it contains a *witness* α_i such that $\{\alpha_1, \alpha_2, \ldots, \alpha_i\} \not\mathrel{\mkern-3mu\vrule\mkern1mu\sim} \gamma$. An identification algorithm is said to *identify β in the limit* if, given any sufficient presentation for β, the output sequence converges to β. An identification algorithm identifies Σ in the limit, if it is able to identify any $\beta \in \Sigma$ in the limit. □

Since we place induction in a logical context, it makes sense not to distinguish between logically equivalent hypotheses. That is, β is *logically* identified in the limit if the output sequence converges to β' such that $\models \beta' \leftrightarrow \beta$. A presentation for β is *logically* sufficient if it contains a witness for any γ such that $\not\models \gamma \leftrightarrow \beta$. In the sequel, we will only consider logical identification, and omit the adjective logical.

2.2 I-relations

After having defined identification in the limit in terms of inductive consequence relations, we now turn to the question: what does it take for inductive consequence relations to behave sensibly? We will first consider some useful properties, and then combine these properties into formal system **I**. We consider this system to be the weakest possible system defining inductive consequence relations.

The first two properties follow from the definition of identification in the limit. Suppose that α_i is a witness for γ, i.e., $\{\alpha_1, \alpha_2, \ldots, \alpha_i\} \not\mathrel{\mkern-3mu\vrule\mkern1mu\sim} \gamma$, then any extended set of observations should still refute γ, i.e., $\{\alpha_1, \alpha_2, \ldots, \alpha_i\} \cup A \not\mathrel{\mkern-3mu\vrule\mkern1mu\sim} \gamma$ for any $A \subseteq \Gamma$. Conversely, if $B \mathrel{\mkern-3mu\vrule\mkern1mu\sim} \beta$ then also $B' \mathrel{\mkern-3mu\vrule\mkern1mu\sim} \beta$ for any $B' \subseteq B$. Assuming that sets of observations can always be represented by their conjunction, this property can be stated as follows:

$$\frac{\models \alpha \rightarrow \beta, \alpha \mathrel{\mkern-3mu\vrule\mkern1mu\sim} \gamma}{\beta \mathrel{\mkern-3mu\vrule\mkern1mu\sim} \gamma} \tag{1}$$

Furthermore, observations cannot distinguish between logically equivalent hypotheses:

$$\frac{\models \beta \leftrightarrow \gamma, \alpha \mathbin{\vdash\!\!\!\!\!-} \beta}{\alpha \mathbin{\vdash\!\!\!\!\!-} \gamma} \tag{2}$$

The other two properties are not derived directly from identification in the limit. Instead, they describe the relation between observations and the hypotheses they confirm or refute. Here, the basic assumption is that induction aims to increase knowledge about some unknown intended model m_0. The observations are obtained from a reliable source, and are therefore true in m_0. On the other hand, hypotheses represent assumptions about the intended model. Together, observations and hypotheses can be used to make predictions about m_0. More specifically, suppose we have adopted hypothesis β on the basis of observations α, and let δ be a logical consequence of $\alpha \wedge \beta$, then we expect δ to be true in m_0. If the next observation conforms to our prediction, then we stick to β; if it contradicts our prediction, β should be refuted. These two principles can be expressed as follows.

$$\frac{\models \alpha \wedge \beta \rightarrow \delta, \alpha \mathbin{\vdash\!\!\!\!\!-} \beta}{\alpha \wedge \delta \mathbin{\vdash\!\!\!\!\!-} \beta} \tag{3}$$

$$\frac{\models \alpha \wedge \beta \rightarrow \delta, \alpha \mathbin{\vdash\!\!\!\!\!-} \beta}{\alpha \wedge \neg \delta \mathbin{\not\vdash\!\!\!\!\!-} \beta} \tag{4}$$

Note that the combination of these rules requires that $\alpha \wedge \beta$ is consistent: otherwise, we would have both $\models \alpha \wedge \beta \rightarrow \delta$ and $\models \alpha \wedge \beta \rightarrow \neg\delta$, and thus both $\alpha \wedge \delta \mathbin{\vdash\!\!\!\!\!-} \beta$ (3) and $\alpha \wedge \delta \mathbin{\not\vdash\!\!\!\!\!-} \beta$ (4). For technical reasons, the inconsistency of $\alpha \wedge \beta$ is not prohibited a priori. In the presence of the other rules, the application of rule (4) can be blocked in this case by adding the consistency of β as a premise (Theorem 4).

Rules (1) and (3) look pretty similar, and can probably be combined into a single rule. Rule (2) is clearly independent from the other rules. Rule (4) is not derivable from the other rules, but it may be if we add a weaker version. These considerations lead to the following system of rules.

Definition 2 (I-relations). The system **I** consists of the following four rules:

Conditional Reflexivity : $\dfrac{\not\models \neg\alpha}{\alpha \mathbin{\vdash\!\!\!\!\!-} \alpha}$

Consistency : $\dfrac{\not\models \neg\alpha}{\neg\alpha \mathbin{\not\vdash\!\!\!\!\!-} \alpha}$

Right Logical Equivalence : $\dfrac{\models \beta \leftrightarrow \gamma, \alpha \mathbin{\vdash\!\!\!\!\!-} \beta}{\alpha \mathbin{\vdash\!\!\!\!\!-} \gamma}$

Convergence : $\dfrac{\models \alpha \wedge \gamma \rightarrow \beta, \alpha \mathbin{\vdash\!\!\!\!\!-} \gamma}{\beta \mathbin{\vdash\!\!\!\!\!-} \gamma}$

If $\Bbb{k}$ is a consequence relation satisfying the rules of I, it is called an *I-relation*.

□

The following lemma gives two useful derived rules in this system.

Lemma 3. *The following rules are derived rules in system* **I***:*

$$\mathbf{S}: \quad \frac{\not\models \neg\beta, \models \beta \to \alpha}{\alpha \Bbb{k} \beta}$$

$$\mathbf{W}: \quad \frac{\not\models \neg\beta, \alpha \Bbb{k} \beta}{\not\models \beta \to \neg\alpha}$$

Proof. (S) Suppose $\not\models \neg\beta$ and $\models \beta \to \alpha$; by Conditional Reflexivity it follows that $\beta \Bbb{k} \beta$, and we conclude by Convergence.

(W) Suppose $\not\models \neg\beta$ and $\alpha \Bbb{k} \beta$; by Consistency it follows that $\neg\beta \not\Bbb{k} \beta$. By Convergence, it follows that $\not\models \alpha \wedge \beta \to \neg\beta$, i.e., $\not\models \beta \to \neg\alpha$. □

Rule S expresses that β is an inductive consequence of α if α is deductively entailed by β; rule W states that β shouldn't deductively entail $\neg\alpha$ if it is an inductive consequence of α (with β consistent in both cases). Rule S hints at the view of induction as reversed deduction, while rule W suggests a connection between induction and finding consistent extensions of a theory. By strengthening one of these rules, we obtain systems for one of two different kinds of induction: strong induction (Section 3) and weak induction (Section 4).

The following theorem shows that system **I** does what it was intended to do.

Theorem 4. *Rules (1)-(4) are derived rules in system* **I***.*

Proof. (1) Suppose $\models \alpha \to \beta$, i.e., $\models \alpha \wedge \gamma \to \beta$ and $\alpha \Bbb{k} \gamma$; we have $\alpha \Bbb{k} \beta$ by Convergence.

(2) Identical to Right Logical Equivalence.

(3) Suppose $\models \alpha \wedge \beta \to \delta$, i.e., $\models \alpha \wedge \beta \to \alpha \wedge \delta$ and $\alpha \Bbb{k} \beta$; by Convergence it follows that $\alpha \wedge \delta \Bbb{k} \beta$. Note that in the presence of rule (1), rule (3) is equivalent to Convergence, since the latter can also be derived from the former: suppose $\models \alpha \wedge \gamma \to \beta$ and $\alpha \Bbb{k} \gamma$, then by (3) $\alpha \wedge \beta \Bbb{k} \gamma$, and since $\models \alpha \wedge \beta \to \beta$, by (1) $\beta \Bbb{k} \gamma$. Since we already showed that (1) follows from Convergence, we conclude that Convergence exactly replaces (1) and (3).

(4) As said earlier, we prove this rule under the assumption that β is consistent. Suppose $\alpha \wedge \neg\delta \Bbb{k} \beta$, then by rule W $\not\models \beta \to \neg(\alpha \wedge \neg\delta)$, i.e., $\not\models \alpha \wedge \beta \to \delta$. From $\alpha \Bbb{k} \beta$ and the consistency of β, it follows that $\alpha \wedge \beta$ is consistent by rule W, as required. □

It should be noted that Conditional Reflexivity is nowhere used in the proof of Theorem 4. This indicates that it can be removed to obtain a truly minimal rule system for induction. However, system **I** possesses a nice symmetry, as shown by the next result.

Theorem 5. *Define* $\alpha \lll \beta$ *iff* $\neg\alpha \not\lll \beta$, *then* κ *is an I-relation iff* $\lll$ *is an I-relation.*

Proof. Using the rewrite rule $\alpha \kappa \beta \Rightarrow \neg\alpha \not\lll \beta$, Conditional Reflexivity rewrites to Consistency and *vice versa*, while Right Logical Equivalence and Convergence rewrite to themselves. Since this rewrite rule is its own inverse, this proves the theorem in both directions. □

This duality will reappear later, as it provides the link between weak and strong induction (Section 4.2).

System **I** has been built on the basis of rules (1)–(4), which in turn were derived from the notion of identification in the limit. The following section rounds off this analysis by demonstrating how one could use inductive consequence relations for performing the perhaps most elementary form of identification: identification by enumeration.

2.3 Identification by enumeration

If we assume that the set of inductive hypotheses is countable, we can formulate a very simple and general identification algorithm (Algorithm 6). We enumerate all the possible hypotheses, and search this enumeration for a hypothesis that is an inductive consequence of the premises seen so far. We stick to this hypothesis until we encounter a new premise which, together with the previous premises, contradicts it: then we continue searching the enumeration.

Algorithm 6 (Identification by enumeration).
Input: a presentation $\alpha_1, \alpha_2, \ldots$ for a target hypothesis $\beta \in \Sigma$, and an enumeration $\beta_1, \beta_2, \ldots$ of all the formulae in Σ.
Output: a sequence of formulae in Σ.

> **begin**
>> $i := 1; k := 1;$
>> **repeat**
>>> **while** $\{\alpha_j | j \leq i\} \not\lll \beta_k$ **do** $k := k + 1;$
>>> **output** β_k;
>>> $i := i + 1;$
>> **forever**;
> **end**.

Algorithm 6 is very powerful, but it has one serious drawback: the enumeration of hypotheses is completely unordered. Therefore, there is much duplication of work in checking hypotheses. There exist more practical versions of this algorithm, that can be applied if the set of hypotheses can be ordered. However, it is clear that if any search-based identification algorithm can achieve identification in the limit, identification by enumeration can as well, provided the inductive consequence relation is well-behaved. The following theorem states that I-relations are well-behaved in this sense.

Theorem 7. *Algorithm 6 performs identification in the limit if $\mathrel{\vert\!\sim}$ is an I-relation.*

Proof. Let α denote the entire presentation, and let β be the target hypothesis, i.e., $\alpha \mathrel{\vert\!\sim} \beta$. Furthermore, let β_n be the first formula in the enumeration, such that $\models \beta_n \leftrightarrow \beta$. We will show that the output sequence converges to β_n if α is sufficient for β.

Suppose β_k, $k < n$ precedes β_n in the presentation. By assumption, $\not\models \beta_k \leftrightarrow \beta$; if the presentation is sufficient, there will be a witness α_i such that $\{\alpha_1, \alpha_2, \ldots, \alpha_i\} \mathrel{\not\vert\!\sim} \beta_k$, so β_k will be discarded.

Since $\models \beta_n \leftrightarrow \beta$ and $\alpha \mathrel{\vert\!\sim} \beta$, it follows by Right Logical Equivalence that $\alpha \mathrel{\vert\!\sim} \beta_n$. By Convergence, $\alpha' \mathrel{\vert\!\sim} \beta_n$ for every initial segment α'. Therefore β_n is never discarded. □

Note that this proof only mentions the rules Right Logical Equivalence and Convergence. As said before, Consistency is needed to ensure that the presentation and the hypothesis can be combined in a meaningful way; Conditional Reflexivity is only needed to preserve the symmetry expressed in Theorem 5.

Induction would be infeasible if it could only be achieved by enumerating hypotheses. Likewise, inductive consequence relations would be useless if nothing stronger than I-relations would exist. In the following two sections, we present two families of inductive consequence relations, the first based on a view of induction as reversed deduction, and the second based on a view of induction as trying to extend the observations consistently. We will thereby adopt a terminology that is more familiar in the field of Machine Learning: observations are called *examples*, and inductive hypotheses are also called *explanations* of the examples.

3 Strong Induction

A *strong* inductive consequence relation is an I-relation that satisfies the following rule:

$$S' : \quad \frac{\models \beta \to \alpha}{\alpha \mathrel{\vert\!\sim} \beta}$$

This is a strengthening of the derived rule S in system I (Lemma 3). The intuition behind strong induction is, that it is a form of reversed deduction in some underlying logic or *base logic*. Rule S' states, that this base logic should allow all valid classical deductions. The base logic might also allow deductions that are classically invalid, but (for instance) plausible. Rule S' is a strengthening of S, because it does not require β to be consistent. In general, inconsistent inductive hypotheses are not very interesting; they arise as a borderline case, similar to tautologies that are deductive consequences of any set of premises. In the present context, this borderline case is instrumental in distinguishing strong induction from weak induction, as we will see in Section 4.

Rule S′ can be derived if we strengthen Conditional Reflexivity to

Reflexivity : $\alpha \mathrel{\vrule height 1.8ex depth 0pt\kern-0.1em\sim} \alpha$

Thus, an I-relation is a strong inductive consequence relation iff it satisfies Reflexivity. In the two rule systems for strong induction to come, Reflexivity replaces Conditional Reflexivity.

3.1   The system SC

The weakest system of rules for strong induction is called **SC**, which stands for Strong induction with a Cumulative base logic. For inductive consequence relations, cumulativity means that if $\beta \mathrel{\vrule height 1.8ex depth 0pt\kern-0.1em\sim} \gamma$, the hypotheses γ and $\beta \wedge \gamma$ inductively explain exactly the same facts. This principle can be expressed by two rules: Right Cut and Right Extension.

Definition 8 (The system **SC**). The system **SC** consists of the following six rules:

Reflexivity : $\alpha \mathrel{\vrule height 1.8ex depth 0pt\kern-0.1em\sim} \alpha$

Consistency : $\dfrac{\not\models \neg\alpha}{\neg\alpha \mathrel{\not\vrule height 1.8ex depth 0pt\kern-0.1em\sim} \alpha}$

Right Logical Equivalence : $\dfrac{\models \beta \leftrightarrow \gamma,\ \alpha \mathrel{\vrule height 1.8ex depth 0pt\kern-0.1em\sim} \beta}{\alpha \mathrel{\vrule height 1.8ex depth 0pt\kern-0.1em\sim} \gamma}$

Convergence : $\dfrac{\models \alpha \wedge \gamma \rightarrow \beta,\ \alpha \mathrel{\vrule height 1.8ex depth 0pt\kern-0.1em\sim} \gamma}{\beta \mathrel{\vrule height 1.8ex depth 0pt\kern-0.1em\sim} \gamma}$

Right Cut : $\dfrac{\alpha \mathrel{\vrule height 1.8ex depth 0pt\kern-0.1em\sim} \beta \wedge \gamma,\ \beta \mathrel{\vrule height 1.8ex depth 0pt\kern-0.1em\sim} \gamma}{\alpha \mathrel{\vrule height 1.8ex depth 0pt\kern-0.1em\sim} \gamma}$

Right Extension : $\dfrac{\alpha \mathrel{\vrule height 1.8ex depth 0pt\kern-0.1em\sim} \gamma,\ \beta \mathrel{\vrule height 1.8ex depth 0pt\kern-0.1em\sim} \gamma}{\alpha \mathrel{\vrule height 1.8ex depth 0pt\kern-0.1em\sim} \beta \wedge \gamma}$

□

Right Cut expresses that a part of an inductive hypothesis, which inductively explains another part, may be cut away from the hypothesis. In the presence of rule S′, it is a strengthening of Convergence. Right Extension states that an inductive hypothesis may be extended by some of the things it explains.

These latter two rules may look suspicious, because β takes the role of both example and hypothesis. For instance, Right Extension might not be applicable in a particular inductive frame, because $\beta \notin \Sigma$. The reader will recall the discussion in Section 1.2, where it was argued that even if this is so, such rules may describe useful properties of the process of (inductive) hypothesis formation. Here we encounter a case in point, because the two new rules interact to produce a rule that is satisfied in any inductive frame of which the consequence relation satisfies the rules of **SC**.

Lemma 9. *In* **SC**, *the following rule can be derived:*

$$\textbf{Compositionality}: \quad \frac{\alpha \mathrel{\vdash\!\sim} \gamma,\, \beta \mathrel{\vdash\!\sim} \gamma}{\alpha \wedge \beta \mathrel{\vdash\!\sim} \gamma}$$

Proof. Suppose $\alpha \mathrel{\vdash\!\sim} \gamma$ and $\beta \mathrel{\vdash\!\sim} \gamma$; by Right Extension we have $\alpha \mathrel{\vdash\!\sim} \beta \wedge \gamma$. Also, because $\alpha \wedge \beta \wedge \gamma \models \alpha \wedge \beta$, we have $\alpha \wedge \beta \mathrel{\vdash\!\sim} \alpha \wedge \beta \wedge \gamma$ by rule S'. Using Right Cut gives $\alpha \wedge \beta \mathrel{\vdash\!\sim} \beta \wedge \gamma$, and since by assumption $\beta \mathrel{\vdash\!\sim} \gamma$, we can cut away β from the righthand side to get $\alpha \wedge \beta \mathrel{\vdash\!\sim} \gamma$. □

Compositionality states that if an inductive hypothesis explains two examples separately, it also explains them jointly. It can be employed to speed up enumerative identification algorithms. Recall that in Algorithm 6 a new hypothesis must be checked against the complete set of previously seen examples. If we already know that the new hypothesis inductively explains some subset of those examples, then by Compositionality the remaining examples can be tested in isolation.

Furthermore, if the search strategy guarantees that the new hypothesis explains all the examples explained by the previous hypothesis, then we only need to test it against the last example which refuted the previous hypothesis. This requires an ordering of the hypothesis space, which in turn requires monotonicity of the base logic. This results in the following stronger system.

3.2 The system SM

There are several ways to define monotonicity of the base logic, for instance by adopting transitivity or contraposition. The next system is obtained by extending **SC** with a rule for contraposition (this makes transitivity a derived property).

Definition 10 (The system **SM**). The system **SM** consists of the rules of **SC** plus the following rule:

$$\textbf{Contraposition}: \quad \frac{\alpha \mathrel{\vdash\!\sim} \beta}{\neg\beta \mathrel{\vdash\!\sim} \neg\alpha}$$

□

As the following lemma shows, this results in a considerably more powerful system.

Lemma 11. *In* **SM**, *the following rules can be derived:*

$$\textbf{Explanation Strengthening}: \quad \frac{\models \gamma \rightarrow \beta,\, \alpha \mathrel{\vdash\!\sim} \beta}{\alpha \mathrel{\vdash\!\sim} \gamma}$$

$$\textbf{Explanation Updating}: \quad \frac{\models \gamma' \rightarrow \gamma,\, \alpha \mathrel{\vdash\!\sim} \gamma,\, \beta \mathrel{\vdash\!\sim} \gamma'}{\alpha \wedge \beta \mathrel{\vdash\!\sim} \gamma'}$$

Proof. (Explanation Strengthening) Suppose $\models \gamma \rightarrow \beta$ and $\alpha \mathrel{|\!\sim} \beta$; by Contraposition, it follows that $\neg\beta \mathrel{|\!\sim} \neg\alpha$. Convergence gives $\neg\gamma \mathrel{|\!\sim} \neg\alpha$, which finally results in $\alpha \mathrel{|\!\sim} \gamma$ by Contraposition.

(Explanation Updating) Suppose $\models \gamma' \rightarrow \gamma$ and $\alpha \mathrel{|\!\sim} \gamma$; by Explanation Strengthening we have $\alpha \mathrel{|\!\sim} \gamma'$. Assuming $\beta \mathrel{|\!\sim} \gamma'$, this gives $\alpha \wedge \beta \mathrel{|\!\sim} \gamma'$ by Compositionality. □

Explanation Strengthening expresses that any γ logically implying some inductive explanation β of a set of examples α is also an explanation of α. Consequently, the set of inductive explanations of a given set of examples is completely determined by its weakest elements according to logical implication. Since logical implication is reflexive and transitive, it is a quasi-ordering on Σ, which can be turned into a partial ordering by considering equivalence classes of logically equivalent formulae (in other words, the Lindenbaum algebra of Σ).

Explanation Updating is a combination of Explanation Strengthening and Compositionality, which shows how to employ this ordering in identification algorithms. It states that if γ is a hypothesis explaining the examples α seen so far but not the next example β, it can be replaced by some γ' which (*i*) logically implies γ and (*ii*) explains β. This clearly shows that we don't need to test the new hypothesis γ' against the previous examples α.

The properties expressed by these rules have been used in many AI-approaches to inductive reasoning (Mitchell 1982, Shapiro 1983). The results in this section have been presented to show how they can be derived systematically within our framework. For instance, we have shown that an important property like Explanation Strengthening requires monotonicity of the base logic.

4 Weak Induction

The ideas described in this section have been the main motivating force for the research reported in this paper. While induction and deduction are closely related, they can be related in more than one way. Weak induction provides an alternative for strong induction, which only considers inductive hypotheses from which the examples are provable. Weak induction aims at supplementing the examples with knowledge which is only implicitly contained in those examples.

In Section 1.1, we provided an example of weak induction: inferring 'every person has exactly one mother' from a collection of facts. This is not a strong inductive argument, since the induced rule does not entail the facts (regardless of the base logic). Rather, the rule does not contradict the facts: it should not imply their falsity. That is, weak inductive consequence relations satisfy the following rule:

$$\mathbf{W'}: \quad \frac{\alpha \mathrel{|\!\sim} \beta}{\not\models \beta \rightarrow \neg\alpha}$$

Note that this disallows the possibility that β is inconsistent, showing that some strong inductive consequence relations are not weak inductive consequence relations.

Rule W$'$ is a strengthening of rule W, and can be derived in **I** if we strengthen Consistency to

Weak Reflexivity : $\neg\alpha \not\Vdash \alpha$

Weak Reflexivity expresses that an inductive hypothesis never explains its negation. It replaces Consistency in the two systems for weak induction we will consider in this section.

4.1 The system WC

The weakest system for weak inductive reasoning is called **WC**. It models weak induction with a cumulative base logic. The principle of cumulativity for weak inductive consequence relations is stated as follows: if $\neg\beta \not\Vdash \gamma$, then β can be added to the inductive hypothesis γ without changing the set of examples it explains. This principle requires weak counterparts of the corresponding rules in **SC**.

Definition 12 (The system **WC**). The system **WC** consists of the following six rules:

Conditional Reflexivity : $\dfrac{\not\models \neg\alpha}{\alpha \Vdash \alpha}$

Weak Reflexivity : $\neg\alpha \not\Vdash \alpha$

Right Logical Equivalence : $\dfrac{\models \beta \leftrightarrow \gamma, \alpha \Vdash \beta}{\alpha \Vdash \gamma}$

Convergence : $\dfrac{\models \alpha \wedge \gamma \rightarrow \beta, \alpha \Vdash \gamma}{\beta \Vdash \gamma}$

Weak Right Cut : $\dfrac{\alpha \Vdash \beta \wedge \gamma, \neg\beta \not\Vdash \gamma}{\alpha \Vdash \gamma}$

Weak Right Extension : $\dfrac{\alpha \Vdash \gamma, \neg\beta \not\Vdash \gamma}{\alpha \Vdash \beta \wedge \gamma}$

□

In this system, we could derive a weak counterpart to Compositionality, expressing that an example, of which the negation is not explained, can be added to the premises. However, this does not express a very useful property. In general, Compositionality itself does not apply to weak inductive reasoning. Consequently, we must always store all previously seen examples, and check them each time we switch to a new inductive hypothesis (an illustration of this will be provided in Section 4.3).

4.2 The system WM

In a monotonic base logic, β does not entail $\neg\alpha$ if and only if α does not entail $\neg\beta$. This property means that a weak inductive consequence relation based on a monotonic base logic is *symmetric*. Again, we stress that although Symmetry is obviously not a property of any form of inductive reasoning, it may be a useful property of the inductive consequence relation involved in weak inductive reasoning.

Definition 13 (The system **WM**). The system **WM** consists of the rules of **WC** plus the following rule:

Symmetry : $\dfrac{\alpha \mathrel{\vdash\mkern-9mu\mid} \beta}{\beta \mathrel{\vdash\mkern-9mu\mid} \alpha}$

$\square$

Similar to **SM**, **WM** induces an ordering of the hypothesis space that can be exploited in enumerative identification algorithms. Search will however proceed in the opposite direction of logically weaker formulae.

Lemma 14. *In* **WM***, the following rule can be derived:*

Explanation Weakening : $\dfrac{\models \beta \rightarrow \gamma, \alpha \mathrel{\vdash\mkern-9mu\mid} \beta}{\alpha \mathrel{\vdash\mkern-9mu\mid} \gamma}$

Proof. Suppose $\models \beta \rightarrow \gamma$ and $\alpha \mathrel{\vdash\mkern-9mu\mid} \beta$; by Symmetry, it follows that $\beta \mathrel{\vdash\mkern-9mu\mid} \alpha$. Convergence gives $\gamma \mathrel{\vdash\mkern-9mu\mid} \alpha$, which finally results in $\alpha \mathrel{\vdash\mkern-9mu\mid} \gamma$ by Symmetry. $\square$

In fact, **SM** and **WM** are interdefinable in the following sense.

Lemma 15. *Define* $\alpha \mathrel{\not\vdash\mkern-9mu\mid} \beta$ *iff* $\neg\alpha \mathrel{\not\vdash\mkern-9mu\mid} \beta$, *then* $\mathrel{\vdash\mkern-9mu\mid}$ *satisfies the rules of* **SM** *iff* $\mathrel{\vdash\mkern-9mu\mid}$ *satisfies the rules of* **WM**.

Proof. Using the rewrite rule $\alpha \mathrel{\vdash\mkern-9mu\mid} \beta \Rightarrow \neg\alpha \mathrel{\not\vdash\mkern-9mu\mid} \beta$, each rule of **SM** rewrites (after re-arranging) to a rule of **WM**: Reflexivity rewrites to Weak Reflexivity, Consistency rewrites to Conditional Reflexivity, Convergence and Right Logical Equivalence rewrite to themselves, Right Cut to Weak Right Extension, Right Extension to Weak Right Cut, and Contraposition rewrites to Symmetry. $\square$

We encountered this transformation before, when we noted that it leaves system **I** invariant (Theorem 5).

4.3 An application of weak induction

In this section, we will illustrate the usefulness of weak induction by applying it to the problem of inducing integrity constraints in a deductive database. Tuples of a database relation (i.e., ground facts) play the role of examples, and hypotheses are integrity constraints on this relation. The induction algorithm is fully described in (Flach 1990), and has also been implemented. In (Flach 1993), we describe how the induced integrity constraints can be utilised for restructuring the database in a more meaningful way. In the current implementation, hypotheses are restricted to functional and multivalued dependencies between attributes.

Suppose `child` is a relation with five attributes: child's first name, father's first and last name, and mother's first and last name. Given the tuples listed in Table 1, we might for example be interested in the attributes that functionally determine the mother's last name (a socalled *functional dependency*).

Table 1. A database relation

```
child(john,frank,johnson,mary,peterson).
child(peter,frank,johnson,mary,peterson).
child(john,robert,miller,gwen,mcintyre).
child(ann,john,miller,dolly,parton).
child(millie,frank,miller,dolly,mcintyre).
```

Two such dependencies that are satisfied in Table 1 are:[4]

$$\text{child}(N, \_, FL, \_, ML1) \land \text{child}(N, \_, FL, \_, ML2) \rightarrow ML1 = ML2$$

$$\text{child}(\_, FF, FL, \_, ML1) \land \text{child}(\_, FF, FL, \_, ML2) \rightarrow ML1 = ML2$$

The first formula states that child's first name and father's last name determine mother's last name, and the second formula says that father's first and last names determine mother's last name. Note that these formulae are not logical consequences of the tuples, nor are the tuples logical consequences of the formulae.

How would we induce these dependencies? According to Explanation Weakening, we can start with the strongest hypothesis: all mothers have the same last name (it is determined by the empty set of attributes). This is expressed by the following formula:

$$\text{child}(\_, \_, \_, \_, ML1) \land \text{child}(\_, \_, \_, \_, ML2) \rightarrow ML1 = ML2$$

Since this formula is inconsistent with the tuples in Table 1, we will make minimal changes in order to get weaker constraints, which is done by unifying variables on the lefthand side.

For instance, the first and third tuple lead to the following false formula:

---

[4] We follow the Prolog conventions: all variables are universally quantified, and the underscores denote unique variables.

```
child(john, frank, johnson, mary, peterson) ∧
child(john, robert, miller, gwen, mcintyre)
        → peterson = mcintyre
```

The formula is false because = is interpreted as syntactical identity. It shows how we can make minimal changes to the original formula: by unifying variables in those positions for which the tuples have different values. This leads to the following three hypotheses:

$$child(\_, FF, \_, \_, ML1) \wedge child(\_, FF, \_, \_, ML2) \rightarrow ML1 = ML2$$

$$child(\_, \_, FL, \_, ML1) \wedge child(\_, \_, FL, \_, ML2) \rightarrow ML1 = ML2$$

$$child(\_, \_, \_, MF, ML1) \wedge child(\_, \_, \_, MF, ML2) \rightarrow ML1 = ML2$$

Each of these hypotheses is again tested for consistency with the data.

If we search in a breadth-first fashion, we will eventually encounter all sets of attributes that determine the mother's last name. Note that, any time we switch to a new hypothesis, we have to check it against the *complete* set of tuples (Compositionality does not hold).

In this setting, there are rather strong restrictions on both Γ (the tuples) and Σ (the functional dependencies). They are needed to ensure convergence of the induction process, and also block properties like Symmetry. On the other hand, Γ should be rich enough to allow sufficient presentations for any hypothesis in Σ (they should form what Shapiro (1983) calls an *admissible pair*). For instance, let Σ be the set of *multivalued dependencies* that hold for a given database relation. An example of such a dependency is

```
child(N1, FF1, FL1, MF, ML) ∧
child(N2, FF2, FL2, MF, ML)
        → child(N1, FF2, FL2, MF, ML)
```

which states that children have all the fathers of any child of a certain mother. Such dependencies can be learned in exactly the same way as functional dependencies. The point is, that Γ should now contain positive *and negative* ground facts, since a given multivalued dependency can only be refuted by two tuples in the relation and one tuple known to be not in the relation.

5 Conclusion and Future Work

The contributions presented in this paper are twofold. First of all, we have given minimal conditions for inductive consequence relations, which are powerful enough to allow identification in the limit. On the other hand, these conditions are liberal enough as to leave room for non-standard forms of inductive

56

reasoning. Our second contribution lies in identifying weak induction as such a non-standard form of induction. We have illustrated the usefulness of weak induction by applying it to the problem of inducing integrity constraints in a deductive database.

We are currently working on the model-theoretic counterpart of the proof-theoretic characterisation presented in this paper. On the basis of such a model theory, we should be able to substantiate our claim that the rules of system **I** indeed express necessary properties of an inductive consequence relation. Another topic of interest is the study of induction with respect to other base logics, such as modal, temporal and intuitionistic logics.

Acknowledgements

I would like to thank John-Jules Meyer, Yao-Hua Tan, Cees Witteveen, and the two anonymous referees for their insightful remarks.

References

Flach, P.A.: "Inductive characterisation of database relations," in: Z.W. Ras, M. Ze-mankowa & M.L. Emrich (eds.), *Proc. International Symposium on Methodologies for Intelligent Systems*, Amsterdam: North-Holland (1990) 371-378. Full version appeared as ITK Research Report no. 23.

Flach, P.A.: "An analysis of various forms of 'jumping to conclusions'," in: K.P. Jan-tke (ed.), *Analogical and Inductive Inference AII'92*, Lecture Notes in Artifical Intelligence 642, Berlin: Springer Verlag (1992) 170-186.

Flach, P.A.: "Predicate invention in Inductive Data Engineering," in: P.B. Bradzil (ed.), *Proc. European Conference on Machine Learning ECML'93*, Lecture Notes in Artifical Intelligence 667, Berlin: Springer Verlag (1993) 83-94.

Gabbay, D.M.: "Theoretical foundations for non-monotonic reasoning in expert sys-tems," in: K.R. Apt (ed.), *Logics and Models of Concurrent Systems*, Berlin: Springer Verlag (1985) 439-457.

Gärdenfors. P.: *Knowledge in Flux*, Cambridge, MA: The MIT Press, 1988.

Gärdenfors, P.: "Belief revision and nonmonotonic logic: two sides of the same coin?" in: *Proc. Ninth European Conference on AI*, London: Pitman (1990) 768-773.

Gold, E.M.: "Language identification in the limit," in: *Information and Control* 10 (1967), 447-474.

Kraus, S., D. Lehmann and M. Magidor: "Nonmonotonic reasoning, preferential models and cumulative logics," in: *Artificial Intelligence* 44 (1990) 167-207.

Mitchell, T.M.: "Generalization as search," in:*Artificial Intelligence* 18 (1982) 2, 203-226.

Shapiro, E.Y.: *Algorithmic program debugging*. Cambridge MA: MIT Press, 1983.

Shoham, Y.: "A semantic approach to nonmonotonic logics," in: *Proc. Eleventh In-ternational Joint Conference on AI*, Los Altos, CA: Morgan Kaufmann (1987) 1304-1310.

Zadrozny, W.: *On rules of abduction*. IBM Research Report (August 1991).

Automated Reasoning with Uncertainties

Flávio S. Corrêa da Silva[1], Dave S. Robertson[2], Jane Hesketh[2]

[1] Instituto de Matemática e Estatística – Cid. Universitária "ASO" – PO Box 20570 – 01498 São Paulo SP Brazil – E-mail: fcs@ime.usp.br
[2] Dept. of Artificial Intelligence – Univ. of Edinburgh – 80 South Bridge – Edinburgh – Scotland EH1 1HN – E-mail: {dr/jane}@aisb.ed.ac.uk

Abstract. In this work we assume that uncertainty is a multifaceted concept and present a system for automated reasoning with multiple representations of uncertainty.

We present a case study on developing a computational language for reasoning with uncertainty, starting with a semantically sound and computationally tractable language and gradually extending it with specialised syntactic constructs to represent measures of uncertainty, while preserving its unambiguous semantic characterization and computability properties. Our initial language is the language of normal clauses with SLDNF as the inference rule, and we select three specific facets of uncertainty for our study: *vagueness*, *statistics* and *degrees of belief*.

The resulting language is *semantically sound* and *computationally tractable*. It also admits relatively efficient implementations employing $\alpha - \beta$ *pruning* and *caching*.

1 Introduction

When reasoning we frequently use uncertain information, i.e., information that is incomplete, vague, only partially reliable or based on statistical associations. Hence, when building automated reasoning systems, we frequently need tools and mechanisms to represent uncertainty.

In this work we present a *system for automated reasoning with multiple representations of uncertainty:* uncertainty is a multifaceted concept, and because of this there are several techniques for measuring it. Our focus in this work is on problems which present more than one of these facets, problems, hence, for which it is important to differentiate several kinds of uncertainty.

We present a case study on developing a computational language for reasoning with uncertainty, starting with a semantically sound and computationally tractable language and gradually extending it to represent measures of uncertainty, preserving its unambiguous semantic characterisation and computability properties. Our initial language is the language of *normal clauses with SLDNF as the inference rule* (i.e., the language of pure PROLOG (Kunen 1989)), which is expressive enough to represent a significant portion of first-order logic, admits computationally tractable implementations, and has a well defined formal semantics.

We select three specific facets of uncertainty for our study, which are not exhaustive but cover many situations found in practical problems. These facets

are (i) *vagueness*, which describes the extent to which a non-categorical statement is true - a vague predicate is one which truth-value admits intermediate
values between *true* and *false* (e.g., the predicate "fat" qualifying the weight of a
person); *statistics*, which describes the likelihood of selecting an element or class
of elements belonging to the domain of discourse; and *degrees of belief*, which
describe the belief apportioned to statements represented by sentences in our
language.

With each of these facets we associate a specific measure. We associate *fuzzy
measures* to vagueness (Dubois and Prade 1988), *probabilities on the domain* to
statistics (Bacchus 1990b) and *probabilities on possible worlds* to degrees of belief (Corrêa da Silva and Bundy 1991, Nilsson 1986, Shafer 1976). The resulting
language is *semantically sound* and *computationally tractable*, using in its implementation the standard optimisation techniques of $\alpha - \beta$ *pruning* and *caching*.

In Section 2 we review the main concepts of fuzzy set theory and probability theory which are used throughout the rest of the work. In Section 3 we
introduce a logic programming language that can treat fuzzy predicates. The
language treats negation by finite failure and is sound with respect to com-
pleted models. In Section 4 we extend this language to deal with probabilities
on the domain. The language implements a significant subset of the logic L_p
(Bacchus 1990b), extended with fuzzy predicates. The logic L_p was known to
have computable subsets, but we are not aware of any previous implementations
of it. In Section 5 we introduce the concepts of possible worlds and degrees of
belief to the language. These concepts are introduced in a way that establishes
close relations between our formalism and other well-known formalisms like Incidence Calculus (Bundy 1985, Corrêa da Silva and Bundy 1991), Probabilistic
Logic (Nilsson 1986) and the Dempster-Shafer Theory of Evidence (Shafer 1976,
Fagin and Halpern 1989a). Finally, Section 7 summarises and concludes this
work.

2   General Definitions

In this section we introduce the concept of *fuzzy sets and relations*, to be used
later in the interpretation of fuzzy sentences. Then we review the basic concepts
of *probability theory* and its extensions to fuzzy events.

2.1   Fuzzy measures

A fuzzy membership function measures the degree to which an element belongs
to a subset or, alternatively, the degree of similarity between the class (subset)
to which an element belongs and a reference class. Formally, a fuzzy subset F of
a referential set D is defined by an arbitrary mapping $\mu_F : D \to [0, 1]$, in which,
for an element $d \in D$, $\mu_F(d) = 1$ corresponds to the intuitive notion that $d \in F$
and $\mu_F(d) = 0$ to the notion that $d \notin F$ (Dubois and Prade 1989).

Set-theoretic operations can be extended to fuzzy sets by means of *triangular
norms and conorms*. A *triangular norm* is any function $T : [0, 1] \times [0, 1] \to [0, 1]$
such that:

- $T(x, 1) = x$ (boundary condition);
- $x_1 \leq x_2, y_1 \leq y_2 \Rightarrow T(x_1, y_1) \leq T(x_2, y_2)$ (monotonicity);
- $T(x, y) = T(y, x)$ (commutativity);
- $T(T(x, y), z) = T(x, T(y, z))$ (associativity).

The *conorm of a triangular norm* is the function $S : [0, 1] \times [0, 1] \rightarrow [0, 1]$ defined by:

$$S(x, y) = 1 - T(1 - x, 1 - y).$$

Furthermore, following (Dubois and Prade 1989), any function $C : [0, 1] \rightarrow [0, 1] : C(\mu_F(d)) = 1 - \mu_F(d)$ obeys the requirements as extension of complementation.

Not all algebraic properties of set operations are necessarily shared by triangular norms and conorms. In fact, as presented in (Klement 1982), the only norms and conorms that are also *distributive* and *idempotent* - i.e., that obey the following rules:

- $\left. \begin{cases} S(x, T(y, z)) = T(S(x, y), S(x, z)) \\ T(x, S(y, z)) = S(T(x, y), T(x, z)) \end{cases} \right\}$ (distributivity);
- $T(x, x) = x$ and $S(x, x) = x$ (idempotency)

- are $T = min$ and $S = max$ - known as Zadeh's triangular norms and conorms. Henceforth, in order to keep fuzzy set operations as close as possible to conventional set operations, we adopt the following functions as our extended set operations of intersection, union and complementation:
   - intersection: $\mu_{A \cap B}(x) = min\{\mu_A(x), \mu_B(x)\}$;
   - union: $\mu_{A \cup B}(x) = max\{\mu_A(x), \mu_B(x)\}$;
   - complementation: $\mu_{\neg A}(x) = 1 - \mu_A(x)$.
These are the most commonly used definitions of fuzzy set operations.

2.2 Probability measures

Given a finite set D, an *algebra* χ_D on D is a set of subsets of D such that (i) $D \in \chi_D$; (ii) $A \in \chi_D \Rightarrow \neg A \in \chi_D$; (iii) $A, B \in \chi_D \Rightarrow A \cup B \in \chi_D$.

Any subset of D is called an *event* on D. Events belonging to χ_D are called *measurable events*.

The *basis* χ'_D of an algebra χ_D is the subset of χ_D such that (i) $\{\} \notin \chi'_D$; (ii) $A, B \in \chi'_D \Rightarrow A \cap B = \{\}$; (iii) $K \in \chi_D \Rightarrow \exists A_1, ..., A_n \in \chi'_D : K = \bigcup_1^n A_i$.

A *probability measure* on χ_D is a function $\mathcal{P} : \chi_D \rightarrow [0, 1]$ such that (i) $\mathcal{P}(D) = 1$ (total probability); (ii) $A \cap B = \{\} \Rightarrow \mathcal{P}(A \cup B) = \mathcal{P}(A) + \mathcal{P}(B)$ (finite additivity).

As shown in (Fagin and Halpern 1989a), once $\mathcal{P}$ is defined for χ'_D it can be extended to the whole algebra by finite additivity. This is useful as we can specify a probability measure by defining its value only for the elements of χ'_D.

Given two measurable events $A, B \in \chi_D$, the *conditional probability* $\mathcal{P}(A|B)$ is defined as:

$$P(A|B) = \begin{cases} \frac{P(A \cap B)}{P(B)}, & P(B) \neq 0 \\ 0, & P(B) = 0 \end{cases}$$

Two measurable events A, B are called *independent* iff $P(A|B) = P(A)$ which, as a corollary, gives that $P(A \cap B) = P(A) \times P(B)$.

The set D can be partitioned into m subsets $D_1, ..., D_m$ such that (i) $D_i \cap D_j = \{\}, i, j = 1, ..., m$, and (ii) $D = \bigcup_1^m D_i$.

We can have independent algebras (two algebras χ_1 and χ_2 are *independent* iff each event $X_i \in \chi_1$ is independent of every event $Y_j \in \chi_2$ and vice-versa) χ_{Di} and probability measures P_i for each set D_i. If we assume that all events in each χ_{Di} are *pairwise independent*, we can extend measures to cartesian products of the sets D_i of a partition of D: the cartesian product of a collection of bases of algebras of elements $D_1, ..., D_m$ of a partition of D is the basis χ' of an algebra of the cartesian product of the sets $D_1, ..., D_m$, and the measure P on the corresponding algebra χ is defined as:

- $P : \chi \to [0, 1]$.
- $P(\mathbf{A}) = \prod_1^m P_i(A_i)$.

where

- $\mathbf{A} = [A_1, ..., A_m]$,
- $A_i \in \chi_{Di}$,
- P_i is the probability measure defined on χ_{Di}.

Probability measures can be extended to *non-measurable events*, i.e., sets $A_j \in 2^D \setminus \chi_D$. Given D, χ_D and P, we define the *inner and outer extensions to* P (P_* and P^*, respectively) as (Dudley 1989):

- $P_*, P^* : 2^D \to [0, 1]$
- $P_*(A) = sup\{P(X) : X \subseteq A, X \in \chi_D\} = P(\bigcup X : X \subseteq A, X \in \chi'_D)$
- $P^*(A) = inf\{P(X) : A \subseteq X, X \in \chi_D\} = P(\bigcup X : X \cap A \neq \{\}, X \in \chi'_D)$

Finally, inner and outer measures can be extended to cartesian products of a partition of D. Given a collection $D_1, ..., D_m$ of elements of a partition of D, and given also the algebras χ_{Di} and probability measures P_i of each $D_i, i = 1, ..., m$, we have:

- $P_{m*}, P_m^* : 2^{D_1 \times ... \times D_m} \to [0, 1]$
- $P_{m*}(A) = sup\{P_m(X) : X \subseteq A, X \in \chi\} = P_m(\bigcup X : X \subseteq A, X \in \chi')$.
- $P_m^*(A) = inf\{P_m(X) : A \subseteq X, X \in \chi\} = P_m(\bigcup X : X \cap A \neq \{\}, X \in \chi')$.

The measures P_{m*} and P_m^* can be regarded as approximations from below and from above to the probabilities of non-measurable events: if we could evaluate the probability $P_m(A)$, then we would have that $P_{m*}(A) \leq P_m(A) \leq P_m^*(A)$. Indeed, for measurable events we have that $P_{m*}(A) = P_m(A) = P_m^*(A)$.

As shown in (Fagin and Halpern 1989b), the best approximations we have for conditional probabilities of non-measurable events can be given by the following expressions:

$$\mathcal{P}_*(A|B) = \begin{cases} \frac{\mathcal{P}_*(A\cap B)}{\mathcal{P}_*(A\cap B)+\mathcal{P}^*(\neg A\cap B)}, & \mathcal{P}_*(A\cap B)+\mathcal{P}^*(\neg A\cap B)\neq 0 \\ 0, & \mathcal{P}_*(A\cap B)+\mathcal{P}^*(\neg A\cap B)=0 \end{cases}$$

$$\mathcal{P}^*(A|B) = \begin{cases} \frac{\mathcal{P}^*(A\cap B)}{\mathcal{P}^*(A\cap B)+\mathcal{P}_*(\neg A\cap B)}, & \mathcal{P}^*(A\cap B)+\mathcal{P}_*(\neg A\cap B)\neq 0 \\ 0, & \mathcal{P}^*(A\cap B)+\mathcal{P}_*(\neg A\cap B)=0 \end{cases}$$

For the case of measures on χ, these expressions can be stated as:

$$P_{m*}(A|B) = \begin{cases} \frac{\mathcal{P}_{m*}(A\cap B)}{\mathcal{P}_{m*}(A\cap B)+\mathcal{P}_m^*(\neg A\cap B)}, & \mathcal{P}_{m*}(A\cap B)+\mathcal{P}_m^*(\neg A\cap B)\neq 0 \\ 0, & \mathcal{P}_{m*}(A\cap B)+\mathcal{P}_m^*(\neg A\cap B)=0 \end{cases}$$

$$\mathcal{P}_m^*(A|B) = \begin{cases} \frac{\mathcal{P}_m^*(A\cap B)}{\mathcal{P}_m^*(A\cap B)+\mathcal{P}_{m*}(\neg A\cap B)}, & \mathcal{P}_m^*(A\cap B)+\mathcal{P}_{m*}(\neg A\cap B)\neq 0 \\ 0, & \mathcal{P}_m^*(A\cap B)+\mathcal{P}_{m*}(\neg A\cap B)=0 \end{cases}$$

2.3 Probabilities of fuzzy events

A sentence containing vague predicates defines a fuzzy set of elements of the domain of discourse (or of elements of the cartesian product of members of one of the partitions of the domain of discourse). Hence, if we allow fuzzy predicates in our language, we must be prepared to specify the probability of fuzzy events.

In (Klement 1982) the concept of algebra is extended to fuzzy sets and in (Piasecki 1988, Smets 1982, Turksen 1988) the definition of the probability of a fuzzy event is presented, reputed as originally by L. Zadeh. A *fuzzy algebra* on D is defined by analogy with the concept of an algebra. It is a set χ_D^F of fuzzy subsets of D, such that (i) $\mu(A) = $ constant $\Rightarrow A \in \chi_D^F$; (ii) $A \in \chi_D^F \Rightarrow \neg A \in \chi_D^F$; (iii) $A, B \in \chi_D^F \Rightarrow A \cup B \in \chi_D^F$.

Given an algebra χ_D and a probability measure $\mathcal{P}$ on χ_D, the probability of the fuzzy subset $A \in \chi_D^F$ is defined for every measurable A (i.e., for every $A \in \chi_D$), and is given by the Lebesgue-Stieltjes integral

$$\mathcal{P}^F(A) = \int_D \mu(A) d\mathcal{P}$$

From the computational point of view, we can access upper and lower bounds for this integral, related to the extreme values of the membership function in $A \cap A_i, A_i \in \chi_D'$:

$$\sum_{A_i \subseteq A} P(A_i) \times min\{\mu(a_i): a_i \in A_i \cap A\} \leq \mathcal{P}^F(A) \leq \sum_{A_i \cap A \neq \{\}} P(A_i) \times max\{\mu(a_i): a_i \in A_i \cap A\}$$

These expressions can be extended to the non-measurable cases and to $2^{D_1 \times ... \times D_m}$, where $D_1, ..., D_m$ form a partition of D. Given a non-measurable fuzzy event A, we have:

$$\sum_{A_i \subseteq A} P_m(A_i) \times min\{\mu(a_i): a_i \in A_i \cap A\} \leq \mathcal{P}_m^F(A) \leq \sum_{A_i \cap A \neq \{\}} P_m(A_i) \times max\{\mu(a_i): a_i \in A_i \cap A\}$$

And for the case of conditional probabilities, we have:

$$\mathcal{P}_{m*}^{F}(A|B) = \begin{cases} \dfrac{\mathcal{P}_{m*1}}{\mathcal{P}_{m*2}+\mathcal{P}_{m3}^{*}}, & \mathcal{P}_{m*2}+\mathcal{P}_{m3}^{*} \neq 0 \\ \\ 0, & otherwise \end{cases}$$

$$\mathcal{P}_{m}^{F*}(A|B) = \begin{cases} min\{1,\dfrac{\mathcal{P}_{m1}^{*}}{\mathcal{P}_{m2}^{*}+\mathcal{P}_{m*3}}\}, & \mathcal{P}_{m2}^{*}+\mathcal{P}_{m*3} \neq 0 \\ \\ 0, & otherwise \end{cases}$$

where

$\mathcal{P}_{m*1} = \sum_{A_i \subseteq [A\cap B]} \mathcal{P}_m(A_i) \times min\{\mu(a_i) : a_i \in A_i \cap [A\cap B]\}$

$\mathcal{P}_{m*2} = \sum_{A_i \subseteq [A\cap B]} \mathcal{P}_m(A_i) \times max\{\mu(a_i) : a_i \in A_i \cap [A\cap B]\}$

$\mathcal{P}_{m*3} = \sum_{A_i \subseteq [\neg A\cap B]} \mathcal{P}_m(A_i) \times min\{\mu(a_i) : a_i \in A_i \cap [\neg A\cap B]\}$

$\mathcal{P}_{m1}^{*} = \sum_{A_i \cap [A\cap B]\neq\{\}} \mathcal{P}_m(A_i) \times max\{\mu(a_i) : a_i \in A_i \cap [A\cap B]\}$

$\mathcal{P}_{m2}^{*} = \sum_{A_i \cap [A\cap B]\neq\{\}} \mathcal{P}_m(A_i) \times min\{\mu(a_i) : a_i \in A_i \cap [A\cap B]\}$

$\mathcal{P}_{m3}^{*} = \sum_{A_i \cap [\neg A\cap B]\neq\{\}} \mathcal{P}_m(A_i) \times max\{\mu(a_i) : a_i \in A_i \cap [\neg A\cap B]\}$

3   A Language Supporting Fuzzy Predicates

The relationship between fuzzy logics and the resolution principle is well established. Since (Lee 1972), one of the pioneering works in the area, several proposals have been made that aim at richer languages in respect of both the logical and the fuzzy relations supported.

In (Lee 1972) the language is limited to *definite clauses* (Apt 1987) *allowing fuzzy predicates with truth-values always greater than 0.5*. The semantics of the relevant connectives is defined according to Zadeh's triangular norms and conorms and resolution is extended to propagate truth-values in a way that is sound and complete with respect to the Herbrand interpretation of sets of clauses. Several implementations based on (Lee 1972) have been proposed, e.g., the ones described in (Hinde 1986, Ishizuka and Kanai 1985, Orci 1989).

More recent developments (Fitting 1988, Fitting 1990, Kifer and Subrahmanian 1991, Shapiro 1983, Van Emden 1986) have focused on fixpoint semantics, either working with definite programs or approaching the definition of negation by means other than finite failure. We adopt negation by finite failure here, in order to have the more conventional languages which are based on this principle (e.g., pure PROLOG) as proper subsets of our language. This choice is corroborated by the results found in (Turi 1989, Kunen 1989), which determine large classes of *normal programs* with a well-defined declarative semantics.

3.1   Reasoning with fuzzy predicates

The language presented here is defined after (Kunen 1989). The class of logic programs supported by this language is that of *function-free normal programs* under restrictions of *non-cyclicality*, *strictness with respect to queries*, and *allowedness* (see definitions of these terms in (Turi 1989, Kunen 1989, Corrêa da Silva 1992)), and its inference procedure - *SLDNF* - is known to be *sound* and *complete* with respect to the model of the *Clark's completion* of programs in the language (Kunen 1989):

Theorem 1. *Given a program P and a query ψ:*
1. *$Comp(P) \models \psi$ iff ψ belongs to the success set of P ($\psi R\sigma$);*
2. *$Comp(P) \models \neg\psi$ iff ψ belongs to the finite failure set of P (ψF).*

This defines a rich subset of first-order logic with a computationally efficient inference procedure and a formally specified declarative semantics.

A fuzzy predicate can be defined by analogy with the concept of fuzzy sets previously presented. The interpretation of predicates can be generalised to a function $I(p) : D^n \rightarrow [0,1]$, with the extreme values corresponding to the previous values $\top$ and $\bot$ (namely, $\top \equiv 1$ and $\bot \equiv 0$). This function can be construed as a fuzzy membership function and the logical connectives can be interpreted as fuzzy set operators – '$\neg$' corresponding to complementation, '$\vee$' corresponding to union, '$\wedge$' corresponding to intersection, and '$\leftrightarrow$' corresponding to set-equivalence. Intuitively, the semantics of a closed formula becomes a "degree of truth", rather than simply one value out of $\{\top, \bot\}$. Let τ denote this value and $T(\psi, \tau)$ state that "the truth-degree of ψ is τ". This evaluation can be made operational using an *extended SLDNF (e-SLDNF)* procedure, to be related to the model of an *extended completion* of a program P ($e\text{-}Comp(P)$). We assume that the *unit clauses* (and only they) in the program express truth-degrees, that is, unit clauses are of the form $T(p, \tau)$, where $\tau > 0$.

The *extended completion* of a program P ($e\text{-}Comp(P)$) is defined as presented in Fig. 1.

A model for a program containing fuzzy predicates is any interpretation for which every expression φ occurring in $e\text{-}Comp(P)$ has a truth-value $\tau > 0$.

Two classes of formulae can be identified in $e\text{-}Comp(P)$:

- *unit formulae*, generated by rule 1 or from the unit clauses occurring in P; and
- *equivalence formulae*, i.e., the remaining ones, all of them containing the connective $\leftrightarrow$.

The connectives occurring in $e\text{-}Comp(P)$ are interpreted according to the truth-functions defined below:
Assuming that:

- $T(\delta, \tau_\delta)$, and
- $T(\psi, \tau_\psi)$

We have that:

- $T((\delta \wedge \psi), \tau) \Rightarrow \tau = min\{\tau_\delta, \tau_\psi\}$
- $T((\delta \vee \psi), \tau) \Rightarrow \tau = max\{\tau_\delta, \tau_\psi\}$
- $T((\neg\delta), \tau) \Rightarrow \tau = 1 - \tau_\delta$
- $\begin{cases} T((\delta \leftrightarrow \psi), 1) \Rightarrow \tau_\delta = \tau_\psi \\ T((\delta \leftrightarrow \psi), 0) \Rightarrow \tau_\delta \neq \tau_\psi \end{cases}$

Rules:

1. $$\frac{Def_p=\{\}}{\forall \mathbf{X}[T(\neg p(\mathbf{X}),1)]}$$

2. $$\frac{Def_p=\{p(\mathbf{t}_i)\leftarrow\psi_i:i=1,...,k\}\neq\{\}}{\forall \mathbf{X}[T(p(\mathbf{X}),\tau)\leftrightarrow max\{\tau_i:(\mathbf{X}=\mathbf{t}_i)}$$
$$\wedge[(\psi_i\neq\{\}\wedge T(\psi_i,\tau_i))$$
$$\vee(\psi_i=\{\}\wedge T(p(\mathbf{t}_i),\tau_i))]\}=\tau]$$

   where
   (a) Def_p is the set of clauses in P with p in the head;
   (b) $\mathbf{x}, \mathbf{t}_i$ are tuples of variables ($[x_1, ..., x_m]$) and terms ($[t_{1i}, ..., t_{mi}]$), respectively;
   (c) $\mathbf{x} = \mathbf{t}_i$ stands for $x_1 = t_{1i} \wedge ... \wedge x_m = t_{mi}$;
   (d) ψ_i are (possibly empty) conjunctions of literals;
   (e) the connective $\leftrightarrow$ stands for equivalence.

Axioms:

1. equality axioms (Mendelson 1987);
2. $t(x) \neq x$ for each term in which x occurs.

Fig. 1. Extended completion of a program P

The completion of a conventional program defines a unique model for the program. For the extended completion to do the same, a necessary condition is to fix the truth-values for the unit clauses occurring in P as values greater than 0. This condition is also sufficient, as all the other formulae in $e\text{-}Comp(P)$ – i.e., the equivalence formulae and the unit formulae generated by rule 1 – must have truth-values equal to 1 in the model of the program.

Our notation for logic programs and the $e\text{-}SLDNF$ procedure is as follows:

- φ_i are literals;
- p_i, q_i are positive literals;
- g_i are positive ground literals;
- δ_i, ψ_i are (possibly empty) conjunctions of literals;
- σ, π are substitutions;
- R^e stands for "returns with a truth-value greater than 0": $\psi R^e (\sigma, \tau)$ holds iff $e\text{-}SLDNF$ succeeds, assigning a truth-value τ to ψ, with the substitution σ as an answer;
- F^e stands for "fails": ψF^e holds iff $e\text{-}SLDNF$ fails, implying on the assignment of a truth-value $\tau = 0$ to ψ.
- *true* stands for the empty query clause;
- *yes* stands for identity substitution.

$e\text{-}SLDNF$ is defined inductively as presented in Fig. 2.

1. $true\ R^e\ (yes, 1)$

2. $\dfrac{(q,\delta),max\left\{\begin{array}{l}\tau_i:[p_i \leftarrow \psi_i],\sigma_i=mgu(q,p_i),(\psi_i,\delta)\sigma_i\ R^e\\(\pi_i,\tau_i)\vee[p_i \leftarrow],\sigma_i=mgu(q,p_i),(\delta)\sigma_i\ R^e\\(\pi_i,\tau_i'),T((p_i)\sigma_i,\tau_i''),min\{\tau_i',\tau_i''\}=\tau_i\end{array}\right\}=\tau}{(q,\delta)\ R^e\ (\sigma\pi,\tau)}$

   where $\sigma\pi$ is the substitution that generates τ and the ψ_i are non-empty conjunctions.

3. $\dfrac{(\neg g,\delta),g\ R^e\ (yes,\tau'),\tau'<1,\delta\ R^e\ (\sigma,\tau''),min\{(1-\tau'),\tau''\}=\tau}{(\neg g,\delta)\ R^e\ (\sigma,\tau)}$

   $\dfrac{(\neg g,\delta),gF^e,\delta\ R^e\ (\sigma,\tau)}{(\neg g,\delta)\ R^e\ (\sigma,\tau)}$

4. $\dfrac{(q,\delta),\neg\exists[p \leftarrow\psi]:\exists mgu(q,p)}{(q,\delta)\ F^e}$

   $\dfrac{(q,\delta),\forall[p_i \leftarrow\psi_i]:\exists\sigma=mgu(q,p_i)\Rightarrow(\psi_i,\delta)\sigma\ F^e}{(q,\delta)\ F^e}$

5. $\dfrac{(\neg g,\delta),g\ R^e\ (yes,1)}{(\neg g,\delta)\ F^e}$

Fig. 2. $e\text{-}SLDNF$

4 A Language Supporting Probabilities on the Domain

The problem of representing and reasoning with statistical knowledge has received some attention recently (Bacchus 1990b, Halpern 1990). This problem can be roughly characterised as the problem of being able to represent in a first-order language terms of the form $\mathcal{P}_{\mathbf{x}}(\psi)$, to be read as "the probability of selecting a vector of instances for the variables in $\mathbf{x}$ that make ψ true".

In (Abadi and Halpern 1989) we have the result that the set of valid formulae for first-order logic containing statistical terms is not recursively enumerable, implying that a complete proof procedure for this logic does not exist. Two different ways of constraining the language to achieve proof-theoretic completeness have been proposed:

- in (Bacchus 1990b) the *probability measures* are relaxed to *non-σ-additive measures*, that is, the general probability axiom stating that "the probability of any *(infinitely) countable* set of pairwise disjoint events equals the sum of the probabilities of those events" is reduced to the case of *finite* sets of events. Moreover, the measures range on *real closed fields* (Shoenfield 1967) rather than on real numbers.
- in (Halpern 1990) the domain of discourse is *bounded in size*, i.e., it contains a number of elements not greater than a fixed N.

Our base language to be extended to contain statistical expressions obeys all these constraints: its domain is always finite and of fixed cardinality, so it is always bounded in size, σ-additivity coincides with finite additivity for finite domains and, as we intend to *compute* probabilities, field-valued measures are sufficient since, as pointed out in (Bacchus 1988), "computers are only capable of dealing with rational numbers (and only a finite set of them)".

On the other hand, the language introduced here extends the aforementioned results in two senses:

- we allow the occurrence of *fuzzy events*, i.e., statistical events that are characterised by fuzzy sets, and
- following a line suggested in (Halpern 1990), we admit the existence of *non-measurable events* and the consequent need for *inner and outer approximations* for statistical measures.

4.1 Reasoning with probabilities

Given a program P, the set of solutions with truth-values greater than 0 for a query ψ is always finite. This set also defines a fuzzy set of tuples of elements of D – the domain of P.

If our language is extended to accommodate the specification of probability measures of algebras of a partition of D through their bases, the set of solutions of ψ can be interpreted as a fuzzy event in the appropriate cartesian product of D, and upper and lower bounds can be evaluated for its probabilities using the measure of the corresponding cartesian product algebra.

The language is extended as follows:

- special unit formulae of the form $\mathcal{P}(S^c, \rho)$ are used to specify probability measures for D, i.e., a collection of expressions of the form $\mathcal{P}(S^c_{ij}, \rho_{ij})$ is attached to P, where the S^c_{ij} form the bases of algebras χ_{Di} of a partition of D and ρ_{ij} is the probability of S^c_{ij};
- some definitions are implicitly assumed as part of our inference procedure: the definitions of the operations of *addition* (+) and *multiplication* (×), of the *relations* > and =, and of the properties of *non-negativity* ($\rho \geq 0 \leftarrow \mathcal{P}(S^c, \rho)$), *finite additivity* ($\mathcal{P}(\cup_1^n S^c_i, \rho) \leftarrow \mathcal{P}(S^c_1, \rho_1), ..., \mathcal{P}(S^c_n, \rho_n), \rho = \rho_1 + ... + \rho_n$) and *total probability* ($\mathcal{P}(D, 1)$).
- special second-order expressions of the forms $\mathcal{P}_*(S, \psi, \rho_*)$ and $\mathcal{P}^*(S, \psi, \rho^*)$ are introduced, to be read as "the lower and the upper bounds for the probability of having a tuple of instances for the variables in S which satisfies ψ are ρ_* and ρ^*".
- special second-order expressions of the forms $\mathcal{P}_*(S, \psi_1|\psi_2, \rho_*)$ and $\mathcal{P}^*(S, \psi_1|\psi_2, \rho^*)$ are introduced, to be read as "the lower and the upper bounds for the probability of having a tuple of instances for the variables in S which satisfies ψ_1 given ψ_2 are ρ_* and ρ^*".

$\mathcal{P}_*(S, \psi, \rho_*)$ and $\mathcal{P}^*(S, \psi, \rho^*)$ are evaluated as follows:

1. generate K_ψ, the finite fuzzy set of tuples of instances of the free variables in ψ which associate a non-zero truth-degree τ to ψ.

If ψ does not have free variables, K_ψ is the singleton set containing the tuple of terms occurring in ψ with its respective truth-degree.

If ψ contains free variables, then K_ψ is generated by substituting exhaustively each free variable in ψ by elements of D and then selecting the substitutions which generate the desired truth-degrees.

2. generate K_ψ^S - the projection of K_ψ over S: select from the tuple of free variables in ψ those which are also in S, and extract the corresponding tuples of instances from K_ψ.

3. If $K_\psi^S \neq \{\}$ then:

(a) generate the cartesian product algebra and measure of the same arity as the tuples in K_ψ^S assuming the elements of D to be statistically independent.

(b) generate ρ_* and ρ^*:

$$\rho_* = \sum_{\mathbf{S}_i \subseteq K_\psi^S} \mathcal{P}_m(\mathbf{S}_i) \times min\{\tau : \mu(\mathbf{K}) = \tau, \mathbf{K} \in \mathbf{S}_i \cap K_\psi^S\}, \mathbf{S}_i \in \chi_D'$$

$$\rho^* = \sum_{\mathbf{S}_i \cap K_\psi^S \neq \{\}} \mathcal{P}_m(\mathbf{S}_i) \times max\{\tau : \mu(\mathbf{K}) = \tau, \mathbf{K} \in \mathbf{S}_i \cap K_\psi^S\}, \mathbf{S}_i \in \chi_D'$$

where m is the arity of the tuples in K_ψ^S.

If $K_\psi^S = \{\}$ then make $\rho_* = \rho^* = \tau$, where $\mathcal{T}(\psi, \tau)$.

$\mathcal{P}_*(S, \psi_1 | \psi_2, \rho_*)$ and $\mathcal{P}^*(S, \psi_1 | \psi_2, \rho^*)$ are evaluated as follows:

1. generate $K_{(\psi_1, \psi_2)}^S$ and $K_{(\neg\psi_1, \psi_2)}^S$.

2. generate $min_\wedge, min_\wedge', min_\wedge^\neg, max_\wedge, max_\wedge'$ and $max_\wedge^\neg$:

$$min_\wedge = \sum_{\mathbf{S}_i \subseteq K_{(\psi_1, \psi_2)}^S} \mathcal{P}_m(\mathbf{S}_i) \times min\{\tau : \mu(\mathbf{K}) = \tau, \mathbf{K} \in \mathbf{S}_i \cap K_{(\psi_1, \psi_2)}^S\}, \mathbf{S}_i \in \chi_D'$$

$$min_\wedge' = \sum_{\mathbf{S}_i \cap K_{(\psi_1, \psi_2)}^S \neq \{\}} \mathcal{P}_m(\mathbf{S}_i) \times min\{\tau : \mu(\mathbf{K}) = \tau, \mathbf{K} \in \mathbf{S}_i \cap K_{(\psi_1, \psi_2)}^S\}, \mathbf{S}_i \in \chi_D'$$

$$min_\wedge^\neg = \sum_{\mathbf{S}_i \subseteq K_{(\neg\psi_1, \psi_2)}^S} \mathcal{P}_m(\mathbf{S}_i) \times min\{\tau : \mu(\mathbf{K}) = \tau, \mathbf{K} \in \mathbf{S}_i \cap K_{(\neg\psi_1, \psi_2)}^S\}, \mathbf{S}_i \in \chi_D'$$

$$max_\wedge = \sum_{\mathbf{S}_i \cap K_{(\psi_1, \psi_2)}^S \neq \{\}} \mathcal{P}_m(\mathbf{S}_i) \times max\{\tau : \mu(\mathbf{K}) = \tau, \mathbf{K} \in \mathbf{S}_i \cap K_{(\psi_1, \psi_2)}^S\}, \mathbf{S}_i \in \chi_D'$$

$$max_\wedge' = \sum_{\mathbf{S}_i \subseteq K_{(\psi_1, \psi_2)}^S} \mathcal{P}_m(\mathbf{S}_i) \times max\{\tau : \mu(\mathbf{K}) = \tau, \mathbf{K} \in \mathbf{S}_i \cap K_{(\psi_1, \psi_2)}^S\}, \mathbf{S}_i \in \chi_D'$$

$$max_\wedge^\neg = \sum_{\mathbf{S}_i \cap K_{(\neg\psi_1, \psi_2)}^S \neq \{\}} \mathcal{P}_m(\mathbf{S}_i) \times max\{\tau : \mu(\mathbf{K}) = \tau, \mathbf{K} \in \mathbf{S}_i \cap K_{(\neg\psi_1, \psi_2)}^S\}, \mathbf{S}_i \in \chi_D'$$

3. generate ρ_* and ρ^*:

$$\rho_* = \begin{cases} \frac{min_\wedge}{max_\wedge' + max_\wedge^\neg}, & max_\wedge' + max_\wedge^\neg \neq 0 \\ 0, & max_\wedge' + max_\wedge^\neg = 0 \end{cases}$$

$$\rho^* = \begin{cases} min\{1, \frac{max_\wedge}{min_\wedge' + min_\wedge^\neg}\}, & min_\wedge' + min_\wedge^\neg \neq 0 \\ 0, & min_\wedge' + min_\wedge^\neg = 0 \end{cases}$$

Since probabilities are completely defined by measures on the constants of the language, terms of the forms $\mathcal{P}_*(S, \psi, \rho_*)$, $\mathcal{P}^*(S, \psi, \rho^*)$, $\mathcal{P}_*(S, \psi_1 | \psi_2, \rho_*)$ and $\mathcal{P}^*(S, \psi_1 | \psi_2, \rho^*)$ never occur as heads of program clauses. Moreover, these terms only admit truth-degrees in $\{0, 1\}$.

5 A Language Supporting Degrees of Belief

5.1 Adding possible worlds

The concept of *possible worlds* has been evoked frequently as a useful device to aid modelling uncertainty (see for example (Bacchus 1990b, Bundy 1985, Fagin and Halpern 1989a, Nilsson 1986)). The general idea is the assumption that there is a collection of *worlds* (or *states*, or *interpretations*), each of them assigning different truth-values to the formulae in our language. Intuitively, a possible world should be viewed as a conceivable hypothetical scenario upon which we can construct our reasoning.

Given a program P and a set of possible worlds $\Omega = \{\omega_1, ...\}$, a *rigid formula* is a formula which is always assigned the same truth-value in all possible worlds.

We assume in our language that, given a program P, each possible world ω_i assigns a different fuzzy truth-value to the set of unit clauses in P. We assume that the other clauses occurring in P, i.e., that the logical dependency and statistical relations expressed in P, are rigid.

Ideally, we should keep track of every possible world independently, and repeatedly apply the machinery presented in the previous sections for each of them each time we activated P with a query ψ. This procedure becomes computationally intractable as the size of Ω gets bigger (notice that Ω is not even required to be finite. Obviously it would not be possible to keep track computationally of an infinite set of possible worlds). Alternatively, we should be able to calculate singular truth-values like the minimum and the maximum values occurring in Ω for each clause: given a program P with unit clauses of the form $\mathcal{T}_*(C_i, \tau_{*i})$ and $\mathcal{T}^*(C_i, \tau_i^*)$ (representing minimum and maximum truth-degrees, respectively), we should be able to derive the values $\mathcal{T}_*(\psi, \tau_*)$ and $\mathcal{T}^*(\psi, \tau^*)$ for a query ψ.

It is not possible, however, to obtain these values for any query given only the singular values for the unit clauses, as the example below shows:

Example 1. Consider the following program:

$r(a) \leftarrow p(a), q(a).$
$s(a) \leftarrow p(a).$
$s(a) \leftarrow q(a).$
$\mathcal{T}_*(p(a), 0.2).\ \mathcal{T}^*(p(a), 0.8).$
$\mathcal{T}_*(q(a), 0.3).\ \mathcal{T}^*(q(a), 0.6).$

Assume further that the truth-degrees have come from the possible worlds in Ω, according to Table 1 (values underlined):

$$\Omega = \{\omega_1, \omega_2, \omega_3\}$$

	ω_1	ω_2	ω_3
$\mathcal{T}(p(a))$	0.2	0.5	0.8
$\mathcal{T}(q(a))$	0.4	0.6	0.3

Table 1. Truth-degrees in Ω

Using the procedure introduced in Fig. 2 for each possible world separately, the results in Table 2 follow:

	ω_1	ω_2	ω_3
$T(r(a))$	0.2	0.5	0.3
$T(s(a))$	0.4	0.6	0.8

Table 2. Derived Truth-degrees in Ω

which indicate that (values underlined, Table 2):

$T_*(r(a), 0.2). \ T^*(r(a), 0.5).$
$T_*(s(a), 0.4). \ T^*(s(a), 0.8).$

Both $T^*(r(a), 0.5)$ and $T_*(s(a), 0.4)$ depend on information which is not given in the initial program, thus cannot be derived from it unless we use additional knowledge.

Approximate solutions can be obtained for T_* and T^*, i.e., we can obtain the values $\hat{T}_*$ and $\hat{T}^*$, such that $\hat{T}_*(\psi) \leq T_*(\psi)$ and $\hat{T}^*(\psi) \geq T^*(\psi)$ for any query ψ.

It is not difficult to verify that the following recursive rules satisfy these conditions:

$$r \leftarrow p \Rightarrow \hat{T}_*(r) = \hat{T}_*(p)$$
$$\hat{T}^*(r) = \hat{T}^*(p)$$

$$r \leftarrow P, Q \Rightarrow \hat{T}_*(r) = min\{\hat{T}_*(P), \hat{T}_*(Q)\}$$
$$\hat{T}^*(r) = min\{\hat{T}^*(P), \hat{T}^*(Q)\}$$

$$r \leftarrow P \Rightarrow \hat{T}_*(r) = max\{\hat{T}_*(P), \hat{T}_*(Q)\}$$
$$r \leftarrow Q \quad \hat{T}^*(r) = max\{\hat{T}^*(P), \hat{T}^*(Q)\}$$

$$r \leftarrow \neg p \Rightarrow \hat{T}_*(r) = 1 - \hat{T}^*(p)$$
$$\hat{T}^*(r) = 1 - \hat{T}_*(p)$$

where $p, q, r, \ldots$ denote atoms and $P, Q, R, \ldots$ denote conjunctions of literals. When applied to the example above, these rules give:

$\hat{T}_*(r(a), 0.2). \ \hat{T}^*(r(a), 0.6).$
$\hat{T}_*(s(a), 0.3). \ \hat{T}^*(s(a), 0.8).$

which obey the desired inequality conditions.

5.2 Reasoning with possible worlds

The e-$SLDNF$ procedure and the completion e-$Comp(P)$ presented in Section 3 must be changed to accommodate the bounds for the truth-degrees across possible worlds. The *completion* of P is redefined as $*\text{-}Comp(P)$ as presented in Fig. 3.

Rules:

1. $$\frac{Def_p=\{\}}{\begin{array}{l}\forall X[\mathcal{T}_*(\neg p(X),1)]\\ \forall X[\mathcal{T}^*(\neg p(X),1)]\end{array}}$$

2. $$\frac{Def_p=\{p(\mathbf{t}_i)\leftarrow\psi_i:i=1,...,k\}\neq\{\}}{\forall X[\mathcal{T}_*(p(X),\tau_*)\leftarrow max\{\tau_{*i}:(X=\mathbf{t}_i)\wedge[(\psi_i\neq\{\},\mathcal{T}_*(\psi_i,\tau_{*i}))\vee}$$
$$(\psi_i=\{\},\mathcal{T}_*(p(\mathbf{t}_i),\tau_{*i}))]\}=\tau_*]$$

$$\forall X[\mathcal{T}^*(p(X),\tau^*)\leftarrow max\{\tau_i^*:(X=\mathbf{t}_i)\wedge[(\psi_i\neq\{\},\mathcal{T}^*(\psi_i,\tau_i^*))$$
$$\vee(\psi_i=\{\},\mathcal{T}^*(p(\mathbf{t}_i),\tau_i^*))]\}=\tau^*]$$
where

(a) Def_P is the set of clauses in P with p in the head;
(b) $\mathbf{x}, \mathbf{t}_i$ are tuples of variables ($[x_1,...,x_m]$) and terms ($[t_{1i},...,t_{mi}]$), respectively;
(c) $\mathbf{x}=\mathbf{t}_i$ stands for $x_1=t_{1i}\wedge...\wedge x_m=t_{mi}$;
(d) the scope of the existential quantifier are the variables occurring in the bodies of the clauses in Def_P;
(e) ψ_i are (possibly empty) conjunctions of literals;
(f) the connective $\leftrightarrow$ stands for equivalence.

Axioms: the same as in Fig. 1.

Fig. 3. $*\text{-}Comp(P)$

A model for a program P is any interpretation for which every expression occurring in $*\text{-}Comp(P)$ has a value $\tau^*>0$.

In order to redefine the inference procedure as $*\text{-}SLDNF$, we need the following in our notation for the success and finite failure set:

- R_*, R^* :
$\psi R_*(\psi,\tau_*)$ holds iff $*\text{-}SLDNF$ succeeds, assigning τ_* to ψ as a lower bound for its truth-degree;
$\psi R^*(\psi,\tau^*)$ holds iff $*\text{-}SLDNF$ succeeds, assigning τ^* to ψ as an upper bound for its truth-degree.
- F_*, F^* :
ψF_* holds iff $*\text{-}SLDNF$ fails, assigning $\tau_*=0$ to ψ;
ψF^* holds iff $*\text{-}SLDNF$ fails, assigning $\tau^*=0$ to ψ.

$*\text{-}SLDNF$ is defined inductively as presented in Fig. 4.

This language subsumes the one presented in the previous section, having that language as the particular class of programs in which all truth-degrees are rigid.

1. $true\ R_* \ (yes, 1).$
   $true\ R^* \ (yes, 1).$

2. $$\frac{(q,\delta), max \left\{ \begin{array}{l} \tau_{*i} : [p_i \leftarrow \psi_i], \sigma_i = mgu(q,p_i), \\ (\psi_i, \delta)\sigma_i\ R_*\ (\pi_i, \tau_{*i}) \lor \\ [p_i \leftarrow], \sigma_i = mgu(q,p_i), (\delta)\sigma_i\ R_*\ (\pi_i, \tau'_i), \\ \mathcal{T}_*((p_i)\sigma_i, \tau''_i), min\{\tau'_i, \tau''_i\} = \tau_{*i} \end{array} \right\} = \tau_*}{(q,\delta)\ R_*\ (\sigma\pi, \tau_*)}$$

$$\frac{(q,\delta), max \left\{ \begin{array}{l} \tau_i^* : [p_i \leftarrow \psi_i], \sigma_i = mgu(q,p_i), \\ (\psi_i, \delta)\sigma_i\ R^*\ (\pi_i, \tau_i^*) \lor \\ [p_i \leftarrow], \sigma_i = mgu(q,p_i), (\delta)\sigma_i\ R^*\ (\pi_i, \tau'_i), \\ \mathcal{T}^*((p_i)\sigma_i, \tau''_i), min\{\tau'_i, \tau''_i\} = \tau_i^* \end{array} \right\} = \tau^*}{(q,\delta)\ R^*\ (\sigma\pi, \tau^*)}$$

where $\sigma\pi$ are the substitutions that generate τ_* and τ^* and the ψ_i are non-empty conjunctions.

$$\frac{(\neg g, \delta), g\ R^*\ (yes, \tau'), \tau' < 1, \delta\ R_*\ (\sigma, \tau''), min\{(1-\tau'), \tau''\} = \tau_*}{(\neg g, \delta)\ R_*\ (\sigma, \tau_*)}$$

$$\frac{(\neg g, \delta), g\ R_*\ (yes, \tau'), \tau' < 1, \delta\ R^*\ (\sigma, \tau''), min\{(1-\tau'), \tau''\} = \tau^*}{(\neg g, \delta)\ R^*\ (\sigma, \tau^*)}$$

3. $$\frac{(\neg g, \delta), gF^*, \delta\ R_*\ (\sigma, \tau_*)}{(\neg g, \delta)\ R_*\ (\sigma, \tau_*)}$$
$$\frac{(\neg g, \delta), gF_*, \delta\ R^*\ (\sigma, \tau^*)}{(\neg g, \delta)\ R^*\ (\sigma, \tau^*)}$$

4. $$\frac{(q,\delta), \neg\exists[p \leftarrow \psi]: \exists mgu(q,p)}{(q,\delta)\ F_*}$$
$$\frac{(q,\delta), \neg\exists[p \leftarrow \psi]: \exists mgu(q,p)}{(q,\delta)\ F^*}$$
$$\frac{(q,\delta), \forall[p_i \leftarrow \psi_i]: \exists \sigma = mgu(q,p_i) \Rightarrow (\psi_i, \delta)\sigma\ F_*}{(q,\delta)\ F_*}$$
$$\frac{(q,\delta), \forall[p_i \leftarrow \psi_i]: \exists \sigma = mgu(q,p_i) \Rightarrow (\psi_i, \delta)\sigma\ F^*}{(q,\delta)\ F^*}$$

5. $$\frac{(\neg g, \delta), g\ R^*\ (yes, 1)}{(\neg g, \delta)\ F_*}$$
$$\frac{(\neg g, \delta), g\ R_*\ (yes, 1)}{(\neg g, \delta)\ F^*}$$

Fig. 4. **-SLDNF*

5.3 Probabilities on the domain with possible worlds

Probability evaluations take into account the bounds for truth-degrees across possible worlds. The syntax of the language can be as before for declaring probabilities, but the evaluation procedure must be changed. In the case of $\mathcal{P}_*(S, \psi, \rho_*)$ we must:

1. generate $K_{\psi*}$, the finite fuzzy set of tuples of instances of the free variables in ψ which associate a non-zero lower bound for the truth-degree τ_* to ψ.

If ψ does not have free variables, $K_{\psi*}$ is the singleton set containing the tuple of terms occurring in ψ with its respective bound for the truth-degree.

If ψ contains free variables, then $K_{\psi*}$ is generated by substituting exhaustively each free variable in ψ by elements of D and then selecting the substitutions which generate the desired bounds for truth-degrees.

2. generate $K_{\psi*}^S$ – the projection of $K_{\psi*}$ over S: select from the tuple of free variables in ψ those which are also in S, and extract the corresponding tuples of instances from $K_{\psi*}$.

3. case 1: $K_{\psi_*}^S \neq \{\}$

(a) generate the cartesian product algebra and measure of the same arity as the tuples in $K_{\psi_*}^S$ assuming the elements of D to be statistically independent.

(b) generate ρ_*:

$$\rho_* = \sum \mathbf{S}_{i \subseteq K_{\psi_*}^S} \, \mathcal{P}_m(\mathbf{S}_i) \times min\{\tau_* : \mu_*(\mathbf{K}) = \tau_*, \mathbf{K} \in \mathbf{S}_i \cap K_{\psi_*}^S\}, \mathbf{S}_i \in \mathcal{X}_D'$$

case 2: $K_{\psi_*}^S = \{\}$:

make $\rho_* = \tau_*$, where $\hat{\mathcal{T}}_*(\psi, \tau_*)$.

In the case of $\mathcal{P}^*(S, \psi, \rho^*)$, we must:

1. generate K_{ψ}^*, the finite fuzzy set of tuples of instances of the free variables in ψ which associate a non-zero upper bound for the truth-degree τ^* to ψ.

If ψ does not have free variables, K_{ψ}^* is the singleton set containing the tuple of terms occurring in ψ with its respective bound for the truth-degree.

If ψ contains free variables, then K_{ψ}^* is generated by substituting exhaustively each free variable in ψ by elements of D and then selecting the substitutions which generate the desired bounds for truth-degrees.

2. generate K_{ψ}^{*S} – the projection of K_{ψ}^* over S: select from the tuple of free variables in ψ those which are also in S, and extract the corresponding tuples of instances from K_{ψ}^*.

3. case 1: $K_{\psi}^{*S} \neq \{\}$

(a) generate the cartesian product algebra and measure of the same arity as the tuples in K_{ψ}^{*S} assuming the elements of D to be statistically independent.

(b) generate ρ^*:

$$\rho^* = \sum \mathbf{S}_{i \cap K_{\psi}^{*S} \neq \{\}} \, \mathcal{P}_m(\mathbf{S}_i) \times max\{\tau^* : \mu^*(\mathbf{K}) = \tau^*, \mathbf{K} \in \mathbf{S}_i \cap K_{\psi}^{*S}\}, \mathbf{S}_i \in \mathcal{X}_D'$$

case 2: $K_{\psi}^{*S} = \{\}$:

make $\rho^* = \tau^*$, where $\hat{\mathcal{T}}^*(\psi, \tau^*)$.

In the cases of $\mathcal{P}_*(S, \psi_1 | \psi_2, \rho_*)$ and $\mathcal{P}^*(S, \psi_1 | \psi_2, \rho^*)$, we must:

1. generate $K_{(\psi_1, \psi_2)}^{*S}$, $K_{(\neg\psi_1, \psi_2)}^{*S}$, $K_{(\psi_1, \psi_2)_*}^{S}$ and $K_{(\neg\psi_1, \psi_2)_*}^{S}$.

2. generate $min_\wedge, min_\wedge', min_\wedge^\neg, max_\wedge, max_\wedge'$ and $max_\wedge^\neg$:

$$min_\wedge = \sum \mathbf{S}_{i \subseteq K_{(\psi_1, \psi_2)_*}^S} \, \mathcal{P}_m(\mathbf{S}_i) \times min\{\tau_* : \mu_*(\mathbf{K}) = \tau_*, \, \mathbf{K} \in \mathbf{S}_i \cap K_{(\psi_1, \psi_2)_*}^S\}, \mathbf{S}_i \in \mathcal{X}_D'$$

$$min_\wedge' = \sum \mathbf{S}_{i \cap K_{(\psi_1, \psi_2)}^{*S} \neq \{\}} \, \mathcal{P}_m(\mathbf{S}_i) \times min\{\tau_* : \mu_*(\mathbf{K}) = \tau_*, \, \mathbf{K} \in \mathbf{S}_i \cap K_{(\psi_1, \psi_2)}^{*S}\}, \mathbf{S}_i \in \mathcal{X}_D'$$

$$min_\wedge^\neg = \sum \mathbf{S}_{i \subseteq K_{(\neg\psi_1, \psi_2)_*}^S} \, \mathcal{P}_m(\mathbf{S}_i) \times min\{\tau_* : \mu_*(\mathbf{K}) = \tau_*, \, \mathbf{K} \in \mathbf{S}_i \cap K_{(\neg\psi_1, \psi_2)_*}^S\}, \mathbf{S}_i \in \mathcal{X}_D'$$

$$max_\wedge = \sum \mathbf{S}_{i \cap K_{(\psi_1, \psi_2)}^{*S} \neq \{\}} \, \mathcal{P}_m(\mathbf{S}_i) \times max\{\tau^* : \mu^*(\mathbf{K}) = \tau^*, \, \mathbf{K} \in \mathbf{S}_i \cap K_{(\psi_1, \psi_2)}^{*S}\}, \mathbf{S}_i \in \mathcal{X}_D'$$

$$max_\wedge' = \sum \mathbf{S}_{i \subseteq K_{(\psi_1, \psi_2)_*}^S} \, \mathcal{P}_m(\mathbf{S}_i) \times max\{\tau^* : \mu^*(\mathbf{K}) = \tau^*, \, \mathbf{K} \in \mathbf{S}_i \cap K_{(\psi_1, \psi_2)_*}^S\}, \mathbf{S}_i \in \mathcal{X}_D'$$

$$max_\wedge^\neg = \sum \mathbf{S}_{i \cap K_{(\neg\psi_1, \psi_2)}^{*S} \neq \{\}} \, \mathcal{P}_m(\mathbf{S}_i) \times max\{\tau^* : \mu^*(\mathbf{K}) = \tau^*, \, \mathbf{K} \in \mathbf{S}_i \cap K_{(\neg\psi_1, \psi_2)}^{*S}\}, \mathbf{S}_i \in \mathcal{X}_D'$$

3. generate ρ_* and ρ^*:

$$\rho_* = \begin{cases} \frac{min_\wedge}{max'_\wedge + max^-_\wedge}, & max'_\wedge + max^-_\wedge \neq 0 \\ 0, & max'_\wedge + max^-_\wedge = 0 \end{cases}$$

$$\rho^* = \begin{cases} min\{1, \frac{max_\wedge}{min'_\wedge + min^-_\wedge}\}, & min'_\wedge + min^-_\wedge \neq 0 \\ 0, & min'_\wedge + min^-_\wedge = 0 \end{cases}$$

6 Adding Probabilities on Possible Worlds

Different worlds can have different likelihoods. Given a set of possible worlds Ω, we can define a *probability measure* $\mathcal{B}$ to represent these likelihoods. The *expected value* for the truth-degree of a clause ψ can be defined as $\mathcal{B}(\psi) = \int_\Omega \tau d\beta$, where $\mathcal{T}(\psi, \tau)$.

When the sets ω of possible worlds in which sentences have "non-zero" truth-degrees are measurable, this defines a straightforward extension of Nilsson's probabilistic logic (Nilsson 1986) to deal with fuzzy predicates. If we consider the non-measurable cases, then the language extends the so-called *Dempster-Shafer structures* (Fagin and Halpern 1989a, Corrêa da Silva and Bundy 1990), which are expressive enough to represent what other important mechanisms to represent degrees of belief can represent, such as Dempster-Shafer Belief and Plausibility Measures, Possibilistic Logic (Dubois and Prade 1988, Ruspini 1989) and Incidence Calculus (Bundy 1985, Corrêa da Silva and Bundy 1991).

Given expressions of the form $\mathcal{B}_*(\psi, \beta_*)$ and $\mathcal{B}^*(\psi, \beta^*)$ for the unit clauses occurring in a program P – where β_* and β^* represent the *inner* and the *outer extensions* for the measure $\mathcal{B}$ – it is not possible to derive the degrees of belief for all queries on P, unless the statistical dependency among clauses is known (Bundy 1985). Nonetheless, *bounds* can be derived for these degrees of belief. For programs without fuzzy predicates, these bounds can be defined by the following rules (from (Ng and Subrahmanian 1992)):

$$r \leftarrow p \Rightarrow \mathcal{B}_*(r) = \mathcal{B}_*(p)$$
$$\mathcal{B}^*(r) = \mathcal{B}^*(p)$$

$$r \leftarrow P, Q \Rightarrow \mathcal{B}_*(r) \geq max\{0, [\mathcal{B}_*(P) + \mathcal{B}_*(Q) - 1]\}$$
$$\mathcal{B}^*(r) \leq min\{\mathcal{B}^*(P), \mathcal{B}^*(Q)\}$$

$$r \leftarrow P \Rightarrow \mathcal{B}_*(r) \geq max\{\mathcal{B}_*(P), \mathcal{B}_*(Q)\}$$
$$r \leftarrow Q \quad \mathcal{B}^*(r) \leq min\{1, [\mathcal{B}^*(P) + \mathcal{B}^*(Q)]\}$$

$$r \leftarrow \neg p \Rightarrow \mathcal{B}_*(r) = 1 - \mathcal{B}^*(p)$$
$$\mathcal{B}^*(r) = 1 - \mathcal{B}_*(p)$$

where $p, q, r, \ldots$ denote atoms and $P, Q, R, \ldots$ denote conjunctions of literals.

When a program contains fuzzy information, these rules can be further refined, since we have that $\hat{\mathcal{T}}_*(\psi) \leq \mathcal{B}(\psi) \leq \hat{\mathcal{T}}^*(\psi)$ for any clause ψ:

$$r \leftarrow p \Rightarrow \overset{.}{\mathcal{B}}_*(r) = \overset{.}{\mathcal{B}}_*(p)$$
$$\overset{.}{\mathcal{B}}^*(r) = \overset{.}{\mathcal{B}}^*(p)$$

$$r \leftarrow P, Q \Rightarrow \mathcal{B}_*(r) \geq \overset{.}{\mathcal{B}}_*(r) = max\{\overset{.}{\mathcal{T}}_*(r), [\overset{.}{\mathcal{B}}_*(P) + \overset{.}{\mathcal{B}}_*(Q) - 1]\}$$
$$\mathcal{B}^*(r) \leq \overset{.}{\mathcal{B}}^*(r) = min\{\overset{.}{\mathcal{T}}^*(r), \overset{.}{\mathcal{B}}^*(P), \overset{.}{\mathcal{B}}^*(Q)\}$$

$$r \leftarrow P \Rightarrow \mathcal{B}_*(r) \geq \overset{.}{\mathcal{B}}_*(r) = max\{\overset{.}{\mathcal{T}}_*(r), \overset{.}{\mathcal{B}}_*(P), \overset{.}{\mathcal{B}}_*(Q)\}$$
$$r \leftarrow Q \quad \mathcal{B}^*(r) \leq \overset{.}{\mathcal{B}}^*(r) = min\{\overset{.}{\mathcal{T}}^*(r), [\overset{.}{\mathcal{B}}^*(P) + \overset{.}{\mathcal{B}}^*(Q)]]\}$$

$$r \leftarrow \neg p \Rightarrow \overset{.}{\mathcal{B}}_*(r) = 1 - \overset{.}{\mathcal{B}}^*(p)$$
$$\overset{.}{\mathcal{B}}^*(r) = 1 - \overset{.}{\mathcal{B}}_*(p)$$

In what follows we introduce these concepts into our language.

6.1 Reasoning with probabilities on possible worlds

The inference procedure defined in the previous sections can be extended to deal with degrees of belief. We define, in addition to *-SLDNF and *-Comp(P) previously presented, the procedure and completion rules for evaluating degrees of belief in a program P presented in Fig. 5 and Fig. 6, in which the following notational conventions are adopted:

- $\psi R_{\beta*}(\psi, \beta_*)$ holds iff *-SLDNF succeeds, assigning β_* to ψ as a lower bound for its truth-degree;
- $\psi R_\beta^*(\psi, \beta^*)$ holds iff *-SLDNF succeeds, assigning β^* to ψ as an upper bound for its truth-degree;
- $\psi F_{\beta*}$ holds iff *-SLDNF fails, assigning $\beta_* = 0$ to ψ;
- ψF_β^* holds iff *-SLDNF fails, assigning $\beta^* = 0$ to ψ.

Rules:

1. $$\frac{Def_P = \{\}}{\forall \mathbf{X}[\overset{.}{\mathcal{B}}_*(\neg p(\mathbf{X}), 1)]}$$
$$\forall \mathbf{X}[\overset{.}{\mathcal{B}}^*(\neg p(\mathbf{X}), 1)]$$

2. $$\frac{Def_P = \{p(\mathbf{t}_i) - \psi_i : i = 1, \ldots, k\} \neq \{\}}{\forall \mathbf{X}[\overset{.}{\mathcal{B}}_*(p(\mathbf{X}), \beta_*) \leftarrow max\{\beta_{*_i} : (\mathbf{X} = \mathbf{t}_i) \wedge [(\psi_i \neq \{\}, \overset{.}{\mathcal{B}}_*(\psi_i, \beta_{*_i}))}$$
$$\vee(\psi_i = \{\}, \overset{.}{\mathcal{B}}_*(p(\mathbf{t}_i), \beta_{*_i}))]\} = \overset{.}{\beta}_*, \mathcal{T}_*(p(\mathbf{X}, \tau_*), max\{\overset{.}{\beta}_*, \tau_*\} = \beta_*]$$

$$\forall \mathbf{X}[\overset{.}{\mathcal{B}}^*(p(\mathbf{X}), \beta^*) \leftarrow \sum \{\beta_i^* : (\mathbf{X} = \mathbf{t}_i) \wedge [(\psi_i \neq \{\}, \overset{.}{\mathcal{B}}^*(\psi_i, \beta_i^*))$$
$$\vee(\psi_i = \{\}, \overset{.}{\mathcal{B}}^*(p(\mathbf{t}_i), \beta_i^*))]\} = \overset{.}{\beta}^*, \mathcal{T}^*(p(\mathbf{X}, \tau^*), min\{\overset{.}{\beta}^*, \tau^*\} = \beta^*]$$

Axioms: the same as in Fig. 1.

Fig. 5. β-Comp(P)

1. $true\ R_{\beta_*}\ (yes,1)$.
   $true\ R_\beta^*\ (yes,1)$.

$$(q,\delta),\ max \left\{ \begin{array}{l} \beta_{*i}:[p_i \leftarrow \psi_i],\sigma_i=mgu(q,p_i),\\ (\psi_i,\delta)1z\sigma_i\ R_{\beta_*}\ (\pi_i,\beta_{*i})\vee[p_i\leftarrow],\\ \sigma_i=mgu(q,p_i),(\delta)\sigma_i\ R_{\beta_*}\ (\pi_i,\beta_i'),\\ \mathcal{B}_*(p_i\sigma_i,\beta_i''),\beta_{*i}=\beta_i'+\beta_i''-1 \end{array} \right\} =$$

2. $$\frac{\begin{array}{c} \beta_*',\mathcal{T}_*((q,\delta),\tau_*),\\ max\{\tau_*,\beta_*'\}=\beta_* \end{array}}{(q,\delta)\ R_{\beta_*}\ (\sigma\pi,\beta_*)}.$$

$$(q,\delta),\ \sum \left\{ \begin{array}{l} \beta_i^*:[p_i\leftarrow\psi_i],\sigma_i=mgu(q,p_i),\\ (\psi_i,\delta)\sigma_i\ R_\beta^*\ (\pi_i,\beta_i^*)\vee[p_i\leftarrow],\\ \sigma_i=mgu(q,p_i),(\delta)\sigma_i\ R_\beta^*\ (\pi_i,\beta_i'),\\ \mathcal{B}^*(p_i\sigma_i,\beta_i''),min\{\beta_i',\beta_i''\}=\beta_i^* \end{array} \right\} =$$

$$\frac{\begin{array}{c} \beta'^*,\mathcal{T}^*((q,\delta),\tau^*),\\ min\{\tau^*,\beta'^*\}=\beta^* \end{array}}{(q,\delta)\ R_\beta^*\ (\sigma\pi,\beta^*)}.$$

where $\sigma\pi$ are the substitutions that generate β_* and β^* and the ψ_i are non-empty conjunctions.

$$\frac{\begin{array}{c} (\neg g,\delta),g\ R_\beta^*\ (yes,\beta'),\beta'<1,\delta\ R_{\beta_*}\ (\sigma,\beta''),\\ \mathcal{T}_*((\neg g,\delta),\tau_*),max\{\tau_*,(1-\beta')+\beta''-1\}=\beta_* \end{array}}{(\neg g,\delta)\ R_{\beta_*}\ (\sigma,\beta_*)}.$$

$$\frac{\begin{array}{c} (\neg g,\delta),g\ R_{\beta_*}\ (yes,\beta'),\beta'<1,\delta\ R_\beta^*\ (\sigma,\beta''),\\ \mathcal{T}^*((\neg g,\delta),\tau^*),min\{\tau^*,(1-\beta'),\beta''\}=\beta^* \end{array}}{(\neg g,\delta)\ R_\beta^*\ (\sigma,\beta^*)}.$$

3. $$\frac{(\neg g,\delta),gF_\beta^*,\delta\ R_{\beta_*}\ (\sigma,\beta_*)}{(\neg g,\delta)\ R_{\beta_*}\ (\sigma,\beta_*)}.$$
   $$\frac{(\neg g,\delta),gF_{\beta_*},\delta\ R_\beta^*\ (\sigma,\beta^*)}{(\neg g,\delta)\ R_\beta^*\ (\sigma,\beta^*)}.$$

4. $$\frac{(q,\delta),\nexists[p\leftarrow\psi]:\exists mgu(q,p)}{(q,\delta)\ F_{\beta_*}}$$
   $$\frac{(q,\delta),\nexists[p\leftarrow\psi]:\exists mgu(q,p)}{(q,\delta)\ F_\beta^*}$$
   $$\frac{(q,\delta),\forall[p_i\leftarrow\psi_i]:\exists\sigma=mgu(q,p_i)\Rightarrow(\psi_i,\delta)\sigma\ F_{\beta_*}}{(q,\delta)\ F_{\beta_*}}$$
   $$\frac{(q,\delta),\forall[p_i\leftarrow\psi_i]:\exists\sigma=mgu(q,p_i)\Rightarrow(\psi_i,\delta)\sigma\ F_\beta^*}{(q,\delta)\ F_\beta^*}$$

5. $$\frac{(\neg g,\delta),g\ R_\beta^*\ (yes,1)}{(\neg g,\delta)\ F_{\beta_*}}.$$
   $$\frac{(\neg g,\delta),g\ R_{\beta_*}\ (yes,1)}{(\neg g,\delta)\ F_\beta^*}$$

Fig. 6. β-SLDNF

6.2 Dealing with conditional beliefs

We may want to constrain our queries to a specific set of possible worlds in which a statement is believed to be (to some extent) true. In other words, we may be interested in measuring *conditional beliefs* on queries.

If we had the values for the inner and outer measures $\mathcal{B}_*(\psi)$ and $\mathcal{B}^*(\psi)$, we could evaluate conditional beliefs by using the expressions given in (Fagin and Halpern 1989b):

$$\mathcal{B}_*(\psi_1|\psi_2) = \begin{cases} \frac{\mathcal{B}_*(\psi_1,\psi_2)}{\mathcal{B}_*(\psi_1,\psi_2)+\mathcal{B}^*(\neg\psi_1,\psi_2)}, \mathcal{B}_*(\psi_1,\psi_2)+\mathcal{B}^*(\neg\psi_1,\psi_2)\neq 0 \\ 0, \mathcal{B}_*(\psi_1,\psi_2)+\mathcal{B}^*(\neg\psi_1,\psi_2)=0 \end{cases}$$

$$\mathcal{B}^*(\psi_1|\psi_2) = \begin{cases} \frac{\mathcal{B}^*(\psi_1,\psi_2)}{\mathcal{B}^*(\psi_1,\psi_2)+\mathcal{B}_*(\neg\psi_1,\psi_2)}, \mathcal{B}^*(\psi_1,\psi_2)+\mathcal{B}_*(\neg\psi_1,\psi_2)\neq 0 \\ 0, \mathcal{B}^*(\psi_1,\psi_2)+\mathcal{B}_*(\neg\psi_1,\psi_2)=0 \end{cases}$$

However, we can only access the values $\hat{\mathcal{B}}_*(\psi) \leq \mathcal{B}_*(\psi)$ and $\hat{\mathcal{B}}^*(\psi) \geq \mathcal{B}^*(\psi)$ for a clause ψ. Since we have that (Fagin and Halpern 1989b):

$$[\mathcal{B}_*(\psi_1|\psi_2), \mathcal{B}^*(\psi_1|\psi_2)] \subseteq [\frac{\mathcal{B}_*(\psi_1,\psi_2)}{\mathcal{B}^*(\psi_2)}, \frac{\mathcal{B}^*(\psi_1,\psi_2)}{\mathcal{B}_*(\psi_2)}]$$

We immediately have that:

$$[\mathcal{B}_*(\psi_1|\psi_2), \mathcal{B}^*(\psi_1|\psi_2)] \subseteq [\frac{\hat{\mathcal{B}}_*(\psi_1,\psi_2)}{\hat{\mathcal{B}}^*(\psi_2)}, \frac{\hat{\mathcal{B}}^*(\psi_1,\psi_2)}{\hat{\mathcal{B}}_*(\psi_2)}]$$

Hence, we adopt these expressions as approximations for the lower and upper bounds for conditional degrees of belief:

- $\hat{\mathcal{B}}_*(\psi_1|\psi_2) = \frac{\hat{\mathcal{B}}_*(\psi_1,\psi_2)}{\hat{\mathcal{B}}^*(\psi_2)}$,
- $\hat{\mathcal{B}}^*(\psi_1|\psi_2) = min\{1, \frac{\hat{\mathcal{B}}^*(\psi_1,\psi_2)}{\hat{\mathcal{B}}_*(\psi_2)}\}$

7 Summary and Discussion

There has been a lot of debate on which formalism to measure uncertainty is the most general, and many researchers have recently defended the view that there is not a most general formalism but that different formalisms are better to measure different facets of uncertainty.

In the present work we adopted the latter view. We also avoided the simplification that *a single* facet of uncertainty should be selected at the end, therefore accepting that multiple measures could have to be considered within a single representation language.

Assuming this point of view, we explored the feasibility of performing automated reasoning about a domain containing more than one facet of uncertainty by (i) selecting three of these facets and their corresponding measures; (ii) incorporating them in a resolution-based, first-order, clausal theorem prover; and (iii) implementing this theorem prover as a PROLOG meta-interpreter.

An important aspect of any knowledge representation schema for automated reasoning is to have a clearly and rigorously specified semantics for its expressions and operations, so we were careful about providing a model theory for our language and guaranteeing the soundness of its inference procedures.

The main expected contribution of this work was the evidential proof that multiple measures of uncertainty are useful in knowledge representation and inference, and that they can (and should) be treated conjointly within a single representation language. Nevertheless, we believe that the language which was constructed and implemented to constitute this proof presents interest in itself as the prototype of a language to implement knowledge-based systems about domains pervaded with uncertainty. With this in mind, we explored some possibilities to improve its computational efficiency in time, which presented some positive results.

One aspect of our language is the variable coarseness of the results it produces. The language is a proper extension of several simpler theorem provers (e.g., Lee's language (1972), Halpern's logic (1990), the logic Lp (Bacchus 1988, Bacchus 1990a), Nilsson's logic (1986), and when "projected" onto one of these languages it produces results at least as precise as those (i.e., if the result is an interval, it is going to be at least as tight as the one produced by the simpler language). In those more complex cases in which the extensions are needed, however, the uncertainty intervals generated by our language grow rapidly in width. It is a topic for further research whether we can specify particular classes of problems with special structural properties such that more precise results (i.e. tighter intervals) can be obtained.

Another limitation of the language is the presupposition of a single source of information for a program (i.e., a single agent to assign belief and truth-degrees to expressions), and the consideration of only those problems which can be treated monotonically. It is still an open question whether a richer language, capable of treating non-monotonicities and multiple agents (which can be independent, partially dependent or totally dependent), can be constructed in such a way that the language has a clear declarative semantics and is computationally tractable.

Acknowledgements

The authors profited from comments and suggestions from many researchers along the development of this work. We would like to thank especially Fahiem Bacchus, Alan Bundy, Didier Dubois, John Fox, Jérôme Lang, Jeff Paris, Henri Prade, Sandra Sandri and V.S. Subrahmanian. The first author was sponsored by CNPq - Conselho Nacional de Desenvolvimento Cientíifico e Tecnológico (Brazil) - grant nr. 203004/89.2. The final production and presentation of this paper was partially supported by FAPESP - Fundação de Amparo à Pesquisa no Estado de São Paulo (Brazil) - grant nr 92/4323-0.

78

References

Abadi, M., and J.Y. Halpern: *Decidability and Expressiveness for First-Order Logics of Probability*. IBM Research Report **RJ 7220**, 1989.

Apt, K.F.: *Introduction to Logic Programming*. Centre for Mathematics and Computer Science Report **CSR 8741**, 1987.

Bacchus, F.: *Representing and Reasoning with Probabilistic Knowledge*. University of Alberta, 1988.

Bacchus, F.: "Lp, a Logic for Representing and Reasoning with Statistical Knowledge," in: *Computational Intelligence* **6** (1990a) 209-231.

Bacchus, F.: *Representing and Reasoning with Probabilistic Knowledge*. MIT Press, 1990b.

Bundy, A.: "Incidence Calculus: a Mechanism for Probabilistic Reasoning," in: *Journal of Automated Reasoning* **1** (1985) 263-284.

Corrêa da Silva, F.S.: *Automated Reasoning with Uncertainties*. University of Edinburgh, Department of Artificial Intelligence, 1992.

Corrêa da Silva, F.S., and A. Bundy: *On Some Equivalence Relations Between Incidence Calculus and Dempster-Shafer Theory of Evidence*. 6th Conference on Uncertainty in Artificial Intelligence, 1990.

Corrêa da Silva, F.S., and A. Bundy: *A Rational Reconstruction of Incidence Calculus*. University of Edinburgh, Department of Artificial: Intelligence Report **517**, 1991.

Dubois, D., and H. Prade: "An Introduction to Possibilistic and Fuzzy Logics," in: P. Smets et al. (eds.), *Non-standard Logics for Automated Reasoning* Academic Press, 1988.

Dubois, D., and H. Prade: "Fuzzy Sets, Probability and Measurement," in: *European Journal of Operational Research* **40** (1989) 135-154.

Dudley, R.M.: *Real Analysis and Probability*. Wadsworth & Brooks/Cole, 1989.

Fagin, R., and J.Y. Halpern: *Uncertainty, Belief, and Probability.* IBM Research Report **RJ 6191**, 1989a.

Fagin, R., and J.Y. Halpern: *A New Approach to Updating Beliefs*. IBM Research Report **RJ 7222**, 1989.

Fitting, M.: "Logic Programming on a Topological Bilattice," in: *Fundamenta Informaticae* **XI** (1988) 209-218.

Fitting, M.: "Bilattices in Logic Programming," in: *Proceedings of the 20th International Symposium on Multiple-valued Logic*, 1990.

Halpern, J.Y.: "An Analysis of First-Order Logics of Probability," in: *Artificial Intelligence* **46** (1990) 311-350.

Halpern, J. Y., and R. Fagin: *Two Views of Belief: Belief as Generalised Probability and Belief as Evidence*. IBM Research Report **RJ 7221**, 1989.

Hinde, C.J.: "Fuzzy Prolog," in: *International Journal of Man-Machine Studies* **24** (1986) 569-595.

Ishizuka, M., and K. Kanai: "Prolog-ELF Incorporating Fuzzy Logic." in: *IJCAI'85 - Proceedings of the 9th International Joint Conference on Artificial Intelligence*, 1985.

Kifer, M., and V.S. Subrahmanian: "Theory of Generalized Annotated Logic Programs and Its Applications," in: *Journal of Logic Programming* **12**, 1991.

Klement, E.P.: "Construction of Fuzzy σ-algebras Using Triangular Norms," in: *Journal of Mathematical Analysis and Applications* **85** (1982) 543-565.

Kunen, K.: "Signed Data Dependencies in Logic Programs," in: *Journal of Logic Programming* **7** (1989) 231-245.

Lee, R.C.T.: "Fuzzy Logic and the Resolution Principle," in: *Journal of the ACM* **19** (1972) 109-119.

Mendelson, E.: *Introduction to Mathematical Logic* (3rd. ed). Wadsworth & Brooks/Cole, 1987.

Nilsson, N.J.: "Probabilistic Logic," in: *Artificial Intelligence* **28** (1986) 71-87.

Ng, R., and V.S. Subrahmanian: "Probabilistic Logic Programming," in: *Information and Computation* **101**, 1992.

Orci, I.P.: "Programming in Possibilistic Logic," in: *International Journal of Expert Systems* **2** (1989) 79-96.

Piasecki, K.: "Fuzzy p-Measures and their Application in Decision Making," in: J. Kacprzyk and M. Fedrizzi (eds.), *Combining Fuzzy Imprecision with Probabilistic Uncertainty in Decision Making.* Berlin heidelberg: Springer Verlag, 1988.

Ruspini, E.H.: "On the Semantics of Fuzzy Logic," in: *SRI International* **475**, 1989.

Saffiotti, A.: "An AI View of the Treatment of Uncertainty," in: *The Knowledge Engineering Review* **2** (1987) 75-97.

Shafer, G.: *A Mathematical Theory of Evidence.* Princeton University Press, 1976.

Shapiro, E.Y.: "Logic Programming with Uncertainties - a Tool for Implementing Rule-based Systems," in: *IJCAI'83 - Proceedings of the 8th International Joint Conference on Artificial Intelligence*, 1983.

Shoenfield, J.R.: *Mathematical Logic.* Addison-Wesley, 1967.

Smets, P.: "Probability of a Fuzzy Event: An Axiomatic Approach," in: *Fuzzy Sets and Systems* **7** (1982) 153-164.

Turi, D.: *Logic Programs with Negation: Classes, Models, Interpreters.* Centre for Mathematics and Computer Science Report **CSR 8943**, 1989.

Turksen, I.B.: "Stochastic Fuzzy Sets: a Survey," in: J. Kacprzyk and M. Fedrizzi (eds.), *Combining Fuzzy Imprecision with Probabilistic Uncertainty in Decision Making.* Berlin, Heidelberg: Springer Verlag, 1988.

Van Emden, M.H.: "Quantitative Deduction and its Fixpoint Theory," in: *Journal of Logic Programming* **1** (1986) 37-53.

An Axiomatic Approach to Systems of Prior Distributions in Inexact Reasoning

Jonathan Lawry* and George M. Wilmers

Department of Mathematics, University of Manchester
Manchester M13 9PL, U.K.
E-mail: mbbgpla@hpa.mcc.ak.uk/george@ma.man.ac.uk

Abstract. We describe an axiomatic approach to the *a priori* choice of hierarchies of second order probability distributions within the context of inexact reasoning. In this manner we give an epistemological characterisation of a certain hierarchy of symmetric Dirichlet priors up to a parameter.

1 Motivation

One of the fundamental problems in the development of expert systems is how to make decisions based on uncertain or inexact knowledge. For example, an expert system for medical diagnosis and prognosis might consist of a knowledge base as follows :

- 80% of patients with symptoms S have disease D
- Between 2% and 5% of patients are of blood group B and have disease D
- Patients of blood group B with symptom S are more likely than not to have disease D

A wide range of such inexact knowledge bases occurring in practice may reasonably be represented by linear equality or inequality constraints on the subjective belief function of the expert from whom the information was collected. This assumes that each individual has a belief function which allocates a numerical value, usually normalised so that it lies between zero and one, to each proposition. For the following we shall consider that all belief functions are probability functions. Hence, the above example could be formulated as:

$$\begin{aligned} E(S \wedge D) &= 0.8 \times E(S) \\ 0.02 \leq E(B \wedge D) &\leq 0.05 \\ E(S \wedge B \wedge D) &> 0.5 \times E(S \wedge B) \end{aligned}$$

for some probability function E.

We consider only propositional languages with binary connectives and negation where the literals are the fundamental observable phenomena relating to the domain of discussion. Clearly then, in most cases the knowledge base will

---

* Supported by a Science and Engineering Research Council Award

not provide sufficient information to uniquely determine a probability value for every sentence of such a language. Therefore, to select a single probability function defined on the whole language, we must make *a priori* assumptions. These take the form of an *inference process*, N, which for a given knowledge base C, defines for every sentence θ of the language a corresponding real value $N_C(\theta)$ consistent with C. This inference process may then be incorporated as part of the inference engine of the expert system.

Given the uncertainty regarding the probability function E, we feel that it is natural to define a second order distribution on belief functions (Paris et al. 1991, Paris et al., to appear). This accords with the feeling that human experts do not always precisely define a subjective belief function but rather have some general intuition regarding their beliefs relative to a knowledge base. Thus, an inference process to select a particular belief function need only be used when a precise decision is required. We aim to develop epistemologically based systems of axioms identifying particular classes of second order distributions. Such classes of priors are naturally applicable to many areas of inexact reasoning; in particular, any such class of second order distributions naturally defines an inference process the properties of which can be investigated.

2 Mathematical Formulation

We use the formulation of inference process developed by Paris and Vencovska in a number of papers including (Paris and Vencovska 1991). Let $L^{(n)}$ be a language of the propositional calculus consisting of the propositional variables $p_1, \ldots, p_n$ with connectives $\wedge, \vee$ and $\neg$. The sentences of $L^{(n)}$ are denoted by $SL^{(n)}$. Now a probability function on $SL^{(n)}$ is a function E from $SL^{(n)}$ into $[0, 1]$ which satisfies the following axioms:

(i) $\models \theta \implies E(\theta) = 1$

(ii)   if $\models \neg(\theta \wedge \varphi)$ then $E(\theta \vee \varphi) = E(\theta) + E(\varphi)$

which together imply:

(iii)   if $\models \theta \leftrightarrow \varphi$ then $E(\theta) = E(\varphi)$

The condition (iii) means that we can define E on the Lindenbaum algebra, $\mathcal{L}^{(n)}$, of equivalence classes for the equivalence relation of logical equivalence (i.e., for $\varphi, \theta \in SL^{(n)}$ the algebra consists of equivalence classes $\overline{\theta}$ such that $\varphi \in \overline{\theta}$ iff $\varphi \leftrightarrow \theta$). Now by the disjunctive normal form theorem, every sentence of $L^{(n)}$ is equivalent to a disjunction of sentences of the form $\bigwedge_i^n p_i^{\epsilon i}$ where $\epsilon_i \in \{0, 1\}$ and $p^1 = p, p^0 = \neg p$. The equivalence classes containing these sentences form the atoms of $\mathcal{L}^{(n)}$ relative to the natural ordering on boolean algebras and hence we refer to them as atoms. Clearly for a language of size n there are 2^n atoms which we enumerate by

$$\alpha_j^{(n)} = \bigwedge_{i=1}^{n} p_i^{\epsilon_i^j}$$

where

$$j = 2^n - \sum_{i=1}^{n} \epsilon_i^j 2^{n-i}$$

Since the $\bar{\alpha}_i^{(n)}$ are disjoint and $\bigvee_i^{2^n} \bar{\alpha}_i^{(n)} = \top$ it follows that a probability function E on $\mathcal{L}^{(n)}$ is uniquely defined by its values on the $\alpha_i^{(n)}$ for $i = 1, \ldots, 2^n$. Therefore our knowledge base can be expressed in terms of linear constraints on $E(\bar{\alpha}_i^{(n)})$ for $i = 1, \ldots, 2^n$. Further, if we define

$$V^{(n)} = \{\mathbf{x} \in [0,1]^{2^n} | \sum_{i=1}^{2^n} x_i = 1\} \subset [0,1]^{2^n}$$

then there is a one to one correspondence from points in $V^{(n)}$ onto probability functions on $\mathcal{L}^{(n)}$. This is to say that for all $\mathbf{x}$ in $V^{(n)}$, $\mathbf{x}$ defines a probabability function on $\mathcal{L}^{(n)}$ such that $E(\bar{\alpha}_i^{(n)}) = x_i$ and for all probability functions E with $E(\bar{\alpha}_i^{(n)}) = x_i$, $\mathbf{x}$ is in $V^{(n)}$. To avoid clumsy notation we associate sentences of $L^{(n)}$ with their equivalence classes in $\mathcal{L}^{(n)}$ from now on.

Let $\mathcal{V}^{(n)}$ be the σ-algebra of Borel sets generated by the intervals of $V^{(n)}$. Then any *a priori* choice of a second order distribution corresponds to a choice of probability function, $Prob^{(n)}$, on $\mathcal{V}^{(n)}$. For the scope of this paper we assume that $Prob^{(n)}$ has a density function $f^{(n)}$ such that for all R in $\mathcal{V}^{(n)}$

$$Prob^{(n)}(R) = \int_R f^{(n)}(\mathbf{x}) dV^{(n)}$$

where integration is carried out with respect to the uniform measure on $\mathcal{V}^{(n)}$.

Definition 1 *Let $\mathcal{F}$ be the class of all density functions which are continuous on the interior of $V^{(n)}$.*

Henceforth, we make a smoothness assumption in this paper by restricting our attention to densities in $\mathcal{F}$.

If C is a knowledge base of linear constraints, then C corresponds to a convex subset of $V^{(n)}$ denoted also by C. Therefore, any $f^{(n)}$ in $\mathcal{F}$ which is integrable on C naturally defines a density function on C given by

$$\frac{f^{(n)}(\mathbf{x})}{\int_C f^{(n)}(\mathbf{x}) dV^{(n)}}$$

where by notational convention integration is carried out in relative dimension if C is a lower dimensional region of $V^{(n)}$. If, in this case, the integral of $f^{(n)}$ on C does not exist, then for the scope of this paper we leave the conditional density function undefined.

With the same convention we define for any R in $\mathcal{V}^{(n)}$

$$Prob^{(n)}(R|C) = \frac{\int_{R \cap C} f^{(n)}(\mathbf{x}) dV^{(n)}}{\int_C f^{(n)}(\mathbf{x}) dV^{(n)}}$$

In this context a rather natural inference process is the **Center of Mass inference process** ($CM^{f^{(n)}}$), so called because it selects the center of mass of a convex region C relative to a prior density $f^{(n)}$. More formally , if

$$CM_C^{f^{(n)}}(\alpha_i^{(n)}) = \frac{\int_C x_i f^{(n)}(\mathbf{x}) dV^{(n)}}{\int_C f^{(n)}(\mathbf{x}) dV^{(n)}} = y_i$$

for $i = 1, \ldots, 2^n$, then $\mathbf{y}$ is the center of mass of the region C calculated according to the density $f^{(n)}$. Since C is convex, $\mathbf{y}$ is a point in C, and hence the inference process selects a probability function E consistent with the knowledge base C. Note, however, that if the dimension of C is less than $2^n - 1$ then $f^{(n)}$ may not be integrable on C in which case $CM_C^{f^{(n)}}(\alpha_i^{(n)})$ is undefined for $i = 1, \ldots, 2^n$. The inference process $CM^{f^{(n)}}$ for the case when $f^{(n)}$ is the uniform measure, has been investigated by several authors (e.g. Paris and Vencovska (1991, to appear)).

Up to now we have considered the language $L^{(n)}$ as fixed. However, if we allow n to vary by adding propositional variables so that $L^{(n)} = \{p_1, \ldots, p_n\}$, and then for each value of $n \geq 1$ define a probability measure $Prob^{(n)}$ with density $f^{(n)}$, we obtain a hierarchy of prior densities denoted $\{f^{(n)}\}$. In the next section we propose an axiomatic framework for the *a priori* choice of a hierarchy of densities, and then go on to give some results related to this sytem of axioms.

3   Axiomatic Framework

The problem of choosing second order densities has parallels with the old statistical problem of defining priors for use in Bayesian inference. It has often been pointed out that for some types of Bayesian reasoning the choice of prior is relatively unimportant assuming large sample sizes. Furthermore, Bayesian statisticians have, in spite of the arguments put forward by (Johnson 1932) and (Carnap 1952), tended to adopt a rather ad hoc approach to selecting priors. In the present context of inexact reasoning, however, the choice of priors is of fundamental importance and hence we feel it is necessary to develop an approach based on epistemological considerations.

The traditional response to the problem, attributed to Laplace in the case $n = 1$ (see (Zabel 1965) for discussion), is that in the absence of any other information the principle of insufficient reason forces us to choose $f^{(n)}$ to be the uniform distribution (i.e $Prob^{(n)}(R)$ proportional to the volume of R for $R \in \mathcal{V}^{(n)}$). However, we shall demonstrate, at least for the more general n dimensional problem, that this is unsatisfactory.

The epistemological conditions that we propose can be separated into two categories: **global conditions** which describe relationships between different levels of the hierarchy, and **local conditions** which are defined for fixed n. The first axiom, marginality, is a global condition.

A1 (Marginality) For all $n > 1$ if $\alpha_i^{(n-1)}$ for $i = 1, \ldots, 2^{n-1}$ denote the atoms of $L^{(n-1)}$ then

$$Prob^{(n)}(\bigwedge_{i=1}^{2^{n-1}} E(\alpha_i^{(n-1)}) < t_i) = Prob^{(n-1)}(\bigwedge_{i=1}^{2^{n-1}} E(\alpha_i^{(n-1)}) < t_i)$$

Expressed in terms of densities: let $\{f^{(n)}\}$ be a hierarchy of prior densities and let

$$Y_i = X_{2i-1} + X_{2i} \; for \; i = 1, \ldots, 2^{n-1}$$

If $h^{(n)}(\mathbf{y})$ is the marginal density function of $\mathbf{Y}$ induced by $f^{(n)}$, then $\{f^{(n)}\}$ is said to satisfy **marginality** if

$$\forall \, n > 1 \; h^{(n)}(\mathbf{y}) = f^{(n-1)}(\mathbf{y}).$$

Note that in our enumeration the atoms of $L^{(n-1)}$ are related to those of $L^{(n)}$ by

$$\alpha_{2j}^{(n)} \vee \alpha_{2j-1}^{(n)} = \alpha_j^{(n-1)} \; where \; \alpha_{2j-1}^{(n)} = \alpha_j^{(n-1)} \wedge p_n \; and \; \alpha_{2j}^{(n)} = \alpha_j^{(n-1)} \wedge \neg p_n$$

This axiom is motivated by the consideration that adding another propositional variable p_n to the language $L^{(n-1)}$ should not effect our knowledge of sentences that do not contain p_n. The axiom of marginality is sufficient to guarantee this in the presence of an axiom which allows the permutation of variables (see axiom A2). Marginality is strongly related to the following condition on inference processes.

Definition 2 *Suppose $N(L^{(n)})$ is a family of inference processes dependent on the language $L^{(n)}$. This family is said to be **language invariant** if for $L^{(n)} \subseteq L^{(n+m)}$ and C a set of constraints on $L^{(n)}$*

$$N_C(L^{(n)})(\theta) = N_C(L^{(n+m)})(\theta) \; \forall \theta \in SL^{(n)}$$

Theorem 3 *If $f^{(n)} \in \mathcal{F}$ and $f^{(n)}(\mathbf{x}) > 0$ for all $\mathbf{x}$ in the interior of $V^{(n)}$, then $CM^{f^{(n)}}$ satisfies language invariance, iff $\{f^{(n)}\}$ satisfies marginality.*

We can now see that the assumption of the uniform measure is unsatisfactory in that it is inconsistent with marginality. In other words, if $Prob^{(n)}$ is defined to be the uniform measure at each level n then the hierarchy of priors does not satisfy marginality. In addition, we observe that the uniform density is a special case of the symmetric Dirichlet system of densities given by

$$d(\lambda, 2^n) = \Gamma(\lambda)[\Gamma(\frac{\lambda}{2^n})^{-2^n}] \prod_{i=1}^{2^n} x_i^{\frac{\lambda}{2^n}-1}$$

where λ is a parameter on $(0, \infty)$ corresponding to the uniform distribution when $\lambda = 2^n$. This system of priors is frequently used in Bayesian reasoning and has been justified in this context by (Johnson 1932) and (Carnap 1952). The inconsistency of the uniform measure with marginality is clarified by the next result.

Theorem 4 *If $\{d(\lambda, 2^n)\}$ is a hierarchy of symmetric Dirichlet priors then $\{d(\lambda, 2^n)\}$ satisfies marginality iff $\lambda > 0$ is a constant independent of n.*

Our second axiom is the local symmetry condition that the density $f^{(n)}$ should be invariant under permutations of the literals of the language.

A2 (Weak Renaming) Let $\sigma : \mathcal{L}^{(n)} \longmapsto \mathcal{L}^{(n)}$ be an automorphism on the Lindenbaum algebra such that for all propositional variables p_i

$$\sigma(p_i) = p_j^\epsilon \ where \ \epsilon \in \{0, 1\}$$

For each such σ there is a corresponding permutation of each $\mathbf{x} \in V^{(n)}$ such that

$$\sigma(x_i) = x_j \iff \sigma(\alpha_i^{(n)}) = \alpha_j^{(n)}$$

Then $f^{(n)}$ satisfies **weak renaming** if

$$\forall \mathbf{x} \in V^{(n)} \ f^{(n)}(\sigma(\mathbf{x})) = f^{(n)}(\mathbf{x})$$

This axiom seems intuitively justified because simply renaming the literals should not alter the *a priori* information content of the system.

A3 (Non Nullity)

$$Prob^{(n)}(E(\alpha_i^{(n)}) \in I) > 0 \ for \ all \ non \ empty \ open \ intervals \ I \subseteq [0, 1].$$

In terms of densities this means that for all such intervals $I \subseteq [0, 1] \ \exists \mathbf{x} \in V^{(n)}$ such that $x_i \in I$ and $f^{(n)}(\mathbf{x}) > 0$.

A problem that seems to occur regularly in relation to knowledge bases for expert systems is as follows. Suppose we have total knowledge regarding specific atoms of $SL^{(n-1)}$; this is to say our knowledge base consists of constraints of the form $E(\alpha_i^{(n-1)}) = t$. If a new propositional variable p_n is then added to the language, and we have no prior information either of the weights to be allocated to the new atoms $p_n \wedge \alpha_i^{(n-1)}$ and $\neg p_n \wedge \alpha_i^{(n-1)}$, or what the relationship is between these and the other atoms of $L^{(n)}$, then we use the final two axioms.

A4 (Weak Atomic Independence) For $n \geq 2$ the distribution $Prob^{(n)}$ satisfies weak atomic independence if

$$Prob^{(n)}(E(p_n | \alpha_i^{(n-1)}) < x \ | E(\alpha_i^{(n-1)}) = t \ )$$

$$= Prob^{(n)}(E(p_n | \alpha_i^{(n-1)}) < x \ | \bigwedge_{j \neq i} (E(\alpha_{2j}^{(n)}) = s_{2j} \wedge E(\alpha_{2j-1}^{(n)}) = s_{2j-1}))$$

for all $s_{2j}, s_{2j-1}, t, x \in [0,1]$ where $j = 1, \ldots, 2^{n-1}$ subject to $\sum_{j \neq i} s_{2j} + s_{2j-1} = 1 - t$.

Less formally, weak atomic independence states that for all $j \in \{1, \ldots, 2^{n-1}\}$ $E(\alpha_{2i}^{(n)})$ and $E(\alpha_{2i-1}^{(n)})$ are independent of the probability of the other atoms of $L^{(n)}$ up to consistency with the constraint $E(\alpha_i^{(n-1)}) = t$.

A5 (Relative Ignorance) The distribution $Prob^{(n)}$ satisfies relative ignorance if for $x, t \in [0,1], n \geq 2$

$$Prob^{(n)}(E(p_n|\alpha_i^{(n-1)}) < x | E(\alpha_i^{(n-1)}) = t)$$

is independent of t.

In other words the probability of p_n occurring, given that $\alpha_i^{(n-1)}$ has occurred, is independent of $E(\alpha_i^{(n-1)})$. The idea here is that since the constraint $E(\alpha_i^{(n-1)}) = t$ provides no information about p_n, the relative distribution of weight between the atoms $p_n \wedge \alpha_i^{(n-1)}$ and $\neg p_n \wedge \alpha_i^{(n-1)}$ should be independent of t. The next section gives a number of results related to this axiom system.

4 Multiplicativity and Dirichlet Priors

The prior densities considered in this section have the form $f^{(n)} = \prod_{i=1}^{2^n} g^{(n)}(x_i)$ where $g^{(n)} : [0,1] \to \mathbf{R}^+$ and we refer to such priors as **multiplicative**. A good example are symmetric Dirichlet priors described earlier. The next result illustrates the connection between multiplicative priors and weak atomic independence. All results in this section concern priors in $\mathcal{F}$ which satisfy weak renaming and non nullity.

Theorem 5 *Let $\{f^n\}$ be a hierarchy of prior densities satisfying marginality. For all $n \geq 1$ let $f^{(n)}$ be a density in $\mathcal{F}$ which satisfies weak renaming and non nullity. Then the following are equivalent*

(i) $\forall n \geq 2$ $f^{(n)}$ *satisfies weak atomic independence*
(ii) $\forall n \geq 1$ $f^{(n)}$ *is multiplicative*

Thus assuming weak atomic independence we are able to further restrict our attention to multiplicative priors. In fact, we now limit ourselves to the following class of smooth multiplicative priors.

Definition 6 *Let $\mathcal{F}_\Pi$ be the class of multiplicative priors of the form $f^{(n)}(\mathbf{x}) = \prod_{i=1}^{2^n} g(x_i)$ where $g : (0,1) \to \mathbf{R}^+$ is twice differentiable on $(0,1)$.*

We now give a result demonstrating the equivalence, in this context, between accepting the axiom of relative ignorance and restricting attention to symmetric Dirichlet priors.

Theorem 7 *If $f^{(n)}$ is in $\mathcal{F}_\Pi$ and satisfies non nullity, then $f^{(n)}$ satisfies relative ignorance iff $f^{(n)}$ is a symmetric Dirichlet prior.*

The following corollary shows that for the class of densities $\mathcal{F}_\Pi$, the axioms A1, A2, A3 and A5 characterise the hierarchy of symmetric Dirichlet priors up to a parameter λ independent of n.

Corollary 8 *If $\{f^{(n)}\}$ is a hierarchy of priors satisfying marginality such that for all $n \geq 1$ $f^{(n)}$ is in $\mathcal{F}_\Pi$ and satisfies non nullity, weak renaming, and relative ignorance, then $f^{(n)}(\mathbf{x}) = d(\lambda, 2^n)(\mathbf{x})$ where $\lambda > 0$ is a constant independent of n.*

5 Comments

From a theorem of De Finetti it follows that Carnap's continuum for inductive inference on sequences of trials with n possible outcomes is equivalent to Bayesian inference assuming a symmetric Dirichlet prior (see (Carnap 1952) or (Zabel 1965)). In view of this and the above results an open question worthy of consideration is what relationship exists between axioms A1 to A5 and the logical conditions of Carnap? For instance, one symmetry principle of Carnap's states that the probability of a particular propositional variable, p, occurring at the next trial is dependent only on the total number of trials and the number of occurrences of p in previous trials. There has been much criticism of this principle on the basis that it fails to take into account information on frequencies of frequencies which can be used to estimate the probabilities of literals (Good 1965). In the light of this it would be interesting to know if analogous criticisms can be made regarding A4 and A5. In addition, given the failure of Carnap's programme to justify the choice of a value for λ, it would be interesting to know if there are natural axioms for systems of priors which together with axioms A1 to A5 would choose a particular λ.

It is important to note that we are not claiming the above axioms are natural laws justifying Dirichlet priors, neither is it our intention to propound any one system of axioms. Rather we aim to demonstrate the relationship between particular hierarchies of priors and epistemological conditions. Indeed, we are investigating a number of other axioms, some of which are inconsistent with A1 to A5. For example:

Epistemic Independence

$$Prob^{(n)}(E(p_i) < t_i \mid \bigwedge_{j \neq i} E(p_j) < t_j\ ) = Prob^{(n)}(E(p_i) < t_i)$$

where $j = 1, \ldots, n$

This condition states that $E(p_j)$ for $j \neq i$ provides no information about $E(p_i)$ and is based on the idea that since we have no knowledge of relationships between the propositional variables we assume them independent.

Hierarchical Independence For $n \geq 2$

$$Prob^{(n)}(E(p_n | \alpha_i^{(n-1)}) < x \ | E(\alpha_i^{(n-1)}) = t \ )$$

is independent of n.

This is motivated by the feeling that for constraints $E(\alpha_i^{(n-1)}) = t$ the degree of uncertainty regarding $E(p_n \wedge \alpha_i^{(n-1)})$ is the same for each level of the hierarchy.

It can be shown that both hierarchical and epistemic independence are inconsistent with A1 to A5 for densities in $\mathcal{F}_{\Pi}$. Hierarchical independence together with A2, A3 and A5 characterise the hierarchy of symmetric Dirichlet priors $\{d(\kappa 2^n, 2^n)\}$ where $\kappa > 0$ is a constant. Clearly this is inconsistent with the hierarchy characterised by A1, A2, A3 and A5 (corollary 8). Similarly we can show that any hierarchy of priors in $\mathcal{F}_{\Pi}$ satisfying epistemic independence and A1 to A3 is also inconsistent with the hierarchy of corollary 8.

References

Carnap, R.: *Continuum of Inductive Methods.* Chicago: University of Chicago Press, 1952.

Good, I.J.: *The Estimation of Probabilities: An Essay on Modern Bayesian Methods.* M.I.T Press, 1965.

Good, I.J.: *Good Thinking: The Foundations of Probability and its Applications.* University of Minnesota Press, 1983.

Johnson, W.E.: "Probability: The Deductive and Inductive Problems," in: *Mind*, Vol. XLI, No. 164 (1932) 27.

Paris, J., and A. Vencovska: "A Method for Updating Justifying Minimum Cross Entropy," in: *The Journal of Approximate Reasoning*, to appear.

Paris, J., and A. Vencovska: "Principles of Uncertain Reasoning," in: *Proceedings of the second International Colloquium on Cognitive Science*, San Sebastian, Spain, 1991.

Paris, J., A. Vencovska, and G.M. Wilmers: "A Note on Objective Inductive Inference," in: De Glas, M., and D, Gabbay (eds.). *Proceedings of the First World Conference on the Foundations of Artificial Intelligence* Paris: Association Francaise pour l'Intelligence Artificialle (1991) 407-412.

Paris, J., A. Vencovska, and G.M. Wilmers: "A Natural Prior Probability Distribution Derived From The Propositional Calculus," in: *The Annals of Pure and Applied Logic*, to appear.

Zabel, S.L.: "Symmetry and its Discontents," in: *Causation, Chance, and Credence*, Vol 1. M.I.T. Press (1965) 155-190.

Contradiction Removal Semantics
with Explicit Negation

Luís Moniz Pereira, José J. Alferes, Joaquim N. Aparício

CRIA, Uninova and DCS, U. Nova de Lisboa
2825 Monte da Caparica, Portugal
E-mail: {lmp/jja/jna}@fct.unl.pty

Abstract. Well Founded Semantics for logic programs extended with eXplicit negation ($WFSX$) is characterized by the fact that, in any model, whenever $\neg a$ (the explicit negation of a) holds, then $\sim a$ (the negation by default of a) also holds.

When explicit negation is used, contradictions may be present (e.g., a and $\neg a$ both hold for some a). We introduce a way the notion of removing some contradictions through identifying the set of models obtained by revising closed world assumptions. One such unique model is singled out as the contradiction removal semantics ($CRSX$). When contradictions do not arise, the contradiction removal semantics coincides with $WFSX$.

1 Introduction

We begin the paper by briefly reviewing the $WFSX$ semantics introduced in (Pereira and Alferes 1992) and by presenting some examples when $WFSX$ semantics is used. For a motivation regarding $WFSX$, see the introduction to (Pereira et al. 1994 – in this volume). Since some programs may have no semantics because they contain a contradiction and $WSFX$ does not directly deal with contradictions, we introduce the $CRSX$, a process of identifying negative literals such as sources of inconsistencies, and show how contradictions may be removed. For each alternative way of removing contradiction in program P, we construct a program P' such that $WFSX(P')$ is consistent. We then present some properties concerning the $CRSX$ semantics.

2 Language

Given a first order language *Lang* (Przymusinska and Przymusinski 1990), an extended logic program is a set of rules of the form

$$H \leftarrow B_1, \ldots, B_n, \sim C_1, \ldots, \sim C_m \qquad m \geq 0, n \geq 0$$

where $H, B_1, \ldots, B_n, C_1, \ldots, C_m$ are classical literals. A (syntactically) classical literal (or explicit literal) is either an atom A or its explicit negation $\neg A$. We also use the symbol $\neg$ to denote complementary literals in the sense of explicit negation. Thus $\neg\neg A = A$. The symbol $\sim$ stands for negation by default[1]. $\sim L$ is called a default literal. Literals are either classical or default. A set of rules stands for all its ground instances w.r.t. *Lang*. When $n = m = 0$ we may simply write H instead of $H \leftarrow$.

As in (Przymusinska and Przymusinski 1990), we expand our language by adding to it the proposition **u** such that for every interpretation I, $I(\mathbf{u}) = 1/2$. By a non-negative program we mean a program whose premises are either classical literals or **u**. Given a program P we denote by $\mathcal{H}_P$ (or simply $\mathcal{H}$) its Herbrand base. If S is a set of literals $\{L_1, \ldots, L_n\}$, by $\sim S$ we mean the set $\{\sim L | L \in S\}$.

If S is a set of literals then we say S is *contradictory* (resp. *inconsistent*) iff there is classical literal L such that $\{L, \neg L\} \subseteq S$ (resp. $\{L, \sim L\} \subseteq S$). In this case we also say that *S is contradictory w.r.t. to L*, (resp. *S is inconsistent w.r.t. to L*). S is agnostic w.r.t. L iff neither $L \in S$ nor $\sim L \in S$.

3 *WFSX* overview

In this section we briefly review $WFSX$ semantics for logic programs extended with explicit negation. For full details the reader is referred to (Pereira and Alferes 1992).

$WFSX$ follows from WFS plus one basic "coherence" requirement:

$$\neg L \Rightarrow \sim L \tag{1}$$

i.e., (if L is explicitly false, L must be false) for any explicit literal L.

Example 1. Consider program $P = \{a \leftarrow \sim b, \quad b \leftarrow \sim a, \quad \neg a \leftarrow \}$.

If $\neg a$ were to be simply considered as a new atom symbol, say a', and WFS used to define the semantics of P (as suggested in (Prymusinski 1990)), the result would be $\{\neg a, \sim \neg b\}$, so that $\neg a$ is true and a is undefined. We insist that $\sim a$ should hold, and that a should not hold, because $\neg a$ does. Accordingly, the WFSX of P is $\{\neg a, b, \sim a, \sim \neg b\}$, since b follows from $\sim a$.

We begin by providing a definition of interpretation for programs with explicit negation which incorporates coherence from the start.

Definition 1 Interpretation. By an interpretation I of a language *Lang* we mean any set $T \cup \sim F$[2], where T and F are disjoint subsets of classical literals over the Herbrand base, and if $\neg L \in T$ then $L \in F$ (coherence)[3]. The set T contains all ground classical literals *true* in I, the set F contains all ground

---

[1] This designation has been used in the literature instead of the more operational *"negation as failure (to prove)"*. Another appropriate designation is *"implicit negation"*, in contradistinction to *"explicit negation"*.

[2] By $\sim\{a_1, \ldots, a_n\}$ we mean $\{\sim a_1, \ldots, \sim a_n\}$.

[3] For any literal L, if L is explicitly false L must be false. Note that the complementary condition "if $L \in T$ then $\neg L \in F$" is implicit.

classical literals *false* in I. The truth value of the remaining classical literals is *undefined* (The truth value of a default literal $\sim L$ is the 3-valued complement of L.)

We next extend with an additional rule the P modulo I transformation of (Przymusinska and Przymusinski 1990), itself an extension of the Gelfond-Lifschitz modulo transformation, to account for coherence.

Definition 2 P/I **transformation.** Let P be an extended logic program and let I be an interpretation. By P/I we mean a program obtained from P by performing the following three operations for every atom A :

- Remove from P all rules containing a default premise $L =\sim A$ such that $A \in I$.
- Remove from P all rules containing a non–default premise L (resp. $\neg L$) such that $\neg L \in I$ (resp. $L \in I$).
- Remove from all remaining rules of P their default premises $L =\sim A$ such that $\sim A \in I$.
- Replace all the remaining default premises by proposition $\mathbf{u}$[4].

The resulting program P/I is by definition non-negative, and it always has a unique $least(P/I)$, where $least(P/I)$ is:

Definition 3 Least-operator. We define $least(P)$, where P is a non-negative program, as the set of literals $T \cup \sim F$ obtained as follows:

- Let P' be the non-negative program obtained by replacing in P every negative classical literal $\neg L$ by a new atomic symbol, say $'\neg\_L'$.
- Let $T' \cup \sim F'$ be the least 3-valued model of P'.
- $T \cup \sim F$ is obtained from $T' \cup \sim F'$ by reversing the replacements above.

The least 3-valued model of a non-negative program can be defined as the least fixpoint of the following generalization of the van Emden–Kowalski least model operator Ψ for definite logic programs:

Definition 4 Ψ^* **operator.** Suppose that P is a non-negative program, I is an interpretation of P and A is a ground atom. Then $\Psi^*(I)$ is an interpretation defined as follows:

- $\Psi^*(I)(A) = 1$ iff there is a rule $A \leftarrow A_1, \ldots, A_n$ in P such that $I(A_i) = 1$ for all $i \leq n$.
- $\Psi^*(I)(A) = 0$ iff for every rule $A \leftarrow A_1, \ldots, A_n$ there is an $i \leq n$ such that $I(A_i) = 0$.
- $\Psi^*(I)(A) = 1/2$, otherwise.

---

[4] The special proposition u is *undefined* in all interpretations.

To avoid incoherence, a partial operator is defined that transforms any non-contradictory set of literals into an interpretation, whenever no contradiction[5] is present.

Definition 5 The *Coh* operator. Let $I = T \cup \sim F$ be a set of literals such that T is not contradictory. We define $Coh(I) = I \cup \sim \{\neg L \mid L \in T\}$.

Definition 6 The Φ operator. Let P be a logic program and I an interpretation, and let $J = least(P/I)$. If $Coh(J)$ exists we define $\Phi_P(I) = Coh(J)$. Otherwise $\Phi_P(I)$ is not defined.

Example 2. For the program of example 1 we have

$$P/\{\neg a, b, \sim a, \sim \neg b\} = \{b \leftarrow; \neg a \leftarrow\},$$

$$least(P/\{\neg a, b, \sim a, \sim \neg b\}) = \{\neg a, b, \sim a\}$$

and:

$$Coh(\{\neg a, b, \sim a\}) = \{\neg a, b, \sim a, \sim \neg b\}.$$

Definition 7 WFS with explicit negation. An interpretation I of an extended logic program P is called an Extended Stable Model (XSM) of P iff $\Phi_P(I) = I$. The F-least Extended Stable Model is called the Well Founded Model. The semantics of P is determined by the set of all $XSMs$ of P.

Example 3. Let $P = \{a \leftarrow \sim b, \sim c; b \leftarrow \sim a; \neg c \leftarrow \sim d\}$. This program has a least model $M_1 = \{\sim d, \neg c, \sim c, \sim \neg a, \sim \neg b, \sim \neg d\}$ and two Extended Stabel Models $M_2 = M_1 \cup \{\sim a, b\}$ and $M_3 = M_1 \cup \{a, \sim b\}$. Considering model M_1 we have for $P/M_1 = \{a \leftarrow \mathbf{u}; b \leftarrow \mathbf{u}; c' \leftarrow\}$, and

$$least(P/M_1) = J = \{\sim d, c', \sim a', \sim b', \sim d', \sim c\} = \{\sim d, \sim \neg d, \neg c, \sim c, \sim \neg a, \sim \neg b\}.$$

Example 4. Let P be:
$$a \leftarrow \sim a \ (i)$$
$$b \leftarrow \sim a \ (ii)$$
$$\neg b \leftarrow \quad (iii)$$

After the transformation, program P' has a rule $b' \leftarrow$, and there is no way in proving $\sim b$ from rules (i) and (ii). And we have $least(P'/\{b', \sim b, \sim a'\}) = \{b', \sim a'\} = M$ which corresponds to the model $\{\neg b, \sim \neg a\}$ if the coherence principle is not applied. In our case we have $Coh(M) = \{\neg b, \sim b, \sim \neg a\}$ which is the intended result.

Definition 8 Contradictory program. An extended logic program P is contradictory iff it has no model, i.e., there exists no interpretation I such that $\Phi_P(I) = I$.

---

[5] We say a set of literals S is contradictory iff for some literal L, $L \in S$ and $\neg L \in S$.

4 Revising contradictory extended logic programs

Once we introduce explicit negation programs are liable to be contradictory:

Example 5. Consider program $P = \{a \leftarrow \; ; \neg a \leftarrow \sim b\}$. Since we have no rules for b, by CWA it is natural to accept $\sim b$ as true. By the second rule in P we have $\neg a$, leading to an inconsistency with the fact a. Thus no set containing $\sim b$ may be a model of P.

We argue that the CWA may not be held of atom b since it leads to a contradiction. We show below how to revise[6] this form of contradiction by making a suitable revision of the incorrect CWA on b. The semantics we introduce identifies $\{a, \sim \neg a\}$ as the intended meaning of P, where b is revised to undefined. Assuming b false leads to a contradiction; revising it to true instead of undefined would not minimize the revised interpretation.

4.1 Contradictory well founded model

In order to revise possible contradictions we need to identify those contradictory sets implied by applications of CWA. The main idea is to compute all consequences of the program, even those leading to contradictions, as well as those arising from contradictions. The following example provides an intuitive preview of what we intend to capture:

Example 6. Consider program P :

$$a \leftarrow \sim b \;\text{(i)} \quad d \leftarrow a \quad \text{(iii)}$$
$$\neg a \leftarrow \sim c \;\text{(ii)} \quad e \leftarrow \neg a \;\text{(iv)}$$

1. $\sim b$ and $\sim c$ hold since there are no rules for either b or c
2. $\neg a$ and a hold from 1 and rules (i) and (ii)
3. $\sim a$ and $\sim \neg a$ hold from 2 and inference rule (1)
4. d and e hold from 2 and rules (iii) and (iv)
5. $\sim d$ and $\sim e$ hold from 3 and rules (iii) and (iv), as they are the only rules for d and e
6. $\sim \neg d$ and $\sim \neg e$ hold from 4 and inference rule (1).

The whole set of literals is then:

$$\{\sim b, \sim c, \neg a, a, \sim a, \sim \neg a, d, e, \sim d, \sim e, \sim \neg d, \sim \neg e\}.$$

N. B. We extend the language with the special symbol $\perp$. For every pair of classical literals $\{L, \neg L\}$ in the language of P we implicitly assume a rule $\perp \leftarrow L, \neg L$[7].

---

[6] We treat contradictory programs extending the approach of (Pereira et al. 1991a, Pereira et al. 1991b).

[7] This is not strictly necessary but simplifies the exposition. Furthermore, without loss of generality, we only consider rules $\perp \leftarrow L, \neg L$ for which rules for both L and $\neg L$ exist in P. We also use the notation $\perp_L$ to denote the head of rule $\perp \leftarrow L, \neg L$.

Definition 9 Pseudo–interpretation. A pseudo–interpretation (or p–interpretation for short) is a possibly contradictory set of ground literals from the language of a program.

We extend the Θ operator (Przymusinska and Przymusinski 1990) from the class of interpretations to the class of p–interpretations, and we call this the Θ^x operator (x standing for eXtended).

Definition 10 The Θ^x operator. Let P be a logic program and J a p–interpretation. The operator $\Theta_J^x : \mathcal{I} \rightarrow I$ on the set $\mathcal{I}$ of all 3-valued p–interpretations of P is defined as follows: If $I \in \mathcal{I}$ is a p–interpretation of P and A is a ground classical literal then $\Theta_J^x(I)$ is the p–interpretation defined by:

1. $\Theta_J^x(I)(A) = 1$ iff there is a rule $A \leftarrow L_1, \ldots, L_n$ in P such that for all $i \leq n$ either $\hat{J}(L_i) = 1$, or L_i is positive and $I(L_i) = 1$;
2. $\Theta_J^x(I)(A) = 0$ iff one of the following holds:
   (a) for every rule $A \leftarrow L_1, \ldots, L_n$ in P there is an $i \leq n$, such that either $\hat{J}(L_i) = 0$, or L_i is positive and $I(L_i) = 0$;
   (b) $\hat{J}(\neg A) = 1$;
3. $\Theta_J^x(I)(A) = 1/2$ otherwise.

Note that the only difference between this definition and the definition of Θ operator introduced in (Przymusinska and Przymusinski 1990) is condition (2b) capturing the coherence requirement, or inference rule (1). Furthermore, since it is defined over the class of p–interpretations, it allows that for a given literal L, we may have $\Theta_J^x(I)(L) = 1$ as well as $\Theta_J^x(I)(L) = 0$.

Proposition 11. For every p–interpretation J, the operator Θ_J^x is monotone and has a unique least fixed point given by $\Theta_J^x {\uparrow}^w$, also denoted by $\Omega^x(J)$[8].

Definition 12 p–model. Given a program, a p–model is a p–interpretation I such that:

$$I = \Omega^x(I) \tag{2}$$

Remark. Note that if a p–model M is contradictory w.r.t. to L then M is inconsistent w.r.t. to L by virtue of inference rule (1), although the converse is not true.

Definition 13 Well Founded Model. The pseudo Well Founded Model M_P of P is the F–least p–model.

The non–minimal models satisfying (2) above are the (pseudo) Extended Models (XMs for short). To compute the p–model M_P, we define the following transfinite sequence $\{I_\alpha\}$:

---

[8] Recall (Przymusinska and Przymusinski 1990) that the F-least interpretation used to compute the least fixed point of $\Theta_J^x {\uparrow}^w$ is $\sim\mathcal{H}_P$.

$$I_0 = \langle \emptyset, \emptyset \rangle$$
$$I_{\alpha+1} = \Omega^x(I_\alpha) = \Theta^x_{I_\alpha}\uparrow^w$$
$$I_\delta = \bigcup_{\alpha<\delta} I_\alpha \text{ for limit ordinal } \delta$$

Equivalently, the pseudo well founded model M_P of P is the F–least fixed point of (2) and is given by $M_P = I_\lambda = \Omega^x \uparrow \lambda$.

Definition 14. A program P is contradictory iff $\perp \in M_P$.

Example 7. Recall the program of example 6:

$$P = \{a \leftarrow \sim b \; ; \neg a \leftarrow \sim c \; ; d \leftarrow a \; ; e \leftarrow \neg a\}.$$

$$\Theta^{\uparrow 0}_{I_0} = \{\sim a, \sim\neg a, \sim b, \sim\neg b, \sim c, \sim\neg c, \sim d, \sim\neg d, \sim e, \sim\neg e\}$$
$$\Theta^{\uparrow 3}_{I_0} = \Theta_{I_0}(\Theta^{\uparrow 2}_{I_0}) = \{\sim b, \sim c, \sim\neg b, \sim\neg c, \sim\neg d, \sim\neg e\} = \Theta^{\uparrow w}_{I_0} = I_1$$
$$\Theta^{\uparrow 3}_{I_1} = \Theta_{I_1}(\Theta^{\uparrow 2}_{I_1}) = \{a, d, \neg a, e, \sim b, \sim\neg b, \sim c, \sim\neg c, \sim\neg d, \sim\neg e\} = \Theta^{\uparrow w}_{I_1} = I_2$$
$$\Theta^{\uparrow 2}_{I_2} = \Theta_{I_2}(\Theta^{\uparrow 1}_{I_2}) = \{a, \sim\neg a, \neg a, \sim a, d, \sim\neg d, e, \sim\neg e, \sim b, \sim\neg b, \sim c, \sim\neg c, \sim d, \sim\neg d, \sim e\} =$$
$$= \Theta^{\uparrow w}_{I_2} = I_3$$
$$\Theta^{\uparrow 2}_{I_3} = \Theta_{I_3}(\Theta^{\uparrow 1}_{I_3}) = \{a, \sim\neg a, \neg a, \sim a, d, \sim\neg d, e, \sim\neg e, \sim b, \sim\neg b, \sim c, \sim\neg c, \sim d, \sim\neg d, \sim e\} =$$
$$= \Theta^{\uparrow w}_{I_3} = I_4 = I_3$$

so the program is contradictory.

4.2 Removing the contradiction

In order to get revised non–contradictory consistent models we must know where a contradiction arises. In this section we identify sets of default literals true by CWA whose revision to undefined can remove contradiction, by withdrawing the support of the CWAs on which the contradiction depends.

Definition 15 Dependency set. A Dependency Set of a literal L in a program P, represented as $DS(L)$, is obtained as follows:

1. If L is a classical literal:
   (a) if there are no rules for L then the only $DS(L) = \{L\}$.
   (b) for each rule $L \leftarrow B_1, \ldots, B_n (n \geq 0)$ in P for L, there exists one $DS_k(L) = \{L\} \cup \bigcup_i DS_{j(i)}(B_i)$ for each different combination k of one $j(i)$ for each i.
2. For a default literal $\sim L$:
   (a) if there are no rules in P for L then a $DS(\sim L) = \{\sim L\}$.
   (b) if there are rules for L then choose from every rule for L a single literal. For each such choice there exist several $DS(\sim L)$; each contains $\sim L$ and one dependency set of each default complement[9] of the chosen literals.

---

[9] The default complement of a classical literal L is $\sim L$; that of a default literal $\sim L$ is L.

(c) if there are rules for $\neg L$ then there are, **additionally**, dependency sets $DS(\sim L) = \{\sim L\} \cup DS_k(\neg L)$ for each k.

Example 8. $P = \{a \leftarrow \sim b \; ; \neg a \leftarrow \sim c \; ; d \leftarrow a \; ; e \leftarrow \neg a\}$. In this case we have the following dependency sets:

$$
\begin{array}{llll}
DS(\sim b) & = \{\sim b\} & DS_1(\sim a) & = \{\sim a, b\} \\
DS(\sim c) & = \{\sim c\} & DS_2(\sim a) & = \{\sim a, \neg a, \sim c\} \\
DS(a) & = \{a, \sim b\} & & \\
DS(\neg a) & = \{\neg a, \sim c\} & & \\
DS_1(\sim d) & = \{\sim d\} \cup DS_1(\sim a) & = \{\sim d, \sim a, b\} & \\
DS_2(\sim d) & = \{\sim d\} \cup DS_2(\sim a) & = \{\sim d, \sim a, \neg a, \sim c\} & \\
DS(\perp_a) & = \{\perp_a, a, \neg a, \sim b, \sim c\} & &
\end{array}
$$

Definition 16 Support of a literal. A support $SS_M(L)$ w.r.t. to a model M is a non–empty dependency set $DS(L)$ such that $DS(L) \subseteq M$. If there exists a $SS_M(L)$ we say that L is supported in M.

For simplicity, a support w.r.t. the pseudo WFM M_P of P can be represented by $SS(L)$.

Definition 17 Support of a set of literals. A support w.r.t. to a model M is:

$$SS_{M\,k}(\{L_1, \ldots, L_n\}) = \bigcup_i SS_{M\,j(i)}(L_i)$$

For each combination k of $j(i)$ there exists one support of sets of literals.

With the notion of support we are able to identify which literals support a contradiction, i.e., the literal $\perp$. In order to remove a contradiction we must change the truth value of at least one literal from each support set of $\perp$. One issue is for which literals we allow to initiate a change of their truth values; another is how to specify a notion of minimal change.

As mentioned before, we only wish to initiate revision on default literals true by *CWA*. To identify such *revising* literals we first define:

Definition 18 Default support. A default literal $\sim A$ is default supported w.r.t. M if **all** supports $SS_M(\sim A)$ have only default literals.

Example 9. Let $P = \{\neg a; \; a \leftarrow \sim b; \; b \leftarrow c; \; c \leftarrow d\}$. The only support of $\perp$ is $\{\neg a, a, \sim b, \sim c, \sim d\}$, and default supported literals are $\sim b$, $\sim c$, and $\sim d$. Here we are not interested in revising the contradiction by undefining $\sim b$ or $\sim c$ because they depend on $\sim d$. The reason is that we are attempting to remove only those contradictions based on *CWA*s. Now, the *CWA* of a literal that is supported on another depends on the *CWA* of the latter.

In order to make more precise what we mean we first present two definitions:

Definition 19 Self supported set. A set of default literals S is self supported w.r.t. a model M iff there exists a $SS_M(S) = S$.

Definition 20 Revising and co–revising literals. Given a program P with pseudo well-founded model M_P, we define co–$\mathcal{R}_P$, the *co–revising literals* induced by P, as the set of literals belonging to some minimal self supported set w.r.t. M_P. We define $\mathcal{R}_P$, the *revising literals*, as the set of co–revising literals L such that $\neg L \notin M_P$. The next examples motivate these definitions.

Example 10. Let $P = \{\neg p; \ p \longleftarrow \sim a; \ \neg a \longleftarrow \sim b\}$.

The co-revising literals are $\{\sim a, \sim b\}$ and the revising are $\{\sim b\}$. The difference is that to revise $\sim a$, one needs to change the truth value of $\neg a$ as well, in order to maintain coherence. To revise $\sim b$, there is no such need. Revising $\neg a$ only is not enough since then $\sim a$ becomes true by default.

Example 11. In the program of example 9, the self supported sets w.r.t. M_P are $\{\sim b, \sim c, \sim d\}$, $\{\sim c, \sim d\}$, and $\{\sim d\}$. Thus the only revising literal is $\sim d$. Note how the requirement of minimality ensures that only CWA literals not depending on other CWAs are revising. In particular:

Proposition 21.

1. If there are no rules for L, then $\sim L$ is a co–revising literal.
2. If there are no rules for L nor for $\neg L$, then $\sim L$ is a revising literal.
3. If $\sim L$ is co–revising and default supported, then it is revising.

An atom can also be false by CWA if it is involved in a positive *"loop"*. Such cases are also accounted for:

Example 12. Let P_1 and P_2 be:

$$P_1 = \{\neg a; \ a \longleftarrow \sim b; \ b \leftarrow b, c\}$$
$$P_2 = \{\neg a; \ a \longleftarrow \sim b; \ b \leftarrow b; \ b \leftarrow c\}$$

For P_1 self supported sets are: $\{\sim b, \sim c\}$, $\{\sim b\}$, and $\{\sim c\}$. Thus $\sim b$ and $\sim c$ are revising. For P_2 the only minimal self supported set is $\{\sim c\}$ thus only $\sim c$ is revising. The only support set of $\sim b$ is $\{\sim b, \sim c\}$. In P_2 it is clear that $\sim b$ depends on $\sim c$. So $\sim b$ is not revising. In P_1 the truth of $\sim b$ can support itself. Thus $\sim b$ is also revising.

Another class of literals is needed in the sequel. Informally, indissociable literals are those that strongly depend on each other, so that their truth value must always be the same. It is impossible to change the truth value of one without changing the truth value of another. So:

Definition 22 Indissociable set of literals. A set of default literals S is indissociable iff

$$\forall \sim a, \sim b \in S \quad \sim a \in \bigcap_i SS_i(\sim b) \ .$$

i.e., each literal in S belongs to every support of every literal in S.

Proposition 23. If S is a minimal self supported set and the only $SS(S)$ is S, then S is an indissociable set of literals.

Example 13. In P below, $\{\sim a, \sim b, \sim c\}$ is a set of indissociable literals:

$$
\begin{array}{ll}
\neg p \leftarrow & a \leftarrow b \\
p \leftarrow \sim a & b \leftarrow c \\
& c \leftarrow a
\end{array}
$$

Example 14. Let P be:

$$
\begin{array}{lll}
\neg p \leftarrow & a \leftarrow b & a \leftarrow c \\
p \leftarrow \sim a & b \leftarrow a &
\end{array}
$$

We have:

$$
\begin{array}{l}
SS(\sim c) = \{\sim c\} \\
SS(\sim b) = \{\sim a, \sim b, \sim c\} \\
SS(\sim a) = \{\sim a, \sim b, \sim c\}
\end{array}
$$

and the unique indissociable set of literals is $\{\sim c\}$, which is also the set of revising literals.

Given the revising literals we have to find one on which the contradiction rests. This is done by finding the supports of $\perp$ where revising literals occur only as leaves (these constitute the $\perp$ assumption sets):

Definition 24 Assumption set. Let P be a program with (pseudo) WFM M_P and $L \in M_P$. An assumption set $AS(L)$ is defined as follows, where $\mathcal{R}_P$ is the set of the revising literals induced by P :

1. If L is a classical literal:
   (a) if there is a fact for L then the only $AS(L) = \{\}$.
   (b) for each rule $L \leftarrow B_1, \ldots, B_n (n \geq 1)$ in P for L such that $\{B_1, \ldots, B_n\} \subseteq M_P$, there exists one $AS_k(L) = \bigcup_i AS_{j(i)}(B_i)$ for each different combination k of one $j(i)$ for each i.
2. For a default literal $\sim L$:
   (a) if $\sim L \in \mathcal{R}_P$, then the only $AS(\sim L) = \{\sim L\}$.
   (b) if $\sim L \in co - \mathcal{R}_P$, then there is a $AS(\sim L) = \{\sim L\}$.
   (c) if $\sim L \notin co - \mathcal{R}_P$, then choose from every rule for L a single literal whose default complement belongs to M_P. For each such choice there exist several $AS(\sim L)$; each contains one assumption set of each default complement of the chosen literals.
   (d) if $\neg L \in M_P$, then there are, **additionally**, assumption sets $AS(\sim L) = AS_k(\neg L)$ for each k.

Definition 25. A program P is *revisable* iff no assumption set of $\perp$ is empty.

This definition entails that a program P is not revisable if $\perp$ has some support without co–revising literals.

Example 15. Consider $P = \{\neg a;\ a \leftarrow \sim b\ ; b \leftarrow \sim c\ ; c\}$ with

$$M_P = \{\bot, a, \sim a, \neg a, \sim b, c\}.$$

The only support of $\bot$ is $SS(\bot) = \{\bot, a, \sim a, \neg a, \sim b, c\}$. $co - \mathcal{R}_P = \{\}$. Thus $AS(\bot) = \{\}$ and the program is not revisable.

Definition 26 Removal set. A Removal Set (RS) of a literal L of program P is a set of literals formed by the union of one **non–empty** subset from each $AS_P(L)$.

Note that, although the program may induce revising literals, this is not enough for a program to be revisable.

In order to make minimal changes that preserve the indissociability of literals we define:

Definition 27 Minimal contradiction removal sets. Let R be a minimal removal set of $\bot$. A Minimal Contradiction Removal Set of program P is the smallest set $MCRS$ such that $R \subseteq MCRS$ and $MCRS$ is inclusive of indissociable literals.

Definition 28 Contradiction removal sets. A contradiction removal set (or CRS for short) of a program P is either a $MCRS$ or the union of $MCRS$s.

Example 16. Consider $P = \{a \leftarrow \sim b\ ;\ b \leftarrow \sim a\ ;\ \neg a\}$.

$$DS(\neg a) = \{\}\ DS(a) = \{\sim b\}\ DS(\sim b) = \{a\}$$

$$DS(\bot_a) = DS(a) \cup DS(\neg a) \supseteq \{\neg a, a, \sim b\}$$

The M_P is obtained as follows:

$$I_0 = \emptyset$$
$$I_1 = \{\neg a, \sim \neg b\} = \Theta_{I_0}^x \uparrow w \qquad I_3 = \{\neg a, \sim a, \sim \neg b, b\} = \Theta_{I_2}^x \uparrow w$$
$$I_2 = \{\neg a, \sim a, \sim \neg b\} = \Theta_{I_1}^x \uparrow w \qquad I_4 = \{\neg a, \sim a, \sim \neg b, b\} = \Theta_{I_3}^x \uparrow w$$
$$I_5 = I_4$$

$M_P = \{\neg a, \sim a, b, \sim \neg b\}$ and $\bot_a \notin M_P$; thus the program is non–contradictory.

Example 17. Consider $P = \{a \leftarrow \sim b\ ; \neg a \leftarrow \sim c\ ; d \leftarrow a\ ; e \leftarrow \neg a\}$.

Since $\sim b$ and $\sim c$ are both revising literals $AS(\bot) = \{\sim b, \sim c\}$. The contradiction removal sets are:

$$CRS_1 = RS_1(\bot_a) = \{\sim b\}$$
$$CRS_2 = RS_2(\bot_a) = \{\sim c\}$$
$$CRS_3 = RS_3(\bot_a) = \{\sim b, \sim c\}$$

Example 18. Let P be:

$$a \leftarrow \sim b \qquad \neg a \leftarrow \sim f$$
$$\neg a \leftarrow \sim d \qquad \neg d \leftarrow \sim e$$

with $M_P = \{\sim b, \sim \neg b, \sim d, \sim e, \sim \neg e, \sim f, \sim \neg f, a, \neg a, \neg d, \sim a, \sim \neg a\}$.

Note that $\sim d$ is not co–revising, since there exists $SS(\sim d) = \{\sim d, \neg d, \sim e\}$. The revising literals are $\sim b$, $\sim e$, and $\sim f$. The assumption sets are:

$$AS_1(\bot) = \{\sim b, \sim e\}$$
$$AS_2(\bot) = \{\sim b\}$$
$$AS_3(\bot) = \{\sim b, \sim f\}$$

Thus the only contradiction removal set is $\{\sim b\}$.

Example 19. Consider the program $P = \{\neg a; a \leftarrow \sim d; \neg d \leftarrow \sim e\}$. We have $M_P = \{\sim e, \sim \neg e, \neg d, \sim d, a, \neg a, \sim \neg a, \sim a\}$ which is contradictory. The only revising literal is $\sim e$ and $\sim d$ is a co–revising literal. Hence one $AS(\sim d) = \{\sim d\}$ and the other $AS(\sim d) = \{\sim e\}$. The only CRS is $\{\sim d, \sim e\}$.

4.3 Contradiction free programs

Next we show that for each contradiction removal set there is a non-contradictory program obtained from the original one by a simple update. Based on these programs we define the $CRSX$ semantics.

Definition 29 CWA inhibition rule. The CWA inhibition rule for an atom A is $A \leftarrow \sim A$.

Any program P containing a CWA inhibition rule for atom A has no models containing $\sim A$.[10]

Definition 30 Contradiction free program. For each contradiction removal set CRS_i of a program P we engender the contradiction free program:

$$P_{CRS_i} =_{def} P \cup \{A \leftarrow \sim A | \sim A \in CRS_i\} \qquad (3)$$

Proposition 31. For any contradiction removal sets i and j, $CRS_i \subseteq CRS_j \Rightarrow M_{P_{CRS_j}} \subseteq M_{P_{CRS_i}}$.

Theorem 32 Soundness of contradiction free programs. A contradiction free program P_{CRS} is non–contradictory, i.e., it has $WFSX$ semantics, and $M_{P_{CRS}} \subseteq M_P$.

---

[10] This rule can be seen as the *productive* integrity constraint $\leftarrow \sim A$. In fact, since the WF Semantics implicitly has in it the *productive* constraint $\leftarrow A, \sim A$, the inhibition rule can be seen as the minimal way of expressing by means of a program rule that $\sim A$ leads to an inconsistency, forcing A not to be false.

Example 20. Consider the program P :

$$a \leftarrow \sim b \qquad \neg c \leftarrow \sim d$$
$$b \leftarrow \sim a, \sim c \qquad c \leftarrow \sim e$$

The well founded model is

$$M_P = \{\bot_c, \sim d, \sim \neg d, \sim e, \sim \neg e, \neg c, c, \sim \neg c, \sim c, \sim b, \sim \neg b, a, \sim \neg a\}.$$

The contradiction removal sets are:

$$CRS_1 = \{\sim d\} \quad CRS_2 = \{\sim e\} \quad CRS_3 = \{\sim d, \sim e\}$$

with CRS_1 and CRS_2 being minimal w.r.t. set inclusion.

- $P_{CRS_1} = P \cup \{d \leftarrow \sim d\}$, with the unique model

$$M_P = \{\sim e, \sim \neg e, c, \sim \neg c, \sim b, \sim \neg b, a, \sim \neg a, \sim \neg d\}.$$

- $P_{CRS_2} = P \cup \{e \leftarrow \sim e\}$, with well founded model

$$M_P = \{\sim d, \neg c, \sim c, \sim \neg a, \sim \neg b, \sim \neg d\}.$$

- $P_{CRS_3} = P \cup \{e \leftarrow \sim e, d \leftarrow \sim d\}$ with well founded model

$$M_P = \{\sim \neg a, \sim \neg b, \sim \neg e, \sim \neg d\}.$$

Definition 33 $CRSX$ **Semantics.** Given a revisable contradictory program P, let CRS_i be any contradiction removal set for P. An interpretation I is a $CRSX$ model of P iff:

$$I = \Phi_{P_{CRS_i}}(I) \ . \tag{4}$$

The least (w.r.t. $\subseteq$) $CRSX$ model of P is called the $CRWFM$ model[11].

The contradiction removal semantics for logic programs extended with explicit negation is defined by the $WFSX$ well founded models of the revised programs defined by (4), representing the different forms of revising a contradictory program.

Example 21. For program P_1 of Example 12 the assumption sets are $AS_{1_1} = \{\sim b\}$ and $AS_{1_2} = \{\sim b, \sim c\}$. Thus the only CRS is $\{\sim b\}$, and the only $CRSX$ model is $\{\neg a, \sim a, \sim c\}$. For program P_2 the only assumption set is $AS_2 = \{\sim c\}$. Thus the only CRS is $\{\sim c\}$, and the only $CRSX$ model is $\{\neg a, \sim a\}$.

---

[11] This model always exists (cf. theorem 35.)

Example 22. Let P be:

$$a \leftarrow \sim b \qquad b \leftarrow c$$
$$\neg a \leftarrow \sim c \qquad c \leftarrow b$$

The only self supported set is $S = \{\sim b, \sim c\}$. Moreover the only support of S is itself. Thus $\sim b$ and $\sim c$ are revising and indissociable. As the only assumption set of $\perp$ is $\{\sim b, \sim c\}$ there are three removal sets: $\{\sim b\}$, $\{\sim c\}$, and $\{\sim b, \sim c\}$. Without indissociability one might think that for this program there would exist three distinct ways of removing the contradiction. This is not the case, since the $XSMs$ of P_{R_1}, P_{R_2}, and P_{R_3} are exactly the same, i.e., they all represent the same revision of P. This is accounted for by introducing indissociable literals in minimal contradiction removal sets. In fact there exists only one $MCRS$ $\{\sim b, \sim c\}$ and thus the only contradiction free program is P_{R_3}.

Theorem 34. For every i, j

$$CRS_i \neq CRS_j \Rightarrow WFM(P_{CRS_i}) \neq WFM(P_{CRS_j}) \ .$$

Theorem 35. The collection of contradiction free programs is a upper semi–lattice under set inclusion of rules in programs, and the set of revised models under set inclusion is a lower semi-lattice. There is a one–to–one correspondence between elements of both semi-lattices.

Acknowledgements

We thank Esprit BRA Compulog (no. 3012) and Compulog 2 (no. 6810), INIC and JNICT for their support.

References

Alferes, J.J., and L.M. Pereira: "On logic program semantics with two kinds of negation," in: K. Apt (ed.), *IJCSLP'92*, MIT Press (1992) 574-588.

Dung, P.M., and P. Ruamviboonsuk: "Well founded reasoning with classical negation," in: A. Nerode, W. Marek, and V. S. Subrahmanian (eds.), *LPNMR'91*, MIT Press (1991) 120-132.

Gelfond, M., and V. Lifschitz: "The stable model semantics for logic programming,"in: R. A. Kowalski and K. A. Bowen (eds.), *5th ICLP*, MIT Press (1988) 1070-1080.

Gelfond, M., and V. Lifschitz: "Logic programs with classical negation," in: Warren and Szeredi (eds.), *ICLP*, MIT Press (September 1990) 579-597.

Inoue, K.: "Extended logic programs with default assumptions," in: Koichi Furukawa (ed.), *ICLP'91*, MIT Press (1991) 490-504.

Kowalski, R.: "Problems and promises of computational logic," in: John Lloyd (ed.), *Computational Logic Symposium*, Springer-Verlag (1990) 1-36.

Kowalski, R., and F. Sadri: "Logic programs with exceptions," in: Warren and Szeredi (eds.), *ICLP*, MIT Press (1990) 598-613.

Lloyd, J.W.: *Foundations of Logic Programming.* Symbolic Computation. Springer-Verlag, 1984.

Pereira, L.M. and J.J. Alferes: "Well founded semantics for logic programs with explicit negation," in: B. Neumann (ed.), *ECAI'92*, John Wiley & Sons, Ltd. (1992) 102-106.

Pereira, L.M., J.J. Alferes, and J.N. Aparício: "Contradiction Removal within Well Founded Semantics," in: A. Nerode, W. Marek, and V. S. Subrahmanian 102-106. (eds.) *LPNMR*, MIT Press (1991a) 105-119.

Pereira, L.M., J.J. Alferes, and J.N. Aparício: "The extended stable models of contradiction removal semantics," in: P.B arahona, L.M. Pereira, and A. Porto (eds.) *EPIA'91*, LNAI 541, Springer-Verlag (1991b) 105-119.

Pereira, L.M., J.J. Alferes, and J.N. Aparício: "Default theory for well founded semantics with explicit negation," in: D. Pearce and G. Wagner (eds.) *Logics for AI - JELIA'92*, LNAI 633, Springer-Verlag (1992a) 339-356.

Pereira, L.M., J. J. Alferes, and J. N. Aparício: "Well founded semantics with explicit negation and default theory," Technical report, AI Centre, Uninova, March 1992 (Submitted).

Pereira, L.M., J.N. Aparício, and J.J. Alferes: "Counterfactual reasoning based on revising assumptions," in: V. Saraswat and K. Ueda (eds.), *ILPS*, MIT Press, (1991c), 566-580.

Pereira, L.M., J.N. Aparício, and J.J. Alferes: "Hypothetical reasoning with well founded semantics," in: B.Mayoh (ed.), *Third Scandinavian Conf. on AI.* IOS Press, 1991d.

Pereira, L.M., J.N. Aparício, and J.J. Alferes: "Nonmonotonic reasoning with well founded semantics," in: K.Furukawa (ed.), *ICLP91*, MIT Press (1991e) 475-489.

Pereira, L.M., J.N. Aparício, and J.J. Alferes: "Non-monotonic reasoning with logic programming," in: *Journal of Logic Programming. Special issue on Nonmonotonic reasoning*, 1993 (to appear).

Pereira, L.M., J.N. Aparício, and J.J. Alferes: "Logic Programming for Non–Monotonic Reasoning." *In this volume*

Przymusinska, H., and T. Przymusinski: "Semantic issues in deductive databases and logic programs," in: R. Banerji (ed.), *Formal Techniques in Artificial Intelligence.* North Holland, 1990.

Przymusinski, T.: "Extended stable semantics for normal and disjunctive programs," in: Warren and Szeredi (eds.), *ICLP'90*, MIT Press (1990) 459-477.

Przymusinski, T.C.: "A semantics for disjunctive logic programs," in: D. Loveland, J. Lobo, and A. Rajasekar (eds.), *ILPS Workshop on Disjunctive Logic Programs*, 1991.

VanGelder, A., K.A. Ross, and J.S. Schlipf: "The well-founded semantics for general logic programs," in: *Journal of the ACM*, 38 (3) (1991) 620-650.

Wagner, G.: "A database needs two kinds of negation," in: B. Thalheim, J. Demetrovics, and H-D. Gerhardt (eds.), *MFDBS'91*, Springer-Verlag (1991) 357-371.

Logic Programming for Non–Monotonic Reasoning

Luís Moniz Pereira, Joaquim N. Aparício, José J. Alferes

CRIA, Uninova and DCS, U. Nova de Lisboa
2825 Monte da Caparica, Portugal
E-mail: {lmp/jna/jja}@fct.unl.pt

Abstract. Our purpose is to develop a modular systematic method of representing nonmonotonic reasoning problems with the Well Founded Semantics of extended logic programs augmented with eXplicit negation (WFSX), and augmented by its Contradiction Removal Semantics (CRSX) when needed. We show how to cast in the language of such logic programs forms of non-monotonic reasoning like defeasible reasoning and hypothetical reasoning, and apply them to different domains of knowledge representation, for instance taxonomic hierarchies and reasoning about actions. We then abstract a modular systematic method of representing non-monotonic problems in logic programming.

1 Introduction

Recently, several authors have showed the importance of introducing an explicit second kind of negation within logic programs, in particular for use in deductive databases, knowledge representation, and nonmonotonic reasoning (Dung and Ruamviboonsuk 1991, Gelfond and Lifschitz 1990, Inoue 1991, Kowalski and Sadri 1990, Kowalski 1990, (Pereira et al., 1991a, 1991b, 1991c), Wagner 1991, Przymusinski 1991).

It has been argued (Pereira et al., 1991a, 1991b, 1991c, 1992b) that well founded semantics are adequate to capture nonmonotonic reasoning if we interpret the least model provided by the semantics (called the Well Founded Model (*WFM*) of a program) as the skeptical view of the world, and the other models (called Extended Stable (*XM*) Models) as alternative enlarged consistent belief sets. A consequence of the well founded property is that the intersection of all models is itself a model belonging to the semantics.

Several proposals for extending logic programming semantics with a second kind of negation have been advanced. One such extension is the Answer Set (AS) semantics (Gelfond and Lifschitz 1990), which is an extension of Stable Model (SM) semantics (Gelfond and Lifschitz 1988) from the class of logic programs (Lloyd 1984) to those with a second form of negation. In (Kowalski and Sadri 1990) another proposal for such extension is introduced (based on the SM semantics), where implicitly a preference of negative information (exceptions) over positive information is assumed. However, AS semantics is not well founded. The meaning of the program is defined as the intersection of all answer-sets, and it is known that the computation of this intersection is computationally expensive. Another extension to include a second kind of negation is suggested by Przymusinski in (Przymusinski 1990). Although the set of models identified by this extension is well founded, the results are less intuitive (Alferes and Pereira 1992) with respect to the coexistence of both forms of negation. Based on the XSM semantics, Przymusinski (1991) also introduces a Stationary semantics where the second form of negation is classical negation. But classical negation entails that the logic programs under Stationary semantics no longer admit a procedural reading.

Well Founded Semantics with Explicit Negation (WFSX) (Pereira and Alferes 1992), is an extension of Well Founded Semantics WFS (VanGelder et al., 1990) including a second form of negation called *explicit negation*, which preserves the well founded property (cf. (Alferes and Pereira 1992) for a comparison of the above approaches) and admits procedural reading.

When a second form of negation is introduced, contradictions may be present (i.e., l and $\neg l$ hold for some l) and no semantics is given by WFSX[1]. In (Pereira et al., in this book) the authors define CRSX extending WFSX by introducing the notion of removing some contradictions and identifying the models obtained by revising closed world assumptions supporting those contradictions. One unique model, if any such revised model exists, is singled out as the contradiction free semantics. When no contradiction is present CRSX semantics reduces to WFSX semantics.

Here, using CRSX (which is assumed (Pereira et al., in this book)), we show how to cast in the language of logic programs extended with explicit negation different forms of non-monotonic reasoning such as defeasible reasoning and hypothetical reasoning, and apply it to diverse domains of knowledge representation such as taxonomic hierarchies and reasoning about actions.

Our final purpose is to identify a modular systematic method of representing some nonmonotonic reasoning problems with the CRSX semantics of logic programs.

2 Defeasible Reasoning

In this section we show how to represent defeasible reasoning with logic programs extended with explicit negation. We want to express defeasible reasoning and give a meaning to sets of rules (some of them being defeasible) when contradictions arise from the application of defeasible rules. For instance, we want to represent defeasible rules such as *birds normally fly* and *penguins normally don't fly*. Given a penguin, which is a bird, we adopt the skeptical point of view and none of the conflicting rules applies. Later on we show how to express preference for one rule over another in case they conflict and both are applicable. Consider for the moment a simpler version of this problem:

---

[1] In (Pereira et al., 1992a, 1992b) it is shown how WFSX relates to default theory.

Example 1. Consider the statements:

(i) Normally birds fly. (ii) Penguins don't fly. (iii) Penguins are birds. (iv) a is a penguin.

represented by the program P (with obvious abreviations, where *ab* stands for abnormal [2]):

$$f(X) \leftarrow b(X), \sim ab(X) \text{ (i)} \quad b(X) \leftarrow p(X) \text{ (iii)}$$
$$\neg f(X) \leftarrow p(X) \qquad \text{(ii)} \quad p(a) \qquad \text{(iv)}$$

Since there are no rules for $ab(a)$, $\sim ab(a)$ holds and $f(a)$ follows. On the other hand, we have $p(a)$, and $\neg f(a)$ follows from rule (ii). Thus the program model $\mathcal{M}_P$ is contradictory. In this case we argue that the first rule gives rise to a contradiction depending on a CWA on $ab(a)$ and so must not conclude $f(a)$. The intended meaning requires $\neg f(a)$ and $\sim f(a)$. We say that in this case a revision occcurs in the CWA of predicate instance $ab(a)$, which must turn to undefined. $\sim f(a)$ follows from $\neg f(a)$ in the semantics.

In this case CRSX identifies one contradiction removal set $CRS = \{\sim ab(a)\}$. The corresponding contradiction free program is $P \cup \{ab(a) \leftarrow \sim ab(a)\}$, and the corresponding model $CRWFM = \{p(a), \sim \neg p(a), b(a), \sim \neg b(a), \neg f(a), \sim f(a), \sim \neg ab(a)\}$.

In the example above the revision process is simple and the information to be revised is clearly the CWA about the abnormality predicate, so something can be said about a flying. However, this is not always the case, as shown in the following example:

Example 2. Consider the statements represented by P below:

(i) Normally birds fly. (ii) Normally penguins don't fly. (iii) Penguins are birds.

$$f(X) \leftarrow b(X), \sim ab_1(X) \text{ (i)}$$
$$\neg f(X) \leftarrow p(X), \sim ab_2(X) \text{ (ii)}$$
$$b(X) \leftarrow p(X) \qquad \text{(iii)}$$

Consider a penguin a, a bird b, and a rabbit c which does not fly; i.e., the facts are: $F = \{p(a), b(b), r(c), \neg f(c)\}$.

Remark. Facts F above and rule *(iii)* in P play the role of non–defeasible information, and should hold whichever world view one may choose for the interpretation of P together with those facts.

---

[2] $\sim$ is used for negation instead of the more usual *not* for expressing implicit or default negation (cf. failure to prove).

– W.r.t. the bird b everything is well defined and we have:

$$\left\{ \begin{array}{c} \sim ab_1(b), b(b), f(b), \sim\neg b(b), \sim\neg f(b), \sim\neg ab_1(b), \\ \sim\neg ab_2(b), \sim ab_2(b), \sim p(b), \sim\neg p(b) \end{array} \right\}$$

which says that bird b flies, $f(b)$, and it can't be shown it is a penguin, $\sim p(b)$. This is the intuitive result, since we may believe that b flies (because it is a bird) and it is not known to be a penguin, and so rules (i) and (ii) are non–contradictory w.r.t. bird b.

– W.r.t. the penguin a use of rules (i) and (ii) provoke a contradiction in $\mathcal{M}_P$: by rule (i) we have $f(a)$ and by rule (ii) we have $\neg f(a)$. Thus nothing can be said for sure about a flying or not, and the only non–ambiguous conclusions we may infer are:

$$\{ p(a), b(a), \sim\neg p(a), \sim\neg b(a), \sim\neg ab_1(a), \sim\neg ab_2(a) \}$$

Note that we are being skeptical w.r.t. $ab_1(a)$ and $ab_2(a)$, whose negation by CWA would give rise to a contradiction.

– W.r.t. c rules (i) and (ii) do not give rise to contradiction since $\sim p(c)$ and $\sim b(c)$ both hold, and we have:

$$\left\{ \begin{array}{c} r(c), \neg f(c), \sim p(c), \sim b(c), \sim\neg r(c), \sim f(c), \sim\neg p(c), \sim\neg b(c), \\ \sim\neg ab_1(c), \sim\neg ab_2(c), \sim ab_1(c), \sim ab_2(c) \end{array} \right\}$$

The least p–model of $P' = P \cup F$ using WFSX is[3]:

$$\begin{aligned} \mathcal{M}_{P'} = \{ & p(a), b(a), \sim\neg p(a), \sim\neg b(a), \sim\neg ab_1(a), \sim\neg ab_2(a), \sim ab_2(a), \\ & \sim\neg f(a), \sim f(a), \neg f(a), \sim ab_1(a), f(a), \\ & b(b), \sim\neg b(b), \sim\neg p(b), \sim\neg ab_1(b), \sim\neg ab_2(b), \sim ab_1(b), \sim ab_2(b), \\ & \neg f(c), \sim f(c), \sim p(c), \sim\neg p(c), \sim\neg b(c), \sim\neg f(c), \sim b(c), \\ & \sim\neg ab_1(c), \sim\neg ab_2(c), \sim ab_1(c), \sim ab_2(c) \} \end{aligned}$$

A contradiction arises concerning penguin a ($f(a)$ and $\neg f(a)$ both hold) because of the (closed world) assumptions on $ab_1(a)$ and $ab_2(a)$; the contradiction removal set is $CRS = \{\sim ab_1(a), \sim ab_2(a)\}$. Using CRSX we can determine formally the CRS above.

2.1 Exceptions

The notion of exception may be expressed in two different ways.

---

[3] Note that the difference between the $\mathcal{M}'_P$ model presented and the set of literals considered as the intuitive result in the previous remark differ precisely in the truth valuation of predicate instances $ab_1(a)$, $ab_2(a)$ and $f(a)$.

2.1.1. Exceptions to predicates.

Example 3. We express that the rule $flies(X) \leftarrow bird(X)$ applies whenever possible but can be defeated by exceptions using the rule:

$$flies(X) \leftarrow bird(X), \sim ab(X) \tag{1}$$

If there is a bird b and a bird a which is known not to fly (and we don't know the reason why) we may express it by $\neg flies(a)$. In this case $\neg flies(a)$ establishes an *exception to the conclusion predicate* of the defeasible rule, and the meaning of the program[4] is:

$$\left\{ \begin{array}{ll} bird(b), \sim ab(b), \sim\neg ab(b), \sim\neg bird(b), \sim\neg flies(b), flies(b) \\ bird(a), \qquad\quad \sim\neg ab(a), \sim\neg bird(a), \neg flies(a), \sim flies(a) \end{array} \right\}$$

Note that nothing is said about $ab(a)$, i.e., the CWA on $ab(a)$ is avoided ($\{\sim ab(a)\}$ is the CRS) since it would give rise to a contradiction on $flies(a)$. This is the case where we know that bird a is an exception to the *normally birds fly* rule, by taking the fact into account that it does not fly: $\neg flies(a)$.

2.1.2. Exceptions to rules.

A different way to express that a given fact is an exception is to say that a given rule must not be applicable to that fact. To state that an element is an exception to a specific rule rather than to its conclusion predicate (more than one rule may have the same conclusion), we state that the element is abnormal w.r.t. the rule, i.e., the rule is not applicable to the element: if element a is an exception we express it as $ab(a)$.

In general we may want to express that a given X is abnormal under certain conditions. This is the case, for example, where we want to express penguins are abnormal w.r.t. the flying birds rule above, as follows:

$$ab(X) \leftarrow penguin(X) \tag{2}$$

Rule (2) together with the non–defeasible rule $bird(X) \leftarrow penguin(X)$ add that *penguins are birds which are abnormal w.r.t. flying*. Similarly of dead birds; i.e., $ab(X) \leftarrow bird(X), dead(X)$ adding that *dead birds are abnormal w.r.t. flying*. Alternatively, given $\neg flies(X) \leftarrow dead(X)$, the non–abnormality of dead bird a w.r.t. flying, i.e., $\sim ab(a)$, may not be consistently assumed since it leads to a contradiction regarding $flies(a)$ and $\neg flies(a)$.

A stronger form of exception may be used to state that any element of a type (say penguin as an element of the type bird), X is considered an exception unless one knows it explicitly not to be one: $ab(X) \leftarrow \sim\neg penguin(X)$. One cannot apply defeasible rule (1) unless X is known not to be a penguin.

---

[4] This is a simplified version of Example 1.

2.2 Exceptions to exceptions

In general we may extend the notion of exceptioned rules to exception rules themselves, i.e., exception rules may be defeasible. This will allow us to express an exception to the exception rule for birds to fly, and hence the possibility that an exceptional penguin may fly, or that a dead bird may fly. In this case we want to say that the exception rule is itself a defeasible rule:

$$ab(X) \leftarrow bird(X), dead(X), \sim ab\_deadbird(X)$$

2.3 Preferences among rules

We may express now preference between two rules, stating that if one rule may be used, this constitutes an exception to the use of the other rule:

Example 4.

$$f(X) \leftarrow b(X), \sim ab_1(X) \text{ (i)}$$
$$\neg f(X) \leftarrow p(X), \sim ab_2(X) \text{ (ii)}$$
$$b(X) \leftarrow p(X) \qquad\qquad \text{(iii)}$$

In some cases we want to apply the most specific information; above, there should be (since a penguin is a specific kind of bird) an explicit preference for the non–flying penguins rule over the flying birds rule:

$$ab_1(X) \leftarrow p(X), \sim ab_2(X) \tag{3}$$

If we have also $penguin(a)$ and $bird(b)$ the unique model is:

$$\left\{ \begin{array}{l} \sim ab_2(b), b(b), \sim p(b), \sim\neg f(b), \sim ab_1(b), f(b), \\ \sim ab_2(a), p(a), b(a), ab_1(a), \sim f(a) \end{array} \right\}$$

Rule (3) says that if a given penguin is not abnormal w.r.t. non–flying then it must be considered abnormal w.r.t. flying. So we infer that b is a flying bird, a (being a penguin) is also a bird, and that there is no evidence that it flies $\sim f(a)$.

3 Representation of Hierarchical Taxonomies

In this section we illustrate how to represent taxonomies with logic programs with explicit negation. In this representation we wish to express general absolute (i.e., non–defeasible) rules, defeasible rules, exceptions to defeasible rules, as well as exceptions to exceptions, by explicitly making preferences among defeasible rules. As we've seen, when defeasible rules contradict each other and no preference rule is present, none of them is considered applicable in the most skeptical reading. We want to be able to express preference for one defeasible rule over another whenever they conflict. In taxonomic hierarchies we wish to express that in the presence of contradictory defeasible rules we prefer the one with most specific information (e.g., for a penguin, which is a bird, we want to conclude that it doesn't fly).

Example 5. The statements, facts and preferences about the domain are:

(1) Mammals are animals.   (6) Normally animals don't fly.
(2) Bats are mammals.   (7) Normally bats fly.
(3) Birds are animals.   (8) Normally birds fly.
(4) Penguins are birds.   (9) Normally penguins don't fly.
(5) Dead animals are animals. (10) Normally dead animals don't fly.

(11) Pluto is a mammal.   (12) Tweety is a bird.
(13) Joe is a penguin.   (14) Dracula is a bat.
(15) Dracula is a dead animal.

(16) Dead bats do not fly though bats do.
(17) Dead birds do not fly though birds do.
(18) Dracula is an exception to the above preferences.

Our representation of the hierarchy is the program:

$$
\begin{array}{llll}
animal(X) \leftarrow mammal(X) & (1) & mammal(pluto) & (11) \\
mammal(X) \leftarrow bat(X) & (2) & bird(tweety) & (12) \\
animal(X) \leftarrow bird(X) & (3) & penguin(joe) & (13) \\
bird(X) \leftarrow penguin(X) & (4) & bat(dracula) & (14) \\
animal(X) \leftarrow dead\_animal(X) & (5) & dead\_animal(dracula) & (15) \\
\neg flies(X) \leftarrow animal(X), \sim ab_1(X) & (6) \\
flies(X) \leftarrow bat(X), \sim ab_2(X) & (7) \\
flies(X) \leftarrow bird(X), \sim ab_3(X) & (8) \\
\neg flies(X) \leftarrow penguin(X), \sim ab_4(X) & (9) \\
\neg flies(X) \leftarrow dead\_animal(X), \sim ab_5(X) & (10)
\end{array}
$$

with the implicit hierarchical preference rules (greater specificity):

$$
\begin{array}{l}
ab_1(X) \leftarrow bat(X), \sim ab_2(X) \\
ab_1(X) \leftarrow bird(X), \sim ab_3(X) \\
ab_3(X) \leftarrow penguin(X), \sim ab_4(X)
\end{array}
$$

and the explicit problem statement preferences:

$$
\begin{array}{ll}
ab_2(X) \leftarrow dead\_animal(X), bat(X), \sim ab_5(X) & (16) \\
ab_3(X) \leftarrow dead\_animal(X), bird(X), \sim ab_5(X) & (17) \\
ab_5(dracula) & (18)
\end{array}
$$

As expected, this program has exactly one model (coinciding with the minimal WFSX model) which is non–contradictory, no choices are possible and everything is defined in the hierarchy.

Thus pluto doesn't fly, and isn't an exception to any of the rules; tweety flies because it's a bird and an exception to the "animals don't fly" rule; joe doesn't fly because it's a penguin and an exception to the "birds fly" rule.

Note that although dracula is a dead animal, which by default don't fly (cf. rule (10)) it is also considered an exception to this very same rule. Furthermore, rule (16) saying that "dead bats normally do not fly" is also exceptioned by dracula and thus the "bats fly" rule applies and dracula flies. Note that preferences rules must be present in order to prevent contradictions from arising.

4 Hypothetical Reasoning

In hierarchies complete taxonomies are given, leaving no choices available. This is not always the case in hypothetical reasoning.

4.1 Hypothetical facts and rules

In some cases we want to be able to hypothesize about the applicability of rules or facts. This is distinct from just not having any knowledge at all about rules or facts.

Hypothetical facts. Consider this simple example: *John and Nixon are quakers* and *John is a pacifist* represented by the program

$$P_1 = \{quaker(john) \ \ pacifist(john) \ \ quaker(nixon)\} \ .$$

The $\mathcal{M}_{P_1}$ (which is the only XM model) is:

$$\left\{ \begin{array}{l} quaker(nixon), \ \sim pacifist(nixon), \ \sim \neg quaker(nixon), \ \sim \neg pacifist(nixon), \\ quaker(john), \quad pacifist(john), \quad \sim \neg quaker(john), \quad \sim \neg pacifist(john) \end{array} \right\}$$

and expresses exactly what is intended, i.e., John and Nixon are quakers, John is a pacifist and we have no reason to believe Nixon is a pacifist, in this or any other model (there aren't any others in fact). Now suppose we want to add:

$$Nixon \ might \ be \ a \ pacifist. \tag{4}$$

In our view we wouldn't want in this case to be so strong as to affirm $pacifist(nixon)$, thereby not allowing for the possibility of Nixon not being a pacifist. What we are prepared to say is that Nixon might be a pacifist if we don't have reason to believe he isn't and, vice-versa, that Nixon might be a non–pacifist if we don't have reason to believe he isn't one. Statement (4) is thus expressed as:

$$pacifist(nixon) \leftarrow \sim \neg pacifist(nixon) \tag{5}$$

$$\neg pacifist(nixon) \leftarrow \sim pacifist(nixon) \tag{6}$$

The first rule states that Nixon is a pacifist if there is no evidence against it. The second rule makes a symmetric statement. Let P_2 be the program P together with these rules. P_2 has a minimal model $\mathcal{M}_{P_2}$ (which is non–contradictory):

$$\left\{ \begin{array}{l} quaker(nixon), \qquad\qquad\qquad \sim \neg quaker(nixon), \\ quaker(john), \ pacifist(john), \ \sim \neg quaker(john), \sim \neg pacifist(john) \end{array} \right\}$$

and two more XMs: $XSM_1 = \mathcal{M}_{P_2} \cup \{pacifist(nixon), \sim \neg pacifist(nixon)\}$ and $XSM_2 = \mathcal{M}_{P_2} \cup \{\neg pacifist(nixon), \sim pacifist(nixon)\}$. which is the result we were seeking. Statements of the form of (4) we call *unknown possible facts*; they are expressed in the form of (5) and (6). They can be read as a fact and its negation, each of which can be assumed only if this is consistent to do so.

Hypothetical rules. Consider the well known Nixon–diamond example using hypothetical rules instead of defeasible ones.

We represent these rules as named rules (in the fashion of (Poole 1988)) where the rule name may be present in one model as true, and in others as false.

Normally quakers are pacifists.	Normally republicans are hawks.
Pacifists are non hawks.	Hawks are non pacifists.
Nixon is a quaker and a republican.	Pacifists are non hawks.
There are other republicans.	There are other quakers.

The corresponding logic program is:

$$
\begin{aligned}
pacifist(X) &\leftarrow quaker(X), hypqp(X) \\
hypqp(X) &\leftarrow \sim\neg hypqp(X) \\
hawk(X) &\leftarrow republican(X), hyprh(X) \\
hyprh(X) &\leftarrow \sim\neg hyprh(X) \\
\neg hawk(X) &\leftarrow pacifist(X) \\
\neg pacifist(X) &\leftarrow hawk(X)
\end{aligned}
\qquad
\begin{aligned}
&quaker(nixon) \\
&republican(nixon) \\
&quaker(another\_quaker) \\
&republican(another\_republican)
\end{aligned}
$$

where the following rules are also added, making each normality instance rule about Nixon hypothetical rather than defeasible (c.f. the representation of defeasible rules in Sect. 2):

$$
\begin{aligned}
hypqp(nixon) &\leftarrow \sim\neg hypqp(nixon) & hyprh(nixon) &\leftarrow \sim\neg hyprh(nixon) \\
\neg hypqp(nixon) &\leftarrow \sim hypqp(nixon) & \neg hyprh(nixon) &\leftarrow \sim hyprh(nixon)
\end{aligned}
$$

as represented in Fig. 1.

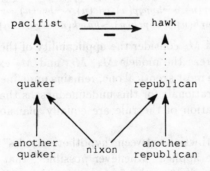

Fig. 1: The Nixon–diamond

The whole set of models is represented in Fig. 2.

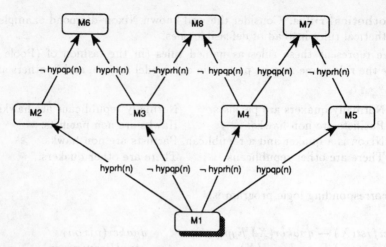

Fig. 2: Models of the Nixon–diamond problem using hypothetical rules, where edge labels represent the hypothesis being made when going from one model to another.

where the models (with obvious abbreviations) are:

$M_1 = \{qua(n), rep(n), \sim\neg qua(n), \sim\neg rep(n),$
$qua(a\_qua), \sim\neg qua(a\_qua), \sim rep(a\_qua), \sim\neg rep(a\_qua),$
$hypqp(a\_qua), \sim\neg hypqp(a\_qua), pac(a\_qua), \sim\neg pac(a\_qua),$
$hyprh(a\_qua), \sim\neg hyprh(a\_qua), \sim\neg pac(a\_qua), \sim hawk(a\_qua)$
$rep(a\_rep), \sim\neg rep(a\_rep), \sim qua(a\_rep), \sim\neg qua(a\_rep)$
$hyprp(a\_rep), \sim\neg hyprp(a\_rep), rep(a\_rep), \sim\neg rep(a\_rep),$
$hypqp(a\_rep), \sim\neg hypqp(a\_rep), \sim pac(a\_rep), \sim\neg hawk(a\_rep)\}$
$M_2 = M_1 \cup \{hyprh(n), \sim\neg hyprh(n), hawk(n), \sim\neg hawk(n), \neg pac(n), \sim pac(n)\}$
$M_3 = M_1 \cup \{\neg hypqp(n), \sim hypqp(n), \sim pac(n), \sim\neg hawk(n)\}$
$M_4 = M_1 \cup \{\neg hyprh(n), \sim hyprh(n), \sim hawk(n), \sim\neg pac(n)\}$
$M_5 = M_1 \cup \{hypqp(n), \sim\neg hypqp(n), pac(n), \sim\neg pac(n), \neg hawk(n), \sim hawk(n)\}$
$M_6 = M_2 \cup \{\neg hypqp(n), \sim hypqp(n), \sim pac(n), \sim\neg hawk(n)\}$
$M_7 = M_4 \cup \{hypqp(n), \sim\neg hypqp(n), pac(n), \sim\neg pac(n), \sim\neg hawk(n)\}$
$M_8 = M_3 \cup \{\neg hyprh(n), \sim hyprh(n), \sim hawk(n), \sim\neg pac(n)\}$

The models M_2 and M_6 consider the applicability of the *republicans are hawks* normality rule, whereas the models M_4, M_5, and M_8 explore not applying it. Model M_1, being the most skeptical one, remains undefined about the applicability of the rule. The rationale for this undefinedness is that since the application and the non–application of the rule are equally plausible, one should remain undecided about it.

Note here the distinction between "hypothetical rules" and "defeasible rules". While the latter are applied "whenever possible", that is, unless their applications lead to contradiction, the former provide equally plausible alternative extensions.

Remark. Note that with this form of representation we might as well add *abqp* or ¬*abqp*, explicit negative information and positive information are treated in the same way. In this case we may now hypothesize about the applicability and non–applicability of each normality rule. However, the most skeptical model (where no hypotheses are made) is still identical to the one where normality rules are interpreted as defeasible rules, the difference being that in the first case no revision is enforced since the $\mathcal{M}_P$ model is non–contradictory.

5 Application to Reasoning About Actions

We now apply the programing methodology used above to some reasoning about action problems and show that it gives correct results. The situation calculus notation (McCarthy and Hayes 1987) is used, where predicate $holds(P, S)$ expresses that property or fluent P holds in situation S; predicate $normal(P, E, S)$ expresses that in situation S, event or action E does not normally affect the truth value of fluent P; the term $result(E, S)$ names the situation resulting from the occurrence of event E in situation S.

5.1 The Yale Shooting Problem

This problem, supplied in (Hanks and Dermott 1986), will be represented in a form nearer to the one in (Kowalski and Sadri 1990).

Example 6. The problem and its formulation are as follows:
- Initially (in situation $s0$) a person is alive: $holds(alive, s0)$.
- After loading a gun the gun is loaded: $holds(loaded, result(load, S))$.
- If the gun is loaded then after shooting it the person will not be alive:

$$\neg holds(alive, result(shoot, S)) \leftarrow holds(loaded, S).$$

- After an event things normally remain as they were (frame axioms), i.e:
  - properties holding before the event will normally still hold afterwards:
  $$holds(P, result(E, S)) \leftarrow holds(P, S), \sim ab(P, E, S) \ (pp)^5$$
  - and properties not holding before the event will normally not hold afterwards:
  $$\neg holds(P, result(E, S)) \leftarrow \neg holds(P, S), \sim ab(\neg P, E, S) \ (np)^6$$
  Consider the question "What holds and what doesn't hold after the loading of a gun, a period of waiting, and a shooting ?" represented as two queries:

$$\leftarrow holds(P, result(shoot, result(wait, result(load, s0))))$$
$$\leftarrow \neg holds(P, result(shoot, result(wait, result(load, s0))))$$

With this formulation the $\mathcal{M}_P$ model is the only XM Model. The subset of its elements that match with at least one of the queries is[7]:

$$\{holds(loaded, s3), \sim\neg holds(loaded, s3), \neg holds(alive, s3), \sim holds(alive, s3)\}$$

---

[5] pp stands for positive persistence.

[6] np stands for negative persistence;the use of $\neg$ as a functor permits a more compact representation of (pp) and (np), with a single ab predicate.

[7] Where s3 denotes the term result(shoot,result(wait,result(load,s0))).

which means that in situation s3 the gun is loaded and the person is not alive. This result coincides with the one obtained in (Kowalski 1990) for *holds*.

5.2 The Stolen Car Problem

The "Stolen Car Problem" (Kautz 1986) is expressed as follows:

1. I leave my car parked and go away: $holds(pk, s0)$.
2. I return after a while and the car is not there, i.e., after n wait events the car is not parked were I left it: $\neg holds(pk, s_n)$ where s_n represents the expression $r(w, \dots, r(w, s0) \dots)$ comprising n wait events.
3. After an event things normally remain as they were, represented as in the previous example.
4. In which situations S, between $s0$ and s_{n-1}, is the car parked and in which is it not?

Using CRSX the result agrees with common sense, and avoids the counterintuitive outcome that the car is parked in the situation just before I return, given by (Kautz 1986, Lifschitz 1986, Shoham 1988).

The WFSX assigns no meaning to the program since the pseudo *WFM* contains both $\neg holds(pk, s_n)$ (by 2) and $holds(pk, s_n)$ (by 1 and the frame axioms). The only assumption set of the contradiction is:

$$\{\sim ab(pk, w, s0), \sim ab(pk, w, s_1), \dots, \sim ab(pk, w, s_{n-1}\}$$

showing that a contradiction results on assuming persistence at every wait event. So, there are n contradiction removal sets, namely:

$$CRS_1 = \{\sim ab(pk, w, s0)\}, \ \dots, \ CRS_n = \{\sim ab(pk, w, s_{n-1})\} \ .$$

Accordingly:

- The $CRWFM$ is $\{holds(pk, s0), \neg holds(pk, s_n)\}$.
- There are n more $CRXSM$s:

$$CRXSM_1 = \{holds(pk, s0), holds(pk, s_1), \neg holds(pk, s_n)\}$$
$$\dots$$
$$CRXSM_n = \{holds(pk, s0), \dots, holds(pk, s_{n-1}), \neg holds(pk, s_n)\}$$

This can be interpreted in the following way:

- In the most skeptical view ($CRWFM$) one can only say for sure that the car was parked when I left it, and not parked when I returned. It is undefined whether the car was parked in all other intermediate situations.
- For each intermediate situation there is the possibility (a $CRXSM$) that the car was still parked.

Note how the set of $CRXSM$s can be read as the disjunct: either the car disappeared in situation s_1 or in situation s_2 or ... or in situation s_{n-1}.

6   Summary of Our Representation Method

In this section we summarize and systematize the representation method adopted
in all the above examples. The type of rules for which we propose a representation is, in our view, general enough to capture a wide domain of nonmonotonic
problems. Each type of rule is described in a subsection by means of a schema
in natural language and its corresponding representation rule.

Definite Rules. *If A then B.* The representation is: $B \leftarrow A$.
Definite Facts. *A is true.* The representation is: A. *A is false.* The repre-
sentation is: $\neg A$.
Defeasible (or maximally applicable) Rules. *Normally if A then B.*
The representation is:

$$B \leftarrow A, \sim ab.$$

where $\sim ab$ is a new predicate symbol. As an example consider the rule
"Normally birds fly". Its representation is: $fly(X) \leftarrow bird(X), \sim ab(X)$.
Defeasible Facts are a special case of *Defeasible Rules* where A is absent.
Known Exceptions to Defeasible Rules. *Under certain conditions
COND there are known exceptions to the defeasible rule* $H_1 \leftarrow B_1, \sim ab_1$.

$$ab_1 \leftarrow COND.$$

As an example, the representation of the exception "Penguins are exceptions
to the "normally birds fly" rule (i.e., rule $f \leftarrow b, \sim abb$)" is: $abb \leftarrow penguin$.
Possible Exceptions to Defeasible Rules. *Under certain conditions
COND there are no possible exceptions to the defeasible rule* $H_1 \leftarrow B_1, \sim ab_1$.

$$ab_1 \leftarrow \sim \neg COND.$$

As an example, the representation of the exception "Animals not known to
be not a penguin are exceptions to the "normally birds fly" rule (i.e., the
rule $f \leftarrow b, \sim abb$)" is: $abb \leftarrow \sim \neg penguin$.
Preference rules are a special kind of exception to defeasible rules:
Preference Rules. *Under conditions COND, prefer to apply the defeasible
rule* $H_1 \leftarrow B_1, \sim ab_1$ *instead of the defeasible rule* $H_2 \leftarrow B_2, \sim ab_2$.

$$ab_1 \leftarrow COND, \sim ab_2.$$

As an example consider "For penguins, if the rule that says "normally penguins don't fly" is applicable then inhibit the "normally birds fly" rule". This
is represented as: $ab\_b \leftarrow penguin(X), \sim ab\_penguin(X)$.
Unknown Possible Fact. *F might be true or not* (in other words, the
possibility or otherwise of F should be considered).

$$F \leftarrow \sim \neg F.$$
$$\neg F \leftarrow \sim F.$$

Hypothetical (or possibly applicable) Rules. *Rule "If A then B" may or may not apply.* Its representation is:

$$B \leftarrow A, hyp$$
$$hyp \leftarrow \sim\neg hyp$$
$$\neg hyp \leftarrow \sim hyp$$

where *hyp* is a new predicate symbol. As an example consider the rule. "Quakers might be pacifists". Its representation is:

$$pacifist(X) \leftarrow quaker(X), hypqp(X).$$

$$hypqp(X) \leftarrow \sim\neg hypqp(X).$$
$$\neg hypqp(X) \leftarrow \sim hypqp(X).$$

Acknowledgements

We thank ESPRIT BRA projects COMPULOG, COMPULOG II, INIC, JNICT, and Gabinete de Filosofia do Conhecimento for their support.

References

Alferes, J.J., and L.M. Pereira: "On logic program semantics with two kinds of negation," in: *IJCSLP'92*. MIT Press, 1992.

Dung, P.M., and P. Ruamviboonsuk: "Well founded reasoning with classical negation," in: A. Nerode, W. Marek, and V.S. Subrahmanian (eds.), *Workshop on LPNMR*. MIT Press, 1991.

Gelfond, M., and V. Lifschitz: "The stable model semantics for logic programming," in: R.A. Kowalski and K.A. Bowen (eds.), *5th ICLP*, MIT Press (1988) 1070-1080..

Gelfond, M., and V. Lifschitz: "Logic programs with classical negation," in: Warren and Szeredi (eds.), *ICLP*, MIT Press (1990) 579-597.

Hanks, S., and D. McDermott: "Default reasoning, nonmonotonic logics and the frame problem," in: *AAAI86* (1986) 328-333.

Inoue, K.: "Extended logic programs with default assumptions," in: K.Furukawa (ed.), *8th ICLP*, MIT Press (1991) 490–504.

Kautz, H.: "The logic of persistence," in: *AAAI'86* (1986) 401.

Kowalski, R.: "Problems and promises of computational logic," in: J.Lloyd (ed.), *Computational Logic Symposium* Springer-Verlag (1990) 1–36.

Kowalski, R., and F.Sadri: "Logic programs with exceptions," in: Warren and Szeredi (eds.), *ICLP*, MIT Press (1990) 598-613.

Lifschitz, V.: "Pointwise circumscription," in: *AAAI'86* (1986) 406.

Lloyd, J.W.: *Foundations of Logic Programming.* Symbolic Computation. Springer-Verlag, 1984.

McCarthy, J., and P.J. Hayes: *Some Philosophical Problems from the Standpoint of Artificial Intelligence.* Readings in Nonmonotonic Reasoning. M. Kaufmann Inc. (1987) 26-45.

Pereira, L.M., and J.J. Alferes: "Well founded semantics for logic programs with explicit negation," in: *ECAI'92*. John Wiley & Sons, Ltd, 1992.

Pereira, L.M., J.J. Alferes, and J.N. Aparício: "Contradiction removal semantics with explicit negation." *In this book.*

Pereira, L.M., J.J. Alferes, and J.N. Aparício: "Default theory for well founded semantics with explicit negation," in: *JELIA '92*, 1992a.

Pereira, L.M., J.J. Alferes, and J.N. Aparício: "Well founded semantics with explicit negation and default theory," Technical report, AI Center, Uninova, 1992b. *Submitted.*

Pereira, L.M., J.N. Aparício, and J.J. Alferes: "Counterfactual reasoning based on revising assumptions," in: V.Saraswat and K.Ueda (eds.), *ILPS*, MIT Press (1991a) 566-580.

Pereira, L.M., J.N. Aparício, and J.J. Alferes: "Hypothetical reasoning with well founded semantics," in: B.Mayoh (ed.) *Third Scandinavian Con. on AI.* IOS Press, 1991b.

Pereira, L.M., J.N. Aparício, and J.J. Alferes. "Nonmonotonic reasoning with well founded semantics," in: K. Furukawa (ed.) *ICLP91*, MIT Press (1991c) 475-489.

Poole, D.L.: "A logical framework for default reasoning," in: *Journal of AI*, 36 (1), (1988) 27-47.

Przymusinski, T.: "Extended stable semantics for normal and disjunctive programs," in: Warren and Szeredi (eds.) *ICLP90*, MIT Press (1990) 459-477.

Przymusinski, T.C.: "A semantics for disjunctive logic programs," in: D. Loveland, J. Lobo, and A. Rajasekar (eds.), *ILPS Workshop on Disjunctive Logic Programs*, 1991.

Shoham, Y.: *Reasoning about Change: Time and Change from the Standpoint of Artificial Intelligence.* MIT Press, 1988.

VanGelder, A., K.A. Ross, and J.S. Schlipf: "The well-founded semantics for general logic programs," in: *Journal of the ACM* (1990) 221-230.

Wagner, G.: "A database needs two kinds of negation," in: B. Thalheim, J. Demetrovics, and H-D. Gerhardt (eds.), *MFDBS'91*, Springer-Verlag (1991) 357-371.

Agent Oriented Programming:
An overview of the framework and summary of recent research

Yoav Shoham

Computer Science Department, Stanford University, Stanford, CA 94305
E-mail: shoham@flamingo.stanford.edu

Abstract. This is a short overview of the *agent oriented programming* (AOP) framework. AOP can be viewed as an specialization of *object-oriented programming*. The state of an agent consists of components called beliefs, choices, capabilities, commitments, and possibly others; for this reason the state of an agent is called its *mental state*. The mental state of agents is captured formally in an extension of standard epistemic logics: beside temporalizing the knowledge and belief operators, AOP introduces operators for commitment, choice and capability. Agents are controlled by *agent programs*, which include primitives for communicating with other agents. In the spirit of *speech-act theory*, each communication primitives is of a certain type: informing, requesting, offering, and so on. This paper describes these features in a little more detail, and summarizes recent results and ongoing AOP-related work.

1 Introduction

Agent Oriented Programming is a proposed new programming paradigm, based on a societal view of computation. Although new, the proposal benefits from extensive previous research. Indeed, the discussion here touches on issues that are the subject of much current research in AI, issues which include the notion of agenthood and the relation between a machine and its environment. Many of the ideas here intersect and interact with the ideas of others. In this overview, however, I will not place this work in the context of other work. That, as well as more details on AOP, appear in (Shoham 1993), and subsequent publications which are mentioned below.

1.1 What is an agent?

The term 'agent' is used frequently these days. This is true in AI, but also outside it, for example in connection with data bases and manufacturing automation. Although increasingly popular, the term has been used in such diverse ways that it has become meaningless without reference to a particular notion of agenthood. Some notions are primarily intuitive, others quite formal. In several longer publications I outline several senses of agenthood that I have discerned in the AI literature. Given the limited space, here I will directly present "my" sense of agenthood.

I will use the term '(artificial) agents' to denote entities possessing formal versions of mental state, and in particular formal versions of beliefs, capabilities, choices, commitments, and possibly a few other mentalistic-sounding qualities. What will make any hardware or software component an agent is precisely the fact that one has chosen to analyze and control it in these mental terms.

The question of what an agent is now replaced by the question of what can be described in terms of knowledge, belief, commitment, *et cetera*. The answer is that *anything* can be so described, although it is not always advantageous to do so. D. Dennett proposes the "intentional stance," from which systems are ascribed mental qualities such as intentions and free will (Dennett 1987). The issue, according to Dennett, is not whether a system really is intentional, but whether we can coherently view it as such. Similar sentiments are expressed by J. McCarthy in his 'Ascribing Mental Qualities to Machines' paper (McCarthy 1979), who also distinguishes between the 'legitimacy' of ascribing mental qualities to machines and its 'usefulness.' In other publications I illustrate the point through the light-switch example. It is perfectly coherent to treat a light switch as a (very cooperative) agent with the capability of transmitting current at will, who invariably transmits current when it believes that we want it transmitted and not otherwise; flicking the switch is simply our way of communicating our desires. However, while this is a coherent view, it does not buy us anything, since we essentially understand the mechanism sufficiently to have a simpler, mechanistic description of its behavior. In contrast, we do not have equally good knowledge of the operation of complex systems such as robots, people, and, arguably, operating systems. In these cases it is often most convenient to employ mental terminology; the application of the concept of 'knowledge' to distributed computation, discussed below, is an example of this convenience.

1.2 Agent- versus object-oriented programming

Adopting the sense of agenthood just described, I have proposed a computational framework called *agent oriented programming* (AOP). The name is not accidental, since from the engineering point of view AOP can be viewed as a specialization of the *object-oriented programming* (OOP) paradigm. I mean the latter in the spirit of Hewitt's original Actors formalism, rather than in some of the senses in which it used today. Intuitively, whereas OOP proposes viewing a computational system as made up of modules that are able to communicate with one another and that have individual ways of handling incoming messages, AOP specializes the framework by fixing the state (now called *mental state*) of the modules (now called *agents*) to consist of precisely-defined components called beliefs (including beliefs about the world, about themselves, and about one another), capabilities, choices, and possibly other similar notions. A computation consists of these agents informing, requesting, offering, accepting, rejecting, competing, and assisting one another. This idea is borrowed directly from the *speech act* literature. Speech-act theory categorizes speech, distinguishing between informing, requesting, offering and so on; each such type of communicative act involves different presuppositions and has different effects. Speech-act theory has been applied in AI, in natural language research as well as in plan recognition. To my knowledge, AOP and McCarthy's Elephant2000 language are the first attempts to base a programming language in part on speech acts. Fig. 1 summarizes the relation between AOP and OOP.[1]

Framework:	OOP	AOP
Basic unit:	object	agent
Parameters defining state of basic unit:	unconstrained	beliefs, commitments, capabilities, choices, ...
Process of computation:	message passing and response methods	message passing and response methods
Types of message:	unconstrained	inform, request, offer, promise, decline, ...
Constraints on methods:	none	honesty, consistency, ...

Fig. 1. OOP versus AOP

1.3 On the use of pseudo-mental terminology

The previous discussion referred to mentalistic notions such as belief and commitment. In order to understand the sense in which I intend these, it is instructive to consider the use of logics of knowledge and belief in AI and distributed computation. These logics, which were imported directly from analytic philosophy first to AI and then to other areas of computer science, describe the behavior of machines in terms of notions such as knowledge and belief. In computer science these mentalistic-sounding notions are actually given precise computational meanings, and are used not only to prove properties of distributed systems, but to program them as well. A typical rule in such a 'knowledge based' systems is "if processor A does not *know* that processor B has received its message, then processor A will not send the next message." AOP augments these logics with formal notions of choices, capabilities, commitments, and possibly others. A typical rule in the resulting systems will be "if agent A *believes* that agent B has *chosen* to do something harmful to agent A, then A will *request* that B change its choice." In addition, temporal information is included to anchor belief, choices and so on in particular points in time.

Here again we may benefit from some ideas in philosophy and linguistics. As in the case of knowledge, there exists work in exact philosophy on logics for choice and ability. Although they have not yet had an effect in AI comparable to that of logics of knowledge and belief, they may in the future.

---

[1] There is one more dimension to the comparison, which I omitted from the table, and it regards inheritance. Inheritance among objects is today one of the main features of OOP, constituting an attractive abstraction mechanism. I have not discussed it since it is not essential to the idea of OOP, and even less so to the idea of AOP. Nevertheless a parallel can be drawn here too.

Intentional terms such as knowledge and belief are used in a curious sense in the formal AI community. On the one hand, the definitions come nowhere close to capturing the full linguistic meanings. On the other hand, the intuitions about these formal notions do indeed derive from the everyday, common sense meaning of the words. What is curious is that, despite the disparity, the everyday intuition has proven a good guide to employing the formal notions in some circumscribed applications. AOP aims to strike a similar balance between computational utility and common sense.

2   Overview of the AOP Framework

A complete AOP system will include three primary components:

- A restricted formal language with clear syntax and semantics for describing a mental state. The mental state will be defined uniquely by several modalities, such as belief and commitment.
- An interpreted programming language in which to program agents, with primitive commands such as REQUEST and INFORM. The semantics of the programming language will depend in part on the semantics of mental state.
- An 'agentifier,' converting neutral devices into programmable agents.

In the remainder of this paper I will start with an short discussion of the mental state. I will then present a general family of agent interpreters, a simple representative of which has already been implemented. I will end with a summary of recent research results and outstanding questions related to AOP.

3   On the Mental State of Agents

The first step in the enterprise is to define agents, that is, to define the various components of a mental state and the interactions between them. There is not a unique 'correct' definition, and different applications can be expected to call for specific mental properties.[2]

In related past research by others in AI three modalities were explored: belief, desire and intention (giving rise to the pun on BDI agent architectures). Other similar notions, such as goals and plans, were also pressed into service. These are clearly important notions; they are also complex ones, however, and not necessary the most primitive ones. Cohen and Levesque, for example, propose to reduce the notion of *intention* to those of *goal* and *persistence*. We too start with quite basic building blocks, in fact much more basic that those mentioned so far. We currently incorporate two modalities in the mental state of agents: *belief* and *obligation* (or *commitment*). We also define *decision* (or *choice*) as an obligation to oneself. Finally, we include a third cateogry which is not a mental

---

[2] In this respect our motivation here deviates from that of philosophers. However, I believe there exist sufficient similarities to make the connection between AI and philosophy mutually beneficial.

construct *per se*, *capability*. There is much to say on the formal definitions of these concepts; some of results described in the final section address this issue.

By restricting the components of mental state to these modalities I have in some informal sense excluded representation of motivation. Indeed, we do not assume that agents are 'rational' beyond assuming that their beliefs, obligations and capabilities are internally and mutually consistent. This stands in contrast to the other work mentioned above, which makes further assumptions about agents acting in their own best interests, and so on. Such stronger notions of rationality are obviously important, and I am convinced that in the future we will wish to add them. However, neither the concept of agenthood nor the utility of agent oriented programming depend on them.

4 A Generic Agent Interpreter

The behavior of agents is governed by programs; each agent is controlled by his own, private program. Agent programs themselves are not logical entities, but their control and data structures refer to the mental state of the agent using the logical language.[3]

The basic loop   The behavior of agents is, in principle, quite simple. Each agent iterates the following two steps at regular intervals:

1. Read the current messages, and update your mental state (including your beliefs and commitments);
2. Execute the commitments for the current time, possibly resulting in further belief change. Actions to which agents are committed include communicative ones such as informing and requesting.

The process is illustrated in Fig. 2; dashed arrows represent flow of data, solid arrows temporal sequencing.

5 Summary of Results and Ongoing Research

A more detailed discussion of AOP appears in (Shoham 1993); the implemented interpreter is documented in (Torrance 1991). Ongoing collaboration with the Hewlett Packard corporation is aimed at incorporating features of AOP in the New Wave[TM] architecture.

Work on mental state is proceeding on different fronts. Work on the 'statics' of mental state include (Moses and Shoham 1993), where we provide some results on the connection between knowledge and (one kind of) belief, and Thomas's (1992), which tackles the notions of capability, plan and intentions; more results on these topics are forthcoming. Other work begins to address dynamic aspects of

---

[3] However, an early design of agent programs by J. Akahani was entirely in the style of logic programming; in that framework program statements themselves were indeed logical sentences.

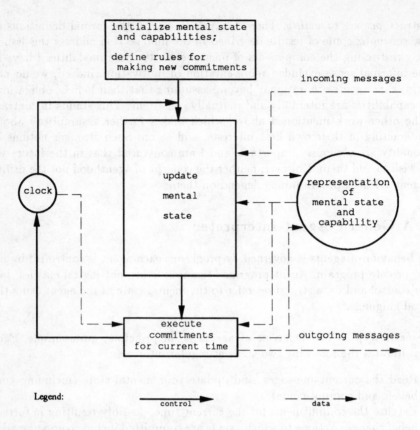

Fig. 2. A flow diagram of a generic agent interpreter

mental state. Lin and Shoham (1992b) investigate formal notions of memory and learning. Del Val and Shoham (to appear) address the logic of belief revision; specifically, the postulates of belief update are shown to be derivable from a formal theory of action. The theory used there is the 'provably correct' theory presented in (Lin and Shoham 1991).

In parallel to the logical aspects of action and mental state, we have investigated algorithmic questions. We have proposed a specific mechanism for tracking how beliefs change over time, called *temporal belief maps* (Isozaki and Shoham 1992). In (Brafman et al. 1993) we show that, similarly to distributed systems, the formal notion of knowledge can be applied to algorithmic robot motion planning.

Finally, we are interested in how multiple agents can function usefully in the presence of other agents. In particular, we are interested in mechanisms that minimize conflicts among agents, and have been investigating the utility of social laws in computational settings. Shoham and Tennenholtz (to appear) propose a general framework for representing social laws within a theory of action, and investigate the computational complexity of automatically synthesizing useful social laws; we also study a special case of traffic laws in a restricted robot environment. In (Shoham and Tennenholtz 1992) we study ways in which such conventions emerge automatically in a dynamic environment.

References

Brafman, R.I., J.-C. Latombe, and Y. Shoham: "Towards Knowledge-Level Analysis of Motion Planning," in: *Proc. AAAI*, Washington, 1993.

Del Val, A,. and Y. Shoham: "Belief update and theories of action," in: *Journal of Logic, Language and Information*, 1993 (to appear).

Dennett, D.C.: *The Intentional Stance.* Cambridge, MA: MIT Press, 1987.

Isozaki, H., and Y. Shoham: "A mechanism for reasoning about time and belief," in: *Proc. Conference on Fifth Generation Computer Systems*, Japan, 1992.

Lin, F., and Y. Shoham: "Provably correct theories of action," (preliminary report) in: *Proc. NCAI*, Anaheim, CA: 1991.

Lin, F., and Y. Shoham: *Concurrent actions in the situation calculus.* Stanford working document, 1992.

Lin, F., and Y. Shoham: *On the persistence of knowledge and ignorance.* Stanford working document, 1992.

McCarthy, J.: *Ascribing Mental Qualities to Machines.* Stanford AI Lab, Memo 326, 1979.

Moses, Y. and Y. Shoham: "Belief as Defeasible Knowledge," in: *Journal of Artificial Intelligence*, 64 (2) (1993), 299-322.

Shoham, Y.: "Agent Oriented Programming," in: *Journal of Artificial Intelligence*, 60 (1) (1993) 51-92.

Shoham, Y., and M. Tennenholtz: "Computational Social Systems: offline design," in: *Journal of Artificial Intelligence*, to appear.

Shoham, Y., and M. Tennenholtz: "Emergent conventions in multi-Agent systems," in: *Proc. KR*, Boston, 1992.

Thomas, B.: *A logic for representing action, belief, capability, and intention.* Stanford working document, 1992.

Torrance, M.: *The AGENT0 programming manual.* Stanford technical report, 1991.

An Application of Temporal Logic for Representation and Reasoning About Design

Keiichi Nakata*

Department of Artificial Intelligence, University of Edinburgh
80 South Bridge, Edinburgh EH1 1HN, Scotland
E-mail: keiichi@ai.ed.ac.uk

Abstract. This paper presents an approach to the application of temporal logic in order to represent and manipulate knowledge about physical systems in the design task. Focusing on the functional aspect of devices, we view the design task as achieving a desired behaviour of a device and its environment. Devices and environmental knowledge such as laws of physics are described in terms of causal rules, which are used to construct a model of the most likely behaviour of the system. Instead of giving a structural specification for design, a behavioural specification, which consists of the desired sequence of events, is provided, and it is compared with the predicted behaviour of the system for evaluation. The modification of the causal rule set is performed analogously to the design modification. Although computationally complex, this method sheds light on the formal treatment of temporal constraints and knowledge in design.

1 Introduction

One of the main features of an artefact is its function. The necessity for a certain function within the world is often the motivation to create an object, and an important factor which stimulates design. From this standpoint, it is reasonable to represent a device in terms of its functions. For instance, a door-bell has the function of notifying the people in the building when a visitor operates a trigger (typically a switch) outside. We can see that a function has its input and output, where input can be seen as the precondition to the consequent which is the output. If we apply a broad definition of 'causality', it is possible to describe functions as causations. In the case of a door-bell, we can see the operation of a switch as the 'cause' for the bell to ring.

. Such representation and reasoning about design in terms of functions and behaviours can be found in the works by Freeman and Newell (1971) and Barrow (1984). The former suggested the validity of representing physical devices as functions and demonstrated the method of configuration task in terms of functions. The latter suggested a formal method of verifying the correctness of

---

* The author is funded by The Murata Overseas Scholarship Foundation and the Overseas Research Students Awards Scheme (Ref. ORS/9214048).

digital circuits by comparing the intended and actual behaviours. More recently, Sembugamoorthy and Chandrasekaran (1986) introduced *functional representation* as a formal representation for the functioning of a device at various levels of abstraction, and the work by Iwasaki and Chandrasekaran (1992) integrates functional representation with qualitative simulation for the design verification task. The work presented in this paper adds an additional aspect of description, namely a temporal feature. None of the contributions above provided an explicit way to represent temporal constraints.

The idea put forward in this paper is the application of temporal logic to represent and reason about the functions in design. Focusing on the characteristics of functionality of the devices as described above, the type of design problems we deal with here are those involving temporal transients, in other words, the design of artefacts which have significant temporal aspects. Also, we concentrate on the feasibility of the design from its functional point of view, and not optimisation. We represent and manage causal knowledge in the temporal logic devised by Yoav Shoham (1988). Although introduced as a means of dealing with the frame problems, the formality and the nonmonotonic feature of Shoham's logic suits nicely the description and the computation of the design task.

The main contribution of this paper is the investigation of the application of temporal logic to handle temporal constraints and maintain temporal relations between events in the design task. There has so far been a relatively small amount of research on the formal description and utilisation of temporal constraints in design. We are looking at practical, medium-size design problems and have so far worked on the domain of logic circuits. Primarily, we have tested on the configuration of set-reset flip-flop circuits, the verification of asynchronous circuits such as counters, and the configuration of JK flip-flop circuits. We obtained reasonable solutions for these problems, and based on this result we are evaluating the efficiency of the current implementation. The examples given in this paper are rather abstract to put emphasis on the logical foundation of this approach.

2 Formal Description of Design

The relationship between the world and an artefact can be formally described as follows:

$$E, S, D \models B \tag{1}$$

where

E: Environment (the laws of physics, causality)
S: Scenario (boundary conditions, sequence of factual events)
D: Design
B: Behaviour

This formula denotes that given an environment, a scenario and a design of an artefact, the behaviour of the system (including the environment) can be modelled. The design task is to create the set D, given E and S, which exhibits B, which is the desired behaviour. In order to construct D, all the others should be known, or at least be partially specified.

From now on we will use the word *system* to mean the union of the all premises (i.e., $E \cup S \cup D$).

Notice that this formulation suggests that the behavioural model B is non-monotonic. Suppose B_1 is a model such that

$$E, S, D \models B_1. \tag{2}$$

When a new condition p is added to the premise creating the model B_2 such that

$$(E, S, D) \land p \models B_2 \tag{3}$$

it is intuitively obvious that B_2 does not subsume B_1. For example, adding a condition that the device is to work under zero gravity to the existing design of a flushing toilet changes the behaviour of the system.

3 Shoham's Temporal Logic

Shoham (1988) introduces the language *CI* which deals with causality. The initial purpose of devising this language was to provide a temporal language which enables us to deal with frame problems, such as the Yale Shooting Problem. Logic *CI* is a nonmonotonic temporal language and provides the most likely model for a sound and consistent *causal theory* by chronologically minimising the changes. In other words, we prefer the model where things would remain the same as long as possible. In this way we can obtain a reasonable prediction given all the information available.

A causal theory Ψ consists of *causal rules* and *inertial rules*. A causal rule is of the form

$$\Phi \land \Theta \supset \Box \varphi \tag{4}$$

where

φ: a formula $\text{TRUE}(t_1, t_2, p)$, indicating that the proposition p holds between time points t_1 and t_2
Φ: a (possibly empty) conjunction of the 'necessary' formulae $\Box \varphi$
Θ: a (possibly empty) conjunction of the 'contingent' formulae $\Diamond \varphi$

and describes that the conditions Φ and Θ *causes* $\Box \varphi$. It is important to note that the latest time point in the antecedent always precedes the initial time point of the consequent.[2]

Inertial rules have the same form as the causal rules but the consequents are potential terms $\text{POTEN}(t_1, t_2, \text{p}-q)$, indicating that the proposition q *potentially*

---

[2] Implying that the cause always precedes the effect.

holds, i.e., if nothing that prevents or terminates q is known, between time points t_1 and t_2.

Causal rules and inertial rules with empty Φ are called *boundary conditions* since their consequents are asserted as facts instead of causal consequence.

This language is attractive for our purpose, because:

- It is declarative.
- It provides a facility to represent default conditions.
- Given a sound and consistent causal theory, we can obtain a single model for the information available.
- It can be integrated with other techniques such as qualitative reasoning (Kuipers 1986).

Because it is declarative, we can readily add new causal rules and boundary conditions without altering existing rules. The 'contingent' terms can be regarded as default assumptions. Since there are many factors to be taken into consideration in design, it is often useful to be able to specify default conditions for efficiency.

A causal theory is *sound* when there are no conflicting defaults in the theory; it is *consistent* when no two rules with the same premise have contradictory conclusions. In the logic CI, a sound and consistent causal theory has a most preferred model, which is chronologically minimal.[3]

By extending the language from the propositional case to the first-order case (see (Bell 1991) for instance), we can incorporate other useful reasoning methods such as qualitative reasoning. This capability is advantageous when considering the integration of the reasoning techniques.

4 Behavioural Specification

Let us return to the formula 1. The design task was to construct D from other factors. E can be considered to be given since this is the knowledge about the world (in the sense of physics) and the domain specific knowledge. This leaves S and B to be provided. First we will focus on the latter, the behaviour of the system. We will begin by defining the *behavioural specification*.

Definition (Behavioural specification). The *behavioural specification* of design is the sequence of events and states which are desirable and necessary for the performance of the artefact. Formally, a behavioural specification BS is a set of atomic formulae φ_i with a temporal total ordering.

Intuitively, the behaviour of a system can be depicted by a sequence of events, which together with the events in the surrounding environment constitutes a *history*. The idea is to specify a history which is most desirable for the system. It is important to notice that it is not only the history of the behaviour of the

---

[3] *The unique c.m.i. theorem*, where c.m.i. stands for 'chronologically maximally ignorant'.

device, but of the whole system. We should take into account the changes in the environmental conditions that the operation of device might impose. For instance, the door-bell not only should ring, but should be noticed by those inside the building. The recognition of the bell ringing is beyond the behaviour of the door-bell itself, but is an important effect of the operation of the device.

The events specified in the behavioural specification should be totally ordered over time. We must specify the time point or an interval of time during which an event is taking place.

An example of a behavioural specification for the door-bell looks as follows.

$$BS = \{(1, 1, switch(on)), (2, 3, ring(bell)), (4, 4, notify(person(inside))))\}$$

Each event is represented as $(T_{begin}, T_{end}, Event)$ where T_{begin} and T_{end} respectively denote the initial and terminal time points in which the $Event$ takes place. The behavioural specification above then reads *"(we want something that when we) turn on the switch it rings the bell for an interval of time and notifies the person inside the building"*. For simplicity, appropriate integers are assigned to the time points which designates the total ordering of the events; however, this does not prevent us from assigning temporal symbols instead of integers and defining their orderings as we do later.

Now we move on to S, the scenario of the system. A scenario is a sequence of events which are known as facts. In causal theory, it is a set of boundary conditions, hence the events in a scenario are base formulae and potential terms.

A scenario in the door-bell example might be

$$S = \{\text{POTEN}(1, \infty, \text{p}-powerSupply(on)), \Box(1, \infty, deaf(person(inside))))\}$$

which reads, *"the power supply is assured to be on unless it is turned off, and the person inside the building is deaf"*.[4] The significance of having the set S separate from other factors is that unlike the environment, we can have more than one scenario for the prediction task. Assuming that there might be more than one possible behaviour of a device depending on the conditions we assume to be present, we can test them by merely replacing the scenario set without altering the other factors. This retains the modularity of knowledge involved.

To summarise, the factors in the system, the behavioural specification, scenario, environment and design have the following properties.

Behavioural specification is a set of desired events with temporal total order specifying their sequence $\varphi \in BS$. Given a behaviour B, ideally the purpose of design is to achieve $BS = B$.

Scenario is a set of boundary conditions which are the facts and the assumptions. $\Box\varphi$, POTEN$\varphi \in S$.

---

[4] The readers may notice that by giving a scenario that the person to be notified is deaf, the ringing a bell as has been specified in BS is not sufficient. This invokes the necessity of another device for the deaf person.

Environment is a set of physical laws and causal knowledge involved in the domain. $\Psi \in E$.

Design is a causal theory in which each rule represents a component of a device. $\Psi \in D$.

5 Design Verification

Once the prediction of the behaviour is obtained (we will call this the 'predicted behaviour'), the task now is to see if it fulfills the behavioural specification. Given a set of events in the behavioural specification and the predicted behaviour which is the set of events in the c.m.i. model, the design verification is to detect the difference between the two histories. If there is no discrepancy between the two, we can conclude that the current design with the provided scenario satisfies the specification. If discrepancies exist, then the design should be modified.

5.1 Detection of discrepancies

Discrepancies between two histories arise when the two have contradictory or different sequences of events. For instance, if the sequence of the events (propositions) p, q, r is actually $p \rightarrow q \rightarrow r$ in one history and $p \rightarrow r \rightarrow q$ in the other, the two histories can be considered to have a discrepancy. There is always a history that acts as a model (*behavioural specification*) and one that is to be verified (*predicted behaviour*).

We begin with identifying the basic discrepancies. As we discuss later, most discrepancies are expected to be a combination of the basic ones. Here I first describe the basic ones in the propositional case and discuss the first-order case.

5.2 Basic discrepancies

There are typically three basic discrepancies here: (1) insufficiency (propositions missing), (2) redundancy (have extra undesirable propositions), and (3) divergence (different histories). These cases are described in Table 1. In the first two cases, the histories compared are basically the same but with some parts being inconsistent. Precisely speaking, in the third there are two distinct cases: propositions q_n being irrelevant to p_n (which is equivalent to having '—' in their places) and q_n being $\neg p_n$. It should be noted that the time points (t_n) are not absolute, but relative: they merely describe the order in which these events occur.

These histories can be illustrated as described in Fig. 1. Notice that in the redundancy there might be a case when the extra proposition is not diverging (i.e., keeping the history on the same track). It should not affect the history for as long as it introduces no inconsistency.

MODEL	insufficient	redundant	divergence
(t_1,p_1)	(t_1,p_1)	(t_1,p_1)	(t_1,p_1)
(t_2,p_2)	(t_2,p_3)	(t_2,p_2)	(t_2,p_2)
(t_3,p_3)	(t_3,p_4)	(t_3,q)	(t_3,q_3)
(t_4,p_4)	(t_4,p_5)	(t_4,p_3)	(t_4,q_4)
(t_5,p_3)	—	(t_5,p_4)	(t_5,q_5)
—	—	(t_6,p_5)	—

Table 1. Three basic cases of discrepancies: *insufficient* — a proposition missing, *redundant* — an extra proposition, *divergence* — histories diverging.

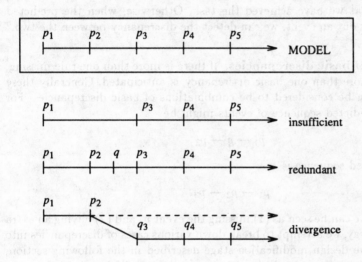

Fig. 1. Three cases of basic discrepancies.

In the first-order case, the basic discrepancies are the same as the propositional case except that the comparison of the events involves a unification process. For instance, if the next event occurring in the model is $value(1)$ and the prediction gives $value(X)$ (where X is a variable), then these two events are consistent provided that the variable X has not been instantiated to another value at the previous time point. Also owing to the semantics of the first-order logic, two terms are inconsistent not only when they are contradictory by negation (e.g., $p(a)$ and $\neg p(a)$) but semantically (e.g., $value(output(+))$ and $value(output(-))$).

5.3 Analysis of discrepancies

Comparison of the histories. As mentioned earlier, since the discrete time points attached to the events have no significance other than the definition of the ordering among the events, the sequence of events should be compared by their relative orderings. The basic strategy is to start from the earliest time points of two histories, and proceed chronologically until the first discrepancy is found. Since the behavioural specification consists of *necessary* sequence of events, all events in it should appear in the predicted behaviour. On the other hand, we can skip some of the intermediate events in the predicted history which do not appear in the behavioural specification as irrelevant or unimportant events. If the predicted behaviour contains all the events in the behavioural specification, we can judge that we have achieved the task. Otherwise, when the predicted behaviour misses out an event, we can detect the discrepancy between the two.[5]

Combination of basic discrepancies. If there is more than one rule missing, or redundant, more than one basic discrepancy is anticipated. Generally these discrepancies can be considered to be combinations of basic discrepancies. For example, the predicted sequence of events might be

$$p_1 \rightarrow q \rightarrow p_3$$

when the expected sequence is

$$p_1 \rightarrow p_2 \rightarrow p_3.$$

The predicted one can be seen as (1) missing the event p_2 and (2) having an extra event q. In this way, we attempt to break down various cases of discrepancies into basic ones. In the design modification stage described in the following section, each basic discrepancy can be dealt with separately, simplifying the task.

5.4 Compilation of devices

Once the behaviour of a device is modelled and proved to be plausible, it would be stored in the library for later use. For example, once the causal rule description of a solar cell is considered to be reasonable, it will be listed along with other devices. The rules can be made abstract if there is no secondary effect during its operation. Those events which would affect the environment (e.g., the increase in temperature, turning the light on, etc.) are called *external* events, as opposed to *internal* events, which occur only within a device (e.g., change in the flow within closed pipe circuit, increase of pressure within a container, etc.). Given an input event p_{input} and the output p_{output}, and the chains of events $q_1...q_n$ between them, i.e.,

$$p_{input} \rightarrow q_1 \rightarrow ... \rightarrow q_n \rightarrow p_{output},$$

---

[5] In cases where such intermediate events are not specified explicitly, we can assume that the specification 'doesn't care' how the succeeding events should be achieved.

we need only to keep explicit those external events among q_i which would affect other histories. In this causal chain, there are at most $n+1$ causal rules involved. Assuming that the external events are q_4 and q_{11}, then the set of rules can be reduced to

$$\Box(t,t,p_{input}) \wedge \Theta_1 \supset \Box(t+1,t+1,q_4)$$

$$\Box(t,t,q_4) \wedge \Theta_2 \supset \Box(t+1,t+1,q_{11})$$

$$\Box(t,t,q_{11}) \wedge \Theta_3 \supset \Box(t+1,t+1,p_{output}).$$

These rules will be the compiled library of the device. It would preserve the temporal order of events, and eliminate events which are irrelevant to the overall behaviour of the device. The compiled library is labelled with the domain in which it was created and loaded when an appropriate environment was specified. This acts as an assignment of the resource available.

6 Design Modification

As the result of design verification, we can identify the point where modifications are necessary in order to obtain a desirable behaviour of the system. Since the primary purpose at this stage is to obtain the event which is essential to occur in order to meet the behavioural specification, the strategy is to assert a rule which 'causes' the desired event. The rule asserted here is typically very abstract. We then proceed to 'prove' the rule using existing rules in the system. The idea is to bring the cause and the effect of the newly added rule as close as possible. Finally, we attempt to bridge the gap by devising a component which provides the effect of the causal rule obtained after this proof procedure.

6.1 Rule assertion and its proof procedure

First we begin by asserting a causal rule which would give the desirable history for the current design. This rule is a very abstract rule which may have no intuitive causality whatsoever, but has an effect of 'forcing' an event which is desirable to occur at a time point later in the occurrence of the premise given. Being a causal rule, it would look like

$$\Box \varphi_P \wedge \Box \varphi_T \supset \Box \varphi_Q \qquad (5)$$

where φ_P and φ_Q are of the form $\text{TRUE}(t_1, t_2, p)$ (base formula, p is a proposition or a first-order formula) and φ_T is a formula that describes the ordering of the temporal variables in the rule.

The object of the operation is to rewrite the causal rule (5) and prove it by existing causal rules. In order to achieve this, the following operations are applied to the antecedent and the consequent of the rule.

- *Antecedent*: Find an alternative rule
- *Consequent*: Perform abduction

Essentially, for $\Box\varphi_P$ in the antecedent, find a causal rule that contains this formula in its antecedent. If such rule exists, say $\Phi_{P1} \wedge \Theta_{P1} \supset \Box\varphi_{P1}$, then $\Box\varphi_P \in \Phi_{P1}$. For the consequent, find a causal rule that has $\Box\varphi_Q$ as its consequent. Assume that such a rule exists, say $\Phi_{Q1} \wedge \Theta_{Q1} \supset \Box\varphi_Q$. Create a rule of the form

$$\Box\varphi_{P1} \wedge \Box\varphi_{T1} \supset \Box\varphi_{Q1} \tag{6}$$

where $\Box\varphi_{Q1} \in \Phi_{Q1}$. Be sure that the temporal constraint $\Box\varphi_T$ and $\Box\varphi_{T1}$ are consistent. A simple example of these operations is illustrated in Fig. 2.

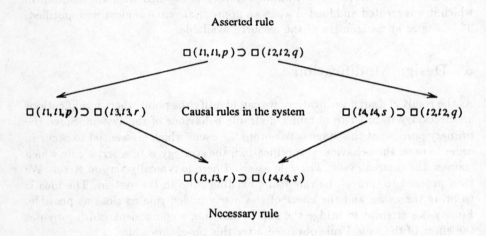

Asserted rule

$\Box(l_1,l_1,p) \supset \Box(l_2,l_2,q)$

$\Box(l_1,l_1,p) \supset \Box(l_3,l_3,r)$ Causal rules in the system $\Box(l_4,l_4,s) \supset \Box(l_2,l_2,q)$

$\Box(l_3,l_3,r) \supset \Box(l_4,l_4,s)$

Necessary rule

Fig. 2. Proof operation of an asserted rule.

At this point there are three possible cases:

1. Rule (6) resembles the existing rule
2. Further operations can be applied
3. Dead end

The causal rule constructed in this manner does not result in the reconstruction of an existing rule, since if there were such rule in the causal theory, it would have been applied at the modelling stage. In the first case, the constructed rule would look like an existing rule but does not subsume it. For instance, a necessary condition could be missing in the new rule, but with all other conditions in the antecedent and the consequent being the same. In this case, rather than just asserting such rule, it would be more reasonable to make the existing rule being applied by devising the missing condition to be fulfilled. Another possible case of resemblance is the difference in the default conditions, but this could end up violating the soundness condition. The second case in the list suggests that the system may be decomposed further. Otherwise (the third case) nothing can be done to it, which suggest that there is no such device present in the current design, or "a device which has such function is necessary". By asserting this rule, we modify the design D and can achieve the required behaviour.

This procedure so far gives the partial solution to the problem since the following must be proved.

- The validity of $\Box \varphi_i \in \Phi_{P1} \quad (i \neq P)$
- The validity of $\Box \varphi_j \in \Phi_{Q1} \quad (j \neq Q)$

That is, the premises other than the one we used in order to construct the new rule must be justified to make this assertion of the new rule valid. In reality, the structure of causal rules are not as simple as those described in Fig. 2. There are typically more than one conditions in the premise, and there may be some default conditions. In such cases, each condition in the premise should be proved by the causal rules in the system, which invokes the chain of proof operations.

The proof is by repetitive application of operations to bring together the antecedent and the consequent of the necessary rule as close as possible.

6.2 Preserving temporal constraints

The constraint for the temporal terms are represented in one of the cases below:

1. Temporal constants ($\in I$) used within base terms: in this case numerical ordering corresponds to the temporal order
2. Temporal variables:
   - Differential description — $t + m \leq t + n$ if $m \leq n$ $m, n \in I$, used within base terms
   - Constraining term — used outside base terms which is of the form $\Box(t_1 \leq ... \leq t_n)$ (or $\Diamond(t_1 \leq ... \leq t_n)$) where t_i are temporal terms appearing in the base term
   - A combination of the two

Temporal constants are typically assigned initially to the boundary conditions. A differential description is typically used for the potential histories (to set up simulation environments). Since the explicit description of the constraining terms are preferred for causal and interval rules, the preservation of temporal constraints in these terms is crucial.

Temporal constraint preservation in rule synthesis. In any operation over an antecedent or the consequent (i.e., expansion using existing rules) the local temporal constraints apply, which preserves the temporal ordering between the temporal variables. This applies to both the causal and interval rules. It is necessary, however, to maintain the temporal ordering in the rule synthesis.

Let $\Box\varphi_A$ and $\Box\varphi_B$ be the antecedent and the consequent of the new (synthesised) rule, which looks like

$$\Box\varphi_A \supset \Box\varphi_B \tag{7}$$

and $t_A = ltp(\varphi_A)$ and $t_B = ltp(\varphi_B)$, where $ltp(\varphi)$ denotes the latest time point for the base formula φ. The syntactic constraint then will be $t_A < t_B$, which should be added as the 'necessary' condition,[6]

$$\Box\varphi_A \wedge \Box(t_A < t_B) \supset \Box\varphi_B \tag{8}$$

6.3   Removing components

Since each rule in the causal theory for design D represents a function of a component, asserting a rule to the set is analogous to adding a new component to the configuration of design. Similarly, the removal or the replacement of a component are performed by removing one or more rules from the theory.

Retracting a causal rule is equivalent to removing a function from which an undesirable event was derived, and, as a result, detaching a component which was responsible for the behaviour. There are essentially two cases for this.

- The causal rule which concluded the event is retractable (i.e., design component rules).
- The causal rule which concluded the event is *not* retractable (i.e., environment causal rules such as laws of physics).

In the first case, removing the rule solves the problem.[7] It is equivalent to removing a component in the design. An alternative is to keep the rule but suppress it from firing by removing the events which satisfy the premise. We will follow the first strategy and not the second since it is always possible to reconstruct the rules which would effectively have the same result.

In the second case, since it is not reasonable to remove the rule (unless we can alter the environment), the strategy will be the second of those mentioned in

---

[6] There is an implicit assumption that there is a well-defined temporal ordering between the temporal variables within a base formula; the *ltp*s become undecidable otherwise.

[7] The implication of removing of the rule can be more problematic. In some cases, the rule may have concluded a desirable event elsewhere, which no longer could be supported. It is, however, possible to reconstruct a causal rule which concludes the desirable event but with different premises: this will invoke yet another design problem.

the previous paragraph, to suppress the rules from firing. We first take a look at the causal rule and see what were the events that caused the rule to fire. The aim now is to choose an event among them and prevent it. By checking which causal rule caused the event, we would have the same task we originally had, but with different events and rules, and at preceding time point. This process continues until we find a retractable rule, or possibly a boundary condition. Theoretically, this process should terminate at some point. The soundness and the consistency of the causal theory must be maintained by monitoring the changes in the rules.

7 Discussion

7.1 The validity of c.m.i. model as the prediction

The unique c.m.i. model shows that there is only one most preferable model for a causal theory (Shoham 1988). This might be too restrictive if we consider the possibility of having multiple possible behaviours of a design. To focus on the most likely outcome would raise the danger of overlooking a non-deterministic aspect of the design. It might be more informative if we could maintain all possible behaviours in order to evaluate the design.

Focusing on the unique model, however, does not exclude other possible behaviours. It is merely suggested as 'the most likely behaviour' under 'given conditions and (default) assumptions'. Typically, a causal theory would result in having different histories depending on whether the default is overridden, since there is no need to state the default conditions in a causal rule when they do not affect the causal outcomes. Whenever the predicted behaviour contradicts with the expected behaviour, there is always a possibility that the default assumed is not appropriate. We can check this by listing out the default conditions used in the modelling process, and if there is any 'wrong' default, it is easily overridden by adding a new boundary condition.[8] In most cases, multiple worlds occur due to lack of information about specific conditions that distinguish the worlds.

There is another case where there arises more than one behaviour. When a variable is universally quantified and there is no need to assign any value to it, there are as many possible worlds as the number of members in the set of individuals semantically assigned to the variable. A typical example of this case is the 'don't care' state in the logic gates. Since there is no restrictions to the value of the variable, assuming the 'most likely' value to it seems to be plausible.

The reason why we think a unique model is appropriate is that it indicates how a device would behave by default. If the designer is satisfied with the outcome, using the default might be good enough, and if not, s/he can find out which default to override. In case of multiple worlds, we can see what 'can' happen, but sometimes the number of alternatives is too high to manage. The process of choosing the 'right' alternative one would nevertheless be the same.[9]

---

[8] By definition, boundary conditions are $\Box$ ('necessary') events.

[9] In this context, we are assuming that a device would behave uniquely under given condition. There are cases when a device should have multiple behaviour, but we think this happens only when the design is under-constrained.

7.2 Unachievable specification

The evaluation-modification cycle of the design process does not always work, especially when there is a conflict in the initial specification. Since one of the results to be obtained after the proof is the construction of a new causal rule (whose causality is necessary to achieve the specification), the new causal rule can be reasonable one or not. For example, the causal rule might give a description of a device which reads "when the power of the magnetic field increases, the mass decreases", or "when a given object is travelling at the speed of light, it accelerates."[10] When such impossible causation is derived as the most plausible among other alternatives, there is something wrong with the behavioural specification.

In such case, there is no way out except to modify the specification. Since there will be some index to the boundary conditions that are responsible for the undesirable events after the failure of the proof, it is possible to figure out the conditions under conflict. Automatic resolution of these conflicts is not in the scope of the current research, but it should be possible to support the designer by indicating the necessary conditions to obtain the desired behaviour.

8 Conclusion

The essence of the approach illustrated in this paper is to treat the functionality of design components in terms of causality. Causal relations among events produce a chronological sequence of events (or a history), which is the behaviour of the whole system in the given environment, scenario and the causal rules describing the design components. We assign the specification of the device in terms of such behaviour, and the design task is to create a causal theory which would have such behaviour as its most likely outcome. The causal rules were manipulated according to Shoham's temporal logic which incorporates the nonmonotonic aspect of the prediction task. The formulation is based on a well-defined theory, with clearly defined theoretical justification.

The advantages of this approach are:

- the behavioural specification of devices allows more intuitive descriptions of the functionality of the system, especially in dynamic systems where the devices interact with the environment, and
- it utilises temporal constraints for design evaluation and modification, which enables the representation of delays and relative timings in the occurrence of the events. Without temporal logic, we must rely on the implicit ordering of events.

On the other hand, the main drawback in the design stage of this approach is its complexity. There are typically a number of rule candidates for the abduction

---

[10] The former is the case when the causal connection is not obvious or non-empirical, but *may be* possible with additional knowledge about physics. The latter is simply impossible to have such an effect in real physics.

process, and the combinatorics become more complex as the number of such rules and the number of conditions in their premise become greater. At this moment, some domain specific heuristics are used to reduce the search space, and some choices are reserved for the human user to decide. This permits the users to incorporate their preference, but as the number of rules increase in more complex domain, it is necessary to introduce more elaborate optimisation procedures to guide search. We are currently investigating the construction of 'most likely' models backwards in time to guide the abduction process. This would limit the number of plausible choices and provide suggestions based on some preference criteria.

Acknowledgements

I would like to thank Dave Robertson and Alan Smaill for fruitful discussions and useful comments on earlier drafts of this paper.

References

Barrow, H. G.:"VERIFY: A Program for Proving Correctness of Digital Hardware Designs," in: *Artificial Intelligence* 24 (1984) 437–491.

Bell, J.: "Extended causal theories," in: *Artificial Intelligence* 48 (1991) 211–224.

Freeman, P., and A. Newell: "A model for functional reasoning in design," in: *Proc. IJCAI-71* (1971) 621–640.

Iwasaki, Y.,and B. Chandrasekaran: "Design verification through function- and behavior- oriented representations: bridging the gap between function and behavior," in: J.S. Gero (ed.), *Artificial Intelligence in Design '92*, Pittsburgh, pages 597–616. Dordrecht: Kluwer Academic Publishers, 1992.

Kuipers, B.: "Qualitative Simulation," in: *Artificial Intelligence* 29 (1986) 289–338.

Sembugamoorthy, V., and B. Chandrasekaran: "Functional Representation of Devices and Compilation of Diagnostic Problem-Solving Systems," in: J.L. Kolodner and C.K. Riesbeck (eds), *Experience, Memory and Reasoning*, pages 47–73. Hillsdale, NJ: Lawrence Erlbaum Associates, 1986.

Shoham, Y.: *Reasoning about Change*. Cambridge, MA: The MIT Press, 1988.

Knowledge Theoretic Properties
of Topological Spaces

Konstantinos Georgatos

Department of Mathematics
Graduate School and University Center
City University of New York
33 West 42nd Street
New York, NY 10036
E-mail: koghc@cunyvm.cuny.edu

Abstract. We study the topological models of a logic of knowledge
for topological reasoning, introduced by Larry Moss and Rohit Parikh
(1992). Among our results is the confirmation of a conjecture by Moss
and Parikh, as well as the finite satisfiability property and decidability
for the theory of topological models.

1 Introduction

We are unable to measure natural quantities with exact precision. Physical devices or bounded resources always introduce a certain amount of error. Because
of this fact, we are obliged to limit our observations to approximate values or,
better, to sets of possible values. Whenever this happens, sets of points, rather
than points, are our subject of reasoning. Thus, the statement *"the amount of
ozone in the upper atmosphere has decreased by 12 per cent"* can never be known
to be true with this precision. What we mean is that the decrease has a value
in the interval $(12 - \epsilon, 12 + \epsilon)$ for some positive real number ϵ. If we are able
to spend more resources (taking more samples, using more precise instruments,
etc.) we may be able to affirm that the value belongs to a smaller interval and
therefore to refine our observation. The topology of intervals in the real line is
our domain of reasoning.

The above limitations do not prevent us from drawing conclusions. In fact
it is enough that we *know* that a certain quantity belongs to a set of possible values. The first hundred decimal points of π are enough for most practical purposes and if we decide to settle for such a value, an algorithm that
computes these decimal points conveys the same knowledge as the actual algorithm that computes π. What we know is exactly the common properties of
all algorithms belonging to the same open set of the algorithms we observe in
the topology of initial segments and this notion of knowledge coincides with
the traditional one (Hintikka 1962, Fagin et al. 1991, Halpern and Moses 1984,
Parikh and Ramanujam 1985): what is known is whatever is true in all states
compatible with the observer's view.

Increase of knowledge is strongly linked with the amount of resources we are
willing to invest. An increase of information is accompanied by an increase in the

effort of acquiring it. This corresponds to the refinement of the open set in the relevant topology. In the formal system introduced in (Moss and Parikh 1992) there are two basic modal operators; K for *knowledge* and □ for *effort*.

A basic advantage of this logic and its semantics over other temporal logics or logics of change is that, though we make no mention of set, we are able to interpret assertions relative to a set of possible states and, at the same time, keep the dependence on the actual state. Topology is a tool for modelling classes of statements with an intuitionistic flavor such as refutative or affirmative assertions (see (Vickers 1989)) and Moss and Parikh's system enables us to treat them in a classical modal framework. In many respects the way we interpret the modal operator K resembles the algebraic semantics of a modal operator used to interpret intuitionistic statements as in (Rasiowa and Sikorski 1968). As the intuitionistic version of a statement is the interior of the subset that represents the classical version of it, KA is satisfied only in the open subsets which are subsets of the interior of the set of points which satisfy a property A.

The fundamental reasoning that this logic tries to capture has many equivalents in recursion theory and elsewhere in Mathematics. The discussion of them is well beyond the scope of this paper and the reader is referred to (Georgatos 1993) and (Moss and Parikh 1992) for a more detailed exposition.

In the following section, we describe the syntax and semantics of the logic and we give complete axiomatisations with respect to subset spaces and topological spaces. In Section 3 we develop a theory for describing the validity problem in topological spaces. In Section 4 we study the model based on the basis of a topological space closed under finite unions, and we prove it equivalent to the topological space that it generates. These results translate to a completeness theorem for topologies, given a finite axiomatisation for the class of spaces which are closed under (finite) intersection and union. In the last section we prove finite satisfiability for the class of topological models and decidability for their theory.

2 The logic

We follow the notation of (Moss and Parikh 1992).

Our language is bimodal and propositional. Formally, we start with a countable set A of *atomic formulae* containing two distinguished elements $\top$ and $\bot$. Then the *language* $\mathcal{L}$ is the least set such that $A \subseteq \mathcal{L}$ and $\mathcal{L}$ is closed under the following rules:

$$\frac{\phi, \psi \in \mathcal{L}}{\phi \wedge \psi \in \mathcal{L}} \qquad \frac{\phi \in \mathcal{L}}{\neg \phi, \Box \phi, K\phi \in \mathcal{L}}$$

The above language can be interpreted inside any spatial context.

Definition 1. Let X be a set and $\mathcal{O}$ a subset of the powerset of X, i.e., $\mathcal{O} \subseteq \mathcal{P}(X)$ such that $X \in \mathcal{O}$. We call the pair $\langle X, \mathcal{O} \rangle$ a *subset space*. A *model* is a triple $\langle X, \mathcal{O}, i \rangle$, where $\langle X, \mathcal{O} \rangle$ is a subset space and i a map from A to $\mathcal{P}(X)$ with $i(\top) = X$ and $i(\bot) = \emptyset$ called *initial interpretation*.

We denote the set $\{(x, U) \mid U \in \mathcal{O},\ x \in U\} \subseteq X \times \mathcal{O}$ with $X \dot\times \mathcal{O}$. For each $U \in \mathcal{O}$ let $\downarrow U$ be the set $\{V \mid V \in \mathcal{O}$ and $V \subseteq U\}$, i.e., the lower closed set generated by U in the partial order $(\mathcal{O}, \subseteq)$.

Definition 2. The *satisfaction relation* $\models_{\mathcal{M}}$, where $\mathcal{M}$ is the model $\langle X, \mathcal{O}, i \rangle$, is a subset of $(X \dot\times \mathcal{O}) \times \mathcal{L}$ defined recursively by (we write $x, U \models_{\mathcal{M}} \phi$ instead of $((x, U), \phi) \in \models_{\mathcal{M}})$:

$$x, U \models_{\mathcal{M}} A \quad \text{iff} \quad x \in i(A), \text{ where } A \in \mathsf{A}$$

$$x, U \models_{\mathcal{M}} \phi \wedge \psi \text{ if } \quad x, U \models_{\mathcal{M}} \phi \text{ and } x, U \models_{\mathcal{M}} \psi$$

$$x, U \models_{\mathcal{M}} \neg \phi \quad \text{if} \quad x, U \not\models_{\mathcal{M}} \phi$$

$$x, U \models_{\mathcal{M}} \mathsf{K}\phi \quad \text{if} \quad \text{for all } y \in U, \quad y, U \models_{\mathcal{M}} \phi$$

$$x, U \models_{\mathcal{M}} \Box\phi \quad \text{if} \quad \text{for all } V \in \downarrow U \text{ such that } x \in V, \quad x, V \models_{\mathcal{M}} \phi.$$

If $x, U \models_{\mathcal{M}} \phi$ for all (x, U) belonging to $X \dot\times \mathcal{O}$ then ϕ is *valid* in $\mathcal{M}$, denoted by $\mathcal{M} \models \phi$.

We abbreviate $\neg\Box\neg\phi$ and $\neg\mathsf{K}\neg\phi$ with $\Diamond\phi$ and $\mathsf{L}\phi$ respectively. We have that

$$x, U \models_{\mathcal{M}} \mathsf{L}\phi \text{ if there exists } y \in U \text{ such that } y, U \models_{\mathcal{M}} \phi$$

$$x, U \models_{\mathcal{M}} \Diamond\phi \text{ if there exists } V \in \mathcal{O} \text{ such that } V \subseteq U,\ x \in V, \text{ and } x, V \models_{\mathcal{M}} \phi.$$

Many topological properties are expressible in this logical system in a natural way. For instance, in a model where the subset space is a topological space, $i(A)$ is *open* whenever $A \to \Diamond\mathsf{K}A$ is valid in this model or $i(A)$ is *nowhere dense* whenever $\mathsf{L}\Diamond\mathsf{K}\neg A$ is valid (cf. (Moss and Parikh 1992)).

Example 1. Consider the set of *real numbers* $\mathbf{R}$ with the usual topology of open intervals. We define the following three predicates:

$$\begin{aligned}
&\texttt{pi where } i(\texttt{pi}) = \{\pi\} \\
&\mathtt{I}_1 \text{ where } i(\mathtt{I}_1) = (-\infty, \pi] \\
&\mathtt{I}_2 \text{ where } i(\mathtt{I}_2) = (\pi, +\infty) \\
&\mathtt{Q} \text{ where } i(\mathtt{Q}) = \{q \mid q \text{ is rational }\}.
\end{aligned}$$

There is no real number p and open set U such that $p, U \models \mathsf{K}\texttt{pi}$ because that would imply $p = \pi$ and $U = \{\pi\}$ and there are no singletons which are open.

A point x belongs to the *closure* of a set W if every open U that contains $x \cap W$. Thus π belongs to the closure of $(\pi, +\infty)$, i.e., every open U that contains π has a point in $(\pi, +\infty)$. This means that for all U such that $\pi \in U$, $\pi, U \models \mathsf{L}\mathtt{I}_2$, therefore $\pi, \mathbf{R} \models \Box\mathsf{L}\mathtt{I}_2$. Following the same reasoning $\pi, \mathbf{R} \models \Box\mathsf{L}\mathtt{I}_1$, since π belongs to the closure of $(-\infty, \pi]$.

A point x belongs to the *boundary* of a set W whenever x belong to the closure of W and $X - W$. By the above, π belongs to the boundary of $(-\infty, \pi]$ Among our results is a solution of a conjecture by the form and $\pi, \mathbf{R} \models \Box(\mathsf{L}\mathtt{I}_1 \wedge \mathsf{L}\mathtt{I}_2)$.

A set W is *closed* if it contains its closure. The interval $i(\mathbf{I}_1) = (-\infty, \pi]$ is closed and this means that the formula $\Box \mathsf{LI}_1 \to \mathbf{I}_1$ is valid.

A set W is *dense* if all opens contain a point of W. The set of rational numbers is dense which translates to the fact that the formula $\Box \mathsf{LQ}$ is valid. To exhibit the reasoning in this logic, suppose that the set of rational numAmong our results is a solution of a conjecture by the formbers was closed then both $\Box \mathsf{LQ}$ and $\Box \mathsf{LQ} \to \mathsf{Q}$ would be valid. This implies that Q would be valid which means that all reals would be rationals. Hence the set of rational numbers is not closed.

The following set of axioms and rules, denoted by **MP***, is sound and complete for the class of topological spaces (see (Georgatos 1993)) while axioms 1 through 10, denoted by **MP**, appeared first and proven sound and complete for the class of subset spaces in (Moss and Parikh 1992). Among our results is a solution ofAmong our results is a solution of a conjecture by the form a conjecture by the form

Axioms

1. All propositional tautologies
2. $(A \to \Box A) \wedge (\neg A \to \Box \neg A)$, for $A \in \mathsf{A}$
3. $\Box(\phi \to \psi) \to (\Box\phi \to \Box\psi)$
4. $\Box\phi \to \phi$
5. $\Box\phi \to \Box\Box\phi$
6. $\mathsf{K}(\phi \to \psi) \to (\mathsf{K}\phi \to \mathsf{K}\psi)$
7. $\mathsf{K}\phi \to \phi$
8. $\mathsf{K}\phi \to \mathsf{KK}\phi$
9. $\phi \to \mathsf{KL}\phi$
10. $\mathsf{K}\Box\phi \to \Box\mathsf{K}\phi$
11. $\Diamond\Box\phi \to \Box\Diamond\phi$
12. $\Diamond(\mathsf{K}\phi \wedge \psi) \wedge \mathsf{L}\Diamond(\mathsf{K}\phi \wedge \chi) \to \Diamond(\mathsf{K}\Diamond\phi \wedge \Diamond\psi \wedge \mathsf{L}\Diamond\chi)$

Rules

$$\frac{\phi \to \psi, \phi}{\psi} \ \mathrm{MP}$$

$$\frac{\phi}{\mathsf{K}\phi} \ \mathsf{K}\text{-Necessitation} \qquad \frac{\phi}{\Box\phi} \ \Box\text{-Necessitation}$$

3   Stability and Splittings

Suppose that X is a set and $\mathcal{T}$ a topology on X. In the following we assume that we are working in the topological space $(X, \mathcal{T})$. Our aim is to find a partition of $\mathcal{T}$, where a given formula ϕ "retains its truth value" for each point throughout a member of this partition. We shall show that there exists a finite partition of this kind.

Definition 3. Given a finite family $\mathcal{F} = \{U_1, \ldots, U_n\}$ of opens, we define the *remainder* of (the principal ideal in $(\mathcal{T}, \subseteq)$ generated by) U_k by

$$\text{Rem}^{\mathcal{F}} U_k \quad = \quad \downarrow U_k - \bigcup_{U_k \subsetneq U_i} \downarrow U_i.$$

Proposition 4. *In a finite set of opens* $\mathcal{F} = \{U_1, \ldots, U_n\}$ *closed under intersection, we have*

$$\text{Rem}^{\mathcal{F}} U_i \quad = \quad \downarrow U_i - \bigcup_{U_j \subset U_i} \downarrow U_j,$$

for $i = 1, \ldots, n$.

Proof.

$$\begin{aligned}
\text{Rem}^{\mathcal{F}} U_i &= \downarrow U_i - \bigcup_{U_i \subsetneq U_h} \downarrow U_h \\
&= \downarrow U_i - \bigcup_{U_i \subsetneq U_h} \downarrow (U_h \cap U_i) \\
&= \downarrow U_i - \bigcup_{U_j \subset U_i} \downarrow U_i.
\end{aligned}$$

We denote $\bigcup_{U_i \in \mathcal{F}} \downarrow U_i$ with $\downarrow \mathcal{F}$.

Proposition 5. *If* $\mathcal{F} = \{U_1, \ldots, U_n\}$ *is a finite family of opens, closed under intersection, then*

1. $\text{Rem}^{\mathcal{F}} U_i \cap \text{Rem}^{\mathcal{F}} U_j = \emptyset$, *for* $i \neq j$,
2. $\bigcup_{i=1}^n \text{Rem}^{\mathcal{F}} U_i = \downarrow \mathcal{F}$, *i.e.,* $\{\text{Rem}^{\mathcal{F}} U_i\}_{i=1}^n$ *is a partition of* $\downarrow \mathcal{F}$. *We call such an* $\mathcal{F}$ *a finite splitting (of* $\downarrow \mathcal{F}$*)*,
3. *if* $V_1, V_3 \in \text{Rem}^{\mathcal{F}} U_i$ *and* V_2 *is an open such that* $V_1 \subseteq V_2 \subseteq V_3$ *then* $V_2 \in \text{Rem}^{\mathcal{F}} U_i$, *i.e.,* $\text{Rem}^{\mathcal{F}} U_i$ *is convex.*

Proof. The first and the third are immediate from the definition.
For the second, suppose that $V \in \downarrow \mathcal{F}$ then $V \in \text{Rem}^{\mathcal{F}} \bigcap_{V \in \downarrow U_i} U_i$.

Every partition of a set induces an equivalence relation on this set. The members of the partition comprise the equivalence classes. Since a splitting induces a partition, we denote the equivalence relation induced by a splitting $\mathcal{F}$ by $\sim_{\mathcal{F}}$.

Definition 6. Given a set of open subsets $\mathcal{G}$, we define the relation $\sim'_{\mathcal{G}}$ on $\mathcal{T}$ with $V_1 \sim'_{\mathcal{G}} V_2$ if and only if $V_1 \subseteq U \Leftrightarrow V_2 \subseteq U$ for all $U \in \mathcal{G}$.

We have the following

Proposition 7. *The relation* $\sim'_{\mathcal{G}}$ *is an equivalence.*

Proposition 8. *Given a finite splitting* $\mathcal{F}$, $\sim'_{\mathcal{F}} = \sim_{\mathcal{F}}$ *i.e., the remainders of* $\mathcal{F}$ *are the equivalence classes of* $\sim'_{\mathcal{F}}$.

Proof. Suppose $V_1 \sim'_{\mathcal{F}} V_2$ then $V_1, V_2 \in \mathsf{Rem}^{\mathcal{F}} U$, where

$$U \;=\; \bigcap \{\, U' \mid V_1, V_2 \subseteq U,\ U' \in \mathcal{F}\,\}.$$

For the other way suppose $V_1, V_2 \in \mathsf{Rem}^{\mathcal{F}} U$ and that there exists $U' \in \mathcal{F}$ such that $V_1 \subseteq U'$ while $V_2 \nsubseteq U'$. Then we have that $V_1 \subseteq U' \cap U$, $U' \cap U \in \mathcal{F}$ and $U' \cap U \subseteq U$ i.e., $V_1 \notin \mathsf{Rem}^{\mathcal{F}} U$.

We state some useful facts about splittings.

Proposition 9. *If $\mathcal{G}$ is a finite set of opens, then* $\mathsf{Cl}(\mathcal{G})$*, its closure under intersection, yields a finite splitting for* $\downarrow\!\mathcal{G}$.

The last proposition enables us to give yet another characterization of remainders: every family of points in a complete lattice closed under arbitrary joins comprises a *closure system*, i.e., a set of fixed points of a closure operator of the lattice (cf. (Gierz et al. 1980).) Here, the lattice is the poset of the opens of the topological space. If we restrict ourselves to a finite number of fixed points then we just ask for a finite set of opens closed under intersection i.e., Proposition 9. Thus a closure operator in the lattice of the open subsets of a topological space induces an equivalence relation, two opens being equivalent if they have the same closure, and the equivalence classes of this relation are just the remainders of the open subsets which are fixed points of the closure operator. The maximum open in $\mathsf{Rem}^{\mathcal{F}} U$, i.e., U, can be taken as the representative of the equivalence class which is the union of all open sets belonging to $\mathsf{Rem}^{\mathcal{F}} U$.

We now introduce the notion of stability corresponding to what we mean by "a formula retains its truth value on a set of opens".

Definition 10. If $\mathcal{G}$ is a set of opens then $\mathcal{G}$ is *stable for* ϕ, if for all x, either $x, V \models \phi$ for all $V \in \mathcal{G}$, or $x, V \models \neg\phi$ for all $V \in \mathcal{G}$, such that $x \in V$.

Proposition 11. *If $\mathcal{G}_1, \mathcal{G}_2$ are sets of opens then*

1. if $\mathcal{G}_1 \subseteq \mathcal{G}_2$ and $\mathcal{G}_2$ is stable for ϕ then $\mathcal{G}_1$ is stable for ϕ ,
2. if $\mathcal{G}_1$ is stable for ϕ and $\mathcal{G}$ is stable for χ then $\mathcal{G}_1 \cap \mathcal{G}_2$ is stable for $\phi \wedge \chi$.

Proof. (a) is easy to see, while (b) is a corollary of (a).

Definition 12. A finite splitting $\mathcal{F} = \{U_1, \ldots, U_n\}$ is called a *stable splitting for* ϕ, if $\mathsf{Rem}^{\mathcal{F}} U_i$ is stable for ϕ for all $U_i \in \mathcal{F}$.

Proposition 13. *If $\mathcal{F} = \{U_1, \ldots, U_n\}$ is a stable splitting for ϕ, so is*

$$\mathcal{F}' = \mathsf{Cl}(\{U_0, U_1, \ldots, U_n\}),$$

where $U_0 \in \downarrow\!\mathcal{F}$.

Proof. Let $V \in \mathcal{F}'$ then there exists $U_l \in \mathcal{F}$ such that $\mathsf{Rem}^{\mathcal{F}'} V \subseteq \mathsf{Rem}^{\mathcal{F}} U_l$ (e.g., $U_l = \bigcap \{U_i \mid U_i \in \mathcal{F}, V \subseteq U_i\}$) i.e., $\mathcal{F}'$ is a *refinement* of $\mathcal{F}$. But $\mathsf{Rem}^{\mathcal{F}} U_l$ is stable for ϕ and so is $\mathsf{Rem}^{\mathcal{F}'} V$ by Proposition 11(a).

The above proposition tells us that if there is a finite stable splitting for a topology then there is a closure operator with finitely many fixed points whose associated equivalence classes are stable sets of open subsets.

Suppose that $\mathcal{M} = \langle X, T, i \rangle$ is a topological model for $\mathcal{L}$. Let $\mathcal{F}_\mathcal{M}$ be a family of subsets of X generated as follows: $i(A) \in \mathcal{F}_\mathcal{M}$ for all $A \in \mathsf{A}$, if $S \in \mathcal{F}_\mathcal{M}$ then $X - S \in \mathcal{F}_\mathcal{M}$, if $S, T \in \mathcal{F}_\mathcal{M}$ then $S \cap T \in \mathcal{F}_\mathcal{M}$, and if $S \in \mathcal{F}_\mathcal{M}$ then $S^\circ \in \mathcal{F}_\mathcal{M}$ i.e., $\mathcal{F}_\mathcal{M}$ is the least set containing $\{i(A)|A \in \mathsf{A}\}$ and closed under complements, intersections and interiors. Let $\mathcal{F}^\circ_\mathcal{M}$ be the set $\{S^\circ | S \in \mathcal{F}_\mathcal{M}\}$. We have $\mathcal{F}^\circ_\mathcal{M} = \mathcal{F}_\mathcal{M} \cap T$. The following is the main theorem of this section.

Theorem 14 Partition Theorem. *Let* $\mathcal{M} = \langle X, T, i \rangle$ *be a topological model. Then there exists a set* $\{\mathcal{F}^\psi\}_{\psi \in \mathcal{L}}$ *of finite stable splittings such that*

1. $\mathcal{F}^\psi \subseteq \mathcal{F}^\circ_\mathcal{M}$ *and* $X \in \mathcal{F}^\psi$, *for all* $\psi \in \mathcal{L}$,
2. *if* $U \in \mathcal{F}^\psi$ *then* $U^\psi = \{x \in U | x, U \models \psi\} \in \mathcal{F}_\mathcal{M}$, *and*
3. *if* ϕ *is a subformula of* ψ *then* $\mathcal{F}^\phi \subseteq \mathcal{F}^\psi$ *and* $\mathcal{F}^\psi$ *is a finite stable splitting for* ϕ,

where $\mathcal{F}_\mathcal{M}$, $\mathcal{F}^\circ_\mathcal{M}$ *as above.*

Proof. By induction on the structure of the formula ψ. In each step we take care to refine the partition of the induction hypothesis.

- If $\psi = A$ is an atomic formula, then $\mathcal{F}^A = \{X, \emptyset\} = \{i(\top), i(\bot)\}$, since T is stable for all atomic formulae. We also have $\mathcal{F}^A \subseteq \mathcal{F}^\circ_\mathcal{M}$ and $X^A = i(A) \in \mathcal{F}_\mathcal{M}$.
- If $\psi = \neg\phi$ then let $\mathcal{F}^\psi = \mathcal{F}^\phi$, since the statement of the proposition is symmetric with respect to negation. We also have that for an arbitrary $U \in \mathcal{F}^\psi$, $U^\psi = U^{\neg\phi}$.
- If $\psi = \chi \wedge \phi$, let

$$\mathcal{F}^\psi = \mathsf{Cl}(\mathcal{F}^\chi \cup \mathcal{F}^\phi).$$

Observe that $\mathcal{F}^\chi \cup \mathcal{F}^\phi \subseteq \mathcal{F}^{\chi \wedge \phi}$.
Now, if $W_i \in \mathcal{F}^\psi$, then there exists $U_j \in \mathcal{F}^\chi$ and $V_k \in \mathcal{F}^\phi$ such that

$$W_i = U_j \cap V_k \quad \text{and} \quad \mathsf{Rem}^{\mathcal{F}^\psi} W_i \subseteq \mathsf{Rem}^{\mathcal{F}^\chi} U_j \cap \mathsf{Rem}^{\mathcal{F}^\phi} V_k$$

(e.g., $U_j = \bigcap\{U_m | W_i \subseteq U_m,\ U_m \in \mathcal{F}^\chi\}$ and $V_k = \bigcap\{V_n | W_i \subseteq V_n,\ V_n \in \mathcal{F}^\phi\}$.) Since $\mathsf{Rem}^{\mathcal{F}^\chi} U_j$ is stable for χ and $\mathsf{Rem}^{\mathcal{F}^\phi} V_n$ is stable for ϕ, their intersection is stable for $\chi \wedge \phi = \psi$, by Proposition 11(b), and so is its subset $\mathsf{Rem}^{\mathcal{F}^\psi} W_i$, by Proposition 11(a). Thus $\mathcal{F}^\psi$ is a finite stable splitting for ψ containing X.
We have that $\mathcal{F}^\psi \subseteq \mathcal{F}_\mathcal{M}$ whenever $\mathcal{F}^\chi \subseteq \mathcal{F}_\mathcal{M}$ and $\mathcal{F}^\phi \subseteq \mathcal{F}^\circ_\mathcal{M}$. Finally, $W_i^\psi = U_j^\chi \cap V_k^\phi$.
- Suppose $\psi = \mathsf{K}\phi$. Then, by induction hypothesis, there exists a finite stable splitting $\mathcal{F}^\phi = \{U_1, \dots, U_n\}$ for ϕ containing X. Let

$$W_i = (U_i^\phi)^\circ,$$

for all $i \in \{1, \dots, n\}$.

Observe that if $x \in U_i - W_i$ then $x, V \models \neg \phi$, for all $V \in \mathsf{Rem}^{\mathcal{F}^\phi} U_i$ and $x \in V$, since $\mathsf{Rem}^{\mathcal{F}^\phi} U_i$ is stable for ϕ, by induction hypothesis.

Now, if $V \in \mathsf{Rem}^{\mathcal{F}^\phi} U_i \cap \downarrow W_i$, for some $i \in \{1 \ldots, n\}$, then $x, V \models \phi$ for all $x \in V$, by definition of W_i, hence $x, V \models \mathsf{K}\phi$ for all $x \in V$.

On the other hand, if $V \in \mathsf{Rem}^{\mathcal{F}^\phi} U_i - \downarrow W_i$ then there exists $x \in V$ such that $x, V \models \neg\phi$ (otherwise $V \subseteq W_i$). Thus we have $x, V \models \neg\mathsf{K}\phi$ for all $x \in V$.

Hence $\mathsf{Rem}^{\mathcal{F}^\phi} U_i \cap \downarrow W_i$ and $\mathsf{Rem}^{\mathcal{F}^\phi} U_i - \downarrow W_i$ are stable for $\mathsf{K}\phi$. Thus, the set

$$F = \{\mathsf{Rem}^{\mathcal{F}} U_i \mid W_i \notin \mathsf{Rem}^{\mathcal{F}} U_i\} \cup \{\mathsf{Rem}^{\mathcal{F}} U_j - \downarrow W_j, \mathsf{Rem}^{\mathcal{F}} U_j \cap \downarrow W_j \mid W_j \in U_j\}$$

is a partition of $\mathcal{T}$ and its members are stable for $\mathsf{K}\phi$. Let $\sim_F$ be the equivalence relation on $\mathcal{T}$ induced by F and let

$$\mathcal{F}^{\mathsf{K}\phi} = \mathsf{Cl}(\mathcal{F}^\phi \cup \{ W_i \mid W_i \in \mathsf{Rem}^{\mathcal{F}^\phi} U_i\}).$$

We have that $\mathcal{F}^{\mathsf{K}\phi}$ is a finite set of opens and $\mathcal{F}^\phi \subseteq \mathcal{F}^{\mathsf{K}\phi}$. Thus, $\mathcal{F}^{\mathsf{K}\phi}$ is finite and contains X. We have only to prove that $\mathcal{F}^{\overline{\mathsf{K}}\phi}$ is a stable splitting for $\mathsf{K}\phi$, i.e., every remainder of an open in $\mathcal{F}^{\mathsf{K}\phi}$ is stable for $\mathsf{K}\phi$.

If $V_1 \not\sim_F V_2$, where $V_1, V_2 \in \mathcal{T}$, then there exists $U = U_i$ or W_i for some $i = 1, \ldots, n$ such that $V_1 \subseteq U$ while $V_2 \not\subseteq U$. But this implies that $V_1 \not\sim_{\mathcal{F}\mathsf{K}_\phi}$ V_2. Therefore $\{\mathsf{Rem}^{\mathcal{F}^{\mathsf{K}_\phi}} U\}_{U \in \mathcal{F}\mathsf{K}_\phi}$ is a refinement of F and $\mathcal{F}^{\mathsf{K}\phi}$ is a finite stable splitting for $\mathsf{K}\phi$ using Proposition 11(a).

We have that $\mathcal{F}^{\mathsf{K}\phi} \subseteq \mathcal{F}^\circ_{\mathcal{M}}$ because $W_i \in \mathcal{F}^\circ_{\mathcal{M}}$, for $i = 1, \ldots, n$. Now if $U \in \mathcal{F}^\psi$ then either $U^{\mathsf{K}\phi} = U$ or $U^{\mathsf{K}\phi} = \emptyset$.

- Suppose $\psi = \Box\phi$. Then, by induction hypothesis, there exists a finite stable splitting $\mathcal{F}^\phi = \{U_1, \ldots, U_n\}$ for ϕ containing X.
Let

$$\mathcal{F}^{\Box\phi} = \mathsf{Cl}(\mathcal{F}^\phi \cup \{U_i \Rightarrow U_j \mid 1 \le i, j \le n\}),$$

where $\Rightarrow$ is the implication of the complete Heyting algebra $\mathcal{T}$ i.e., $V \subseteq U \Rightarrow W$ if and only if $V \cap U \subseteq W$ for $V, U, W \in \mathcal{T}$. We have that $U \Rightarrow W$ equals $(X - (U - W))^\circ$. Clearly, $\mathcal{F}^{\Box\phi}$ is a finite splitting containing X and $\mathcal{F}^\phi \subseteq \mathcal{F}^{\Box\phi}$. We have only to prove that $\mathcal{F}^{\Box\phi}$ is stable for $\Box\phi$. But first, we prove the following claim:

Claim 15. Suppose $U \in \mathcal{F}^\phi$ and $U' \in \mathcal{F}^{\Box\phi}$. Then

$$U' \cap U \in \mathsf{Rem}^{\mathcal{F}^\phi} U \iff V \cap U \in \mathsf{Rem}^{\mathcal{F}^\phi} U \text{ for all } V \in \mathsf{Rem}^{\mathcal{F}^{\Box\phi}} U'.$$

Proof. The one direction is straightforward. For the other, let $V \in \mathsf{Rem}^{\mathcal{F}^{\Box\phi}} U'$ and suppose $V \cap U \notin \mathsf{Rem}^{\mathcal{F}^\phi} U$ towards a contradiction. This implies that there exists $U'' \in \mathcal{F}^\phi$, with $U'' \subset U$, such that $V \cap U \subseteq U''$. Thus, $V \subseteq U \Rightarrow U''$ but $U' \not\subseteq U \Rightarrow U''$. But $U \Rightarrow U'' \in \mathcal{F}^{\Box\phi}$ which contradicts $U' \sim_{\mathcal{F}^{\Box\phi}} V$, by Proposition 8.

Let $U' \in \mathcal{F}^{\Box\phi}$. We must prove that $\text{Rem}^{\mathcal{F}^{\Box\phi}} U'$ is stable for $\Box\phi$.
Suppose that $x, U' \models \neg\Box\phi$. We must prove that

$$x, V' \models \neg\Box\phi$$

for all $V' \in \text{Rem}^{\mathcal{F}^{\Box\phi}} U'$ such that $x \in V'$.

Since $x, U' \models \neg\Box\phi$, there exists $V \in \mathcal{T}$, with $x \in V$ and $V \subseteq U'$, such that $x, V \models \neg\phi$. Since $\mathcal{F}^{\phi}$ is a splitting, there exists $U \in \mathcal{F}^{\phi}$ such that $V \in \text{Rem}^{\mathcal{F}^{\phi}} U$. Observe that $V \subseteq U' \cap U \subseteq U$, so $U' \cap U \in \text{Rem}^{\mathcal{F}^{\phi}} U$, by Proposition 5(c).

By Claim 15, for all $V' \in \text{Rem}^{\mathcal{F}^{\Box\phi}} U'$, we have $V' \cap U \in \text{Rem}^{\mathcal{F}^{\phi}} U$. Thus if $x \in V'$ then $x, V' \cap U \models \neg\phi$, because $\text{Rem}^{\mathcal{F}^{\phi}} U$ is stable for ϕ, by induction hypothesis. This implies that, for all V' such that $V' \in \text{Rem}^{\mathcal{F}^{\Box\phi}} U'$ and $x \in V$, we have $x, V' \models \neg\Box\phi$.
Therefore, $\mathcal{F}^{\Box\phi}$ is a finite stable splitting for $\Box\phi$.
Now $U_i \Rightarrow U_j \in \mathcal{F}_{\mathcal{M}}^{\circ}$ for $1 \leq i, j \leq n$, hence $\mathcal{F}^{\Box\phi} \subseteq \mathcal{F}_{\mathcal{M}}^{\circ}$.
Finally, let U belong to $\mathcal{F}^{\Box\phi}$ and $V_1, \ldots, V_m$ be all opens in $\mathcal{F}^{\phi}$ such that $U \cap V_i \in \text{Rem}^{\mathcal{F}^{\phi}} V_i$, for $i = 1, \ldots, m$. Then $x, U \models \Diamond\neg\phi$ if and only if there exists $j \in \{1, \ldots, m\}$ with $x \in V_j$ and $x, V_j \models \neg\phi$ because $x, V_j \cap U \models \neg\phi$ since $V_j \cap U \in \text{Rem}^{\mathcal{F}^{\phi}} V_j$. This implies that

$$U^{\neg\Box\phi} = U^{\Diamond\neg\phi} = U \cap \bigcup_{i=1}^{m} V_i^{\neg\phi}.$$

Since $U, V_1^{\neg\phi}, \ldots, V^{\neg\phi}$ belong to $\mathcal{F}_{\mathcal{M}}$, so does $U^{\neg\Box\phi}$ and, therefore, $U^{\Box\phi} = U - U^{\neg\Box\phi}$.

In all steps of induction we refine the finite splitting, so if ϕ is a subformula of ψ, then $\mathcal{F}^{\phi} \subseteq \mathcal{F}^{\psi}$ and $\mathcal{F}^{\psi}$ is stable for ϕ using Proposition 11(a).

Theorem 14 gives us a great deal of intuition for topological models. It describes in detail the expressible part of the topological lattice for the completeness result as it appears in (Georgatos 1993) and paves the road for the reduction of the theory of topological models to that of spatial lattices and the decidability result of this section.

4 Basis Model

Let $\mathcal{T}$ be a topology on a set X and $\mathcal{B}$ a basis for $\mathcal{T}$. We denote satisfaction in the models $\langle X, \mathcal{T}, i \rangle$ and $\langle X, \mathcal{B}, i \rangle$ by $\models_{\mathcal{T}}$ and $\models_{\mathcal{B}}$, respectively. In the following proposition we prove that each equivalence class under $\sim_{\mathcal{F}}$ contains an element of a basis closed under finite unions.

Proposition 16. *Let $(X, \mathcal{T})$ be a topological space, and let $\mathcal{B}$ be a basis for $\mathcal{T}$ closed under finite unions. Let $\mathcal{F}$ be any finite subset of $\mathcal{T}$. Then for all $V \in \mathcal{F}$ and all $x \in V$, there is some $U \in \mathcal{B}$ with $x \in U \subseteq V$ and $U \in \text{Rem}^{\mathcal{F}} V$.*

Proof. By finiteness of $\mathcal{F}$, let $V_1, \ldots, V_k$ be the elements of $\mathcal{F}$ such that $V \not\subseteq V_i$, for $i \in \{1, \ldots, k\}$. Since $V_i \neq V$, take $x_i \in V - V_i$ for $i \in \{1, \ldots, k\}$. Since $\mathcal{B}$ is a basis for $\mathcal{T}$, there exist U_x, U_i, with $x \in U_x$ and $x_i \in U_i$, such that U_x and U_i are subsets of V for $i \in \{1, \ldots, k\}$. Set

$$U = (\bigcup_{i=1}^{k} U_i) \cup U_x.$$

Observe that $x \in U$, and $U \in \mathcal{B}$, as it is a finite union of members of $\mathcal{B}$. Also $U \in \mathsf{Rem}^{\mathcal{F}} V$, since $U \in \downarrow V$ but $U \not\subseteq \bigcup \downarrow V_i$ for $i \in \{1, \ldots, k\}$.

Corollary 17. *Let $(X, \mathcal{T})$ be a topological space, $\mathcal{B}$ a basis for $\mathcal{T}$ closed under finite unions, $x \in X$ and $U \in \mathcal{B}$. Then*

$$x, U \models_{\mathcal{T}} \phi \iff x, U \models_{\mathcal{B}} \phi.$$

Proof. By induction on ϕ.

The interesting case is when $\phi = \Box \psi$. Fix x, U, and ψ. By Proposition 14, there exists a finite stable splitting $\mathcal{F}$ for ϕ and its subformulae such that $\mathcal{F}$ contains X and U. Assume that $x, U \models_{\mathcal{B}} \Box \psi$, and $V \in \mathcal{T}$ such that $V \subseteq U$. By Proposition 5(b), there is some $V' \subseteq U$ in $\mathcal{F}$ with $V \in \mathsf{Rem}^{\mathcal{F}} V'$. By Proposition 16, let $W \in \mathcal{B}$ be such that $W \in \mathsf{Rem}^{\mathcal{F}} V'$ with $x \in W$. So $x, W \models_{\mathcal{B}} \psi$, and thus by induction hypothesis, $x, W \models_{\mathcal{T}} \psi$. By stability, twice, $x, V \models_{\mathcal{T}} \psi$ as well.

We are now going to prove that a model based on a topological space $\mathcal{T}$ is equivalent to the one induced by any basis of $\mathcal{T}$ which is lattice. Observe that this enables us to reduce the theory of topological spaces to that of spatial lattices and, therefore, to answer the conjecture of (Moss and Parikh 1992): a completeness theorem for subset spaces which are lattices will extend to the smaller class of topological spaces.

Theorem 18. *Let $(X, \mathcal{T})$ be a topological space and $\mathcal{B}$ a basis for $\mathcal{T}$ closed under finite unions. Let $\mathcal{M}_1 = \langle X, \mathcal{T}, i \rangle$ and $\mathcal{M}_2 = \langle X, \mathcal{B}, i \rangle$ be the corresponding models. Then, for all ϕ,*

$$\mathcal{M}_1 \models \phi \iff \mathcal{M}_2 \models \phi.$$

Proof. It suffices to prove that $x, U \models_{\mathcal{T}} \phi$, for some $U \in \mathcal{T}$, if and only if $x, U' \models_{\mathcal{B}} \phi$, for some $U' \in \mathcal{B}$.

Suppose $x, U \models_{\mathcal{T}} \phi$, where $U \in \mathcal{T}$, then, by Corollary 17, there exists $U' \in \mathcal{B}$ such that $x \in U'$ and $x, U \models_{\mathcal{T}} \phi$. By Corollary 17, $x, U' \models_{\mathcal{B}} \phi$.

Suppose $x, U \models_{\mathcal{B}} \phi$, where $U \in \mathcal{B}$, then $x, U \models_{\mathcal{T}} \phi$, by Corollary 17.

5 Finite Satisfiability

Proposition 19. *Let $\langle X, \mathcal{T} \rangle$ be a subset space. Let $\mathcal{F}$ be a finite stable splitting for a formula ϕ and all its subformulae, and assume that $X \in \mathcal{F}$. Then for all $U \in \mathcal{F}$, all $x \in U$, and all subformulae ψ of ϕ, $x, U \models_{\mathcal{T}} \psi$ iff $x, U \models_{\mathcal{F}} \psi$.*

Proof. The argument is by induction on ϕ. The only interesting case to consider is when $\phi = \Box \psi$.

Suppose first that $x, U \models_{\mathcal{F}} \Box \psi$ with $U \in \mathcal{F}$. We must show that $x, U \models_{\mathcal{T}} \Box \psi$ also. Let $V \in \mathcal{T}$ such that $V \subseteq U$; we must show that $x, V \models_{\mathcal{T}} \psi$. By Proposition 5(b), there is some $V' \subseteq U$ in $\mathcal{F}$ with $V \in \mathrm{Rem}^{\mathcal{F}} V'$. So $x, V' \models_{\mathcal{F}} \psi$, and by induction hypothesis, $x, V' \models_{\mathcal{T}} \psi$. By stability, $x, V \models_{\mathcal{T}} \psi$ also.

The other direction (if $x, U \models_{\mathcal{T}} \Box \psi$, then $x, U \models_{\mathcal{F}} \Box \psi$), is an easy application of the induction hypothesis.

Constructing the quotient of $\mathcal{T}$ under $\sim_{\mathcal{F}}$ is not adequate for generating a finite model because there may still be an infinite number of points. It turns out that we only need a finite number of them.

Let $\mathcal{M} = \langle X, \mathcal{T}, i \rangle$ be a topological model, and define an equivalence relation $\sim$ on X by $x \sim y$ iff

(a) for all $U \in \mathcal{T}$, $x \in U$ iff $y \in U$, and
(b) for all atomic A, $x \in i(A)$ iff $y \in i(A)$.

Further, denote by x^* the equivalence class of x, and let $X^* = \{x^* : x \in X\}$. For every $U \in \mathcal{T}$ let $U^* = \{x^* : x \in X\}$, then $\mathcal{T}^* = \{U^* : U \in \mathcal{T}\}$ is a topology on X^*. Define a map i^* from the atomic formulae to the powerset of X^* by $i^*(A) = \{x^* : x \in i(A)\}$. The entire model $\mathcal{M}$ lifts to the model $\mathcal{M}^* = \langle X^*, \mathcal{T}^*, i^* \rangle$ in a well-defined way.

Lemma 20. *For all x, U, and ϕ,*

$$x, U \models_{\mathcal{M}} \phi \quad \text{iff} \quad x^*, U^* \models_{\mathcal{M}^*} \phi .$$

Proof. By induction on ϕ.

Theorem 21. *If ϕ is satisfied in any topological space, then ϕ is satisfied in a finite topological space.*

Proof. Let $\mathcal{M} = \langle X, \mathcal{T}, i \rangle$ be such that for some $x \in U \in \mathcal{T}$, $x, U \models_{\mathcal{M}} \phi$. Let $\mathcal{F}^{\phi}$ be a finite stable splitting (by Theorem 14) for ϕ and its subformulae with respect to $\mathcal{M}$. By Proposition 19, $x, U \models_{\mathcal{N}} \phi$, where $\mathcal{N} = \langle X, \mathcal{F}, i \rangle$. We may assume that $\mathcal{F}$ is a topology, and we may also assume that the overall language has only the (finitely many) atomic symbols which occur in ϕ. Then the relation $\sim$ has only finitely many classes. So the model $\mathcal{N}^*$ is finite. Finally, by Lemma 20, $x^*, U^* \models_{\mathcal{N}^*} \phi$.

Observe that the finite topological space is a quotient of the initial one under two equivalences. The one equivalence is $\sim_{\mathcal{F}}^{\phi}$ on the open subsets of the topological space, where $\mathcal{F}^{\phi}$ is the finite splitting corresponding to ϕ and its cardinality is a function of the complexity of ϕ. The other equivalence is $\sim_X$ on the points of the topological space and its number of equivalence classes is a function of the atomic formulae appearing in ϕ. The following simple example shows how a topology is formed with the quotient under these two equivalences

Example 2. Let X be the interval $[0, 1)$ of the real line with the set

$$\mathcal{T} \;=\; \{\emptyset\} \cup \{\, [0, \frac{1}{2^n}) \mid n = 0, 1, 2, \dots \,\}$$

as topology. Suppose that we have only one atomic formula, call it A, such that $i(A) = \{0\}$. Then it is easy to see that the model $\langle X, \mathcal{T}, i \rangle$ is equivalent to the finite topological model $\langle X^*, \mathcal{T}^*, i^* \rangle$, where

$$X^* = \{\, x_1, x_2 \,\},$$
$$\mathcal{T}^* = \{\, \emptyset, \{x_1, x_2\} \,\}, \text{ and}$$
$$i(A) = \{\, x_1 \,\}.$$

So the overall size of the (finite) topological space is bounded by a function of the complexity of ϕ. Thus if we want to test whether a given formula is invalid we have a finite number of finite topological spaces where we have to test its validity. Thus we have the following

Theorem 22. *The theory of topological spaces is decidable.*

Observe that the last two results apply for lattices of subsets by Theorem 18.

Acknowledgements

I wish to thank Larry Moss and Rohit Parikh for helpful comments and suggestions.

References

Fagin, R., J.Y. Halpern, and M.Y. Vardi: "A model-theoretic analysis of knowledge," in: *Journal of the Association for Computing Machinery*, 38 (2) (1991) 382–428.

Georgatos, K.: *Modal Logics for Topological Spaces.* Ph.D. Dissertation. City University of New York, 1993.

Gierz, G., K.H. Hoffman, K. Keimel, J.D. Lawson, M.W. Mislove, and D.S. Scott: *A Compendium of Continuous Lattices.* Berlin, Heidelberg: Springer-Verlag, 1980.

Halpern, J.Y., and Y. Moses: "Knowledge and common knowledge in a distributed environment," in: *Proceedings of the Third ACM Symposium on Principles of Distributed Computing* (1984) 50-61.

Hintikka, J.: *Knowledge and Belief.* Ithaca, New York: Cornell University Press, 1962.

Moss. L.S., and R. Parikh: "Topological reasoning and the logic of knowledge," in: Y. Moses (ed.), *Proceedings of the Fourth Conference (TARK 1992)* (1992) 95-105.

Parikh, R., and R. Ramanujam: "Distributed computing and the logic of knowledge," in: R. Parikh (ed.) *Logics of Programs*, number 193 in Lecture Notes in Computer Science, Berlin, New York: Springer Verlag (1985) 256-268.

Rasiowa, H., and R. Sikorski: *The Mathematics of Metamathematics*. Panstwowe Wydawnictwo Naukowe, Warszawa, Poland, second edition, 1968.

Vickers, S.: *Topology via Logic*. Cambridge Studies in Advanced Computer Science. Cambridge: Cambridge University Press, 1989.

Rough Logic for Multi-agent Systems

Cecylia M. Rauszer

Institute of Mathematics, Warsaw University
ul. Banacha 2, 02-097 Warsaw, Poland
E-mail: rauszer@mimuw.edu.pl

Abstract. Reasoning about knowledge is one of the most challenging problems in philosophy, artificial intelligence and logic. Various approaches have been presented, such as nonmonotonic reasoning, fuzzy sets, probabilistic logic, and so on. In this paper we focus on *rough set philosophy* to describe reasoning about knowledge, which is understood as the ability to classify objects. Rough sets are used as a mathematical tool to deal with uncertain and imprecise data. The aim of this paper is to present a complete formal system for reasoning based on incomplete information of a multi-agent system. The logic under consideration is a multi modal logic that can be used as a query language for groups of agents.

1 Introduction

The concept of rough sets has been proposed (Pawlak 1982) as a new mathematical tool to deal with uncertain and imprecise data. In the paper we focus on the rough sets philosophy to model reasoning about knowledge (cf. (Pawlak 1982), (Orłowska 1989), (Rasiowa 1990), (Rauszer 1992a, to appear)).

In our approach, knowledge is understood as the ability to classify objects which are taken from the fixed set U (called the universe of discourse, or shortly *universe*). Any classification is in fact a partition of the universe. Objects being in the same class are indiscernible by means of knowledge provided by the classification. For instance, if $U = \{o_1, o_2, o_3, o_4, o_5\}$ then the classifications (partitions) $\mathcal{E}_s = \{\{o_1, o_2, o_3\}, \{o_4\}, \{o_5\}\}$ and $\mathcal{E}_t = \{\{o_1, o_2\}, \{o_3, o_4\}, \{o_5\}\}$ are examples of knowledge about the universe U. More precisely, $\mathcal{E}_s$ and $\mathcal{E}_t$ given above are treated as knowledge base of agents s and t about the universe U. In the example, the agent s identifies objects o_1, o_2, o_3 and distinguishes objects o_4 and o_5, whereas the agent t identifies o_1 with o_2 and o_3 with o_4 and recognizes o_5.

We will discuss the multi-agent case. We assume that a family of groups of agents T is given and each group perceives the same universe of discourse U. Sometimes, for simplicity, we will refer to elements of T as agents, not groups of agents.

Let $\mathcal{E} = \{\mathcal{E}_t\}_{t \in T}$ be a family of partitions of U, that is, each $\mathcal{E}_t$ is considered as knowledge base of an agent t (of a group of agents t) about U. We extend our semantics so that we can reason about distributed knowledge which is intended to convey information about knowledge of every agent from the group of agents.

We assume that each group of agents can have two kinds of distributed knowledge base, strong and weak.

We say that a group of agents has a *strong distributed knowledge base*, provided objects which are distinguishable for one agent from the group are also distinguishable for the whole group, that is, an agent t with better knowledge plays a dominating role in the group. More precisely, if $\mathcal{E}_s$ is interpreted as knowledge base of an agent s and $\mathcal{E}_t$ as knowledge base of an agent t about the same universe U then $\mathcal{E}_{s \vee t}$ may be viewed as a strong distributed knowledge base of the group $\{s, t\}$, denoted by st, which intuitively may be described as follows: If an agent s knows that an object x is different from objects $x_{j_1}, \ldots, x_{j_m}$, then x has to be different from those objects in $\mathcal{E}_{s \vee t}$. As a consequence we have: if an object x is distinguished from y in $\mathcal{E}_{s \vee t}$, that is, the block $[x]$ is different from the block $[y]$ (in $\mathcal{E}_{s \vee t}$) then it means that at least one of the agents s, t distinguishes x from y. If objects x and y are indiscernible in $\mathcal{E}_{s \vee t}$, then it means that each agent from the group st, according to her knowledge, is not able to distinguish between x and y. For instance, in the above example the partition $\mathcal{E}_s$ better classifies an object o_4 than knowledge $\mathcal{E}_t$. Hence, the class $\{o_4\}$ has to appear in $\mathcal{E}_{s \vee t}$ despite of, using knowledge base $\mathcal{E}_t$ objects o_3 and o_4 are indiscernible.

The notion of a *weak distributed knowledge base* may be interpreted as a classification that preserves less efficient knowledge. This means that if an agent, say t, identifies some objects, then they are indiscernible in each group to which the agent t belongs. If $\mathcal{E}_s$ and $\mathcal{E}_t$ denote knowledge bases of agents s and t, respectively, then we denote by $\mathcal{E}_{s \wedge t}$ a weak distributed knowledge base of the group st. Thus, if $[x] = \{x\} \in \mathcal{E}_{s \wedge t}$, then we infer that there is a consensus of agents s and t about the object x, i.e., $[x] \in \mathcal{E}_s \cap \mathcal{E}_t$. If $\{x_1, \ldots, x_n\} \in \mathcal{E}_{s \wedge t}$, then it means that either there is consensus of the agents s and t about $x_1, \ldots, x_n$ or for any subset of $\{x_1, \ldots, x_n\}$ there is no consensus. For instance, in the above example because of the objects o_3 and o_4 are indiscernible by the agent t, they have to remain indiscernible in $\mathcal{E}_{s \wedge t}$. Moreover, because of o_3 is not distinguished from objects o_1, o_2 by an agent s, the block $\{o_1, o_2, o_3, o_4\}$ is an element of the partition $\mathcal{E}_{s \wedge t}$.

It is shown (in Section 2) that if the family $\mathcal{E} = \{\mathcal{E}_t\}_{t \in T}$ is closed with respect to strong and weak distributed knowledge, then it is a lattice.

In Section 3 we examine lower and upper approximations of sets of objects (Pawlak 1992). Intuitively speaking, by a lower approximation of X determined by a partition of U we mean the set of objects of U that without any doubt belong to X. An upper approximation of X is a set of objects which could be classified as elements of X. Finally, we consider the boundary of X which is in a sense undecidable area of the universe.

Let $\mathcal{E}_t$ be a knowledge base of an agent t and let R_t denote an equivalence relation determined by $\mathcal{E}_t$. Then the t-lower approximation of a set of objects $X \subseteq U$, denoted by $\underline{R}_t(X)$, is intended as knowledge of an agent t about X. In other words, $\underline{R}_t(X)$ is read: *an agent t knows X*. Hence, $\underline{R}_t(X)$ consists of objects which are classified by an agent t as those which, according to knowledge base $\mathcal{E}_t$, have a property given by X. If $\underline{R}_t(X) = X$, then we say that X is t-*defined*.

If $\underline{R}_t(X) \neq X$ then X is t-*rough*. In the former case, the agent t can justify if any object from the universe U belongs to X or to $-X$. In the latter case, the t-boundary of X is a nonempty set, that means that the agent t is unable to decide the membership problem for X.

The next problem is to find methods which allow to represent knowledge in terms of classifications. It turns out that information systems introduced by Pawlak (1982, 1991) provide good models of knowledge. The idea is that information systems may be used as "real" description of a knowledge base. In Section 4 we recall some basic properties of information systems, describing them as tables with columns labelled by attributes and rows labelled by objects. Each row in the data table represents information about a corresponding object. In general, in a given information system we are not able to distinguish all single objects (using attributes provided by the system), since objects can have the same values on some attributes. As a consequence, any set of attributes establishes a partition of the set U of all objects. Suppose now, that $\mathcal{S}_t$ is an information system describing the universe U by means of a set of attributes $\mathbf{A}_t$. Denote it by $(U, \mathbf{A}_t)$, that is, $\mathcal{S}_t = (U, \mathbf{A}_t)$ and let $\mathcal{E}_{\mathbf{A}_t}$ be the partition given by $\mathbf{A}_t$. If $\mathcal{E}_{\mathbf{A}_t} = \mathcal{E}_t$ then we say that $\mathcal{S}_t$ represents knowledge base $\mathcal{E}_t$ of an agent t and call $\mathcal{S}_t$ a *knowledge representation system* of $\mathcal{E}_t$. Clearly, such a representation is not unique.

We show that if $\mathcal{S}_s = (U, \mathbf{A}_s)$ is a knowledge representation system of $\mathcal{E}_s$ and $\mathcal{S}_t = (U, \mathbf{A}_t)$ is a knowledge representation system of $\mathcal{E}_t$, then the system $(U, \mathbf{A}_s \cup \mathbf{A}_t)$ represents a strong distributed knowledge base of the group st i.e., $\mathcal{E}_{s \vee t} = \mathcal{E}_{\mathbf{A}_s \cup \mathbf{A}_t}$. In the case of a weak distributed knowledge base, in general we have $\mathcal{E}_{s \wedge t} \neq \mathcal{E}_{\mathbf{A}_s \cap \mathbf{A}_t}$. Clearly, if $\mathcal{E}_{s \wedge t}$ is a weak distributed knowledge base of $\mathcal{E}_s$ and $\mathcal{E}_t$, then there is a knowledge representation system $(U, \mathbf{A})$ such that the partition determined by $\mathbf{A}$ is equal to $\mathcal{E}_{s \wedge t}$. However, the set of attributes $\mathbf{A}$ need not to be the same as the set $\mathbf{A}_s \cap \mathbf{A}_t$.

It is also shown in Section 4 that the family $\{\mathcal{S}\}_{t \in T}$ of knowledge representation systems may be treated as a lattice. The intuitive meaning of the lattice ordering $\leq$ on this family is that, if $\mathcal{S}_s \leq \mathcal{S}_t$, then the sharpness of perception of U and therefore feature recognitions of objects from the universe U by an agent s is weaker than that of an agent t.

In Section 5 we introduce and examine a formal system called *rough logic*. It is intended as a logic which reflects properties of approximations of knowledge plus some other features of knowledge representation systems. It seems that the logic we have been considering may provide good approximations to reasoning carried out by a knowledge base (Rauszer 1992a). Roughly speaking, our logic is a modal logic with a finite number of modal operators I_t. Each modal operator corresponds to knowledge represented by an information system. A formula of the form $I_t \phi$ might be read as *an agent t knows ϕ*. In other words, $I_t \phi$ represents the t-lower approximation of the set of objects which satisfy ϕ in an information system $\mathcal{S}_t = (U, \mathbf{A}_t)$, that is, $I_t \phi$ represents the set of all positive instances of ϕ.

In Section 6 we present a theorem about knowledge understood as a partition.

Finally, we show that a formula of the form $I_{s \vee t} \phi$ may be treated as distributed knowledge in the sense of (Halpern and Moses 1992). Moreover, if knowledge of an agent t is understood as the set of all positive and negative instances of ϕ, that is, as a formula of the form $I_t\phi \vee I_t - \phi$, then knowledge of an agent is not closed under modus ponens and also some paradoxes of epistemic logic are eliminated. In particular, *what an agent knows is true* and *an agent always knows all the consequences of her knowledge* are not theorems of the logic under consideration.

2 Knowledge Base

In our approach, knowledge is understood as the ability to classify objects. Objects are treated as elements of a real or abstract world called the *universe of discourse* (or *universe*). In our understanding, knowledge concerns the classification of parts of the universe.

We explain this idea more precisely.

Let T be a family of groups o agents that perceive the same universe of discourse U. Any subset X of U is said to be a *concept*. For every $t \in T$, let $\mathcal{E}_t$ denote a partition of U established by a group of agents t. The family $\mathcal{E}_t$ is said to be a *knowledge base of a group t of agents about the universe U*, or simply, a *knowledge base of an agent t*.

Let T be a family of agents (groups of agents) and let for every $t \in T$, $\mathcal{E}_t$ be a knowledge base of an agent t about U. For simplicity, each block from $\mathcal{E}_t$ is denoted by $[x]_t$, instead of $[x]_{\mathcal{E}_t}$. Each block $[x]_t$ is a concept and we call it a *basic concept*. If a basic concept $[x]_t \in \mathcal{E}_t$ contains more than one object, then objects from $[x]_t$ are not distinguishable with respect to the knowledge base $\mathcal{E}_t$.

Let as before, T denote a family of agents and let $\mathcal{E} = \{\mathcal{E}_t\}_{t \in T}$ be a family of all partitions determined by agents from T. Let $\prec$ be a binary relation on $\mathcal{E}$ defined as follows:

$$\mathcal{E}_s \prec \mathcal{E}_t \text{ if and only if } \forall [x]_s \exists [y]_t \; [x]_s \subseteq [y]_t \, .$$

It is not difficult to prove that $\prec$ is an ordering relation on $\mathcal{E}$, that is, $(\mathcal{E}, \prec)$ is a poset.

Denote by $\mathcal{E}_s \wedge \mathcal{E}_t$ the following set:

$$\{[x]_s \cap [y]_t : [x]_s \cap [y]_t \neq \emptyset\}.$$

It is easily proved that $\mathcal{E}_s \wedge \mathcal{E}_t$ is a partition of U and we call this partition a *strong distributed knowledge base* of a group of agents ts. Moreover, if $\mathcal{E}_s \wedge \mathcal{E}_t$ belongs to $\mathcal{E}$ then it is the *infimum* (*inf*) of $\mathcal{E}_s$ and $\mathcal{E}_t$ in $(\mathcal{E}, \prec)$.

Observe that if $\mathcal{E}$ is a family of all partitions of the universe U, then $\mathcal{E}$ is closed with respect to $\wedge$.

Notice also:

Lemma 2.1 *If $\mathcal{E}$ is closed with respect to $\wedge$ then $(\mathcal{E}, \wedge)$ is a lower semi-lattice.*

□

Now put

$\mathcal{E}_s \vee \mathcal{E}_t = \{X \subseteq U : X$ is the union of **all** $[x]_s$ and $[y]_t$ such that $[x]_s \cap [y]_t \neq \emptyset\}.$

It is not difficult to show that $\mathcal{E}_s \vee \mathcal{E}_t$ is a partition of U. We call this partition a *weak distributed knowledge base* of a group of agents ts. Moreover, if the partition $\mathcal{E}_s \vee \mathcal{E}_t$ exists in $\mathcal{E}$, then $\mathcal{E}_s \vee \mathcal{E}_t$ is the *supremum* (*sup*) in $(\mathcal{E}, \prec)$ of $\mathcal{E}_s$ and $\mathcal{E}_t$.

Lemma 2.2 *If a family $\mathcal{E}$ is closed with respect to $\wedge$ and $\vee$, then the structure $(\mathcal{E}, \vee, \wedge)$ is a lattice with the zero element and the unit element.*

Proof: Clearly, the mentioned structure is a lattice. The strong distributed knowledge base of all $\mathcal{E}_s$'s, that is, the $inf\mathcal{E}$ is the zero element and the weak distributed knowledge base of all $\mathcal{E}_s$'s, that is, the $sup\mathcal{E}$ is the unit element in this lattice.

□

Notice, that if $\mathcal{E}$ is the family of all partitions of the universe U then $(\mathcal{E}, \vee, \wedge, \mathbf{0}, \mathbf{1})$ is a lattice. We call every sublattice of the lattice $(\mathcal{E}, \vee, \wedge, \mathbf{0}, \mathbf{1})$ a *lattice of partitions*. The example given below shows that a lattice of partitions needs not to be distributive.

Example 1. Let U consist of five objects $\{o_1, o_2, o_3, o_4, o_5\}$ and let $\mathcal{E}_s = \{\{o_1, o_2\}, \{o_3\}, \{o_4\}, \{o_5\}\}$, $\mathcal{E}_t = \{\{o_1, o_4\}, \{o_2, o_3\}, \{o_5\}\}$ and $\mathcal{E}_w = \{\{o_1, o_2\}, \{o_3, o_4\}, \{o_5\}\}$. Then a strong distributed knowledge base $\mathcal{E}_s \wedge \mathcal{E}_t$ is the following partition of U: $\{\{o_1\}, \{o_2\}, \{o_3\}, \{o_4\}, \{o_5\}\}$, and a weak distibuted knowledge base $\mathcal{E}_s \vee \mathcal{E}_t$ is the partition $\{\{o_1, o_2, o_3, o_4\}, \{o_5\}\}$. Notice that $\mathcal{E}_w \wedge (\mathcal{E}_s \vee \mathcal{E}_t) = \mathcal{E}_w$ and $\mathcal{E}_w \wedge \mathcal{E}_s \vee \mathcal{E}_w \wedge \mathcal{E}_t = \mathcal{E}_s$. Hence, the family $\{\mathcal{E}_s, \mathcal{E}_t, \mathcal{E}_w, \mathcal{E}_s \vee \mathcal{E}_t, \mathcal{E}_s \wedge \mathcal{E}_t\}$ is an example of a non-distributive lattice of partitions. $\mathcal{E}_s \wedge \mathcal{E}_t$ is the zero element and $\mathcal{E}_t \vee \mathcal{E}_t$ is the unit element in this lattice.

□

We finish this section with the following remark. Let T be a family of groups of agents such that $\mathcal{E} = \{\mathcal{E}_t\}_{t \in T}$ is a lattice of partitions, where each $\mathcal{E}_t$ is referred to us as a knowledge base of an agent $t \in T$ about the universe U. It might be easily shown that the relation $\leq$ defined on T as follows:

$$s \leq t \text{ if and only if } \mathcal{E}_t \prec \mathcal{E}_t,$$

is an ordering relation on T. Thus $(T, \leq)$ is a poset. Moreover, one can also prove that $sup\{s, t\}$, denoted by $s \vee t$, and $inf\{s, t\}$, denoted by $s \wedge t$, exist in $(T, \leq)$. Namely, we have

$$s \vee t = sup\{s, t\} \text{ if and only if } \mathcal{E}_{s \vee t} = \mathcal{E}_s \wedge \mathcal{E}_t$$

and

$$s \wedge t = inf\{s, t\} \text{ if and only if } \mathcal{E}_{s \wedge t} = \mathcal{E}_s \vee \mathcal{E}_t.$$

Thus we conclude:

Lemma 2.3 $(T, \vee, \wedge)$ *is a lattice with the zero and unit element provided* $\mathcal{E} = \{\mathcal{E}_t\}_{t \in T}$ *is a lattice of partitions.*

$\square$

3 Lower and Upper Approximation

Observe that some concepts may be expressed as the set-theoretical union of certain basic concepts in a knowledge base about U, but they cannot be defined as the union of basic concepts from another knowledge base. Hence, if a concept cannot be covered by basic concepts from a given knowledge base $\mathcal{E}_t$, then the question arises whether it can be "approximately" defined by $\mathcal{E}_t$. In this section we are going to discuss this problem.

Let $\mathcal{E}_t$ be a knowledge base of an agent t about U and let R_t be the equivalence relation determined by $\mathcal{E}_t$. With every concept X, $X \subseteq U$, we associate three sets: $\underline{R}_t(X)$, $\overline{R}_t(X)$ and $B_t(X)$ called a *t-lower approximation of X, a t-upper approximation of X* and *a t-boundary of X*, respectively, where

$$\underline{R}_t(X) = \{[x]_t : [x]_t \subseteq X\},$$

$$\overline{R}_t(X) = \{[x]_t : [x]_t \cap X \neq \emptyset\},$$

and

$$B_t(X) = \overline{R}_t(X) - \underline{R}_t(X).$$

Intuitively speaking, a t-lower approximation of X is the collection of all elements of the universe which can be classified by an agent t with full certainty, as elements of X, using her knowledge base $\mathcal{E}_t$. A t-upper approximation of X is the collection of all objects from the universe U which can be possibly classified, by an agent t, as elements of X, using her knowledge base $\mathcal{E}_t$. Finally, a boundary of X is in a sense an undecidable area of the universe, that is, none of the objects belonging to $B_R(X)$ can be classified with certainty by an agent t into X or $-X$ as far as her knowledge base $\mathcal{E}_t$ is concerned.

We say that a concept X is *t-definable* if $\underline{R}_t(X) = \overline{R}_t(X)$. Clearly, if X is t-defined, then $\underline{R}_t(X) = X$, $\overline{R}_t(X) = X$ and $B_t(X) = \emptyset$. If for $X \subseteq U$, $\underline{R}_t(X) \neq \overline{R}_t(X)$, then X is said to be *t-rough*.

Example 2. Suppose that we have three groups of agents s, t and w and their knowledge base about the universe $U = \{o_1, o_2, o_3, o_4, o_5\}$ is as follows: $\mathcal{E}_s = \{\{o_1, o_2\}, \{o_3\}, \{o_4, o_5\}\}$, $\mathcal{E}_t = \{\{o_1\}, \{o_2, o_3\}, \{o_4\}, \{o_5\}\}$ and $\mathcal{E}_w = \{\{o_1, o_2\}, \{o_3, o_4\}, \{o_5\}\}$. Take as X the set $\{o_1, o_2\}$. Then $\underline{R}_s(X) = \underline{R}_w(X) = X$ and $\underline{R}_t(X) = \{o_1\}$, $\overline{R}_t(X) = \{o_1, o_2, o_3\}$, and $B_t(X) = \{o_2, o_3\}$. Hence X is s- and w-definable, and X is a t-rough set.

□

Now, we list selected properties of lower and upper approximations and the boundary of any concept. Proofs can be found in (Rauszer, to appear).

The first lemma says that any lower approximation behaves as an interior operation in a topological space and any upper approximation has the same properties as a closure operation in a topological space.

In particular we have:

Lemma 3.1 *Let $\mathcal{E}_t$ be a knowledge base of an agent t and let $X \subseteq U$. Then*

1. *$(U, \underline{R}_t)$ is a topological space, where $\underline{R}_t$ is an interior operation on U, i.e., for every $X \subseteq U$ and $Y \subseteq U$*
   - $\underline{R}_t(X) \subseteq X$,
   - $\underline{R}_t(X) \subseteq \underline{R}_t(\underline{R}_t(X))$,
   - $\underline{R}_t(X) \cap \underline{R}_t(Y) = \underline{R}_t(X \cap Y)$,
   - $\underline{R}_t(U) = U$.
2. *$\mathcal{E}_t$ is a subbasis of the topological space $(U, \underline{R}_t)$.*
3. *$\underline{R}_t(X) = -\overline{R}_t(-X)$, $\overline{R}_t(X) = -\underline{R}_t(-X)$.*
4. *$\underline{R}_t(\overline{R}_t(X)) = \overline{R}_t(X)$ $\overline{R}_t(\underline{R}_t(X)) = \underline{R}_t(X)$.*
5. *X is t-definable if and only if $-X$ is t-definable.*
6. *Let X be t-definable. $X \subseteq Y$ if and only if $X \subseteq \underline{R}_t(Y)$.*
7. *Let Y be t-definable. $X \subseteq Y$ if and only if $\overline{R}_t(X) \subseteq Y$.*

□

Lemma 3.2 *Let T be a family of groups of agents, and let for every $t \in T$, $\mathcal{E}_t$ be a knowledge base of t. The following conditions are true:*

1. *$\mathcal{E}_s \prec \mathcal{E}_t$ if and only if $\underline{R}_t(X) \subseteq \underline{R}_s(X)$.*
2. *$\mathcal{E}_s \prec \mathcal{E}_t$ if and only if $\underline{R}_s(\underline{R}_t(X)) = \underline{R}_t(X)$.*
3. *$\mathcal{E}_s \prec \mathcal{E}_t$ if and only if $\overline{R}_s(X) \subseteq \overline{R}_t(X)$.*
4. *$\mathcal{E}_s \prec \mathcal{E}_t$ if and only if $\overline{R}_s(\overline{R}_t(X)) = \overline{R}_t(X)$.*
5. *$\mathcal{E}_s \prec \mathcal{E}_t$ if and only if $B_s(X) \subseteq B_t(X)$.*
6. *$\mathcal{E}_s \prec \mathcal{E}_t$ implies $\underline{R}_t(\underline{R}_s(X)) = \underline{R}_s(\underline{R}_t(X))$.*

□

Lemma 3.3 *Let T be a family of groups of agents such that $\mathcal{E} = \{\mathcal{E}_t\}_{t \in T}$ is a lattice of partitions. For every set $X \subseteq U$ the following holds:*

1. *$\underline{R}_t(X) \cup \underline{R}_s(X) \subseteq \underline{R}_{t \vee s}(X)$.*
2. *$\underline{R}_{s \wedge t}(X) \subseteq \underline{R}_t(X) \cap \underline{R}_s(X)$.*

3. $\underline{R}_t(\underline{R}_s(X)) \subseteq \underline{R}_t(X)$.

4. $\overline{R}_{s\vee t}(X) \subseteq \overline{R}_t(X) \cap \overline{R}_s(X)$.

5. $\overline{R}_t(X) \cup \overline{R}_s(X) \subseteq \overline{R}_{s\wedge t}(X)$.

6. $\overline{R}_s(X) \subseteq \overline{R}_s(\overline{R}_t(X))$.

7. $B_{s\vee t}(X) \subseteq B_s(X) \cap B_t(X)$.

8. $B_s(X) \cup B_t(X) \subseteq B_{s\wedge t}(X)$.

9. $B_t(X) = B_t(-X)$.

10. $\underline{R}_t(B_t(X)) = B_t(X)$.

11. $B_t(X) = \emptyset$ if and only if $\underline{R}_t(X) = X$. □

Let $\mathcal{E}_t$ be a knowledge base of an agent t and let $X \subseteq U$. Recall that a t-lower approximation $\underline{R}_t(X)$ is meant as the set of all objects which for an agent t, according to her knowledge base $\mathcal{E}_t$ have, without any doubt the property given by the concept X. This enables us to interpret a t-lower approximation of X as *knowledge of an agent t about* X. Thus, the set $\underline{R}_t(X)$ might be viewed as the set of all objects which according to the knowledge of an agent t have the property described by the concept X. In other words, the set $\underline{R}_t(X)$ may be treated as the set of all positive examples of X (for an agent t) or the set of all objects which (for an agent t) belong to X. Hence, if an agent t is able to decide, according to her knowledge base $\mathcal{E}_t$, whether a given object x has the property described by the concept X, that is, she knows with certainty whether x belongs to X or to $-X$, then $\underline{R}_t(X) = X$, which means that X is t-defined. In that case the undecidable area about the concept X, that is, the t-boundary of X is empty. If $\underline{R}_t(X) \neq X$, that is, X is t-rough, then the t-lower aproximation of X might be viewed as the set of all objects which are known by an agent t as objects belonging to X. In that case, a t-upper approximation $\overline{R}_t(X) \neq \emptyset$ and as a consequense $B_t(X) \neq \emptyset$, which means that there is at least one object such that the agent t, according to her knowledge base $\mathcal{E}_t$, is not able to justify whether it has the property X or not.

Thus, the equality:

$$\underline{R}_s \underline{R}_t(X) = \underline{R}_t(X).$$

may be read:

an agent s knows what an agent t knows about X.

Thus, immediately from Lemma 2.3 we have

Example 4. Take the information system $\mathcal{S} = (U, \mathbf{A})$ from the previous example and let $X = \{o_2, o_5\}$. Then the b-lower approximation of X is $\underline{ind}(b)(X) = \{o_5\}$, and the b-upper aproximation of X is $\overline{ind}(b)(X) = \{o_2, o_3, o_5\}$. Thus, the set $\{o_2, o_5\}$ is b-rough in $\mathcal{S}$. Notice that the set $\{o_2, o_5\}$ is $\mathbf{A}$-defined in $\mathcal{S} = (U, \mathbf{A})$. □

It turns out that every knowledge base may be represented as an information system, that is, in the form of an attribute-value table.

To this end let $\mathcal{E}_t$ be a knowledge base about U. It is not difficult to construct an information system $\mathcal{S}_t = (U, \mathbf{A}_t)$ such that $\mathcal{E}_t = \mathcal{E}_{\mathbf{A}_t}$. If for some information system $\mathcal{S}_t = (U, \mathbf{A}_t)$, $\mathcal{E}_t = \mathcal{E}_{\mathbf{A}_t}$ then we call $\mathcal{S}_t = (U, \mathbf{A}_t)$ a *knowledge representation system* (*k.r.s.*) for $\mathcal{E}_t$.

Example 5. Suppose that $\mathcal{E}_s = \{\{o_1, o_2\}, \{o_3\}, \{o_4, o_5\}\}$, $\mathcal{E}_t = \{\{o_1\}, \{o_2, o_3\}, \{o_4\}, \{o_5\}\}$, and $\mathcal{E}_w = \{\{o_1\}, \{o_2, o_3, o_4\}, \{o_5\}\}$ are partitions of U.

Notice that each $\mathcal{E}_u$, where $u \in \{s, t, w\}$ may be represented by $\mathcal{S}_u$ depicted below:

S_t:

U	a	b	c
o_1	1	2	3
o_2	0	1	3
o_3	0	1	3
o_4	2	1	2
o_5	1	3	2

S_s:

U	c	d	e
o_1	3	0	2
o_2	3	0	2
o_3	3	1	0
o_4	2	4	1
o_5	2	4	1

S_w:

U	f	g
o_1	1	1
o_2	0	0
o_3	0	0
o_4	0	0
o_5	2	2

Observe that the strong distributed knowledge base

$$\mathcal{E}_{s \vee t \vee w} = \{\{o_1\}, \{o_2\}, \{o_3\}, \{o_4\}, \{o_5\}\}$$

and the weak distributed knowledge base

$$\mathcal{E}_{s \wedge t \wedge w} = \{o_1, o_2, o_3, o_4, o_5\}$$

of $\mathcal{E}_s, \mathcal{E}_t$ and $\mathcal{E}_w$ may be represented by $\mathcal{S}_{s \vee t \vee w}$ and $\mathcal{S}_{s \wedge t \wedge w}$, respectively, as follows:

$S_{s \vee t \vee w}$:

U	a	b	c	d	e	f	g
o_1	1	2	3	0	2	1	1
o_2	0	1	3	0	2	0	0
o_3	0	1	3	1	0	0	0
o_4	2	1	2	4	1	0	0
o_5	1	3	2	4	1	2	2

and

$S_{s \wedge t \wedge w}$:

U	k
o_1	3
o_2	3
o_3	3
o_4	3
o_5	3

□

From now on the notion knowledge representation system will be used synonymous with information system.

Finally, it seems worthwhile to mention that for the given knowledge representation system $\mathcal{S} = (U, \mathbf{A})$ and $X \subseteq U$, there are several efficient methods for computing sets $\underline{\mathbf{A}}(X)$, $\overline{\mathbf{A}}(X)$ and the boundary of X. One of them is presented in [SR] and says that the upper bound for the time complexity for computing $\underline{\mathbf{A}}(X)$, $\overline{\mathbf{A}}(X)$ and the boundary of X is of order n^2, where n is the number of objects in U.

4 Rough Logic

4.1 Syntax

In this section we are going to define a deductive system which may be served as a logical tool in the investigations of multi-agents systems.

We call this logic *rough logic for multi-agents systems* and denote by R-logic, where R refers to rough.

Let T be a family of groups of agents which perceive the same reality U. Moreover, assume that if $s, t \in T$, then the group st has strong and weak distributed knowledge about U.

Let $\mathbf{A}$ be a finite set of attributes such that $2^{|T|} \leq |\mathbf{A}|$. We associate with every $a \in \mathbf{A}$ a non-empty set V_a, such that $2 \leq |V_a|$ and let $V = \bigcup_{a \in \mathbf{A}} V_a$. Every set V_a may be treated as a domain of an attribute $a \in \mathbf{A}$.

Now, we associate with $\mathbf{A}$ and T a language $\mathcal{L}_{\mathbf{A},T}$ called *the formal language of R-logic*. All elements of $\mathbf{A}$, T and V are treated as constants of $\mathcal{L}_{\mathbf{A},T}$. Elements of $\mathbf{A}$ are called *attribute constants* and denoted by $a, b, c, \ldots$, elements of T are named *agent constants* and denoted $s, t, \ldots$, and elements of V are called *attribute-value constants* and denoted by $v, u \ldots$.

The language $\mathcal{L}_{\mathbf{A},T}$ consists of two levels. The expressions of these levels are called *1-st kind formulae* and *2-nd kind formulae*, respectively. Intuitively, 1-st kind formulae describe relations between knowledge bases understood as a partition of the universe U, whereas 2-nd kind formulae express certain facts about sets of objects of U or approximations of these sets.

To give a formal definition of the sets of formulae, we define first terms of $\mathcal{L}_{\mathbf{A},T}$.

Terms are built up from agent constants, two constants $\mathbf{0}$ and $\mathbf{1}$, and operations: $\vee$ and $\wedge$. More precisely, the *set of all terms* is defined to be the least set $\mathcal{T}$ with the following three properties:

- $\mathbf{0}$ and $\mathbf{1}$ are in $\mathcal{T}$.
- all agent constants are in $\mathcal{T}$,
- $s \vee t$, $s \wedge t$ are in $\mathcal{T}$, whenever s, t are terms.

Formulae of the 1-st kind are built up from terms and a unary operation $\Rightarrow$. In particular, the set F_1 of all *formulae of the 1-st kind* is the smallest set such that

- If $s, t \in \mathcal{T}$, then $s \Rightarrow t \in F_1$.

Intuitively, 1-st kind formulae express a hierarchy between agents, that is determined by their knowledge base. The formula $s \Rightarrow t$ may be interpreted in the following way: a sharpness of recognizing features of objects by an agent s is weaker than that of an agent t.

The set F_2 of all *formulae of the 2-nd kind* is the smallest set containing all atomic formulae which are of the form (a, v), where $a \in \mathbf{A}$ and $v \in V$; it is closed with respect to the propositional connectives $\vee$, $\wedge$, $\rightarrow$, $\leftrightarrow$, $\neg$ and a family $\{I_t\}_{t \in T}$ of modal connectives, that is, the following conditions are satisfied for F_2:

- $(a, v) \in F_2$, for every $a \in \mathbf{A}$ and $v \in V$.
- $\phi \vee \psi$, $\phi \wedge \psi$, $\phi \rightarrow \psi$, $\phi \leftrightarrow \psi$, and $\neg \phi$ are in F_2, whenever ϕ and ψ are in F_2.
- For every $t \in \mathcal{T}$, $I_t \phi \in F_2$, whenever ϕ is in F_2.

The axioms for the R-logic consist of three groups: one for 1-st kind formulae, one for 2-nd kind formulae, and one separate group. Specific axioms express characteristic properties of information systems.

The axioms for 1-st kind formulae are:

(t_1)	$t \Rightarrow t$,	
(t_2)	$s \Rightarrow s \vee t$	$t \Rightarrow s \vee t$,
(t_3)	$s \wedge t \Rightarrow s$	$s \wedge t \Rightarrow t$,

where s and t are any terms.

Now we list axioms for 2-nd kind formulae:

(c)	All axioms for classical logic,
(i_1)	$I_t \phi \rightarrow \phi$,
(i_2)	$I_t \phi \rightarrow I_t I_t \phi$,
(i_3)	$I_t(\phi \wedge \psi) \leftrightarrow (I_t \phi \wedge I_t \psi)$,
(i_4)	$I_t(\phi \vee -\phi)$,

where ϕ is any formula of the second kind, and I_t is any modal operator.

The specific axioms of R-logic are as follows:

1. $(a, v) \wedge (a, u) \leftrightarrow \perp$ for any $a \in \mathbf{A}$, $v, u \in V_a$ and $v \neq u$.
2. $\bigvee_{v \in V_a}(a, v) \leftrightarrow \top$, for every $a \in \mathbf{A}$,
3. $\neg(a, v) \leftrightarrow \bigvee \{(a, u) : u \in V_a, u \neq v\}$, for every $a \in \mathbf{A}$,

where $\phi \vee -\phi =_{df} \top$, $\phi \wedge -\phi =_{df} \perp$ and $\bigvee \phi$ means a finite disjunction.

Specific axioms characterize our notion of knowledge representation system. Observe that the first axiom follows from the assumption that each object can have exactly one value for each attribute. Axiom (2) follows from the assumption that each object in any knowledge representation system $\mathcal{S}$ has a value with respect to every attribute. Hence, the description of objects is complete up to a given set of attributes. In other words, for every $a \in \mathbf{A}$ and every object x, the entry in the row x and the column a (in $\mathcal{S}$ viewed as a table) is nonempty.

The third axiom allows us to figure out negation in such a way that instead of saying that an object does not possess a given property we can say that it has one of the remaining properties. For example, instead of saying that something is not blue we can say it is either red or green or yellow, etc.

We say that a formula ϕ is *derivable in R-logic from a set of formulae* F, denoted by $F \vdash \phi$, provided it can be concluded from F by means of the above axioms and the following rules: modus ponens, and for every term s, t and w

$$\frac{\phi}{I_s \phi},$$

$$\frac{s \Rightarrow t}{I_s \phi \rightarrow I_t \phi} \; ,$$

$$\frac{s \Rightarrow w \quad t \Rightarrow w}{s \vee t \Rightarrow w} \qquad \frac{w \Rightarrow s \quad w \Rightarrow t}{w \Rightarrow s \wedge t} \; ,$$

$$\frac{s \Rightarrow t \quad t \Rightarrow w}{s \Rightarrow w} \; .$$

If ϕ is derivable in R-logic from the empty set, then we write $\vdash \phi$ and say ϕ *is derivable.* Clearly, all classical tautologies are derivable. Also $\vdash \top$ and $\nvdash \bot$.

It is easy to prove

Lemma 4.1 *The following are derivable formulae in R-logic:*

1. $(I_s \phi \vee I_t \phi) \rightarrow I_{s \vee t} \phi$,
2. $I_{s \wedge t} \phi \rightarrow (I_s \phi \wedge I_t \phi)$,
3. $I_s I_t \phi \rightarrow I_s \phi$,
4. $I_s I_t \phi \rightarrow I_t \phi$. □

In the standard way we may prove the Deduction Theorem:

Theorem 4.2 *Let F be a set of formulae of the 2-nd kind. For every formula ϕ and ψ of the 2-nd kind and every modal operator I_s,*

$$F \vdash I_s \phi \rightarrow \psi \text{ if and only if } F \cup \{\phi\} \vdash \psi.$$

□

Consider now the set of all terms T as an abstract algebra $(T, \vee, \wedge, 0, 1)$. Put

$$s \sim t \text{ if and only if } \vdash s \Rightarrow t \text{ and } \vdash t \Rightarrow s.$$

One can prove that $\sim$ is a congruence relation with respect to $\vee$ and $\wedge$. The algebra $(T/\sim, \vee, \wedge, 0, 1)$ will be called the *algebra of terms of R-logic.* For every term t, $\|t\|$ denotes an element in the algebra of terms.

It can be proved:

Lemma 4.3 *The algebra of terms is a lattice. Moreover,*

1. $\|s \vee t\| = \|s\| \vee \|t\|$,

2. $\|s \wedge t\| = \|s\| \wedge \|t\|$, *where $\vee$ and $\wedge$ on the left hand side of the equality are logical connectives and $\vee$ and $\wedge$ on the right hand side of the equality are lattice operations.*

3. *The relation $\leq$ is defined as follows: $\|s\| \leq \|t\|$ if and only if $\vdash s \Rightarrow t$ is an ordering relation on $T/\sim$, where $s \Rightarrow t$ is a formula of the 1-st kind from $\mathcal{L}_{A,T}$.* □

Consider the set of all formulae F_2 of the 2-nd kind as an abstract algebra, that is, as an algebra

$$(F_2, \vee, \wedge, \rightarrow, \neg, \{I_t\}_{t \in T})$$

with binary operations $\vee, \wedge, \rightarrow$, unary operation $\neg$, and modal operators I_t, where $t \in T$.

The relation $\approx$ is defined in F as follows:

$$\phi \approx \psi \text{ if and only if } \vdash \phi \leftrightarrow \psi.$$

The relation $\approx$ is a congruence with respect to the operations $\vee, \wedge, \rightarrow, \neg$ and the modal operators I_t, where t is a term. Thus the set $F_2/_\approx$ can be conceived as an abstract algebra $\mathcal{A} = (F_2/_\approx, \vee, \wedge, \rightarrow, \neg, \{I_t\}_{t \in T})$, called the *Lindenbaum algebra of R-logic*. Let for every formula ϕ, $\|\phi\|$ denote an element of $F_2/_\approx$. In the standard way one can prove the following theorem:

Theorem 4.4 *For every modal operator I_t, the I_t-reduct of the Lindenbaum algebra of R-logic $\mathcal{A}$, that is, the algebra $(F_2/_\approx, \vee, \wedge, \rightarrow, \neg, I_t)$ is a topological Boolean algebra.*

Moreover,

1. $\|\phi\| = 1$ *if and only if ϕ is derivable, where* $1 = \|\top\|$ *is the unit element in* $\mathcal{A}$.
2. $\|\phi \circ \psi\| = \|\phi\| \circ \|\psi\|$,
3. $\| \circ \phi\| = \circ \|\phi\|$,

where $\circ$ on the left hand side of the equality means a logical connective and $\circ$ on the right hand side of the equality means one of the operations in the Lindenbaum algebra of R-logic.

$\square$

4.2 Semantics

Intuitively speaking, formulae of the 1-st kind are meant to describe a hierarchy between groups of agents and formulae of the 2-nd kind are meant as descriptions of subsets of objects obeying properties expressed by these formulae. For instance, a natural interpretation of an atomic formula (a, v) is the set of all objects having value v for the attribute a. Hence, a natural interpretation of a formula of the form $I_t(a, v)$ is a t-lower approximation of the set of all objects having the property v for the attribute a.

Let $\mathcal{L}_{\mathbf{A}, T}$ be the language of R-logic described above determined by $\mathbf{A}$ and T. Let U be a non-empty set such that $|U| \geq 2^T$. Let for every term t, $\mathcal{E}_t$ be a partition of U conceived as a knowledge base of a group of agents t and let $\mathcal{E} = \{\mathcal{E}_t\}_{t \in T}$.

Lemma 4.5 . *The family of all partitions determined by terms, that is, the family $\mathcal{E} = \{\mathcal{E}_t\}_{t \in T}$ is a lattice of partitions.*

Proof: By Lemma 5.3 we know that the algebra of terms of R-logic is a lattice. Put, for every $s, t \in T$,

$$\mathcal{E}_t \prec \mathcal{E}_s \text{ if and only if } ||s|| \leq ||t||,$$

where the relation $\leq$ is defined as in Lemma 5.3

It is not difficult to show that the relation $\prec$ is an ordering relation on $\mathcal{E}$. To prove that $\mathcal{E}$ is a lattice it suffices to assert that for all $\mathcal{E}_s, \mathcal{E}_t$, the infimum and the supremum exist in $\mathcal{E}$. We will only show that $inf\{\mathcal{E}_s, \mathcal{E}_t\}$ exists in $\mathcal{E}$ (for the supremum the proof is similar). Notice, that for any terms s, t, $t \vee s$ is also a term, hence, $\mathcal{E}_{s \vee t} \in \mathcal{E}$. We prove now, that $\mathcal{E}_{s \vee t}$ is upper lower bound of $\mathcal{E}_s$ and $\mathcal{E}_t$ in $\mathcal{E}$. By Lemma 5.3 (3), axiom (t_2) and the definition of $\prec$ we have that $\mathcal{E}_{s \vee t} \prec \mathcal{E}_s$ and $\mathcal{E}_{s \vee t} \prec \mathcal{E}_t$. Now, let $\mathcal{E}_z \prec \mathcal{E}_s$ and $\mathcal{E}_z \prec \mathcal{E}_t$. Then $\vdash x \Rightarrow z$ and $\vdash t \Rightarrow z$, and by the corresponding inference rule we have that $\mathcal{E}_z \prec \mathcal{E}_{s \vee t}$, which was to be shown.

□

Now we are going to define semantics for R-logic. Let $\mathcal{L}_{\mathbf{A},T}$ be the formal language of R-logic defined in the previous subsection. Assume that a universe of discourse U, $|U| \geq 2^T$, is given and let for every $t \in T$, $\mathcal{E}_t$ be a partition of U. Let $\mathcal{S} = (U, \mathbf{A})$ be an information system such that $|U| \geq 2^T$, $|A| \geq 2^T$ and a domain of each attribute contains at least two elements, that is, $|V_a| \geq 2$ for every $a \in \mathbf{A}$. $\mathcal{S} = (U, \mathbf{A})$ is said to be *an information system associated with* $\mathcal{L}_{\mathbf{A},T}$ provided that for every $t \in T$ there is a subset $\mathbf{A}_t$ of $\mathbf{A}$ such that $\mathcal{E}_t = \mathcal{E}_{\mathbf{A}_t}$.

Observe, that for a given language $\mathcal{L}_{\mathbf{A},T}$, an information system associated with $\mathcal{L}_{\mathbf{A},T}$ may be constructed as follows: By the assumption, the powerset of attributes $\mathbf{A}$ of $\mathcal{S} = (U, \mathbf{A})$ is greater than or equal to 2^T, and the power of each attribute domain is at least two. Now, for every $\mathcal{E}_t$, where t is an agent constant, take as $\mathbf{A}_t$ all mappings $a_t : U \rightarrow V_{a_t}$, $a_t \in \mathbf{A}$, such that for every $[x]_t \in \mathcal{E}_t$, there is a $v \in V_{a_t}$ for which $\{o \in U : a_t(o) = v\} = [x]_t$. Clearly, for such defined $\mathbf{A}_t$, $\mathcal{E}_t = \mathcal{E}_{\mathbf{A}_t}$.

If for all $\mathcal{E}_t$, where t is an agent constant, $\mathcal{E}_{\mathbf{A}_t}$ is constructed, then it is also constructed for $\mathcal{E}_{s \vee t}$, where s, t are agent constants. Indeed, if s, t are agent constants, then by Lemma 5.5 the partition $\mathcal{E}_{s \vee t}$ associated to term $s \vee t$ is equal to $\mathcal{E}_s \wedge \mathcal{E}_t$. Hence, as $\mathbf{A}_{s \vee t}$ take $\mathbf{A}_s \cup \mathbf{A}_t$.

Suppose we have defined $\mathbf{A}_z$ for all agent constants z. Thus, $\mathbf{A}_z$ is also defined for all terms z of the form $s \vee t$, where s, t are agent constants. If $\mathcal{E}_{s \wedge t}$ is different from all $\mathcal{E}_{\mathbf{A}_i}$ which have been constructed, then take as $\mathbf{A}_{s \wedge t}$ the mapping $a_{s \wedge t}$, such that for every $[x]_{s \wedge t} \in \mathcal{E}_{s \wedge t}$ there is an $v \in V_{s \wedge t}$ such that $\{o \in U : a_{s \wedge t}(o) = v\} = [x]_{s \wedge t}$, where $a_{s \wedge t}$ is the first unused attribute in $\mathbf{A}$.

Finally, as the required information system take $(U, \bigcup_{t \in T} \mathbf{A}_t)$.

Now, consider the pair $(\mathcal{S}, \mathcal{E})$, where $\mathcal{S} = (U, \mathbf{A})$ is an information system associated with $\mathcal{L}_{\mathbf{A},T}$ and $\mathcal{E} = \{\mathcal{E}_t\}_{t \in T}$ is the family of all partitions determined by terms. Recall, that $\mathcal{E}$ is a lattice of partitions.

We say that 1-st kind formula of the form $s \Rightarrow t$ is *true in* $(\mathcal{S}, \mathcal{E})$, denoted by $\models s \Rightarrow t$, if $\mathcal{E}_t \prec \mathcal{E}_s$ holds in the lattice $\mathcal{E}$.

Let ϕ be a formula of the 2-st kind from $\mathcal{L}_{\mathbf{A},T}$. We say that an object $x \in U$ *satisfies a formula* ϕ in $(\mathcal{S}, \mathcal{E})$, denoted by $x \models_{(\mathcal{S},\mathcal{E})} \phi$ (or short: $x \models \phi$ if the information system $\mathcal{S}$ follows from the context) if and only if the following conditions are satisfied:

1. $x \models (a, v)$ if and only if $a(x) = v$,
2. $x \models \neg\phi$ if and only if $x \not\models \phi$,
3. $x \models \phi \vee \psi$ if and only if $x \models \phi$ or $x \models \psi$,
4. $x \models \phi \wedge \psi$ if and only if $x \models \phi$ and $x \models \psi$,
5. $x \models \phi \rightarrow \psi$ if and only if $x \models \neg\phi \vee \psi$,
6. $x \models \phi \leftrightarrow \psi$ if and only if $x \models \phi \rightarrow \psi$ and $x \models \psi \rightarrow \phi$,
7. For every modal operator I_t, $x \models I_t\phi$ if and only if for all $x_i \in U$ if $x_i \in [x]_t$ then $x_i \models \phi$.

Let $\mathcal{S} = (U, \mathbf{A})$ be an information system associated with $\mathcal{L}_{\mathbf{A},T}$. For any formula ϕ of the 2-nd kind the set $|\phi|_{\mathcal{S}}$, defined by

$$|\phi|_{\mathcal{S}} = \{x \in U : x \models \phi\}$$

will be called a *meaning of the formula* ϕ in $\mathcal{S}$. As before we will omit the subscript $\mathcal{S}$, if the information system $\mathcal{S}$ follows from the context.

Notice, (cf. Lemma 3.3 (Rauszer 1992a)) that for every meaning $|\phi|_{(U,\mathbf{A})}$ of a satisfiable formula ϕ which is a conjunction of atomic formulae of the form (a, v), $a \in \mathbf{A}$, $v \in V_a$ there is a basic concept $[x]$ such that $|\phi|_{(U,\mathbf{A})} = [x]$, and vice versa, for every basic concept $[x]$ there is a formula ϕ such that $[x] = |\phi|_{(U,\mathbf{A})}$.

Now, we list some basic properties of the meaning of formulae. The simple proof of the lemma given below is left to the reader.

Lemma 4.6 *For every atomic formula (a, v) and any formulae ϕ and ψ of the 2-nd kind the following conditions are true:*

1. $|(a, v)| = \{x \in U : a(x) = v\}$.
2. $|\neg\phi| = -|\phi|$.
3. $|\phi \vee \psi| = |\phi| \cup |\psi|$.
4. $|\phi \wedge \psi| = |\phi| \cap |\psi|$.
5. $|\phi \rightarrow \psi| = -|\phi| \cup |\psi|$.
6. $|\phi \leftrightarrow \psi| = |\phi \rightarrow \psi| \cap |\psi \rightarrow \phi|$.
7. $|I_t\phi| = \bigcup_{[x]_t \subseteq |\phi|}[x]_t$, for every $t \in \mathcal{T}$. $\qquad\qquad\square$

Let $\mathcal{S} = (U, \mathbf{A})$ be an information system associated to $\mathcal{L}_{\mathbf{A},T}$. We say that a formula ϕ of the 2-nd kind is *valid in* $(\mathcal{S}, \mathcal{E})$, denoted by $\models \phi$, if $|\phi|_{\mathcal{S}} = U$ for any meaning of ϕ. If any formula ϕ (of the 1-st or of the 2-nd kind) is valid in $(\mathcal{S}, \mathcal{E})$, then we call the pair $(\mathcal{S}, \mathcal{E})$ a *model for* ϕ. If $(\mathcal{S}, \mathcal{E})$ is a model for every formula from a set F, then we say that the pair $\mathcal{S} = (U, \mathbf{A})$ is a *model for* F. Finally, we say that F *implies* ϕ, denoted by $F \models \phi$, if from the fact that $(\mathcal{S}, \mathcal{E})$ is a model of F follows that $(\mathcal{S}, \mathcal{E})$ is a model of ϕ.

The next theorem shows that our axiomatization is sound.

Theorem 4.7 *(soundness) Let F be a set of formulae. If $F \vdash \phi$ then $F \models \phi$.*

$\square$

Suppose now, an information system $\mathcal{S} = (U, \mathbf{A})$ associated with $\mathcal{L}_{\mathbf{A},T}$ is given and let for every term t, $\mathcal{E}_t$ be a corresponding partition of U. Recall that the family $\mathcal{E} = \{\mathcal{E}_t\}_{t \in T}$ is a lattice of partitions.

Lemma 4.8 *There is an isomorphism of the algebra of terms of R-logic on the lattice of partition of $\mathcal{E}$.*
Moreover,

$$||s|| \leq ||t|| \ \text{if and only if} \ \mathcal{E}_t \prec \mathcal{E}_s.$$

Proof: It is easy to show that the mapping h such that for every $t \in T$, $h(||t||) = \mathcal{E}_t$ is the required isomorphism. Notice only, that $h(||s \vee t||) = \mathcal{E}_{s \vee t} = \mathcal{E}_s \wedge \mathcal{E}_t$. $\square$

Let $\mathcal{S} = (U, \mathbf{A})$ be an information system associated with $\mathcal{L}_{\mathbf{A},T}$. Consider the following algebra $\mathcal{P}(U) = (\mathbf{P}(U)/_{=}, \cup, \cap, \rightarrow, -, \{\underline{\mathbf{A}}_t\}_{t \in T})$, where $\mathbf{P}(U)$ is the family of all concepts of U, and for any subsets X, Y of U, $X \rightarrow Y$ means the set $-X \cup Y$, and for every $t \in T$ and $X \subseteq U$, $\underline{\mathbf{A}}_t(X)$ is the $\mathbf{A}_t$-lower approximation of X in $\mathcal{S}$, $\mathbf{A}_t \subseteq \mathbf{A}$. For simplicity, we will denote elements of $\mathcal{P}(U)$ in the same way as subsets of U.

Notice, that every $\underline{\mathbf{A}}_t$-reduct of the algebra $\mathcal{P}(U)$ is a topological Boolean algebra. The unit element $\mathbf{1}$ of $\mathcal{P}(U)$ is the equivalence class $\{X : X = U\}$. For instance, the meaning of any valid formula belongs to $\mathbf{1}$. Indeed, if ϕ is a formula of the 2-nd kind valid in $\mathcal{S}$, then $|\phi|_\mathcal{S} = \{x : x \models \phi\} = U$.

Observe also that

$$|I_t \phi|_\mathcal{S} = \underline{\mathbf{A}}_t |\phi|_\mathcal{S}.$$

Indeed, if $\mathcal{S} = (U, \mathbf{A})$ is an information system associated to $\mathcal{L}_{\mathbf{A},T}$, then for every partition $\mathcal{E}_t$, $t \in T$ there is a subset $\mathbf{A}_t$ of $\mathbf{A}$ such that $\mathcal{E}_t = \mathcal{E}_{\mathbf{A}_t}$. Moreover, for every basic concept $[x]_{\mathbf{A}_t}$ there is a formula ϕ such that $|\phi|_\mathcal{S} = [x]_{\mathbf{A}_t}$. Hence by Lemma 5.6 (7) we conclude the required equality.

Denote by ∇ the set of all meanings of formulae which are provable, that is,

$$\nabla = \{|\phi|_\mathcal{S} : \vdash \phi\}.$$

Lemma 4.9 *For every term t, ∇ is an $\underline{\mathbf{A}}_t$-filter in $\mathcal{P}(U)$.*

Proof: Clearly, ∇ is closed with respect to $\cap$. Notice, that $\mathbf{1}$ belongs to ∇ as for any formula ϕ, $\vdash \phi \vee -\phi$ and $|\phi \vee -\phi|_\mathcal{S} = \mathbf{1}$. Now, let $|\phi|_\mathcal{S} \in \nabla$ and let $|\phi|_\mathcal{S} \subseteq |\psi|_\mathcal{S}$. Then $|\phi \rightarrow \psi|_\mathcal{S} = \mathbf{1}$ and therefore $|\phi| \rightarrow |\psi| \in \nabla$. Hence, $\vdash \psi$, which proves that $|\psi|_\mathcal{S} \in \nabla$. We claim that for every $\underline{\mathbf{A}}_t$, where t is a term, $\underline{\mathbf{A}}_t |\phi|_\mathcal{S} \in \nabla$ provided $|\phi|_\mathcal{S} \in \nabla$ If $|\phi|_\mathcal{S} \in \nabla$, then $\vdash \phi$ and by the necessitation rule, for every modal operator I_t we have $\vdash I_t \phi$. Hence, $|I_t \phi|_\mathcal{S} = \underline{\mathbf{A}}_t |\phi|_\mathcal{S}$ and we infer that $\underline{\mathbf{A}}_t|\phi|_\mathcal{S} \in \nabla$, which ends the proof that ∇ is $\underline{\mathbf{A}}_t$-filter in the algebra $\mathcal{P}(U)$.

$\square$

We prove the following lemma:

Lemma 4.10 *There is one-to-one monomorphism of the Lindenbaum algebra of R-logic $\mathcal{A}$ into $\mathcal{P}(U)$.*

Proof: Let h be a mapping from $F_2/_{\approx}$ into $\mathbf{P}(U)/_=$ such that $h(||\phi||) = |\phi|_\mathcal{S}$, where $|\phi|_\mathcal{S}$ is the meaning of ϕ in $\mathcal{S}$ and ϕ is a formula of the 2-nd kind. Clearly, h is a monomorphism of $\mathcal{A}$ into $\mathcal{P}(U)$. To show that h is one-to-one suppose that for some formulae ϕ and ψ, $||\phi|| \neq ||\psi||$. Then either $\nvdash \phi \rightarrow \psi$ or $\nvdash \psi \rightarrow \phi$. If $\nvdash \phi \rightarrow \psi$ then $|\phi \rightarrow \psi|_\mathcal{S} \notin \nabla$. Therefore, $|\phi|_\mathcal{S} \nsubseteq |\psi|_\mathcal{S}$. Thus $|\phi|_\mathcal{S} \neq |\psi|_\mathcal{S}$. In the latter case the proof is analogous.

$\square$

Now, we prove that our axiomatization is complete.

Theorem 4.11 *(completeness) Let F be a set of formulae and let ϕ be a formula of $\mathcal{L}_{\mathbf{A},T}$. If $F \models \phi$ then $F \vdash \phi$.*

Proof : Let ϕ be a formula of the 1-st kind. Suppose that ϕ is of the form $s \Rightarrow t$. Let $(\mathcal{S}, \mathcal{E})$ be a model for F. Recall that the family $\mathcal{E} = \{\mathcal{E}_t\}_{t \in T}$ is a lattice of partitions. By the assumption, $s \Rightarrow t$ is true in $(\mathcal{S}, \mathcal{E})$, and we conclude that $\mathcal{E}_t \prec \mathcal{E}_s$. Suppose now, that $F \nvdash s \Rightarrow t$. Then $\nvdash s \Rightarrow t$ and by Lemma 5.3 we infer that the relation $||s|| \leq ||t||$ does not hold in the algebra of terms. This proves, by Lemma 5.8, that $\mathcal{E}_t \nprec \mathcal{E}_s$, is a contradiction.

Assume now, that ϕ is a formula of the 2-nd kind and let $F \nvdash \phi$. We show that there is a model for F which is not a model for ϕ. By the assumption $\nvdash \phi$ and by Theorem 5.4 $||\phi|| \neq 1$, where $1 = ||T||$ is the unit element in the Lindenbaum algebra of R-logic $\mathcal{A}$. Let $(\mathcal{S}, \mathcal{E})$ be a model for F and let h be a monomorhpism from $\mathcal{A}$ into $\mathcal{P}(U)$ defined as in Theorem 5.10, that is, $h(||\phi||) = |\phi|_\mathcal{S}$. Clearly, $|\phi|_\mathcal{S} \notin \nabla$, where ∇ is the filter defined above. Thus, because of h is one-to-one we infer that $|\phi|_\mathcal{S} \neq U$, the unit element in the algebra $\mathcal{P}(U)$, which proves that $(\mathcal{S}, \mathcal{E})$ is not a model for ϕ.

$\square$

For every term t define now new modal connectives C_t and Br_t as follows: for any formula of the 2-nd kind ϕ put:

$$C_t\phi \equiv \neg I_t \neg \phi$$

and

$$Br_t\phi \equiv C_t\phi \wedge \neg I_t\phi.$$

It is easy to check that

$$|C_t\phi|_\mathcal{S} = \overline{\mathbf{A}}_t(|\phi|_\mathcal{S}) ,$$

where C_t is the unary connective defined above, and $\overline{\mathbf{A}}_t$ is the upper approximation determined by the relation $ind(\mathbf{A}_t)$ in the information system $\mathcal{S} = (U, \mathbf{A})$ associated with $\mathcal{L}_{\mathbf{A},T}$.

Moreover,

$$|Br_t \phi|_{\mathcal{S}} = B_t(|\phi|_{\mathcal{S}}),$$

where $B_t(|\phi|_{\mathcal{S}})$ means the t-boundary of $|\phi|_s$ in $\mathcal{S}$ determined by $ind(\mathbf{A}_t)$.

Theorem 4.12 Let $\mathcal{S} = (U, \mathbf{A})$ be an information system associated with $\mathcal{L}_{\mathbf{A},T}$ and let $\mathcal{E} = \{\mathcal{E}_t\}_{t \in T}$ be a lattice of partitions, where each $\mathcal{E}_t$ is a partition of U. The following conditions are equivalent:

1. $X \subseteq U$ is t-definable in $\mathcal{S}$.
2. A formula of the form $I_t \phi \leftrightarrow \phi$ is valid in $(\mathcal{S}, \mathcal{E})$, where the meaning of ϕ is X, that is, $|\phi|_{\mathcal{S}} = X$.
3. $Br_t \phi$ is false, where ϕ is as before.
4. $|I_t \phi|_{\mathcal{S}} = X$.

Proof: The proof is very simple. We show only that (1) implies (2). If X is t-definable, then $\underline{\mathbf{A}}_t(X) = X$, and therefore $X = \bigcup_{[x]_B \subseteq X} [x]_B$. Hence, there is a formula ϕ such that $|\phi|_s t = X$. Notice, $|\phi \to I_t \phi|_{\mathcal{S}} = -|\phi|_{\mathcal{S}} \cup |I_t \phi|_{\mathcal{S}} = -X \cup \underline{\mathbf{A}}_t X = U$, which together with axiom (i_1) proves that a formula of the form $I_t \phi \leftrightarrow \phi$ is true in $(\mathcal{S}, \mathcal{E})$.

□

Finally we have

Theorem 4.13 A pair $(\mathcal{S}, \mathcal{E})$ is a model for a formula ϕ if and only if there is a subset $\mathbf{A}_t$ of $\mathbf{A}$ such that the meaning of ϕ in the information system $(U, \mathbf{A}_t)$ is equal to U.

□

5 What an Agent Knows about the Knowledge of Another Agent

We might be interested in investigating whether knowledge $\mathcal{E}_s$ can be expressed in terms of knowledge $\mathcal{E}_t$. In other words, we want to know whether properties of objects expressed in terms of attributes $\mathbf{A}_s$ can be expressed in terms of attributes $\mathbf{A}_t$.

Let us start with some definitions:

We say that a *set of attributes* $\mathbf{A}_t$ *depends on a set of attributes* $\mathbf{A}_s$ in an information system $\mathcal{S} = (U, \mathbf{A})$, abbreviated by $\mathbf{A}_s \to \mathbf{A}_t$, if objects which are identified by $\mathbf{A}_s$ are also identified by $\mathbf{A}_t$. In other words,

$$\mathbf{A}_s \to \mathbf{A}_t \text{ if and only if } ind(\mathbf{A}_s) \subseteq ind(\mathbf{A}_t).$$

Let $\mathcal{L}_{\mathbf{A},T}$ be a formal language of R-logic and let $(\mathcal{S}, \mathcal{E})$ be a model for $\mathcal{L}_{\mathbf{A},T}$. For any $\mathbf{A}_s, \mathbf{A}_t \subseteq \mathbf{A}$ by the st-rule we mean an implication of the form:

$$(a_1, v_1) \wedge \ldots \wedge (a_n, v_n) \rightarrow (b_1, u_1) \wedge \ldots \wedge (b_m, u_m),$$

which is satisfiable by at least one object, where $\mathbf{A}_s = \{a_1, \ldots, a_n\}$ and $\mathbf{A}_t = \{b_1, \ldots, b_m\}$.

Any information system $(U, \mathbf{A}_s \cup \mathbf{A}_t)$ is said to be *consistent*, provided $\mathbf{A}_s \rightarrow \mathbf{A}_t$ holds in $(U, \mathbf{A}_s \cup \mathbf{A}_t)$.

The next theorem follows from results of previous sections:

Theorem 5.1 *Let $\mathcal{S}_{st} = (U, \mathbf{A}_s \cup \mathbf{A}_t)$ be an information system. Then the following conditions are equivalent:*

1. *An agent s knows what an agent t knows about the universe U,*
2. *An information system $\mathcal{S}_{st}$ is consistent,*
3. *The dependency $\mathbf{A}_s \rightarrow \mathbf{A}_t$ holds in $\mathcal{S}$,*
4. *Each st-rule is valid in $\mathcal{S}_{st}$,*
5. $\underline{\mathbf{A}}_s(\underline{\mathbf{A}}_t(X)) = \underline{\mathbf{A}}_t(X)$,
6. *For every $X \subseteq U$, $\underline{\mathbf{A}}_t(X) \subseteq \underline{\mathbf{A}}_s(X)$, $\overline{\mathbf{A}}_s(X) \subseteq \overline{\mathbf{A}}_t(X)$, $B_s(X) \subseteq B_t(X)$,*
7. $\underline{\mathbf{A}}_s([x_1]_t) \cup \ldots \cup \underline{\mathbf{A}}_s([x_k]_t) = U$, *where $\mathcal{E}_{\mathbf{A}_t} = \{[x_1]_t, \ldots, [x_k]_t\}$,*
8. $\mathcal{E}_s \prec \mathcal{E}_t$,
9. *For every $i \leq k$, $\vdash I_s \phi_i \leftrightarrow \phi_i$, where $|\phi_i|_t = [x_i]_t$, and $[x_i]_t$ is a basic concept of an agent t,*
10. $\vdash I_s I_t \phi \leftrightarrow I_t \phi$, *for any formula ϕ.*

Proof: By Lemma 3.4 (1) is equivalent to (5) and (8). Clearly (2) and (3) are equivalent, as well as, (3), (6) and (8). According to the completeness theorem (9) and (8) are equivalent. (5) implies (10) and (10) implies (9).

Now, we show that (7) and (9) are equivalent.

Assume (7). Then for every $i \leq k$, $\underline{\mathbf{A}}_s([x_i]_t) = [x_i]_t$. Otherwise, there is an object o, such that $o \in [x_i]_t$ and $o \notin \underline{\mathbf{A}}_s([x_i]_t)$. Then for some $[x_j]_t$, $i \neq j$ $o \in \underline{\mathbf{A}}_s([x_j]_t) \subseteq [x_j]_t$, and therefore $o \in [x_j]_t$, a contradiction. Thus by the completeness theorem (7) and (9) are equivalent.

We have now shown that all conditions except (4) are equivalent.

Observe, that (4) is equivalent to (8). Indeed, suppose (4). It suffices to prove that for every s-basic concept $[x]_s$ there is a t-basic concept $[x]_t$ such that $[x]_s \subseteq [x]_t$. Take $[x]_s$. Then, there is a formula ϕ which is a conjunction of atomic formulae of the form $(a, v), a \in \mathbf{A}_s$ such that $|\phi|_{(U,\mathbf{A}_s)} = [x]_s$. Now, as the required t-basic concept take $|\phi|_t$ where $\phi \rightarrow \psi$ is a st-rule valid in $\mathcal{S}_{st}$. On the other hand, assume (8) and that there is an st-rule $\phi \rightarrow \psi$ which is not valid in $\mathcal{S}_{st}$. Then by the remark before Lemma 5.6, (Lemma 3.3 in (Rauszer 1992a)) there are basic concepts $[x]_{|\phi|}, [x]_{|\psi|}$ such that $[x]_{|\phi|} \not\subseteq [x]_{|\psi|}$. By (8) and the quoted lemma, there is a t-basic concept $[x]_t$ which contains $[x]_{|\phi|}$. Moreover, there is ψ' such that $\phi \rightarrow \psi'$ is a valid st-rule. A contradiction, which ends the proof of Theorem 6.1.

$\square$

6 Connections with Some Related Results

In the discussion above, $I_t\phi$ might be read *agent t knows* ϕ and $I_{s\vee t}\phi$ might be treated as a strong distributed knowledge of the group of agents st. In other words, the modal connective $I_{s\vee t}$ is interpreted as the syntactical counterpart of a strong distributed knowledge base of the group st.

Observe that for all terms s, t, $I_{s\vee t}$ is complete with respect to axioms for the operator D described in (Halpern and Moses 1992) and called distributed knowledge.

Indeed, for any terms s, t and formulae of the 2-nd kind ϕ, ψ and $\psi_i, i = 1, \ldots, n$ we have:

$$\vdash I_s\phi \to I_{s\vee t}\phi \qquad\qquad \vdash I_t\phi \to I_{s\vee t}\phi\,,$$

$$I_{s\vee t}\phi \wedge I_{s\vee t}(\phi \to \psi) \to I_{s\vee t}\psi\,,$$

and

$$\text{if } \vdash \psi_i \wedge \ldots \wedge \psi_n \to \phi \text{ then } \vdash I_1\psi_1 \wedge \ldots \wedge I_n\psi_n \to I_u\phi\,,$$

where $u = 1 \vee \cdots \vee n$ and $i \leq$ is a term.

In (Grzymala Busse, to appear), (Orlowska 1989), (Rasiowa 1990), knowledge is understood as an ability of agents to describe all positive examples and all negative examples of the concept. More exactly, knowledge of an agent about a concept X is based on the following intuition: If an agent t knows X, then he can decide for any object if it has the property X or the property $-X$. As a consequence, an agent t can decide membership question for the concept X.

In terms of R-logic, knowledge understood in this fashion may be reflected as follows: For every term t and a formula ϕ of the 2-nd kind put

$$K_t\phi =_{def} I_t\phi \vee I_t - \phi,$$

and let $K_t\phi$ be read *an agent t knows* ϕ.

The following properties of modal operators K_t are a simple consequence of the previous lemmas:

Lemma 6.1 *For every terms s, t and formulae of the second kind ϕ, ψ the following holds:*

1. $K_t\phi \to K_t K_t\phi$,
2. $-K_t\phi \to K_t - K_t\phi$,
3. $K_t\phi \wedge K_t\psi \to K_t(\phi \wedge \psi)$,
4. $K_s\phi \vee K_t\phi \to K_{s\vee t}\phi$,
5. $K_{s\wedge t}\phi \to K_s\phi \wedge K_t\phi$.

$\square$

Lemma 6.2 *For every modal operator K_t and formulae ϕ, ψ the following formulae are not provable in R-logic:*

1. $K_t\phi \to \phi$,
2. $(\phi \to \psi \wedge K_t\phi) \to K_t\psi$,
3. $(K_t\phi \wedge K_t(\phi \to \psi)) \to K_t\psi$,
4. $K_t\phi \vee K_t\psi \leftrightarrow K_t(\phi \vee \psi)$,
5. $K_t(\phi \wedge \psi) \to K_t\phi \wedge K_t\psi$.

□

Observe, that conditions (1) and (2) of the above lemma show that certain paradoxes of epistemic logic are eliminated in R-logic with the family of K_t modal connectives. Namely, by (1) *what an agent knows is true* is not longer valid in R-logic. Also the logical omniscience problem (Hintikka 1962) which says *an agent always knows all the consequences of her knowledge* is not valid in our logic.

Moreover, it follows from condition (3) that knowledge of agents, understood as the ability to classify objects as positive and negative instances of a given property, is not closed under modus ponens.

References

Grzymała Busse, J.W.:*LERS- A System for Learning from Examples Based on Rough Sets*, to appear.

Hintikka, J. *Knowledge and Belief.* Chicago: Cornell University Press, 1962.

Halpern J.Y., and Y. Moses: "A guide to completeness and complexity for modal logics of knowledge and belief," in: *Artificial Intelligence*, 54 (1992) 309 - 379.

Minski, M.: "A Framework for representation knowledge," in: P. Winston (ed.), *The Psychology of Computer Vision*, New York: McGraw-Hill (1975) 211-277.

Pawlak, Z.: "Rough sets," in: *International Journal of Computer and Information Sciences*, 11 (1982) 341-346.

Pawlak, Z.: *Rough Sets - Theoretical Aspects of Reasoning about Data.* Kluwer Academic Press, 1992.

Orłowska E.: "Logic for reasoning about knowledge," in: *Zeitschr.f. Math. Logik und Grundlagen d. Math.*, 35 (1989) 559-572.

Rasiowa, H.: "On approximation logics: A survey." in: *Jahrbuch 1990 der Kurt Gödel Gesellschaft*, (1990) 63-87.

Rauszer, C.M.: "Logic for information systems," in: *Fundamenta Informaticae*, vol.16, no 3-4 (1992a) 371-383.

Rauszer, C.M.: "Knowledge representation systems for groups of agents," in: J. Woleński (ed.), *Philosophical Logic in Poland*, Kluwer, to appear.

Rauszer C.M.: "Distributive knowledge representation systems," *ICS Research Report* 22/92, Warsaw: University of Technology, Institute of Computer Science, 1992b.

Skowron, A.: "On topology in information systems," in: *Bulletin of the Polish Academy of Sciences*, vol.36, no 7-8 (1988) 477-479.

Skowron, A., and C.M. Rauszer: "The discernibility matrices and functions in information systems," in: R. Słowiński (ed.), *Decision Support by Experience-Applications of the Rough Sets Theory*, Kluwer Academic Press, 1992.

A Logical Approach to Multi-Sources Reasoning

Laurence Cholvy

ONERA-CERT, 2 avenue Edouard Belin, 31055 Toulouse, France
E-mail: cholvy@dryas.cert.fr

Abstract. This paper presents two logics for reasoning with information from several sources. The main problem is that the information might be contradictory; we show that ordering the different sources according to their reliability is a good way for solving this problem. The two logics which are presented, correspond to two attitudes one can take with respect to such an order.

1 Introduction

In this paper, we focus on the problem of merging autonomous knowledge based systems.

Such a merge is necessary when one wants to access several databases at the same time i.e., when one wants to query several existing databases and obtain answers that combine information from each of them. In this case, the merging may be logical and not necessarly physical. However, the different databases are merged from the point of view of the users who query them and the query evaluator must compute answers with these logically merged data.

A merge is also necessary when one wants to combine the knowledge of different expert systems in order to build an integrated system. For instance, each expert system may be the specialist for a part of a problem and attacking the whole problem requires a merge.

A merge is furthermore required when one wants to combine the beliefs of several agents. For instance, each agent may have some (possibly incomplete) belief about a given situation and one wants to combine these beliefs in order to reason about this situation. A good example is a police investigation that gathers the accounts of the different witnesses. Each witness has some beliefs about the crime: the first one saw a man but could not hear him, the second one heard a woman's voice, the third one saw two people jumping into a car, etc.

Merging several autonomous data/knowledge bases gives rise to different problems. One of them is the problem of global consistency. Even though each separate system may be consistent, the global one obtained by combining them may no longer be consistent.

The problem is then how to deal with this inconsistent set of information. In database terminology, this means: how can we answer queries addressed to the global database if this database is inconsistent? Or, in the language of belief set merging, the question becomes: what can be believed in an inconsistent context?

Simplifying the problem somewhat and assuming that the database can be described by a set of propositional formulae, the problem is: which theorems may be deduced from an inconsistent set obtained by merging different consistent sets?

In Section 2, we describe some work on reasoning with inconsistency. We will first detail approaches which assume that the different pieces of information are equally trusted. Then, we will describe approaches in which additional information is provided that can be used in order to restore consistency. Our solution to the problem of merging incompatible databases belongs to the second kind of approach: we assume that the bases are ordered according to a total order which reflects their reliability. In Section 3, we will show that there are two possible attitudes with respect to such an order. Section 4 and Section 5 will present two logical systems, corresponding to the two attitudes. Links between them are given in Section 6. Relations with the problems of database updates and belief base updates are established in Section 7.

2 Previous Work on Inconsistent Knowledge Bases

2.1 Paraconsistent logics

Classical logic satisfies the principle of "ex falso sequitur quodlibet" that says that everything can be concluded from a contradiction $(A \wedge \neg A) \rightarrow B$. Classical logic collapses under inconsistency: everything can be deduced from an inconsistent database.

Paraconsistent logics are logics that reject the principle of "sequitur quodlibet". We refer to (Besnard 1990) for a survey.

Here, we illustrate a paraconsistent logic C_w, on an example which comes from (Baral et al. 1992).

Example 1. Assume three databases that contain a police inspector's knowledge and two witnesses's accounts: the inspector knows that if a car is black, then it is dark; if it is white, then it is light; nothing can be both light and dark. The first witness, Bill, saw a black car while the second, John, saw two men in a white car. We formalize this information by:

inspector = { *(1) black → dark,   (2) white → light,   (3) ¬ light ∨ ¬ dark* }
Bill =   { *(4) black* }
John =   { *(5) white ,   (6) two*}

The combined knowledge base (*inspector* ∪ *Bill* ∪ *John*) is inconsistent. Using first order logic to reason with this set, we could conclude everything i.e., we could conclude for instance that the car was a limousine. Using C_w, we can conclude (*dark* ∧ *light*) i.e., the inspector cannot know the real type of colour. However, we cannot conclude that the car was a limousine (this is indeed what the inspector does in the real life situation: he does not conclude anything when a contradiction arises).

2.2 Maximal consistent sets

In the next approach, the underlying logic is still classical, but a difference between formulae is made outside the logic; at the meta-level an attempt is made to eliminate the inconsistency by determining maximal consistent subsets.

Combining knowledge bases (Baral et al. 1992) addresses the problem of combining the knowledge of different experts.

They assume a set of consistent theories and a set of integrity constraints. Each theory satisfies the integrity constraints. They aim to combine the given set of theories so that the combined theory is also consistent with respect to the integrity constraints and contains as much consistent information as possible.

According to their approach, the combination of several theories may lead to several resulting theories. So they define the combination of theories as a mapping from a set of theories (the given knowledge bases) and a set of integrity constraints into a set of theories. They provide several alternative definitions of combination functions. For instance, function $Comb1$, takes the union of the theories $T1 \cup \ldots \cup T$ and identifies the maximal subsets that are consistent with the integrity constraints IC.

On the previous example (where there is no integrity constraint), we get the following maximal consistent belief sets.

$$Comb1\{ \ \{ \ inspector, \ Bill, \ John \ \}, \ \emptyset \ \} = \{ \ \{(1), (2), (3), (4), (6)\},$$
$$\{(1), (2), (3), (5), (6)\},$$
$$\{(1), (2), (4), (5), (6)\},$$
$$\{(2), (3), (4), (5), (6)\} \ \}$$

A formula is a theorem of the combined theory iff it is a theorem of all its subsets. So, according to this combination, "there were two men in the car" is deducible from the combined theory, as well as "the car was black or white". However, "the car was black" and "the car was white" are not deducible.

This means that, after combining the accounts of the different witnesses, the inspector can affirm that "there were two men in the car" (since one witness told him and the other denied it) and that "the car was black or white" (since, although the witnesses are contradictory on this point, the first one told him the car was white and the other told him the car was black). However, he can not affirm the real colour of the car.

Sure and doubtful information In (Cholvy 1990) and (Bauval and Cholvy 1991), a similar approach is described for a slightly different context: we try to circumscribe the contradiction as precisely as possible and to distinguish between information that is related to the contradiction and information which is not. The terms "sure information" and "doubtful information" are introduced. Again, the main notions here are the maximal consistent subsets of the database (integrity constraints are not treated separately). A modal logic is used to formally describe the meaning of "sure" and "doubtful" information, but the query evaluator is first order.

For instance, "there were two men in the car" is sure information, since it does not give rise to a contradiction, i.e., it belongs to the intersection of all maximal consistent subsets of the global theory. However "the car was white", "the car was black"...are doubtful information: they are true in one maximal consistent subset and false in another one.

2.3   Paraconsistent logics and extra-information

(Besnard 1990) described the logic $V1$, originally developped by Arruda. $V1$ holds the middle between classical logic and a purely inconsistent logic since it contains two kinds of propositional letters: some that behave classically and some that behave paraconsistently. Its axiomatisation is obtained by adding (as an axiom) the ex-falso quodlibet only for propositions that behave classically.

Making a disctinction between classical and non-classical proposition requires extra-information attaching to propositions and this is the responsibility of the user.

Using $V1$ is impossible when one cannot decide which propositions must behave classically. For instance, the inspector from our example cannot decide, before listening to the witnesses, on which notions they will agree.

2.4   Tagged data and ordered data

(Fagin et al. 1983) dealt with a related problem of updating a database (see Section 7 for a comparision). In order to construct the resulting database in a minimal way (a minimal number of formulae must be rejected) and in order to distinguish between formulae, they introduced the notion of tagged sentences: a tag is a number, attached to a sentence of the global database, which expresses a priority. The lower the tag, the higher the priority during the update process. The sentences that have the tag 0 have the highest priority and cannot be rejected during the update.

Let us reiterate the inspector example in the context of (Fagin et al. 1983) and assume that inspector's formulae are tagged 0, Bill's sentence is tagged 1 and John's sentences are tagged 2. Let us assume that the inspector first listens to Bill. So Bill's account provides an update to his own knowledge. Since there is no contradiction, the result is: $\{(1), (2), (3), (4)\}$. Then he listens to John who tells him (5). As a consequence his knowledge base becomes: $\{(1), (2), (3), (4), (5)\}$. Then John adds (6). Since (6) contradicts the current base and since (6) is tagged 2 (the lowest priority), it is not added. So the inspector's knowledge base is: $\{(1), (2), (3), (4), (5)\}$.

In (Gabbay and Hunter 1991) the authors suggested that reasoning with inconsistency can be studied as a Labelled Deductive System, where deduction is done both on labels and on formulae. (Indeed, in the logic they defined, units of information are labelled formulae).

(Dubois et al. 1992) adapted this approach to the problem of merging knowledge bases in the context of a possibilistic logic: every formula is associated with a tag, referring to the sources of the information: in this way both the level of support of the formula by a source and the reliability of the source itself can be handled.

(Cayrol et al. 1992) finally, assume that the existence of an order on propositions (reflecting some kind of preference). They infer different orders on sets of propositions in such a way that the problem of consistency restoration leads to select consistent subsets which are maximal according to this order.

2.5 Prioritized theories

The last part of (Baral et al. 1992) focus on the combination of prioritized theories. They assume that different knowledge bases may have different priorities. They use priority information when combining the bases. For example, if a base with higher priority contradicts another base with a lower priority, the first one takes precedence over the second. They define two algorithms that combine prioritized theories $T1 \prec T2 \ldots \prec Tk$. The first algorithm, called "bottom-up", starts combining $T1$ and $T2$ with a preference for $T2$. The combined theory then is a set of theories $\{T: T$ is a superset of $T2$ and $T \backslash T2$ is a maximal subset of $T1$ such that T is consistent$\}$. The result is then combined with $T3$ and so on until Tk is reached. The result is finally combined with the set of integrity constraints IC (that have the highest priority). The second algorithm, called "top-down", starts by combining Tk and IC. The result is then combined with $Tk - 1$, and so on until $T1$ is reached.

On the inspector example, the inspector may order the different bases, expressing that: $John \prec Bill \prec inspector$. This means that he estimates that he is himself more reliable than Bill who is himself more reliable than John.

Using the bottom-up algorithm, the results are the two following sets: $\{1, 2, 3, 4, 6\}$ and $\{1, 2, 3, 5, 6\}$.

Using the top-down algorithm, the result of the combination of the three bases generates the set: $\{1, 2, 3, 5, 6\}$.

3 Context of Our Work

We think that the idea of ordering the different sources of information provides a good point of departure since the order may reflect the fact that the sources are not equally reliable.

Reconsider our example. Assume that a first witness, Bill, said that he saw a black car, while a second, John, said that he saw two men in a white car. Assume that the inspector himself has some additional information which is true: for instance, he is sure that the crime was committed on a foggy day. Bringing the fog into play, he might assume that John is less reliable than Bill since he was standing too far from the location of the crime and could not see well because of the fog. So, the inspector may trust him less. In this case, the inspector's prioritization will be: *Inspector>Bill>John.*

We assume that different databases are ordered according to a total order >. However, there are two possible attitudes with respect to this order relation:

- The "suspicious" attitude: suspect all the information provided by a database if this database contradicts a more trustable database. The suspicious attitude of the inspector would lead him to conclude no more than that the car was black.
- The "trusting" attitude: suspect the information provided by a database that contradicts the information provided by a more reliable database; all other information is kept. According the trusting attitude, the inspector will conclude that they were two men in a black car. Indeed, concerning the colour of the car, he trusts Bill more than John, so he can assume that the colour is black. Concerning the number of persons, John provides new information that does not contradict Bill's account.

In the two next sections, we study logical systems for reasoning according to the suspicious attitude (Section 4) and to the trusting attitude (Section 5).

Notice that in both cases, we do not construct the merged database outside the logic, as opposed to (Fagin et al. 1983) and (Baral et al. 1992). We want a system which hypothetically generates the formulae that can be deduced in the merged database. So our approach belongs to the hypothetical approaches along the lines of (Farinas Del Cerro and Herzig 1986, Farinas and Herzig 1992).

4 Merging Two Databases According to the Suspicious Attitude

We assume that our language L is a finite set of propositional variables: p_1, p_2, ... p_L.

We denote the two databases to be merged 1 and 2, respectively. We assume that they are finite sets of literals (positive or negative propositional variables). We also assume that they are consistent i.e., they do not contain both a literal and its negation. But we do not assume that they are complete.

We define a logic, called $FUSION - S(1, 2)$, whose language L' is obtained from L by adding pseudo-modalities i.e., markers on propositional formulae. These pseudo-modalities are:

- $[i_1 i_2]$ where $i_1 \in \{1, 2\}$ and $i_2 \in \{1, 2\}$ and $(i_1 \neq i_2)$

$[i_1 i_2]F$ (where F is a formula of L), will mean that, when considering the total order on $\{1, 2\} : i_1 > i_2$, F is true in the database obtained by virtually merging database i_1 and database i_2.

Notice that the general form of these pseudo modalities allows us to represent the particular case: $[i]F$, $i=1$ or $i=2$, which means that F is true in database i.

189

4.1 Semantics

The semantics of $FUSION - S(1,2)$ is the following:

An interpretation of $FUSION - S(1,2)$ is the pair: $M = (W,r)$, where:

- W is the finite set of all interpretations of the underlying language L.
- r is a set of four equivalence relations between interpretations of W.
  Each pseudo-modality is associated to a relation. So, if $[O]$ is a pseudo-modality, $R(O)$ denotes the associated equivalence relation and $\overline{R}(O)$ its equivalence class. The equivalence classes are defined by:
  $\overline{R}(i)$ is a non empty subset of $W, i = 1,2$
  $\overline{R}(i_1 i_2) = \overline{R}(i_1) \cap \overline{R}(i_2)$ if not empty, $(i_1 \in \{1,2\}, i_2 \in \{1,2\}, i_1 \neq i_2)$
  $\overline{R}(i_1 i_2) = \overline{R}(i_1)$ else $(i_1 \in \{1,2\}, i_2 \in \{1,2\}, i_1 \neq i_2)$

Definition 1. Satisfaction of formulae.
Let F be a formula of L. Let $F1$ and $F2$ be formulae of L'. Let O be a total order on a subset of $\{1,2\}$. Let $M = (W,r)$ be an interpretation of $FUSION - S(1,2)$ and let $w \in W$.

$FUSION - S(1,2), r, w \models F \iff w \models F$
$FUSION - S(1,2), r, w \models [O]F \iff \forall w' w' \in \overline{R}(O) \implies w' \models F$
$FUSION - S(1,2), r, w \models \neg F1 \iff not(FUSION - S(1,2), r, w \models F1)$
$FUSION - S(1,2), r, w \models F1 \wedge F2 \iff (FUSION - S(1,2), r, w \models F1)$ and
$(FUSION - S(1,2), r, w \models F2)$

Definition 2. Valid formulae in $FUSION - S(1,2)$.
Let F be a formula of L'. F is a valid formula (in $FUSION - S(1,2)$) iff
$\forall M = (W,r), \forall w \in W, FUSION - S(1,2), r, w \models F$

We note $FUSION - S(1,2) \models F$, the valid formulae F.

4.2 Axiomatics

Let us first introduce the following formula:

$INC(1,2) = (([1]p_1 \wedge [2]\neg p_1) \vee ([1]\neg p_1 \wedge [2]p_1) \vee \ldots \vee$
$([1]p_L \wedge [2]\neg p_L) \vee ([1]\neg p_L \wedge [2]p_L))$

$INC(1,2)$ expresses that there is a literal whose valuation is not the same in database 1 and database 2. So, $INC(1,2)$ is true when the two databases are contradictory.
  Axioms of $FUSION - S(1,2)$ are:

- $(A0)$ the axioms of propositional logic
- $(A1)$ $[O]\neg F \to \neg[O]F$ if F is a formula of L

- (A2) $[O]F \wedge [O](F \to G) \to [O]G$ if F is a formula of L
- (A3) $INC(1,2) \to ([i_1 i_2]l \longleftrightarrow [i_1]l)$ if l is a literal
- (A4) $\neg INC(1,2) \to ([i_1 i_2]l \longleftrightarrow ([i_1]l \vee [i_2]l))$ if l is a literal

Inference rules of $FUSION - S$ are:

- (Nec) $\vdash F \Longrightarrow \vdash [O]F$ (if F is propositional and O a total order on a subset of $\{1,2\}$)
- (MP) $\vdash F$ and $\vdash (F \to G) \Longrightarrow \vdash G$

Notice that axioms $(A3)$ and $(A4)$ express the suspicious attitude of merging. Let us assume that the order is: $i_1 \geq i_2$. Then, in case of contradiction, the formulae which are true in the merged database are those which are true in database i_1. Else, the formulae which are true in the merged database are those of database i_1 or database i_2.

Remark: This logic will be used to model the merging of two databases $db1$ and $db2$, in the case where they are finite consistent sets of L literals.
Let us note

$$\psi = \bigwedge_{l \in bd1} [1]l \wedge \bigwedge_{bd1 \nvdash c} \neg[1]c \wedge \bigwedge_{l \in bd2} [2]l \wedge \bigwedge_{bd2 \nvdash c} \neg[2]c$$

(where l is a literal and c a clause)

We are interested in finding valid formulae of the form: $(\psi \to [O]F)$, i.e., formulae F which are true in the database obtained by merging $db1$ and $db2$, when the order is O.

We can prove the following facts:

Proposition 3. *Let $bd1$ and $bd2$ two finite sets of L literals and let ψ be the formula previously defined. Let F be a formula of L. Let O be a total order on a subset of $\{1,2\}$.*

$$FUSION - S(1,2) \models (\psi \to [O]F) \iff FUSION - S(1,2) \vdash (\psi \to [O]F)$$

This shows that deriving theorems of the form $(\psi \to [O]F)$ yields all the valid formulae of the form $(\psi \to [O]F)$.

Proposition 4. *Let $bd1$ and $bd2$ two finite sets of L literals and let ψ be the formula previously defined. Let F be a propositional formula. Let O be a total order on a subset of $\{1,2\}$. Then:*
$$FUSION - S(1,2) \vdash (\psi \to [O]F) \quad or \quad FUSION - S(1,2) \vdash (\psi \to \neg[O]F)$$

This shows a kind of completeness of the ψ consequences of the form $[O]F$: whether we will be able to derive that $[O]F$ (i.e., it is the case that F is true under order O), or $\neg[O]F$ (i.e., it is not the case that F is true under order O).

4.3 An example

Let us illustrate the suspicious attitude on the inspector example. Consider two witnesses. The first one, Bill, told the inspector that he saw a black car. The second one, John, told the inspector that he saw two men in a white car. So we consider the two following bases:

$1 = \{black\}$. $2 = \{two, \neg\ black\}$.

Then we consider $\psi = [1]\ black\ \wedge\neg[1]\ two\ \wedge\neg[1]\neg\ two\ \wedge\neg[1]\neg\ black\ \wedge[2]\ two$ $\wedge[2]\neg\ black\ \wedge\neg[2]\neg\ two\ \wedge[2]\ black$

Here are some deductions that the inspector can perform:

$FUSION - S(1,2) \vdash (\psi \rightarrow [12]\ (black))$
$FUSION - S(1,2) \vdash (\psi \rightarrow \neg[12]\ (\neg\ black))$
$FUSION - S(1,2) \vdash (\psi \rightarrow \neg[12]\ two)$
$FUSION - S(1,2) \vdash (\psi \rightarrow \neg[12]\ (\neg\ two))$
$FUSION - S(1,2) \vdash (\psi \rightarrow [21]\ (two\ \wedge\neg\ black))$
$FUSION - S(1,2) \vdash (\psi \rightarrow \neg[21]\ black)$

In other terms, if the inspector trusts Bill more than John, the only thing he can assume is that the car was black. If he trusts John more than Bill, he can only assume that there were two men in a black car.

5 Merging Several Databases According to the Trusting Attitude

We still assume that the language L is a finite set of propositional variables.

We denote with $1, 2 \ldots n$ the n databases to be merged. Again, we assume that the databases are finite, satisfiable but not necessarily complete sets of literals.

The logic we define here is called $FUSION-T(1\ldots n)$. Its pseudo-modalities are :

- $[i_1 i_2 \ldots i_m]$, where $m \geq 1$ and $i_j \in \{1 \ldots n\}$ and $(j \neq k \implies i_j \neq i_k)$

- $[i_1 i_2 \ldots i_m]\ F$ will mean that, when considering the total order on $\{i_1 \ldots i_m\}$: $i_1 > i_2, i_2 > i_3, \ldots i_{m-1} > i_m$, F is true in the database obtained by virtually merging database i_1 and $\ldots$ database i_m.

Notice again that the general form of these pseudo-modalities allows us to represent the particular case: $[i]F, i = 1\ldots n$, which means that F is true in database i.

5.1 Semantics

The semantics of $FUSION-T(1\ldots n)$ is the following: the model of $FUSION-T(1\ldots n)$ is the pair: $I = (W, r)$, where:

- W is the finite set of all the interpretations of the underlying propositional language L

– r is a finite set of equivalence relations between interpretations in W.

Each pseudo-modality is associated with a relation. So, if $[O]$ is a pseudo-modality, $R(O)$ denotes the associated equivalence relation and $\overline{R}(O)$ its equivalence class. The equivalence classes are recursively defined by:

$\overline{R}(i)$ is a nonempty subset of $W, i = 1 \ldots n$

$\overline{R}(i_1 i_2 \ldots i_m)) = f_{i_m}(\ldots(f_{i_2}(\overline{R}(i_1)) \ldots))$ where:

$f_{i_j}(E) = \{w : w \in E \text{ and } w \models L_{i_j E}\}$ and
$L_{i_j E} = \{l : l \text{ literal of } L \text{ such that} : (\forall v \in \overline{R}(i_j) \Longrightarrow v \models l) \text{ and}$
$\qquad\qquad\qquad\qquad\qquad (\exists u \in E \text{ and } u \models l) \}$

Definition 5. Satisfaction of formulae.
(see Section 4.1)

Notice that since the underlying databases are assumed to be satisfiable, we have $\forall i = 1 \ldots n$, $\overline{R}(i) \neq \emptyset$, So, $\overline{R}(O) \neq \emptyset$, whatever the total order O on any subset of $\{1 \ldots n\}$. This means that (virtually) merging several satisfiable databases leads to a satisfiable database. In other terms, in our logic, not all propositional formulae will be true under an order O.

5.2 Axiomatics

Let O be an order $i_1 \ldots i_m$, $m \geq 1$. (i.e., $i_1 > i_2, \ldots, i_{m-1} > i_m$). By convention, we note $O \cup \{i_{m+1}\}$, the order $i_1 \ldots i_m i_{m+1}$.

Axioms of $FUSION - T(1 \ldots n)$ are:

– $(A0)$ Axioms of the propositional logic
– $(A1)$ $[O]\neg F \rightarrow \neg[O]F$
– $(A2)$ $[O]F \wedge [O](F \rightarrow G) \rightarrow [O]G$
– $(A3)$ $[O \cup \{i\}]l \longleftrightarrow [O]l \vee ([i]l \wedge \neg[O]\neg l)$ if l is a literal

Inferences rules of $FUSION - T(1 \ldots n)$ are:

– $(Nec) \vdash F \Longrightarrow \vdash [O]F$ (if F is a propositional formula)
– $(MP) \vdash F$ and $\vdash (F \rightarrow G) \Longrightarrow \vdash G$

Axiom $(A3)$ expresses the trusting attitude. Indeed, we could decompose it in three axioms:

– $(A3.1)$ $[O]l \rightarrow [O \cup \{i\}]\, l$
– $(A3.2)$ $[i]l \wedge \neg[O]\neg l \rightarrow [O \cup \{i\}]\, l$
– $(A3.3)$ $\neg[O]l \wedge \neg[i]l \rightarrow \neg[O \cup \{i\}]\, l$

This means that:
- if a literal is true under order O, then it is still true under order $O \cup \{i\}$, for any i, since, by convention, $O \cup \{i\}$ means that i is the least reliable source.

- if it is the case that a literal is true in database i, and if it is not the case that its negation is true under order O, then it is the case that it is true under $O \cup \{i\}$.

- if it is not the case that a literal is true under order 0 and if it is not the case that it is true in database i then it is not the case that it is true under order $O \cup \{i\}$.

Remark: This logic will be used to model the merging of n databases $db1 \ldots dbn$, in the case where such databases are finite consistent sets of L literals and according the trusting attitude
Let us note

$$\psi = \bigwedge_{i=1}^{n} (\bigwedge_{l \in bdi} [i]l \wedge \bigwedge_{bdi \nvdash c} \neg[i]c)$$

(where l is a literal and c a clause)
We will be interested in finding valid formulae of the form: $(\psi \rightarrow [O]F)$, i.e., formulae F which are true in the database obtained by merging $db1 \ldots dbn$, when the order is O.
We can prove the following facts:

Proposition 6. *Let $bd1 \ldots bdn$ be finite sets of literals and let ψ be the formula previously defined. Let F be a formula of L. Let O be a total order on a subset of $\{1 \ldots n\}$. Then:*

$$FUSION - T(1 \ldots n) \models (\psi \rightarrow [O]F) \iff FUSION - T(1 \ldots n) \vdash (\psi \rightarrow [O]F)$$

Proposition 7. *With the same assumptions as in proposition 3:*

$$FUSION - T(1,2) \vdash (\psi \rightarrow [O]F) \ or \ FUSION - T(1,2) \vdash (\psi \rightarrow \neg[O]F)$$

5.3 An example:

Let us illustrate this machinery on the inspector example. Assume here that the inspector has got some belief about the context of the crime: in fact, the day of the crime was a foggy day. The inspector gathers information from two witnesses: Bill who told him he saw a black car and John who told him he saw two men in a white car. Let us consider three bases :
$1 = \{fog\}$. $2 = \{black\}$. $3 = \{two \wedge \neg black\}$.
We note $\psi = [1] fog \wedge \neg[1] black \wedge \neg[1] \neg black \wedge \neg[1] two \wedge \neg[1] \neg two \wedge \ldots [3]$ $two \wedge [3] \neg black \wedge \neg[3] fog \wedge \ldots$
Here are some formulae that the inspector can deduce according to the trusting attitude:

$FUSION - T(1, 2, 3) \vdash (\psi \rightarrow [123] \ (fog \wedge black \wedge two))$

i.e., when assuming $1 > 2$, $2 > 3$, we can deduce that there were two men in a black car and there was fog.

$FUSION - T(1, 3, 2) \vdash (\psi \rightarrow [132] \ (fog \wedge two \wedge \neg \ black))$

i.e., when assuming $1 > 3$, $3 > 2$, we can deduce that there were two men in a car, that was black, and there was fog.

6 Links Between the Two Attitudes

Proposition 8. *Case of two databases.*[1] *When the two databases to be merged are compatible, then:*
$$FUSION - S(1, 2) \vdash (\psi \rightarrow [O]F) \iff FUSION - T(1, 2) \vdash (\psi \rightarrow [O]F)$$

i.e., when the two databases to be merged are compatible, the merged database obtained with the suspicious attitude is the same than the database obtained with the trusting attitude.

7 Relation with the Problems of Database Updates and Belief Base Updates

Let us first recall some definitions (Katsuno and Mendelzon 1991):

Definition 9. Let m and $m1$ be two interpretations. We define the distance between m and $m1$ by:
$$d(m, m1) = \{p \in L : (p \in m \text{ and } p \notin m1) \text{ or } (p \notin m \text{ and } p \in m1)\}$$

Definition 10. Let m be an interpretation. We define a partial order on the set of interpretations $\leq_m$ by:
$$m1 \leq_m m2 \iff d(m, m1) \subseteq d(m, m2)$$

Then we have the following result:

Proposition 11. *Let f_{i_j} be the functions defined in Section 5.1. Then:*
$$f_{i_j}(E) = \bigcup_{m \in \overline{R}(i_j)} Min(E, \leq_m)$$

So, according to (Katsuno and Mendelzon 1991), $f_{i_j}(E)$ is the set of models of belief base i_j updated by E.

In other terms, the result of merging two databases according to the trusting attitude, such that $i > j$, is equivalent to updating database j with database i.

This also means that the axiomatics given for two sets of literals in Section 5.2 is an axiomatics of an update of atomic belief bases i.e.,
$$\{F : FUSION - T(1, 2) \vdash [ij]F\} \longleftrightarrow j <> i \text{ (notation of Katsuno and}$$
Mendelzon (1991)).

---

[1] With the previous notations.

Generalisation: Merging n databases $1, 2 \ldots n$, according to the trusting attitude and given an order: $i_1 > i_2, \ldots, i_{n-1} > i_n$ means to update i_n with the result of the update of i_{n-1} with the result of the update $\ldots$ of i_2 with i_1, i.e., $\overline{R}(i_1 \ldots i_{n-1} i_n) = \text{models-of}(i_n <> (i_{n-1} <> \ldots (i_2 <> i_1) \ldots))$

Reconsider Winslett's approach (Winslett 1990). The previous proposition shows that adding a conjunction i in a database j according to Winslett's approach, means the merging of i and j, according to the trusting attitude in the order $i > j$.

Besides that, in the classical approaches to database updates, the addition of any information i that contradicts the current state of the database j is rejected. This implies the merging of i and j according to the suspicious attitude and in the order $j > i$.

8 Concluding Remarks and Open Problems

A query evaluator that implements the logics presented here has been developped (Cholvy 1993). It considers queries of the form: $[O]Q$? i.e., "is Q is true under order O?".

It generates three kinds of answers:
* YES, if $FUSION - S(1,2) \models [O]Q(resp, FUSION - T(1,n))$
* NO, if $FUSION - S(1,2) \models \neg[O]Q(resp, FUSION - T(1,n))$
* ?, else

However, the work presented here leaves many problems open:

First, the logics presented here must be extended in the case where databases are sets of clauses. In this context, given the semantics of the trusting attitude, we will be constrained to consider the second definition of $f_{i_j}(E)$ in terms of minimal models (see Section 7) since the first definition given in Section 5.1 can not be applied generally.

Second, we have shown that merging several databases may be achieved according to two attitudes. The so-called trusting attitude corresponds to consecutive updates. So postulates of updates (when restricted to our case of conjunctions) characterize merging. It would be interesting to see what are the postulates that characterize the suspicious attitude.

Finally, we have assumed here that the databases are ordered according to a total order. However, in some applications, the person who gathers the different sources of information cannot order them totally: for instance, the inspector cannot decide which witness is more trustable. In the case of a partial order, we must define a formalism which mixes the logics presented here and the formalisms defined for reasoning in inconsistent contexts with equally trusted information (see Section 2).

References

Besnard P.: "Logics for automated reasoning in the presence of contradictions," in: *Proceedings of Artificial Intelligence: Methodology, systems and applications.* North Holland, 1990.

Bauval A., and L. Cholvy: "Automated reasoning in case of inconsistency," in: *Proceedings of the First World Conference on Fundamentals of AI* 1991.

Baral C., S. Kraus, J. Minker, and V.S. Subrahmanian: "Combining knowledge bases consisting of first order theories," in: *Computational Intelligence* 8-1 (1992).

Cayrol C., R. Royer, and C. Saurel: "Management of preferences in assumption-based reasoning," in: *Proceedings of (IPMU) Conference.* Palma de Mallorca, Spain, 1992.

Cholvy L.: "Querying an inconsistent database," in: *Proceedings of Artificial Intelligence: Methodology, systems and applications.* North Holland, 1990.

Cholvy, L.: "Proving theorems in a multi-source environment," in: *Proceedings of IJ-CAI,* 1993.

Dubois D., J. Lang, and H. Prades: "Dealing with multi-source information in possibilistic logic," in: *Proceedings of ECAI,* 1992.

Fagin R., J. Ullman, and M. Vardi: "On the semantics of updates in databases," in: *Proceedings of ACM TODS,* 1983.

Fagin R., G. Kupper, J. Ullman, and M. Vardi: "Updating logical databases," in: *Advances in Computing Research* 3 (1986).

Farinas Del Cerro L., and A. Herzig: *Reasoning about database updates. Proceedings of the Workshop of Foundations of Deductive Databases and Logic Programming.* Jack Minker Editor, 1986.

Farinas L., and A. Herzig: *Constructive Minimal Changes.* Report IRIT, 1992.

Gabbay D., and A. Hunter: "Making inconsistency respectable," in: *International Workshop on Fundamentals of Artificial Intelligence,* 1991.

Katsuno H., and A. Mendelzon: "Propositional knowledge base revision and minimal change," in: *Artificial Intelligence* 52 (1991).

Winslett M.: *Updating Logical Databases.* Cambridge University Press, 1990.

Situation Theory and Social Structure

Keith Devlin

School of Science, Saint Mary's College of California
Moraga, California 94575, USA
E-mail: devlin@stmarys-ca.edu

Abstract. This paper seeks to utilize situation theory as a framework (or formalism) for the description and analysis of the fundamental social structures that underlie the way we encounter the world, and which influence our behavior and communication in society.
Much of this work is done jointly with Duska Rosenberg. Our collaboration on this project commenced with (Devlin and Rosenberg, to appear), and continues in (Devlin and Rosenberg, in preparation a). In many ways, this paper represents a partial progress report of work leading to our forthcoming monograph (Devlin and Rosenberg, in preparation b).

1 Introduction

The traditional approach to social study, sometimes referred to as 'normative sociology', commences with a collection of empirically identified *social norms* that constitute, or are taken to constitute, our common-sense-view of the world. Normative sociology posits, and then attempts to describe, an objective world of social facts to which our attitudes and actions are a response. What the everyday practice of normative sociology amounts to is constructing a social science by a process of refinement, or quantification, of the initial collection of foundational norms. This enterprise is successful in so far as it improves upon the normative structure it starts with. Human action is explained by reference to the body of social norms taken to be the grounding structure for the theory.

During the 1960s, Garfinkel (1967) and others proposed a radically different approach, known as *ethnomethodology*. Rather than taking a normative social structure as foundational and explain human action in terms of those norms, the ethnomethodologist regards human action as fundamental and seeks to explain *how* human action can give rise to what we perceive as a collection of norms. Thus for the ethnomethodologist, the common-sense-view of the world is taken not as a foundational structure to be improved upon, but as the fundamental *phenomenon* of social study.

The ethnomethodologist, then, seeks to identify, describe, and understand the social *structure* that underlies the way ordinary people (as opposed to experts or theorists) encounter the world and make it intelligible to themselves and to one another. As such, ethnomethodology seeks to provide:

descriptions of a society that its members, (...) use and treat as known in common with other members, and with other members take for granted. Specifically, [it seeks] a description of the way decisions of meanings and fact are managed, and how a body of factual knowledge of social structures is assembled in common sense situations of choice. (Garfinkel 1967: 77.)

By way of an example, consider an utterance of the following sentences:

The baby cried. The mommy picked it up.

These two sentences, uttered by a small child as the opening two sentences of a story, constitute the principal data of a well-known, seminal article in the ethnomethodological literature, Harvey Sacks' *On the Analyzability of Stories by Children* (1972), an article which Rosenberg and I subjected to a situation-theoretic analysis in (Devlin and Rosenberg, to appear).

In his article, Sacks is concerned with natural conversation, and in particular with the way speaker and listener make use of their knowledge of social structure in the utterance and understanding of a simple natural language communication. According to Sacks, the particular choice of words used by a speaker in, say, a description is critically influenced by the speaker's knowledge of social structure, and the listener utilizes his[1] knowledge of social structure in order to interpret, in the manner the speaker intended, the juxtaposition of these words in conversation.

The focus of Sacks' article is the way a *typical* listener understands the two sentences. As Sacks observes, when heard by a typical, competent speaker of English, the utterance is almost certainly heard as referring to a very small human (though the word 'baby' has other meanings in everyday speech) and to that baby's mommy (though there is no genitive in the second sentence, and it is certainly consistent for the mommy to be some other child's mother); moreover it is the baby that the mother picks up (though the 'it' in the second sentence could refer to some object other than the baby). Why do we almost certainly, and without seeming to give the matter any thought, choose this particular interpretation?

To continue, we are also likely to regard the second sentence as describing an action (the mommy picking up the baby) that follows, and is caused by, the action described by the first sentence (the baby crying), though there is no general rule to the effect the sentence order corresponds to temporal order or causality of events (though it often does so).

Moreover, we may form this interpretation without knowing what baby or what mommy is being talked of.

Furthermore, we recognize these two sentences as constituting a *possible description*, and indeed it seems to be in large part because we make such recognition that we understand the two sentences the way we do.

As Sacks notes, what leads us, effortlessly, instantaneously, and almost invariably, to the interpretation we give to this simple discourse, is the speaker and listener's shared knowledge of, and experience with, the social structure that pertains to (the subject matter of) this particular utterance.

---

[1] For definiteness, I shall assume a female speaker and a male listener throughout this paper.

It is this underlying social structure that constitutes Sacks' main interest. Referring to his observations concerning the way typical speakers of English understand the two sentences, summarized above, Sacks says of the social structure he (and we) seek to investigate (1972: 332):

My reason for having gone through the observations I have so far made was to give you some sense, right off, of the fine power of a culture. It does not, so to speak, merely fill brains in roughly the same way, it fills them so that they are alike in fine detail. The sentences we are considering are after all rather minor, and yet all of you, or many of you, hear just what I said you heard, and many of us are quite unacquainted with each other. I am, then, dealing with something real and something finely powerful.

Having identified a phenomenon to be studied, as Garfinkel, Sacks, and the other early ethnomethodologists surely did, the question at once arises as to how one should set about studying that phenomenon. Ethnomethodologists insist that the essence of the discipline is *inquiry*, not theorizing; the ethnomethodologist examines the (empirical) data, holding them up for scrutiny and analysis; she does not use the data as a basis for theory-building. (See, for instance, the remarks of Button (1991: 4–5).)

But how is that examination, that analysis of the data, to be carried out, and how are the ethnomethodologist's findings to be evaluated and validated? Clearly, both description and analysis must, of necessity, be carried out with the aid of language. But then we run into the problem that will inevitably face any deeply foundational study of linguistic issues, what one might term the 'epistemological-bootstrap' problem: successfully using language in order to examine, and communicate to others the results of such examination, the *minutae* by which language functions as a communicative medium.

One need only look at, say, the Sacks' paper to see the difficulties such a fundamental study entails. The ethnomethodological literature is riddled with long, highly complex sentences, often extremely hard to parse, and authors frequently resort to the construction of complex, hyphenated terms in order to try to capture adequately the relevant abstract concepts they wish to examine. Though perhaps frustrating for the reader of an ethnomethodological analysis, this is, in large part, surely unavoidable. As Benson and Hughes argue in (Button 1991: 129):

... sociology is, along with the other human sciences, a 'second order' discipline using the concepts of ordinary language. In which case, an important constraint on sociological inquiry is that the categories, the concepts used, and the methods for using them, must be isomorphic to the ways in which they are used in common-sense reasoning.

The absence of a descriptive and analytic framework 'separate' from the data under consideration, while perhaps a source of frustration to a sociologist trying to follow an ethnomethodological analysis, can present a major obstacle to interdisciplinary research, where people with different areas of expertise wish to pool their knowledge to attack particularly difficult problems; for example, the kind of interdisciplinary research and development work involved in the design of interactive information systems in the context of Computer

Supported Cooperative Work (CSCW), a process in which ethnomethodology is playing an increasingly significant role these days. The relative ease with which say, the chemist, biologist, and physicist can communicate with each other at a fundamental level through the universal language of mathematics and the use of a common methodology (the 'scientific method'), is not matched when an ethnomethodologist becomes part of a systems-design team involving computer scientists, mathematicians, and engineers.

Can some measure of assistance be found through increased 'formality' of language? More specifically, can mathematical formalisms be advantageously introduced?

It is the purpose of this paper, just as it was the purpose of my joint paper with Rosenberg (Devlin and Rosenberg, to appear), to argue that mathematics can indeed be used profitably in carrying out an analysis of phenomena normally alalyzed by ethnomethodologists. That this claim may strike many as *quite obviously false* is, I would suggest, a consequence of a mistakenly narrow view of what mathematics is, or at least what it can be and what it can be used for,[2] an issue I take up in the next section.

The crucial factor to be addressed in attempting to make use of mathematical techniques in this kind of analysis is to fit the mathematics to the data, not the other way round. And that almost certainly requires the development of new mathematical techniques.

My paper with Rosenberg (Devlin and Rosenberg, to appear) presents an analysis of Sacks' article. We attempt to show how situation theory can help formalize some of Sacks' arguments, and we make use of that formalization to examine those arguments in a critical fashion. Our main purpose was not to present an alternative analysis of the same linguistic data, but to demonstrate that situation theory could be used to add precision to an ethnomethodological analysis *already validated as such within the ethnomethodological community*. The added precision we were able to bring to Sacks' arguments brought out some points of his argument that were in need of clarification, a clarification that we were, again by virtue of the situation-theoretic machinery, able to provide. In the course of this study, we were led to new structures and new classes of situation-theoretic constraints, not previously considered in situation theory.

In this present paper, I shall give a brief summary of the discussion of the Sacks' article Rosenberg and I presented in (Devlin and Rosenberg, to appear), taking the situation-theoretic development we presented there a stage further, in particular, showing how situation theory can help describe the way that the constraints that govern normal behavior can arise through interactions in a social context. This leads to the introduction of a new category of situation-theoretic *types* not previously encountered in situation theory. Using these types—I refer to them as *evolved types*—I sketch an alternative (and in my view superior)

[2] A view which, I am afraid, is due in part to the manner in which my fellow mathematicians have traditionally regarded both their subject and its relation to other disciplines, particularly the humanities.

situation-theoretic analysis of the Sacks data than the one Rosenberg and I presented in (Devlin and Rosenberg, to appear).

The machinery I develop here sets the stage for a situation-theoretic investigation of the issue of *possible descriptions*: what is it about certain sequences of utterances that enables agents such as ourselves to recognize, without effort, a sequence of utterances as constituting, or possibly constituting, a description of some object, scene, or event? Though a discussion of this notion occupies a good deal of Sacks' paper, Rosenberg and I did not consider this aspect of Sacks' analysis in (Devlin and Rosenberg, to appear); rather we left that as the topic to be taken up in a later paper (Devlin and Rosenberg, in preparation a), which we are currently working on.

To skeptics that are tempted to read no further, let me at this stage simply quote one of the remarks Sacks makes early in his *mother–baby* article, a remark also addressed to anticipated skeptical readers (Sacks 1972: 330):

... I ask you to read on just far enough to see whether it is or is not the case that the observations [I make] are both relevant and defensible.

2 Mathematics and Sociology

The article by Benson and Hughes (Button 1991: Chapter 6) summarizes the most well-known application of mathematical techniques in sociology, the 'variable analysis' commonly associated with Lazarsfeld. In this approach to social study, various features of a society are denoted by numerical parameters, whose values are then obtained by empirical, investigative techniques (tabulating and counting). As a *statistical* approach, variable analysis can provide useful insights into the behavior of *sections* of a society, consisting of many members, and it may well be possible, on occasion, to particularize from such global findings to understand, and perhaps even predict, aspects of behavior of individual members of such a section. But, being quantitative, it is difficult to see how such techniques could be of much use to ethnomethodology, which concentrates on fundamental, cognitive and social behavior at the level of individuals.

Given the extensive use made of statistical techniques in sociology—in 1971, one commentator estimated (Phillips 1971) that some 90% of published empirical sociology was produced using the statistical manipulation of interview and questionnaire data—it is not surprising that to many sociologists, the phrase 'mathematical techniques' is virtually synonymous with 'statistical (or quantitative) techniques'. For instance, in the article mentioned above, Benson and Hughes claim that mathematical techniques are not appropriate in ethnomethodology, but their argument applies only to *quantitative* techniques, which they appear to confuse with the far more general notion of a 'mathematical technique'. Thus, on page 117 of (Button 1991), we read:

To the extent to which a mathematical system is applied, 'objects' in the target domain must be mapped onto 'objects', *that is numbers*, in the mathematical domain. [My emphasis.]

The authors seem to make two major assumptions here. Firstly, they (wrongly) assume that the only mathematical objects that might be used are numbers. And, even more fundamental, they apparently believe (again erroneously) that a mathematical system can only deal with abstract mathematical objects (be they numbers or other), and not with the same, real objects, agents, and data that the ethnomethodologist is mostly concerned with in her everyday work.

Clearly, then, before we can take another step, we need to be clear what is meant (certainly what I mean) by the word 'mathematics'.

Present-day mathematics evolved in eras when quantization was paramount: commerce, architecture, cartography, engineering, and the laboratory sciences all required numerically-based tools for measurement and computation. In contrast, the kind of mathematics I would suggest might be of assistance in an ethnomethodological analysis would be quite different, based on descriptive rather than numerical concepts. The relevant issues are essentially *descriptive* and *qualitative*, and are, as Benson and Hughes observe, not amenable to techniques that are ultimately *quantitative*. What is required then is *qualitative* or *descriptive* mathematics, not a *quantitative* theory.[3]

Certainly, the *development* of various kinds of mathematics to meet a particular need is not a new phenomenon. The evolution of mathematics is a long series of developments made in response to needs of the time: arithmetic to facilitate trade and commerce among the Sumerians, the Babylonians, and the Egyptians, geometry and trigonometry to support exploration and the construction of buildings by the Greeks, the calculus to allow for a precise study of motion and space in physics in the 17th Century, projective geometry to understand how a three-dimensional world may be represented on a two-dimensional canvas during the Renaissance period, techniques in calculus to meet the demands of structural and (later) electrical engineers in the 19th and early 20th Centuries, parts of logic and discrete methods to facilitate the development of computers in the 20th Century, and more recently developments in topology and knot theory to help understand the genetic material DNA.

There is, as far as I can see, no *a priori* reason that precludes the development of mathematical tools for use in sociology, including ethnomethodology. How much these tools resemble existing parts of mathematics is not clear, and is quite unimportant. What is important is that the machinery will have to be developed with the intended application firmly in mind, by carrying out the kind of study presented in this paper. In particular, the mathematical tools we produce must be designed and used in such a way that their formality does not constrict the application domain. This involves a careful choice of both the *level* at which the

---

[3] Though mathematics has always had qualitative aspects, the quantitative aspects have hitherto dominated, particularly in applications. Indeed, so fundamental has been number and measurement to most of mathematics over its 5,000 year history, that a great deal of the descriptive mathematics that has been used in, say, computer science and linguistics has had to be developed almost from scratch, with those applications in mind, largely based on mathematical logic, one of the few purely qualitative branches of classical mathematics.

mathematics is developed and applied, and the *granularity* of the mathematical framework that is developed at that level. (For instance, Euclidean geometry is an excellent mathematical tool for studying the geometry of the everyday world around us, but not at all suitable for studying the universe on either a cosmic or a subatomic level, when other descriptive mechanisms have to be used.)

The development of mathematical tools to be used in any discipline proceeds by a process of abstraction: fleshing out the abstract structures that underlie the phenomena under consideration, in a fashion consistent with the aims and overall methodology of that discipline. In the case of mathematical tools for use in ethnomethodology, attention needs to be paid to the intrinsic methodology of that particular approach to the study of social phenomena. The aim must be to abstract a mathematical framework *endogenous* to the system, not to port or adapt some mathematical framework developed for other purposes, least of all a framework developed for applications in the natural sciences.

Of course, the result of such a development may well be a mathematical theory that does not look very much like most existing branches of mathematics. If this is the case, then so be it. As Lynch says in (Button 1991: 97):

The policy of ethnomethodological indifference [to 'method'] requires that we put aside strong professional urgings to 'ground' inquiry in a set of *a priori* rules and standard techniques . . .

3 Situation Theory

Though developed initially by a logician (Jon Barwise), situation theory is not, as some have supposed, an attempt to extend classical logic to cover various real-world phenomena, in particular the use of natural language in communication. Such a *bottom-up*, mathematical-logic treatment of natural language has indeed been attempted, most notably by Chomsky, in the case of grammar and syntax, and by Montague in the case of semantics. In contrast, situation theory adopts a very definite *top-down* approach. Starting from the assumption that purposeful action and communication require a certain 'orderliness' in the world, situation theory attempts to develop—or more accurately *abstract*—a conceptual framework with which to describe and study that orderliness.

As a top-down development, situation theory deals with real objects, real agents, and real data, identifying and gradually refining the various abstract structures that arise from, and govern, the behavior and actions of members of a society.[4] (In contrast, bottom-up approaches generally start out with a collection of abstract, mathematical objects, often pure sets and functions, and gradually add structure until a model of the target phenomenon is obtained. In such an approach, the abstract mathematical objects are eventually taken to *represent*, in some sense, various objects and entities in the world.)

---

[4] Hitherto, the 'societies' considered have been linguistic communities or subcommunities thereof, including the case of computers and interactive information-processing systems.

In starting with empirical data, and gradually abstracting an appropriate (for our purposes) framework, we take care, at each stage, to make only the minimal restrictions and refinements necessary to proceed. Though formalization (in the usual sense of this word in mathematics) and axiomatization might well be ultimate goals (at least for some), the important issue is to remain as true to the data as possible; and every new restriction, every new tightening up of a definition, runs the risk of distorting the data or even excluding some features from further consideration. Such a cautious, painstaking, and in some ways deliberately non-committal approach is intensely frustrating to most mathematicians, including myself, but is absolutely necessary if there is to be any hope of achieving the desired aim.

A similar point is made by Jeff Coulter (Button 1991: 39–40), in connection with what he calls 'endogenous logic':[5]

The relative neglect of *symbolic* formalization and axiomatization within Endogenous Logic will not be discussed here: suffice to say, much of the narrowness of scope of traditional formal–logical studies of language may be attributed to attempts to preserve the consistency of a notation system at the expense of discerning fresh and actual logical relationships and connections orientable-to, and made by, practical reasoners in the course of conducting their everyday affairs. Further, an exclusive reliance upon supplementing the classical logical (particularly 'formal semantic') concepts with mathematical ones (especially the one of 'set'), and a related (Carnapian) insistence upon distinguishing between a 'logical' and a 'nonlogical' vocabulary or conceptual apparatus in natural languages, can both be seen now as unnecessary restrictions upon the logical investigation of language-use and cultural *praxis*. The exact extent of the revisions necessary in relation to former conceptions of logical analysis remains an open question.

Of course, even if we decide (as I do) to study, in a top-down fashion, the everyday world of objects, agents, spatial and temporal locations, and the like, that ordinary people see and experience as making up their *environment*, there has to be some initial set of assumptions concerning the kinds of abstract structures to be considered. Something has to distinguish our study from physics, chemistry, biology, psychology, and even from normative sociology and Garfinkel-style ethnomethodology. Though we are, as a driving methodology, taking the world (our data) as it is cut up by the ethnomethodologists, we are, after all, attempting to develop a new way of *looking at* that data. Situation theory is intended to provide a useful alternative view of issues such as linguistic communication and human interaction.

Situation theory is a conceptual framework for the study of *information*. When used as a framework for the study of social phenomena, the result is an

---

[5] There is as yet no such subject as 'endogenous logic'. Rather Coulter has proposed the development of such a logic, and has set out some guidelines for that development. The relationship between situation theory and Coulter's *desiderata* for such a logic is considered in Section 8.

information-theoretic approach to communication and action. To explain what these two statements mean, I refer to Fig. 1.

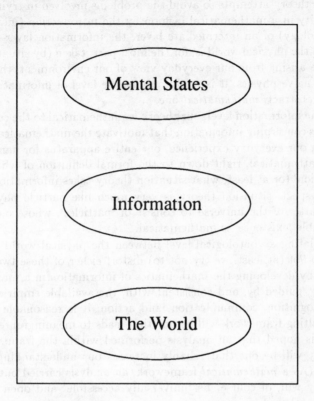

Fig. 1. The information level

In order to study cognition, communication, and action *in a manner that accepts our everyday view of the physical world*, we need to take account of two distinct domains: the (physical) world on the one hand, and mental states on the other.[6] In the case of the former, the physical world, mathematics can provide us with a number of proven techniques and well-worked-out models. Indeed, this is the domain in which the development and use of mathematical techniques has been supremely successful. The same cannot be said for the other domain, the domain of mental states. Though research in artificial intelligence and in cognitive science has attempted to develop the appropriate machinery, this effort has, to date, been largely unsuccessful. Indeed, I see no reason to

---

[6] I am making some element of judgment here. Behaviorism could be said to be an attempt to circumvent the requirement of a model of mental states, by reducing all cognitive activity to the externally manifested stimulus–response activity of the agent. However, few workers these days believe that this approach would be adequate for the kind of purposes outlined in this paper.

assume that mathematical techniques will ever be as successful in providing models of cognitive activity as they have been in modeling the physical world.

Situation theory attempts to avoid the problems involved in trying to model mental activity in a mathematical fashion by the introduction (into the mathematical ontology) of an intermediate layer, the information layer—see Fig. 1. Indeed, since the physical world is, for the most part, taken (by situation theory) to be the one arising from our everyday view of our environment, that is to say, the world of naive physics, it is really only at the level of information that the theory is an abstract, *mathematical* one.

And at the information level, our theory is mathematical to the core. Though the intuitions concerning information that motivate the mathematical treatment are rooted in our everyday experience, our entire apparatus for handling information is mathematical, right down to the formal definition of what we mean by 'information' (or at least, what situation theory takes information to be).

In this respect, situation theory is very much like particle physics, which takes the matter of the universe to consist of 'particles', whose only real and unchallengeable 'existence' is mathematical.

By postulating an ontological level between the physical world and mental states, we do not (at least, we try not to) distort either of those two aspects of reality. And by developing the mathematics of information in a manner that is motivated by, guided by, and consistent with, the available empirical evidence concerning cognition, communication, and action, it is reasonable to suppose that the resulting framework will be one that leads to meaningful results. More precisely, it is hoped that an analysis performed within the framework of situation theory will be one that reliably increases our understanding of various phenomena. (As a *mathematical* framework, an analysis carried out within situation theory will, of course, be 'universally accessible' and open to detailed inspection by others.)

This does not in any way make situation theory a 'theory of everything', not even everything in the cognitive domain. But it does, I believe, result in a framework that has considerable potential utility.

I am very aware that such an approach, indeed any approach that adopts a particular methodological 'stance', risks the fate that, according to Benson and Hughes (Button 1991: 125), befalls variable analysis:

... the burden of the ethnomethodological critique is, as far as variable analysis is concerned, that it sets the conditions for sociological description in advance so that we look at the phenomena through a grid that we impose upon them, *irrespective of whatever properties the phenomena might otherwise display.* [Emphasis as in the original.]

Stepping the path between adopting a particular viewpoint to gain understanding, and allowing the particulars of that viewpoint obscure what is being viewed, is a delicate one, and the best one can do is to keep referring back to the data as it is, and not how we might like it to be. This is, after all, what is done in the natural sciences. In physics, for example, there is no doubt that one is working not with 'the real, physical universe', but with a mathematical idealization, or model, of that domain. What makes the resulting theory so useful is that the physicist constantly compares her model with data from the real world. Occasionally, a discrepancy is found, and the model (not the world) has to be changed, as happened when Newtonian mechanics was found lacking and supplanted (for certain purposes) by the theories of relativity and quantum mechanics. In itself, there is nothing wrong with adopting a particular viewpoint or framework; indeed, without it, it is hard to see how any progress (in developing our understanding) could be made. This procedure only breaks down when the theoretical stance or framework continues to be used in circumstances discovered to be inappropriate.

To the critic who says that such a 'rationalist' (or Leibnizian) approach is not suitable in the case of ethnomethodology, I would say two things:

Firstly, use of a tool does not require a commitment to the framework within which that tool was developed. What counts is how effective that tool is in carrying out the task at hand. Just as the sociologist, psychologist, or phenomenologist, may make use of a computer in her analysis of human activity, without committing to the view that the computer (a Leibnizian device if ever there were one) provides a good model of human cognitive behavior, so too the argument Rosenberg and I present in (Devlin and Rosenberg, to appear) demonstrates, at the very least, that the ethnomethodologist may use situation theory as an effective, analytic tool, without such use requiring or entailing any commitment to our philosophy.

Secondly, it is surely foolish to turn one's back on *any* means to achieve greater understanding of significant aspects of the problem relevant to the purpose of the analysis. Faced with a highly complicated phenomenon—and in studying human behavior, the sociologist is surely faced with a phenomenon as complicated as it gets—the better ways one can find to look at that phenomenon, the greater will be the final understanding.

Presented with an unfamiliar object, the most sensible way to gain a proper understanding of that object is to view, examine, and analyze it in as many different ways as possible, using whatever tools we have at our disposal: look at it from all sides, pick it up, weigh it, X-ray it, take it apart, dissect it, analyze its chemical and physical composition, etc.

Likewise, a well-taken photograph of a country scene, being an accurate *visual* portrayal, will provide me with a pretty good sense of that scene. But my appreciation will be greater, and deeper, if I am also shown a good oil-painting, through which medium the artist can convey many of the aspects of the scene that a photograph cannot capture, aspects relating to mood and emotion and visual texture. A recording of the sounds at the location will provide still further understanding. And greater still will be my appreciation, if the picture and the painting and the sound-recording are accompanied by a poem or a piece of well-written prose, or even, on occasion, by a well-chosen (or inspirationally written) piece of music. (Notice that the painting, sound-recording, poem, prose, or music need not be acknowledged as good *within their respective disciplines* in order to be efficacious in contributing to my overall appreciation of the scene, which comes from a holistic synthesis of all the different portrayals.)

If the aim is to achieve as good an understanding as possible—and this, I take it, is the purpose of interdisciplinary research—then there is likely to be something to be gained by any additional means by which we can describe and analyze the phenomenon of interest. Situation theory is intended to provide one method by which one may gain a measure of understanding of communication and action.

In particular, situation theory offers us better understanding because it forces us to clarify issues that the social science perspective alone will (of necessity) take as given. Taken together, the two approaches make us examine and question issues that would otherwise not be noticed as problematic and non-trivial.

NOTE: *The remainder of this section consists of a brief summary of the basic ideas of situation theory. As such, the exposition is fairly technical, and the reader might prefer to skip ahead to the next section, and come back to this account as and when it proves necessary. A more leisurely, and comprehensive account of elementary situation theory is provided in (Devlin 1991.)*

Situation theory takes its name from the mathematical device introduced in order to take account of context and partiality. A *situation* can be thought of as a limited part of reality. Such parts may have spatio-temporal extent, or they may be more 'abstract,' such as fictional worlds, contexts of utterance, problem domains, mathematical structures, databases, or Unix directories. The status of situations in the ontology of situation theory is equal to that of (say) individuals; the distinction between the two being that situations have a *structure* that plays a significant role in the theory whereas individuals do not. Examples of situations of particular relevance to the subject matter of this paper will arise as the development proceeds.

The basic ontology of situation theory consists of entities that people, or other kinds of agent, individuate and/or discriminates as they make their way in the world: spatial locations, temporal locations, individuals, finitary relations, situations, types, and a number of other, 'higher-order' entities, together with some theorist's conveniences such as parameters.

The objects (known as *uniformities*) in this ontology include the following.

- *individuals* — objects such as tables, chairs, tetrahedra, cubes, people, hands, fingers, etc. that the agent either individuates or at least discriminates (by its behavior) as single, essentially unitary items; usually denoted in our theory by $a, b, c, \ldots$.
- *relations* — uniformities individuated or discriminated by the agent that hold of, or link together specific numbers of, certain other uniformities; denoted by $P, Q, R, \ldots$.
- spatial *locations*, denoted by $l, l', l'', l_0, l_1, l_2$, etc. These are not necessarily like the 'points' of mathematical spaces (though they may be so), but can have spatial extension.

- *temporal locations*, denoted by $t, t', t_0, \ldots$. As with spatial locations, temporal locations may be either points in time or regions of time.
- *situations* — structured parts of the world (concrete or abstract) discriminated by (or perhaps individuated by) the agent; denoted by $s, s', s'', s_0, \ldots$
- *types* — higher order uniformities discriminated (and possibly individuated) by the agent; denoted by $S, T, U, V, \ldots$.
- *parameters* — indeterminates that range over objects of the various types; denoted by $\dot{a}, \dot{s}, \dot{i}, \dot{l}$, etc.

The framework that 'picks out' the ontology is referred to as the *scheme of individuation*. The intuition is that in a study of the activity (both physical and cognitive) of a particular agent or species of agent, we notice that there are certain regularities or *uniformities* that the agent either individuates or else discriminates in its behavior.

For instance, people individuate certain parts of reality as *objects* ('individuals' in our theory), and their behavior can vary in a systematic way according to spatial location, time, and the nature of the immediate environment ('situation types' in our theory).

Information is always taken to be information *about* some situation, and is taken to be in the form of discrete items known as *infons*. These are of the form

$$\ll R, a_1, \ldots, a_n, 1 \gg , \; \ll R, a_1, \ldots, a_n, 0 \gg$$

where R is an n-place relation and $a_1, \ldots, a_n$ are objects appropriate for R (often including spatial and/or temporal locations). These may be thought of as the informational item expressing that objects $a_1, \ldots, a_n$ do, or respectively, do not, stand in the relation R.

Infons are 'items of information'. They are not things that in themselves are true or false. Rather a particular item of information may be true or false *about a certain part of the world* (a 'situation').

Infons may be combined to form what are known as *compound infons*: the permissible combinatory operations consist of conjunction, disjunction, and bounded universal and existential quantification (by parameters). I omit the details in this brief summary.

Given a situation, s, and an infon σ, we write

$$s \models \sigma$$

to indicate that the infon σ is 'made factual by' the situation s, or, to put it another way, that σ is an item of information that is true of s. The official name for this relation is that s *supports* σ. The facticity claim $s \models \sigma$ is referred to as a *proposition*.

It should be noted that this approach treats 'information' as a *commodity*. Moreover a commodity that does not have to be 'true.' Indeed, for every positive infon there is a dual negative infon that can be thought of as the 'opposite' informational item, and both of these cannot be 'true.'

The *types* of the theory are defined by applying two type-abstraction procedures, starting with an initial collection of *basic types*. The basic types correspond to the process of individuating or discriminating uniformities in the world at the most fundamental level. Among the *basic types* are:

TIM : the type of a temporal location;
LOC : the type of a spatial location;
IND : the type of an individual;
REL^n : the type of an n-place relation;
SIT : the type of a situation;
INF : the type of an infon;
PAR : the type of an *parameter*.

For each basic type T other than *PAR*, there is an infinite collection $T_1, T_2, T_3, \ldots$ of *basic parameters*, used to denote arbitrary objects of type T. We generally use the less formal notation $\dot{l}, \dot{t}, \dot{a}, \dot{s}$, etc. to denote parameters (in this case of type *LOC, TIM, IND, SIT*, respectively).

Given an object, x, and a type, T, we write

$$x : T$$

to indicate that the object x is *of* type T.

Most uses of parameters require what are known as *restricted parameters* whose range is more fine grained than the basic parameters. In essence, the mechanism for constructing restricted parameters enables us to make use of parameters restricted to range over any relevant domain. See (Devlin 1991) for details.

There are two kinds of type-abstraction, leading to two kinds of types. First of all there are the *situation-types*. Given a *SIT*-parameter, $\dot{s}$, and a compound infon σ, there is a corresponding *situation-type*

$$[\dot{s} \mid \dot{s} \models \sigma],$$

the *type* of situation in which σ obtains.

This process of obtaining a type from a parameter, $\dot{s}$, and a compound infon, σ, is known as *(situation-) type abstraction*. We refer to the parameter $\dot{s}$ as the *abstraction parameter* used in this type abstraction.

For example,

$$[SIT_1 \mid SIT_1 \models \ll \text{running}, \dot{p}, LOC_1, TIM_1, 1 \gg]$$

(where $\dot{p}$ is a parameter for a person) denotes the type of situation in which someone is running at some location and at some time. A situation s will be of this type just in case someone is running in that situation (at some location, at some time).

As well as situation-types, our theory also allows for *object-types*. These include the basic types *TIM, LOC, IND, REL^n, SIT*, and *INF*, as well as the more fine-grained uniformities described below.

Object-types are determined over some initial situation. Let s be a given situation. If $\dot{x}$ is a parameter and σ is some compound infon (in general having $\dot{x}$ as a constituent), then there is a type

$$[\dot{x} \mid s \models \sigma],$$

the *type* of all those objects x to which $\dot{x}$ may be anchored in the situation s, for which the conditions imposed by σ obtain in s.

This process of obtaining a type from a parameter $\dot{x}$, a situation s, and a compound infon σ, is known as *(object-) type abstraction*. The parameter $\dot{x}$ is known as the *abstraction parameter* used in this type abstraction.

The situation s is known as the *grounding* situation for the type. In many instances, the grounding situation s is 'the world' or 'the environment' we live in (generally denoted by w in my account). For example, the *type* of all people could be denoted by

$$[IND_1 \mid w \models \ll \text{person}, IND_1, l_w, i_{now}, 1 \gg]$$

Constraints, the facilitators and inhibitors of information flow, are abstract links between types of situation. They may be natural laws, conventions, logical (i.e., analytic) rules, linguistic rules, empirical, law-like correspondences, or whatever. Their role in the information chain is quite well conveyed by the use of the word *means*. For instance, consider the statement

smoke means fire.

This expresses a constraint (of the natural law variety). What it says is that there is a lawlike relation that links situations where there is smoke to situations where there is fire. If T_{smoke} is the type of situations where there is smoke present, and T_{fire} is the type of situations where there is a fire, then an agent (eg. a person) can pick up the information that there is a fire by observing that there is smoke (a type T_{smoke} situation) and being aware of, or *attuned to,* the constraint that links the two kinds of situation, denoted by

$$T_{smoke} \Rightarrow T_{fire}$$

(This is read as "T_{smoke} *involves* T_{fire}.")

As a constraint that holds 'because the world is that way', this constraint is one that holds regardless of the presence or absence of any cognitive agent, and is an instance of what is referred to as a *nomic constraint*. For an example of a non-nomic constraint, consider:

FIRE *means fire.*

This describes the linguistic constraint

$$T_{utterance} \Rightarrow T_{fire}$$

that links situations (of type $T_{utterance}$) where someone yells the word FIRE to situations (of type T_{fire}) where there is a fire. Awareness of this constraint involves knowing the meaning of the word FIRE and being familiar with the rules that govern the use of language.

The three types just introduced may be defined as follows:

$$T_{smoke} = [\dot{s} \mid \dot{s} \models \ll \text{smokey}, i, 1 \gg]$$
$$T_{fire} = [\dot{s} \mid \dot{s} \models \ll \text{firey}, i, 1 \gg]$$
$$T_{utterance} = [\dot{u} \mid \dot{u} \models \ll \text{speaking}, \dot{a}, i, 1 \gg \wedge \ll \text{utters}, \dot{a}, \text{FIRE}, i, 1 \gg]$$

The use of the same time parameter i in all three types indicates that there is no time-slippage in either case. The smoke and the fire are simultaneous, and so are the utterance and the fire. In general, parameters keep track of the various informational links that are instrumental in the way constraints operate.

Notice that constraints links types, not situations. On the other hand, any particular instance where a constraint is utilized to make an inference or modify behavior will involve specific situations (of the relevant types). Thus constraints function by relating various regularities or uniformities across actual situations.

4 The Sacks Analysis

I turn now to the examination Rosenberg and I made (Devlin and Rosenberg to appear) of Sacks' analysis of the two-sentence 'story opening':

The baby cried. The mommy picked it up.

The following object-types are particularly central to the analysis (i.e., to our situation-theoretic adaptation of Sacks' own analysis):

– $T_{baby} = [\dot{p} \mid w \models \ll \text{baby}, \dot{p}, t_{now}, 1 \gg]$, the type of all babies,

where $\dot{p}$ is a parameter for a person and w is 'the world', by which I mean any situation big enough to include everything under discussion;

– $T_{mother} = [\dot{p} \mid w \models \ll \text{mother}, \dot{p}, t_{now}, 1 \gg]$, the type of all mothers;
– T_{family}, a type of types, consisting of types such as 'baby', 'mommy', 'daddy', etc.;
– $T_{stage-of-life}$, a type of types, consisting of types such as 'baby', 'child', 'adult', etc.

The first two of the above types correspond to what Sacks refers to as *categories*. The correspondence is sufficiently close that I shall regard the terms 'category' and 'object-type (of individual)' as synonymous.

In addition to categories, Sacks also makes use of what he calls 'categorization devices'. He defines a *(membership) categorization device* (or simply a *device*) to be a non-empty collection of categories, together with rules of application. When endowed with the appropriate structure, the types T_{family} and $T_{stage-of-life}$ each correspond to a *categorization device*.

Categorization devices are structured objects, whose structure plays a role in the cognitive and social activities of agents that discriminate the devices and their component types.

For instance, the type $T_{stage-of-life}$ is linearly ordered:

$$T_{baby} < T_{child} < T_{adolescent} < T_{young-adult} < T_{adult} < T_{elderly}.$$

Of course, there are no clear-cut divisions between any adjacent pair of types in this chain. But when the vagueness of the types is 'factored out', the resulting order is indeed a linear ordering of the device.

People are aware of this ordering, and make use of it in their everyday lives. For instance, it can be used to praise or degrade others, using phrases such as 'acting like an adult' to praise a child, 'acting like a child' to degrade an adult, or 'acting like a baby' to degrade a child. In other words, people make systematic use of a relation

$$less\text{-}than(T, T')$$

between types T, T' in the device $T_{stage-of-life}$, a relation that, subject to vagueness of the types involved, is based on age.

What makes this kind of thing possible is that a society will often attach *values* to the nodes of the structure of a device. For instance, in contemporary American and European society, the optimal point in the stage-of-life device is usually T_{adult}, and progression along the device-ordering, starting from T_{baby}, and proceeding through T_{child}, $T_{adolescent}$, $T_{young-adult}$, and up to T_{adult}, is normally regarded as a steady increase in status in society, with the final step to $T_{elderly}$ regarded as a retrograde step down from the optimum.

The precise valuation may, however, vary from society to society. For example, in certain African tribes, status within the stage-of-life device increases throughout the entire linear ordering, with $T_{elderly}$ regarded as occupying the most-respected, optimal position in the device.

Academic hierarchies provide another, interesting example of a categorization device. For instance, if T_D is a State university-system, the device T_D has a precisely defined hierarchical structure (a tree) having a single top-node (the system president), directly beneath whom are a number of campus-presidents, together with the system-presidents' aids. Beneath each campus-president are the various deans along with the campus-presidents' aids, and so forth. Since the university system will be *defined* (as a university system) in this way, in this case the mathematical realization of the device-structure (a partial ordering) is an accurate model of the reality.

Such a hierarchy is constructed with the intention that the associated valuation is a monotonic one: the higher up the partial ordering one is, the greater is supposed to be the status, with the system-president occupying the most prestigious position of all.

Now, because of the highly visible and fundamental role this kind of structural hierarchy plays in the very establishment and operation of the system, those outside the system, such as journalists or government officials, will generally assume the intended valuation whenever they have dealings with the system. But other groups may attach other valuations to the structure, and indeed may add additional structure to the hierarchy. For instance, many research-oriented academics regard research professors or laboratory directors as occupying the optimal category, ranking well above administrative positions. In this case, the hierarchical structure is the same, what differs is the valuation associated with that structure.

Again, people familiar with the system often assume a linear or partial ranking of the individual institutions in the system, resulting in a corresponding ranking of the individual campus presidents, etc. This structure is additional to, and consistent with, the original system-hierarchy.

Of course, the provision of a mathematically precise structure does not at all amount to a claim that people do in fact act 'mathematically' (whatever that might mean). Rather the use of a mathematical structure simply provides us with a very precise descriptive device to handle one aspect of a highly complex phenomenon. Given such a formal conceptualization of a certain social structure as a mathematical structure with a social valuation, we may then go on to investigate the constraints that govern the way behavior is influenced by those features.

Other structural aspects of devices concern the constraints that link types within a device. I take up this issue next.

As originally developed by Barwise and Perry (1983), and used widely within situation theory and situation semantics (see (Devlin 1991)), constraints provide (are) links between situation-types, links that capture (are) systematic regularities connecting situations of one kind with situations of another. The idea is to provide a mechanism for studying context: the situations are for the most part contexts for the agent, contexts that influence the agent's activity.

Thus (Devlin 1991) provides the following 'standard' picture of constraints. A *constraint* is a particular kind of linkage $S \Rightarrow T$ that connects two situation-types S, T. Given a situation s of type S, the constraint $S \Rightarrow T$ provides the information that there is a situation t of type T. In typical cases, the situation t is, or may be regarded as, an extension of s, and thus the constraint provides information about the larger actuality of which s is part.

In order to address some of the questions Sacks investigates from the perspective of situation theory, it is necessary to extend the notion and theory of constraints quite a bit further. In particular, the notion of a constraint must be extended to cover not just situation-types but object-types as well.

In (Devlin and Rosenberg, to appear), we introduce constraints of the form $U \Rightarrow V$, where

$$U = [\dot{x} \mid u \models \sigma(\dot{x})] \ , \quad V = [\dot{y} \mid v \models \tau(\dot{y})]$$

for some grounding situations u, v and compound (parametric) infons σ, τ. This constraint provides an 'associative link' between objects of type U and objects of type V, in that an agent $\mathcal{A}$ that is aware of, or attuned to, this constraint will, when it encounters an object x of type U *as an object of type U* and, under the same circumstances encounters an object y of type V, will regard, or encounter, y *as an object of type V*. (It is possible that x and y are identical here, in which case we say that the constraint is functioning *reflexively*.)

For example, there is a constraint

$$T_{baby} \Rightarrow T_{mother}$$

such that, if $\mathcal{A}$ is attuned to this constraint and encounters an object B of type T_{baby} and an object M of type T_{mother}, and furthermore, $\mathcal{A}$ encounters B *as an object of type* T_{baby}, then $\mathcal{A}$ will in fact encounter M as an object of type T_{mother}.

In (Devlin and Rosenberg, to appear), we call such a constraint an *associative link*. Associative links are an important special case of what we call *normative constraints*; these are informational constraints that guide the normal behavior of agents.

Of course, though an associative link might provide a situation-theoretic mechanism corresponding to normal behavior, it does not on its own say anything about what evokes a particular link on a given occasion. Indeed, the same may also be said of the more familiar situation-type constraints described in (Devlin 1991): what makes a particular constraint *salient* on a given occasion, so that an agent does in fact modify its behavior in response to that constraint? The answer is, in large part, beyond the scope of situation theory, which sets out to provide a framework for studying cognitive behavior in terms of information flow 'in the world' (i.e., between agents), but does not attempt to provide a theory of mind. However, part of the answer is at the very least closely connected to the issue of just what it is in the world that *supports* a given constraint, the issue I take up next.

Let me start with the more familiar kinds of constraints that link situation-types.[7] To be even more definite, let me take the following oft-used examples of constraints discussed in (Devlin 1991: 91–94):

(C_1)   *smoke means fire*

(C_2)   *the ringing bell means class is over*

(C_3)   COOKIE *means cookie*

C_1 is what is normally referred to as a *nomic* constraint, one that obtains because the world is the way it is. Now, C_1 is a fact about the world, and as such may be represented as an infon, namely

$$\sigma_1 = \ll \text{involves}, T_{smoke}, T_{fire}, l_C, t_C, 1 \gg,$$

where l_C and t_C are the location and time periods in which this constraint obtains. (In particular, l_C includes the surface of the Earth and t_C includes the present epoch.) In fact, according to the situation-theoretic view of the world, when considered as a fact about the world, the constraint C_1 *is* this infon, and

---

[7] The following discussion is taken almost verbatim from (Devlin and Rosenberg to appear). I include it here for the convenience of readers who do not have a copy of that paper to hand.

the factuality of C_1 is expressed by the proposition that σ_1 is supported by the appropriate situation.

The question now is, what is the appropriate situation? It is consistent with the level to which the theory was developed there to take the supporting situation to be the whole world, w, and express the factuality of the constraint C_1 by means of the proposition

$$w \models \sigma_1.$$

For the present analysis, however, such an answer is far too crude. We need to ask ourselves just what it means to say a certain constraint obtains.

Well, the constraint C_1 is a certain regularity in the world, an abstract feature of the world comprising a systematic linkage between situations of the two types T_{smoke} and T_{fire}. But what is the ontological status of this systematic linkage other than a situation? (See (Devlin 1991: 69-85) for a discussion of the nature of situations.) And it is precisely this situation that supports C_1, of course. I shall denote this situation by $Support(C_1)$.

In general, any nomic constraint C will comprise a systematic, informational link between pairs of situations, situations of types T and T', respectively, and as a systematic regularity in the world, this linkage will constitute a situation, which I shall denote by $Support(C)$. This situation will include, in particular, the relevant causality between situations of type T and those situations of type T' to which they are linked. Moreover,

$$Support(C) \models C$$

and $Support(C)$ is in a sense the 'minimal' situation that supports C.

Of course, there is a certain apparent triviality to the above, in that I seem to come close to claiming that it is the constraint that supports the constraint. Well, in a way I am, but the matter is not quite as simple as that, and besides even this *apparent* triviality is not the case for all constraints, and indeed is, in general, characteristic of the nomic constraints. A nomic constraint holds in the world because that is the way the world is; what makes a particular regularity a (nomic) *constraint* is the role it plays in guiding the flow of information. That is to say, in the case of a nomic constraint, the distinction between the regularity (i.e., situation) and the constraint is essentially one of abstraction and functionality.

Thus, an agent that observes instances of smoke being related to fire observes parts of a certain situation, $Support(C_1)$. As a result of a number of such observations, perhaps backed up by other means of acquiring information about smoke and fire, the agent might then come to be aware of, or attuned to, the constraint C_1 (abstraction), and to make use of that constraint (functionality). But the agent is not going to become aware of the *situation* $Support(C_1)$; such highly abstract situations are not the kind of object that agents normally become aware of (as entities in the world).

For a nomic constraint such as C_1, then, it is the very uniformity linking smokey situations to firey situations that constitutes the situation that supports the constraint, and the constraint may be regarded as an *abstraction* from that situation. Turning to the second of the three examples, C_2, things are quite different. Here it is not at all the systematic linkage between situations in which a bell rings and situations in which the class is over that constitutes the supporting situation. The connection between two such situations is not, after all, an aspect of the way the world is, even if we restrict things to the particular educational establishment concerned. Rather the connection exists purely by virtue of some previously established convention. That is to say, the 'minimal' situation that supports C_2, $Support(C_2)$, the situation *by virtue of which* C_2 obtains, is the situation comprising the convention. This is, of course, a highly abstract situation that exists purely as an aspect of the behavior of a certain community. As far as I know, prior to (Devlin and Rosenberg, to appear), situations of this kind had not previously been considered in situation theory. Though they do not readily fall into the category of 'parts of the world' that is often used to explain the concept of a situation, they do arise in a quite natural way when we ask the question "What is it in the world that supports a particular constraint (i.e., infon)?" I shall have more to say on the nature of situations in just a moment.

Of course, a particular student may come to be aware of the constraint C_2 by observing the systematic way ringing bells are followed by the ending of class, without ever being informed that there is a previously established convention to this effect, but this says nothing about what it is in the world that actually *supports* this constraint.

My third example, C_3, is a linguistic constraint connected with the (American) English language. Though one could take the supporting situation to be the regularity that connects uses of the word COOKIE to instances of cookie (i.e., to actual cookies), this would amount to reducing language to a whole bag of isolated words and connections. More reasonable is to take the supporting situation in the case of a linguistic constraint to be the entire language situation; that is to say, the complete collection of rules, norms, and practices that constitutes the English language. Again this is a highly abstract kind of situation, not previously encountered in situation theory (at least not in the form of a situation in the ontology). It is similar in nature to the 'ringing bell means class is over' constraint just discussed, except that the ringing bell support-situation is restricted to one particular constraint whereas the English language situation supports all English meaning relations.

Notice that we have now arrived at a much more general notion of 'situation' than the one explicitly described in (Devlin 1991) (though that treatment simply left open the possibility of extending the notion along the present lines). We may think of situations as aggregates of features of the world that constitute an *aspect* of the world. That aspect may be physical, possibly located in time and/or space, or abstract, perhaps consisting of systematic regularities in the world, as in the case of nomic constraints, or maybe arising from the intentional activity of cognitive agents, as in the case of language or social conventions.

With the discussion of the more familiar kind of constraint behind us now, I turn to the associative links. Consider first the constraint

$$T_{baby} \Rightarrow T_{mother}.$$

This links the two concepts of babies and mothers. What supports it? Well, it is one of the constraints that could be said to be part of the 'world of families'. But in situation-theoretic terms, the 'world of families' constitutes a situation. (More precisely, it constitutes a number of situations, the 'close family' situation and various 'extended family' situations. I shall restrict my attention to the former for the time being.) This situation comprises everything that is part and parcel of being a family, and thus is captured within the existing situation-theoretic framework as $Oracle\,(T_{family})$. (More precisely, as $Oracle_\Gamma(T_{family})$, for an appropriate set of issues Γ. See (Devlin 1991: Section 3.5) for details.) This is the situation that supports the constraint:

$$Oracle\,(T_{family}) \models T_{baby} \Rightarrow T_{mother}.$$

Notice that for an associative link such as this, it is not so much the validity of this proposition that is relevant, as is the issue of whether or not the link is *salient* to the agent at a particular juncture. That is to say, what counts is whether the agent's behavior is governed by, or guided by, the link. And the agent's behavior will be so influenced if it is currently operating in the context $Oracle\,(T_{family})$. I shall write

$$Oracle\,(T_{family}) \,\|{-}\, T_{baby} \Rightarrow T_{mother}$$

to indicate that the constraint $T_{baby} \Rightarrow T_{mother}$ is *salient* in $Oracle\,(T_{family})$.

The notation $s \,\|{-}\, C$ is borrowed from set theory, where it is articulated "s *forces C*".

In general, a given situation will support a great many constraints, many of them irrelevant as far as the agent's current activity is concerned. But for many situations, in particular the ones that arise as contexts for cognitive activity, there is often a 'hierarchy' of constraints, with some constraints being more prevalent (i.e., more likely to influence the agent's behavior) than others. I refer to the prevalence of a particular constraint or constraints in a situation as *salience*, and write

$$s \,\|{-}\, C$$

to indicate that the constraint C is *salient* in the situation s. Clearly,

$$s \,\|{-}\, C \quad \text{implies} \quad s \models C$$

but not conversely.

When an agent acts within a particular context s, its behavior will be strongly influenced by the constraints that are salient to s (among those supported by s). The greater the salience, the more will be the influence, though at this level of analysis I shall not introduce any non-trivial spectrum of salience.

The major complicating factor here is that, in general, an agent will be simultaneously operating in a number of contextual situations, each bringing with it its own salience hierarchy, and the different constraints that are salient in the respective contexts may well 'compete' for influence. Sometimes two constraints will be mutually supportive, but on other occasions salient constraints in two contexts may be mutually contradictory, and the agent must 'choose' between them. How all of this works, or rather what mechanisms may be developed to provide a useful description of this phenomenon, is an issue that needs to be taken up by situation-theorists in due course.

The salience of a particular constraint C in a situation s is often a reflection of the fact that C is closely bound up with the structure of s.

For example, the situation $Oracle\,(T_{family})$ supports many constraints concerning family relationships and the way members of a family behave to each other, including constraints that, while they undoubtedly guide and influence an agent's behavior, do so in a highly peripheral way as far as purposeful activity is concerned, such as the constraint that a family member is human, that husbands are male, etc. On the other hand, some constraints are particularly salient to this situation, in particular those that concern the family relationships that bind the family together as a family, such as the associative link that says a mother is the mother of a child, a husband is the husband of a wife, etc.

In particular, the type $T_{mother\text{-}of}$ acts as a 'fundamental' one within T_{family}, with the types T_{mother} and T_{baby} being linked to, and potentially derivative on, that type. More precisely, the following structural constraints are salient in the device T_{family} :

$$T_{mother} \Rightarrow \exists \ddot{y} T_{mother\text{-}of}$$

$$T_{baby} \;\; \Rightarrow \exists \dot{x} T_{mother\text{-}of}$$

where T_{mother} is the 2-type

$$[\dot{x}, \dot{y} \mid w \models \ll \text{mother-of}, \dot{x}, \dot{y}, t_{now}, 1 \gg].$$

This has the following consequence: in the case where $T_{mother} : T_{family}$ (i.e., T_{mother} is of type T_{family}) and $T_{baby} : T_{family}$, the following implications are salient:

$$p : T_{mother} \;\rightarrow\; \exists q \,(p, q : T_{mother\text{-}of}) \tag{1}$$

$$q : T_{baby} \;\rightarrow\; \exists p \,(p, q : T_{mother\text{-}of}). \tag{2}$$

These two implications are not constraints. In fact they do not have any formal significance in situation theory. They are purely guides to the reader as to where this is all leading.

It should be noted that normative constraints, such as the associative links, are a product of evolution: they evolve along with the society they pertain to. The result of such an evolutionary process is a sort of 'chicken-and-egg' state of affairs, whereby members[8] can be said to behave *according to certain normative constraints*, and indeed on occasions may even explicitly *follow* some of those

---

[8] I generally use the word 'member' in the sociologist's sense, to mean 'member of a society', or, depending on context, 'member of the society under consideration', and use the word 'agent' for the more general notion of any cognitive agent, not necessarily human.

constraints, and yet those constraints obtain *by virtue of the fact that members normally behave that way*. A similar remark can be made about linguistic constraints, of course.

Category-binding constraints constitute another class of constraints that arise from a situation-theoretic analysis of the Sacks paper.[9] A *category-binding constraint* is a link between an activity (i.e., a relation in the ontology) A and a type T. The salience of such a constraint means that a person would normally associate the activity A with objects of type T.

As in the case of associative links, the issue of relevance for a category-binding constraint is salience in a context rather than factuality (i.e., being supported by the context). For instance, in the device $T_{stage\text{-}of\text{-}life}$, the activity of crying is *category bound* to the type T_{baby}; thus

$$Oracle\,(T_{stage\text{-}of\text{-}life})\ \Vdash\ crying \Rightarrow T_{baby}.$$

According to Sacks, evidence that the activity of 'crying' is category-bound to the type T_{baby} in the device $T_{stage\text{-}of\text{-}life}$ is provided by the fact (mentioned earlier) that members recognize a link between the activity of 'crying' and the position of the category T_{baby} in the linear-ordering structure of the device. For instance, a member of T_{child} who cries might be said to be 'acting like a baby' and a member of T_{baby} who does not cry when the circumstances might warrant it, such as following an injury, might be praised as 'acting like a big boy/girl'.

This seems to be an instance of a more general phenomenon, whereby one feature of an activity A being category-bound to a type T_C in a device T_D is that A is closely related to the position of T_C within the structure on T_D.

When category-binding arises, as it generally does, by virtue of the very structure of a particular device, listeners can make use of this tight relationship to obtain what, in a slightly different context, Barwise and Perry (1983: 167–168) have called 'inverse information'.

For example, utterance of the word 'baby' can trigger in the listener a number of different information structures, among them the device $T_{stage\text{-}of\text{-}life}$ and the device T_{family}. Each of these devices will bring to bear different sets of constraints, which will influence subsequent processing in different ways. Hearing the sentence "The baby cried", however, the combination of 'baby' with 'crying' can suggest to the listener that the appropriate device here is $T_{stage\text{-}of\text{-}life}$. Thus, the listener will normally hear the utterance of this sentence in such a way that

$$T_{baby} : T_{stage\text{-}of\text{-}life}.$$

That is to say, this item of information will be available to the listener as he processes the incoming utterance, and will influence the way the input is interpreted.

Since the normal situation-theoretic scenario is for an available context to combine with an utterance to determine information content, the inference of

---

[9] Though Rosenberg and I did not single out these particular constraints in our paper (Devlin and Rosenberg, to appear).

an appropriate context from an utterance (together with other, background information, such as social knowledge) in the way just considered is an instance of 'inverse information'. In his paper, Sacks presents other examples of this phenomenon that arise in everyday discourse. Indeed, as Sacks observes,[10] people often make use of the device of category-binding and inverse information to avoid direct mention of delicate or unpleasant contextual features.

Pulling the various observations together now, here is the situation-theoretic analogue of Sacks' analysis of the two-sentence data.

Let s denote the described situation for the discourse. The situation s will be such that it involves one and only one baby, otherwise the use of the phrase 'the baby' would not be appropriate. In starting a communicative act with the sentence "The baby cried", the speaker is informing the listener that she is commencing a description of a situation, s, in which there is exactly one baby, call it b.

The *propositional content* of the utterance of the first sentence "The baby cried", which in the case of a simple description like the present example is, for speaker and listener, the principal item of information about the described situation that is conveyed, is

$$s \models \ll \text{cries}, b, t_0, 1 \gg$$

where t_0 is the time, prior to the time of utterance, at which the crying took place. In words, in the situation s, the baby b was crying at the time t_0.

Notice that, in the absence of any additional information, the only means available to the listener to identify b is as the referent for the utterance of the phrase 'the baby'. The utterance of this phrase tells the listener two pertinent things about s and b:

$$b : T_{baby} \quad \text{(i.e., } b \text{ is of type } T_{baby}\text{)} \tag{3}$$

where T_{baby} is the type of all babies, and

$$b \text{ is the unique individual of this type in } s. \tag{4}$$

As noted earlier in the discussion of category binding, in addition to the propositional content, the utterance of the entire first sentence "The baby cried" also provides the listener with the information

$$T_{baby} : T_{stage-of-life}. \tag{5}$$

The speaker then goes on to utter the sentence "The mommy picked it up." As in the case of 'the baby', in order for the speaker to make appropriate and informative use of the phrase 'the mommy', the described situation s must contain exactly one individual m who is a mother. In fact we can make a stronger claim: the individual m is the mother of the baby b referred to in the first sentence. For if m were the mother not of b but of some other baby, then the appropriate

---

[10] Though using a different theoretical framework.

form of reference would be 'a mother', even in the case were m was the unique mother in s. The mechanism that produces this interpretation can be described as follows.

Having heard the phrase 'the baby' in the first sentence and 'the mommy' in the second, the following two items of information are salient to the listener:

$$m : T_{mother} \tag{6}$$

$$m \text{ is the unique individual of this type in } s. \tag{7}$$

In addition, I shall show that the following, third item of information is also salient:

$$m \text{ is the mother of } b. \tag{8}$$

Now, as I have already observed, because the activity of *crying* is category-bound to the type T_{baby} in the device $T_{stage\text{-}of\text{-}life}$, following the utterance of the first sentence, the listener's cognitive state is such that the type T_{baby} is of type $T_{stage\text{-}of\text{-}life}$. This type has categories that include T_{baby}, T_{child}, $T_{adolescent}$, T_{adult}, all of which have equal ontological status within this device, with none being derivative on any other. But as soon as the phrase 'the mommy' is heard, the combination of 'baby' and 'mommy' switches the emphasis from the type $T_{stage\text{-}of\text{-}life}$ to the type T_{family}, making salient the following propositions:

$$T_{baby} : T_{family}. \tag{9}$$

$$T_{mommy} : T_{family}. \tag{10}$$

In the T_{family} device, the various family relationships that bind a family together (and which therefore serve to give this device its status as a device) are more fundamental than the categories they give rise to. In particular, the types T_{baby} and T_{mother} are derivative on the type $T_{mother\text{-}of}$ that relates mothers to their babies.

Now, proposition (9) is the precondition for the salience of implication (2), namely

$$q : T_{baby} \ \rightarrow \ \exists p\,(p, q : T_{mother\text{-}of}).$$

Substituting the particular individual b for the variable q, we get

$$b : T_{baby} \ \rightarrow \ \exists p\,(p, b : T_{mother\text{-}of}).$$

But by (3), we know that

$$b : T_{baby}.$$

Thus we have the salient information

$$\text{there is an } m \text{ such that } m, b : T_{mother\text{-}of}. \tag{11}$$

The use of the definite article in the phrase 'the mommy' then makes it natural to take this phrase to refer to the unique m that satisfies (11). Thus the listener naturally takes the phrase 'the mommy' to refer to the baby's mother. This interpretation is reinforced by the completion of the second sentence "...picked it up", since there is a social norm to the effect that a mother picks up and comforts her crying baby. This explains how the fact (8) becomes salient to the listener.

It should be noticed that the switch from the salience of one set of constraints to another was caused by the second level of types in the type-hierarchy. The constraints we were primarily interested in concerned the types T_{mother} and T_{baby}. These types are part of a complex network of inter-relationships (constraints). Just which constraints in this network are salient to the agent is governed by the way the agent encounters the types, that is to say, by *the type(s) of those types*— for instance, whether T_{baby} is regarded (or encountered) as of type $T_{stage-of-life}$ or of type T_{family}. This consideration of the type of the types linked by a constraint represents a much finer treatment of constraints and inference than has hitherto arisen in situation theory. By moving to a second level of typing (i.e., to types of types), we are able to track the way agents use one set of constraints rather than another, and switch from one set to another. The first level of types allows us to capture the informational connections between two objects; the second level allows us to capture the agent's preference of a particular informational connection, and thereby provides a formal mechanism for describing normality.

5 Normality

The informational structure that the situation-theoretic framework, and in particular the type structure, brings to the analysis of the Sacks data results in our avoiding a number of problems that, as we point out in (Devlin and Rosenberg, to appear), Sacks' own argument runs into.

Of the several points in Sacks' analysis that our reformulation in situation-theoretic terms brings to light as in need of clarification, by far the biggest problem we encountered concerns Sacks' *Hearer's Maxim 2*:[11]

(HM2) If some population has been categorized by means of a duplicatively organized device, and a member is presented with a categorized population which *can* be heard as 'coincumbents' of a case of that device's unit, then hear it that way.

As we point out in (Devlin and Rosenberg, to appear), this maxim is logically inconsistent. (The inconsistency shows up dramatically as soon as one tries to recast Sacks' argument in a more mathematical fashion.) The problem lies in the wide scope that results from the use of the word 'can'. The *possibility* of hearing something a certain way does not mean that one 'should' hear it that way: possibility does not imply normality.[12]

---

[11] Sacks, notion of a 'duplicatively organized device', of which the family device is an instance, is somewhat complicated to explain. Since it plays no role in the argument of the present paper, I shall refer readers to (Sacks 1972) or (Devlin and Rosenberg, to appear) for details.

[12] It should be pointed out that this has nothing to do with giving 'possibility' *too* wide a scope; the inconsistency is present even if one adopts the reading, as Sacks surely intended, of 'possibility within the given context.'

The 'fix' we suggest in (Devlin and Rosenberg, to appear) is to replace Hearer's Maxim 2 by the alternative:

(HM2') If some population has been categorized by means of a duplicatively organized device, and a member is presented with a categorized population which would *normally* be heard as coincumbents of a case of that device's unit, then hear it that way. [Emphasis added.]

As we remark in (Devlin and Rosenberg, to appear), from a logical point of view, this appears to verge on the tautologically trivial. But, as we also remarked, it does not appear to be vacuous. Indeed, from the point of view of coming to grips with the issue of normality, we believe it has significant content. Not only does the act of *stating* (HM2') bring the concept of normality into the analysis, indeed as a crucial feature of that analysis, the maxim itself captures the essence of normality with regards to the way people understand certain utterances. (Notice that if you replace 'normally' with some other qualifier in the statement of (HM2'), the resulting maxim is unlikely to be a reliable observation of, or norm for, everyday human behavior.)

The same problem arises for Sacks' *Hearer's Maxim 1*:

(HM1) If two or more categories are used to categorize two or more members of some population, and those categories *can* be heard as categories from the same device, then hear them that way. [Emphasis added.]

Again, the wide scope given by the word 'can' makes this maxim is inconsistent. And once again, my suggestion would be to modify this maxim as follows:

(HM1') If two or more categories are used to categorize two or more members of some population, and those categories would *normally* be heard as categories from the same device, then hear them that way.

We did not dwell on the issue of the inconsistency of (HM1) in (Devlin and Rosenberg, to appear), since this particular maxim was not required for Sacks' final analysis of the two-sentence data, which was our focus of attention at the time.

As mentioned above, the problem with (HM2) only showed up when we were trying to reformulate Sack's argument in situation-theoretic terms. In the situation-theoretic version of the argument, the problem does not arise. Tracking the information flow involved in a 'normal' understanding of Sacks' two sentences, the understanding that (HM2) is intended to lead to (or reflect) falls straight out of the analysis. Our reason for formulating (HM2') was not that it was needed in the situation-theoretic analysis. Rather, (HM2') was our suggestion, *based upon* our situation-theoretic analysis, of the change that needed to be made to (HM2) *in order for Sacks' own argument to work*.

Of course, if Sacks' analysis depends upon normality in a critical fashion, as we suggest, then normality must surely play a role in our own analysis. This is indeed the case, but in a somewhat different guise. In the situation-theoretic framework, the procedural or behavioral notion of *normality* is replaced by the structural notion of *salience*.

In situation-theoretic terms, *normal behavior* in a particular context amounts to acting in accordance with the constraints that are most salient in that context. Thus an investigation of the concept of normality is reduced (or transferred, to use a less value-laden term) to a study of salience, a topic whose importance we stressed in (Devlin and Rosenberg, to appear), but a detailed examination of which was deferred until later.

The apparent triviality of (HM2′) as a maxim is a consequence of (HM2′) being, in effect, a *definition* (or, if you prefer, a *classification*) of normality: "normally do what you would normally do". By moving from a procedural notion to a structural one (salience), this apparent circularity is avoided. More precisely, the vicious circularity of the notion of normality is replaced by the recursive procedure whereby agents use constraints to which they are attuned, or of which they are aware, in order to develop an attunement to, or an awareness of, further constraints. This is the phenomenon I address in the next section.

6 Constraint Formation and Salience

The main function of the situation-theoretic notion of *type-abstraction* is to capture, within the theory, the ability, characteristic of cognitive agents (see (Dretske 1981: 142)) and a propensity in the case of human agents, to recognize, and on occasion to create, similarities between various things in the world and to construct categories (or 'types') of things according to those similarities. It is indeed by virtue of the systematization of an agent's environment provided by means of such typing that the agent is able to behave in what we generally refer to as a 'rational' (as opposed to a random or haphazard) manner.

Thus, for example, people recognize the categories of *baby*, *mother*, *family*, and *stage-of-life*. In situation-theoretic notation, these types may be obtained by means of the following type-abstractions:

- $T_{baby} = [\dot{p} \mid w \models \ll \text{baby}, \dot{p}, t_{now}, 1 \gg]$;
- $T_{mother} = [\dot{p} \mid w \models \ll \text{mother}, \dot{p}, t_{now}, 1 \gg]$;
- $T_{family} = [\dot{e} \mid w \models \ll \text{family-type}, \dot{e}, 1 \gg]$;
- $T_{stage\text{-}of\text{-}life} = [\dot{e} \mid w \models \ll \text{stage-of-life-type}, \dot{e}, 1 \gg]$;

where $\dot{p}$ is a parameter for a person, w is 'the world', i.e., any situation big enough to include everything under discussion, and $\dot{e}$ is a parameter for a type.

Now, each of these identities provides a *structural* dependency of the type on the corresponding property, with the *type T_{baby}* the result of *abstracting* across the *property* 'baby', etc. But this is a theoretical dependency. We could equally well provide a mechanism for recovering the property from the type, if we needed such a device. Maintaining a distinction between properties and types is convenient for the purposes of developing a theory of information, but in terms of the target domain of cognitive agents, properties and types are very much two sides of the same coin, and moreover two sides that look very much alike. (The principal technical difference is that types incorporate the notion of 'truth in a situation' whereas properties are just that, properties, requiring a context in order to encompass truth.)[13]

Nevertheless, despite the somewhat artificial nature of the technical distinction between properties and types, types do help us capture, in a natural way, the notions of *category* and *categorization device* that Sacks uses in his analysis.

The question I want to investigate now is, what does *recognition* (by a person) of a category (i.e., type) amount to, and how does a person *acquire* these categories and the ability to use them (i.e., the ability to place various entities in the appropriate category)?

In the case of *categories* (types of individuals, in situation-theoretic terms), things seem fairly straightforward. Recognition of, or familiarity with, a category (or type) is simply a matter of recognizing those individuals that are in the category (are of the type) and those that are not.[14] Thus, familiarity with the 'baby' category (type T_{baby}) is a matter of recognizing babies (that is to say, recognizing certain individuals *as babies*), and likewise familiarity with the 'mother' category (type T_{mother}) is a matter of knowing what a mother is.

Moreover, *use* of a category in everyday life, including cognition and communication, requires, for the most part, nothing more than the ability to recognize individuals as being of that category. Once I know what a 'baby' is, I can understand references to babies and can myself make reference to babies.

It is at the level of *categorization devices* (types of types) that things get a bit more interesting.

Knowing what a 'family' or a 'stage-of-life' is, and being able to recognize that a certain category is a family category or a stage-of-life category, involves quite a bit more than the ability to recognize an individual as being, or not being, in a certain category (of a certain type). This is in part because of the increased level of abstraction: categorization devices (types of types of individuals) are at a more abstract level than categories (types of individuals). But the most significant difference is that categorization devices have a *structure* that is important *to their being categorization devices*, whereas categories do not.

For instance, familiarity with the family device involves an awareness that a family is not just a collection of two or more persons (or animals of some species), but a collection bound together by certain kinds of relationships, relationships involving geneology and/or certain kinds of legal commitments, and possibly less institutionalized social commitments. That is to say, one cannot know what

---

[13] For an example where the distinction is fairly dramatic, consider the property of 'unicorn-ness', i.e. the property of being a unicorn. This is a meaningful, *bona fide* property, closely related to the properties of being a horse and having a horn. It is a property that figures in many stories, and is part of human culture. However, when abstracted over w, the world, this property leads to the vacuous type, which is only a type in a trivial, degenerate way.

[14] I am speaking here purely of recognition capacity. The issue as to *how*, on a given occasion, a member 'chooses' a particular way of regarding an individual in preference to other, equally valid type-ascriptions, is one I shall take up presently.

a 'family' is (in the sense of having the 'family' categorization device at one's cognitive disposal) without knowing (at least some of) the kinds of relationships that bind families together. (Note that, in (Sacks 1972), Sacks' explicitly includes 'rules of application' in his definition of a categorization device.)

Likewise, familiarity with the stage-of-life device entails knowing at least some of the categories in this device, together with the ordering relation between them, since it is the ordering relation between the various categories that makes this particular device the *stage-of-life* device.

The structure that is an essential part of a categorization device played a significant role in Sacks' analysis of the two-sentence data, and an even greater role in the alternative analysis given by Rosenberg and myself, where the structure associated with (indeed, constitutive of) the family device enabled us to circumvent Sacks' problematical (HM2) maxim.

Now, in (Devlin and Rosenberg, to appear), we did not explicitly introduce a situation-theoretic analogue of a categorization device. Instead, we carried out our argument using the types T_{family} and $T_{stage-of-life}$, plus the oracles of these types, $Oracle(T_{family})$ and $Oracle(T_{stage-of-life})$. It is these latter two, oracle situations that most closely correspond to Sacks' 'family' and 'stage-of-life' categorization devices. Indeed, this is how we implicitly regarded them when we were working on (Devlin and Rosenberg, to appear). We chose to make use of the oracle operator of situation theory, rather than introduce categorization devices as a further entity in the situation-theoretic ontology, for reasons of ontological parsimony. For the level of treatment we are currently able to give for data such as that of Sacks, the oracle situations corresponding to types seem to fulfill our aims. However, we do not rule out the necessity of having to abandon this technical convenience at some future date, and develop a separate situation-theoretic notion of 'categorization device'.

As I mentioned earlier, and as Rosenberg and I argued in (Devlin and Rosenberg, to appear), the pivotal role played by the family-binding relationships in the family device (i.e., in that device *being* a device), is reflected in the fact that the corresponding constraints are *salient* in $Oracle(T_{family})$. Similarly, the various constraints concerning the ordering relation between the various categories in the stage-of-life device are all salient in $Oracle(T_{stage-of-life})$.

Since the constraints that are salient in a particular device constitute an integral part of that device, a member's ability to utilize a categorization device entails an awareness of, or attunement to, the constraints that are salient in that device, and the process of achieving that ability involves acquiring that awareness or attunement. The process whereby a member acquires the ability to utilize a device can be—and, I believe, usually is—a mixture of being told, or otherwise informed, about the device, repeated experience in encountering the device, and perhaps conscious inner reflection on those experiences.

According to the account Rosenberg and I are currently developing, *normal behavior* in a given context amounts to behavior in accordance with the constraints salient (or most salient) in that context. In order to fully appreciate what this means, I need to say something about salience. What I say will, of necessity, be somewhat tentative, since Rosenberg and I have not yet fully worked out what we take to be a satisfactory account of this notion.

'Rational' behavior by an agent amounts to that agent acting and reasoning in accordance with various constraints, constraints that obtain in the context in which that agent is situated. But a given situation will, in general, support a great many constraints, many of them quite possibly of a minor and, to all intents and purposes, irrelevant nature as far as the agent's activity is concerned. This is where the salience 'hierarchy' comes in. The more salient is a constraint C within a given supporting situation s, the more likely is an agent for whom s is a context to be guided by C.

For example, in real-world, environmental situations, the constraint that links smoke to fire is a highly important one, crucial to the agent's survival, and as such is, under normal circumstances, likely to be the most salient in any situation in which there is smoke. On the other hand, one can imagine that a group of people has established a constraint whereby a smoke-signal indicates that the enemy is approaching, and for the members of that group, their context is such that the most salient constraint is the one that links smoke to an approaching enemy. Since the behavior of an agent is most likely to be influenced by the most salient constraints in its current context, different contexts can bring different constraints into play.

A metaphor I find particularly helpful in connection with salience is that of 'living in a situation'. Situations are an attempt to capture, within a rigorously defined ontology, the role played by context in reasoning and communication. Now the key feature of context—what makes it a *context*—is that it guides the flow of information *from without*, it does not play an explicit role. For example, in the case of everyday activity, the way you behave in the home situation differs significantly from your behavior at work, and is different again from the way you act when in a concert hall. Each situation carries with it a distinctive set of rules and norms of behavior, which situation theory treats as constraints. Again, in the case of communication, you make use of different linguistic constraints, depending on whether you are speaking to a small child, to your family, or at work, and different constraints again when speaking a foreign language. Now in each of these cases, you do not make explicit use of any *rules* (except perhaps on very special occasions which need not concern us here); the context does not play an active role in your activity, it simply *establishes the appropriate constraints*. During the course of any particular situated activity, you may be thought of as 'living in the world' that constitutes the context for that activity.

Notice that there is no reason to suppose you are restricted to 'living in' just one situation at a time in this manner. The high degree of abstraction allowed for situations enables us to use the theory to capture many different aspects of behavior at any one time. When playing a game of cards with some friends, for example, your behavior will be guided by the formally specified rules of the game, the linguistic rules governing English language, and the social rules and norms that guide group behavior when among friends. According to the 'living in a situation' metaphor, you may thus be described as simultaneously living in three different situations.

Similarly, to be competent in a particular language amounts to having a familiarity with a certain abstract situation, to 'know one's way around that situation'. Speaking or understanding a particular language can be regarded as 'cognitively living in' the appropriate linguistic situation, in the same way that finding one's way around one's home can be regarded as physically living in that home situation. Learning a new language involves becoming familiar with another linguistic situation, learning to find one's way around that situation.

Of course, salience is not an all-or-nothing state of affairs. Preferential readings, interpretations, or actions can be over-ruled or ignored. Another analogy that I find helpful is to think of salience as analogous to a gravitational field. At any point, the field pulls you in one particular direction, and depending on your circumstances you will follow that pull to a greater or lesser degree. If there are no other forces (constraints, influences) acting on you, you will follow the field in the direction of strongest pull—which itself may well be the resultant of component attractions in a number of different directions. When there are other forces acting on you, you will still be under the influence of the field, but may move in a different direction, a direction that results from the combined effect of the gravitational field and those other forces. *Normality* can be thought of as following the attraction of a 'gravitational field'.

Associative links, which Rosenberg and I introduced in (Devlin and Rosenberg, to appear), are one instance of a class of constraints that reflect/guide normal behavior. The associative link that connects the baby category to the mother category is salient in the family device, i.e.,:

$$Oracle\,(T_{family}) \; \| \!\!- \; T_{baby} \Rightarrow T_{mother}$$

Now, as we claimed in (Devlin and Rosenberg, to appear), associative links are a quite new kind of constraint in situation theory. However, when we ask ourselves how a member would normally become attuned to, or aware of, a constraint such as the one above, we are at once thrown back to the more familiar notion of a situation-theoretic constraint between (environmental) situation-types.

Attunement to the constraint

$$T_{baby} \Rightarrow T_{mother}$$

would normally develop as part of the process of becoming familiar with the 'family' device, $Oracle\,(T_{family})$. The member (presumably a small child) repeatedly encounters situations s in which there is close interaction between a mother and her baby. As a result of these encounters, the member comes to recognize a certain *type* of situation, the type of situation in which there is such interaction. Let T_{bm} denote this situation-type.

Types such as T_{bm} are what I propose to call *evolved* types. Such types cannot normally be defined in an extensional fashion, and thus may not be effectively specified by means of the normal mechanisms for type-abstraction within situation theory. They arise by a process of repeated interaction between certain kinds of agent and the environment. Such agents include people, various species of animal, and neural networks.

In the case of the evolved type T_{bm}, one aspect of particular interest to us at the moment is that it involves two individuals, a baby and a mother. Let $\dot{b}$ be a parameter for a baby, $\dot{m}$ a parameter for a mother. I shall write $T_{bm}(\dot{b}, \dot{m})$ to indicate that the type T_{bm} has $\dot{b}$ and $\dot{m}$ as constituents.

As part of the process of *evolving* the type T_{bm} (i.e., acquiring the ability to discriminate this type), a member will learn that, under such circumstances, the two major participants normally consist of a mother and her baby. This amounts to developing an attunement to the constraint

$$T_{bm}(\dot{b}, \dot{m}) \Rightarrow T_{is}$$

where

$$T_{is} = [\dot{s} \mid \dot{s} \models \ll \text{baby}, \dot{b}, t_{now}, 1 \gg$$
$$\wedge \ll \text{mother}, \dot{m}, t_{now}, 1 \gg$$
$$\wedge \ll \text{mother-of}, \dot{m}, \dot{b}, t_{now}, 1 \gg]$$

A member who is attuned to this constraint, and who encounters a situation that is recognizably of type T_{bm}, will be aware that the individuals to which the parameters $\dot{m}$ and $\dot{b}$ are anchored will normally consist of a mother and her baby.

It is natural to take the support of the above constraint to be the family device, which I am taking to be $Oracle\,(T_{family})$. Indeed, in consequence of the fundamental role played by the the type T_{bm} in the family device, we have the saliency relation:

$$Oracle\,(T_{family}) \;\|\!\!-\; T_{bm}(\dot{b}, \dot{m}) \Rightarrow T_{is}$$

In particular, familiarity with the family device involves the capacity to recognize situations as being of type T_{bm}.

Consider now the listener in Sacks, 'baby–mommy' scenario, who hears the two sentences

The baby cried. The mommy picked it up.

To a native speaker of English, this clearly describes a situation, s, (possibly a fictional one) of type T_{bm}, (in situation-theoretic terminology, s is the *described situation*). Thus, under normal circumstances, the speaker's choice of words and the listener's interpretation of those words are governed by the constraints salient in the family device, in particular the constraint

$$T_{bm}(\dot{b}, \dot{m}) \Rightarrow T_{is}$$

mentioned above. It is this constraint that, for the speaker, leads to the two actors being preferentially described as 'baby' and 'mommy' and, for the listener, leads to the reference of 'the mommy' being heard as the mommy of the baby. And it is this constraint that has, as a derivative, the associative link

$$T_{baby} \Rightarrow T_{mother}$$

As the above discussion indicates, it is possible to dispense with associative links altogether, and work entirely with situation-type constraints such as $T_{bm} \Rightarrow T_{is}$. However, the result of an evolved attunement to such constraints is that members do develop such connections *between objects*, which is to say that they have informational status, which a theory of information ought to reflect. In infon form, the above associative link is written

$$\ll \text{linked}, T_{baby}, T_{mother}, t_{now}, 1 \gg$$

Notice also that normal use of (normative) constraints of the kind under discussion is often unconscious and automatic. Reliance on such constraints is a matter of attunement rather than awareness.

Familiarity with the type T_{bm} also involves attunement to the *category binding* constraint

$$\text{crying} \Rightarrow T_{baby}$$

that links the activity of crying to the category of babies. Again, it would be possible to avoid the introduction of such constraints, and to work instead with situation-type constraints (in the case of this example, going through the type T_{bm}), but again they reflect more closely the basic manner in which these connections figure in the everyday cognitive activity of members, and so it seems sensible to include them. As an informational item, the binding of crying to the category of babies would be written

$$\ll \text{category-bound-to}, \text{crying}, T_{baby}, t_{now}, 1 \gg$$

Notice that the account developed above concerns the relevant information structures 'in the world'. That is to say, I have been trying to identify the informational links that a member will (unconsciously) make use of in order to understand a certain situation (either observed or described). I have not attempted to describe the member's cognitive processes in any way. This could be done. For instance, as part of the process of evolving the type T_{bm}, a member will learn that one of the two individuals concerned is usually referred to as a 'baby' and the other as a 'mother'.

One final remark to conclude this section: the account of normality just developed is very much a contextual one. What I describe is normal behavior *in a given context*. Moreover, that context may be an *evolved* one, built up by a process of the member repeatedly interacting with the environment.

7 So Whose Theory Is It?

Writing in (Psathas 1979), Heritage and Watson (pp. 123–124) set out the central task of the ethnomethodologist as follows:

A central focus of ethnomethodological work is the analysis of the practical sociological reasoning through which social activity is rendered accountable and orderly. Assumed by this concern is the notion that all scenic features of social interaction are occasioned and established as a concerted practical accomplishment, in and through which the parties display for one another their competence in the practical management of social order. As analysts, our interest is to explicate, in respect of naturally occurring occasions of use, the methods by which such orderliness can be displayed, managed, and recognized by members.

The question at once arises, how does one, as Heritage and Watson put it, "explicate ... the methods by which such orderliness can be displayed, managed, and recognized by members"? How does one describe the 'social structure' that Garfinkel, Sacks, and others claim governs the way members encounter the world and interact with one another?

A commonly heard view is that such an analysis of everyday (sociolinguistic) phenomena can only be carried out using the linguistic tools of natural language, relying upon the linguistic competence and everyday experience of both producer and reader of such an analysis in order to capture and describe various features of the observed data. To repeat part of the quotation from Benson and Hughes given in Section 1: "... an important constraint on sociological inquiry is that the categories, the concepts used, and the methods for using them, must be isomorphic to the ways they are used in common-sense reasoning."

But an examination of, say, the Sacks' article considered in this paper will indicate that neither the language nor its use is in any sense 'everyday'. Rather, Sacks adopts (indeed, in his case, helped to develop) a specialized and highly stylized linguistic *genre*, whose complexity varies inversely with the 'everydayness' of the particular phenomenon under discussion. Whether or not there is, nevertheless, an 'isomorphism' between such ethnomethodological use of language and everyday reasoning is of little consequence, since there is quite evidently no *natural* isomorphism. The production and proper understanding of an analysis such as Sacks' involves considerable effort, including the mastery of an entire linguistic *genre*, and an associated ontology, quite unlike 'everyday English' or 'everyday concepts'.

The reason for this linguistic complexity lies in the fact that the goal of the analysis is the identification and description of formal, abstract structures, and everyday language is not well-suited to such a task. Mathematics, on the other hand, is very well-suited to this kind of purpose, since mathematics is, by definition, the study of formal, abstract structures. As a piece of mathematics, the situation-theoretic analysis of the Sacks data presented here (or in (Devlin and Rosenberg, to appear)) is extremely simple—indeed, a mathematician would describe it as essentially 'trivial' (a term that mathematicians generally use in a technical, non-perjoratory way).

But this triviality and appropriateness of the technical, descriptive machinery provided by situation theory comes at a price: it is only easily and readily accessible to those sufficiently familiar with (enough) mathematics. Though by no stretch of the imagination 'everyday use of language', the descriptive machinery of ethnomethodologists such as Sacks is *grounded* in everyday language, and thus is, in principle, accessible to any sufficiently competent English speaker, given only an adequate motivation and enough time. (It took me, a mathematician hitherto unfamiliar with sociology, some six months of fairly intensive effort, including the assistance of Rosenberg, a social scientist familiar with the ethnomethodological literature, before I felt I was able to understand Sacks' analysis reasonably well.) Given the nature of elementary and high school education prevalent through most of the western world, where what 'mathematics' is taught is largely quantitative and algorithmic (as opposed to qualitative and descriptive), for most social scientists, the time, and effort, required to achieve an adequate mastery of the appropriate descriptive tools from mathematics is considerably longer, and indeed may be, for many, inaccessibly long.

However, this is an empirical consequence of the prevailing educational system, not an intrinsic feature of descriptive mathematics. To anyone sufficiently well-versed in mathematics, and familiar with mathematical ontologies, a description carried out with the aid of mathematics is just that: a description. Indeed, to such a person, the situation-theoretic analysis of the Sacks data presented above may well be (and for myself certainly was) much simpler to produce and to understand than a more traditional, ethnomethodological analysis such as Sacks' own. To someone well-versed in mathematics, the use of descriptive and analytic mathematical tools, as in this paper, is a perfectly *natural*, and indeed appropriate, medium for carrying out an investigation of the abstract structures involved in any phenomenon. Such an analysis will be open to inspection and validation by others with a similar background.

There is then, I maintain, no intrinsic difference between the kind of analysis developed by Sacks and the situation-theoretic analysis of the same data developed by Rosenberg and myself. The difference lies in the groups to which the two analyses are, first, accessible and, second, natural. It would probably be too naive to expect that social scientists would rush to learn, and embrace, situation-theoretic, or other descriptive-mathematical, techniques, though I suspect that in due course some will. Much more likely is that increasing numbers of computer scientists, already familiar with the language of mathematics, will find themselves becoming involved in ethnomethodological questions in their work on problems of systems design. If this does indeed turn out to be the case, then it is this group for whom the kind of analysis presented here will be most appropriate. Whether such studies are classified as 'ethnomethodological', or whether they will take their place alongside ethnomethodology as an alternative means of analysis, is of little importance. The crucial issue, surely, is to achieve greater understanding and wider utility of that understanding.

8   Situation Theory as Endogenous Logic

Expression of the need to develop descriptive-mathematical tools for the analysis of social phenomena is not solely restricted to mathematicians, such as myself, who are trying to understand such phenomena. Such a program has been set out by some working within the ethnomethodological tradition. In particular, in (Button 1991: 49), Jeff Coulter sets out the following *desiderata* for a 'logic of language' that is, as he put it 'adequately wedded to *praxis*':

(A) An extension of analytic focus from the proposition or statement, sentence or speech-act, to 'utterance design' or 'turn-at-talk'.

(B) An extension of analytic focus to encompass indexical expressions as components of *sequences* in terms of their logical properties and relations, especially their *inferential affordances*.

(C) A respecification of the concept of 'illocutionary act' to exclude *a prioristic* efforts to isolate 'propositional contents', and more fully to appreciate the socially situated availability of 'what an utterance could be accomplishing' *in situ*, especially in respect of its properties of design, sequential implication and turn-allocation relevances; in other words, its *interactionally* significant properties.

(D) A development of the concept of a *combinatorial* logic for illocutionary activities *in situ*.

(E) A development of an informal or endogenous logic for the *praxis* of person, place, activity, mental predicate and collectivity categorizations, and their interrelationships, among other domains of referential, classificational and descriptive operations. This requires *abandonment* of formal semantic theoretic schemes deriving from set theory, extensionalism, generative- (transformational) grammar, truth-conditional semantics, and componential analysis as resources.

(F) Abandonment of the preoccupation with 'correctness' defined as usage in accord with any rule specified *independently* of an analysis or orientation to ascertainable members' situated relevances, purposes and practices.

(G) Abandonment of *a priori* invocations of mathematical concepts in the analysis of the informal logic of reasoning and communication; only those concepts warranted by studies of actual, *in situ* practical orientations of persons may be employed.

(H) Replacement of the goal of logical regimentation in favor of logical *explication*.

(I) Awareness of the varieties and modalities of what could count as 'rules of use' of linguistic/conceptual resources.

(J) Abandonment of intellectual prejudices and generic characterizations concerning the putative 'vagueness', 'disorderliness', 'ambiguities', 'indeterminacies', 'imprecisions' and 'redundancies' or ordinary language use.

(K) Formalization, but not axiomatization, becomes an objective, but not necessarily the production of an *integrated system* of formalizations.

(L) Adherence to the constraint that formulations of rules of practical reasoning and communication be sensitive to *actual*, and not exclusively hypothetical, cases of *praxis*.

(M) Extension of the concept of a 'logical grammar' to encompass the diversity of phenomena studied as components of conceptual *praxis*, requiring the de-privileging of 'strict categoricity rules' and the fuller exploration of the ties between Logic and Rhetoric.

(N) De-priveleging of all decontextualized standards for the ascription of 'rationality' and 'truth' without sacrificing their position as components of real-worldly reasoning in the arts and sciences of everyday affairs.

(O) Recognition of the priority of *pre*-theoretical conceptualizations of phenomena as constraints upon 'technical' renditions of them.

How close does situation theory come to fulfilling this 'sociologist's wish list' for a 'logic wedded to *praxis*'? The answer is 'very close indeed'. Indeed, not only are all the aims and guiding principles of situation theory consistent with Coulter's requirements, in many cases they are identical. In this section, I examine this issue, taking Coulter's requirements one at a time.

(A) An extension of analytic focus from the proposition or statement, sentence or speech-act, to 'utterance design' or 'turn-at-talk'.

Though situation semantics has hitherto concentrated almost exclusively on propositions, statements, sentences, and speech-acts, as a semantic theory, situation semantics focuses on particular *utterances* of expressions. So in part, Coulter's requirements have already been met by situation semantics. In so far as this is not the case, there is nothing to prevent situation theory being applied to 'utterance design' or 'turn-at-talk'. Indeed, both my paper with Rosenberg (Devlin and Rosenberg, to appear) and this present paper are further steps in this direction, and our forthcoming paper (Devlin and Rosenberg, in preparation a) and monograph (Devlin and Rosenberg, in preparation b) will carry this development further.

(B) An extension of analytic focus to encompass indexical expressions as components of *sequences* in terms of their logical properties and relations, especially their *inferential affordances*.

From its inception, situation semantics took the issue of indexicality very seriously, and requirement (B) could be said to be one of the motivating factors for situation semantics.

(C) A respecification of the concept of 'illocutionary act' to exclude *a prioristic* efforts to isolate 'propositional contents', and more fully to appreciate the socially situated availability of 'what an utterance could be accomplishing' *in situ*, especially in respect of its properties of design, sequential implication and turn-allocation relevances; in other words, its *interactionally* significant properties.

Though the notion of the 'propositional content' of a declarative utterance played a major role in the early work on situation semantics, subsequent developments led to propositional content becoming just one of a number of features of (certain kinds of) utterances. Indeed, in the brief discussion of the five speech-act categories of Searle presented in (Devlin 1991), the *impact* of utterances played a significant, and for some kinds of utterance the most significant, role. Indeed, situation theory appears to be well suited to fulfill the positive requirements listed under (C), and my work with Rosenberg in (Devlin and Rosenberg, to appear) and subsequently has been, and is, moving in this direction.

(D) A development of the concept of a *combinatorial* logic for illocutionary activities *in situ*.

Insofar as situation theory is a 'combinatorial logic', I suppose this aim is met, but it is not at all clear to me just what Coulter has in mind here.

(E) A development of an informal or endogenous logic for the *praxis* of person, place, activity, mental predicate and collectivity categorizations, and their interrelationships, among other domains of referential, classificational and descriptive operations. This requires *abandonment* of formal semantic theoretic schemes deriving from set theory, extensionalism, generative- (transformational) grammar, truth-conditional semantics, and componential analysis as resources.

This expresses very well what current situation theory is trying to achieve, and the means by which it is setting about that task. The inadequacy, and indeed the unsuitability, of set theory and classical logic as a foundation for situation theory was realized quite early on in the development of the subject, and has long since been abandoned in favor of a 'top down' approach that starts off with empirical observations of communication and cognition.

(F) Abandonment of the preoccupation with 'correctness' defined as usage in accord with any rule specified *independently* of an analysis or orientation to ascertainable members' situated relevances, purposes and practices.

As indicated above, as a domain-led development, situation theory has never had such a preoccupation.

(G) Abandonment of *a priori* invocations of mathematical concepts in the analysis of the informal logic of reasoning and communication; only those concepts warranted by studies of actual, *in situ* practical orientations of persons may be employed.

This echoes remarks I have made both in this paper and elsewhere that the task at hand requires new mathematical concepts, abstracted from the target domain.

(H) Replacement of the goal of logical regimentation in favor of logical *explication*.

Again, this is a goal I, and others, have expressed for situation theory.

(I) Awareness of the varieties and modalities of what could count as 'rules of use' of linguistic/conceptual resources.

This principle seems consistent with the development of situation theory to date.

(J) Abandonment of intellectual prejudices and generic characterizations concerning the putative 'vagueness', 'disorderliness', 'ambiguities', 'indeterminacies', 'imprecisions' and 'redundancies' of ordinary language use.

Situations are explicitly designed to capture, or help capture, each of these aspects of ordinary language use. See the discussion of situations in (Devlin 1991).

(K) Formalization, but not axiomatization, becomes an objective, but not necessarily the production of an *integrated system* of formalizations.

This is the substance of the stress Rosenberg and I placed upon the 'toolbox' approach to the development of situation theory for use in sociology.

(L) Adherence to the constraint that formulations of rules of practical reasoning and communication be sensitive to *actual*, and not exclusively hypothetical, cases of *praxis*.

Situation theory has always adhered to this constraint. Likewise, Coulter's final three requirements all seem to be among the principles that guide the development of situation theory, and I will not comment on them individually.

Though initially developed for a different purpose, or at least, for a purpose that many would have supposed was different, it seems then that situation theory comes extremely close to being the kind of theory Coulter has in mind. If 'logic' is taken to mean 'the science of reasoning and inference', as I argue for in (Devlin 1991), then situation theory could be said to be an attempt to develop an 'endogenous logic' in the sense of Coulter.

Though Coulter does not argue against a *mathematical* development of such a 'logic', many sociologists seem to think that a mathematical approach is incompatible with ethnomethodology. As I have argued elsewhere in this essay, for the most part such skepticism seems to be based on an erroneously narrow view of what constitutes mathematics. Admittedly, it may well not be possible to develop endogenous logic in the formal, mathematical fashion of, say, predicate logic. Indeed, it is, I think, unlikely that a single, uniform, mathematical framework will capture all of the features of everyday conversation and human action. But the development and use of mathematical tools *as part of* an 'endogenous logic' should surely provide the sociologist, on occasion, with an additional level of precision not otherwise available. Indeed, the fact is that the additional level of precision that mathematical techniques can afford enabled Rosenberg and myself to identify, and rectify, a number of points of unclarity in what is acknowledged to be an exemplary ethnomethodological analysis. This does not mean that ethnomethodology is likely to become a 'mathematical science' in the sense of physics and chemistry. But it does indicate, quite clearly, that mathematical techniques can make a useful addition to the arsenal of descriptive and analytic tools at the ethnomethodologist's disposal.

References

Barwise, J., and Perry, J.: *Situations and Attitudes.* Bradford Books, MIT Press, 1983.

Button, G. (ed.): *Ethnomethodology and the Human Sciences.* Cambridge University Press, 1991.

Devlin, K.: *Logic and Information,* Cambridge University Press, 1991.

Devlin, K., and D. Rosenberg: "Situation Theory and Cooperative Action," in: *Situation Theory and its Applications,* Volume 3, CSLI Lecture Notes, to appear.

Devlin, K., and D. Rosenberg: "Networked Information Flow Via Stylized Documents," (in preparation a).

Devlin, K., and D. Rosenberg: *The Logical Structure of Social Interaction.* (in preparation b).

Dretske, F.: *Knowledge and the Flow of Information.* Bradford Books, MIT Press, 1981.

Garfinkel, H.: *Studies in Ethnomethodology.* Prentice-Hall, 1967.

Phillips, D.: *Knowledge from What?* Rand McNally, 1971.

Psathas, G.: *Everyday Language: Studies in Ethnomethodology.* New York: Irvington, 1979.

Sacks, H.: "On the Analyzability of Stories by Children," in: J. Gumpertz and D. Hymes (eds.), *Directions in Sociolinguistics. The Ethnography of Communication.* Holt, Rinehart and Winston Inc. (1972) 325-345.

Printing: Weihert-Druck GmbH, Darmstadt
Binding: Theo Gansert Buchbinderei GmbH, Weinheim

Lecture Notes in Artificial Intelligence (LNAI)

Lecture Notes in Computer Science

曲一线科学备考

第6次修订

全彩版

初中 物理

知识清单

物　理

主　　编：曲一线

本册主编：张树刚

本册副主编：马桂如　张树勇　卢桂梅

本册编委：李学军　张安珍　郑彦飞

首都师范大学出版社
·北京·

教育科学出版社
·北京·

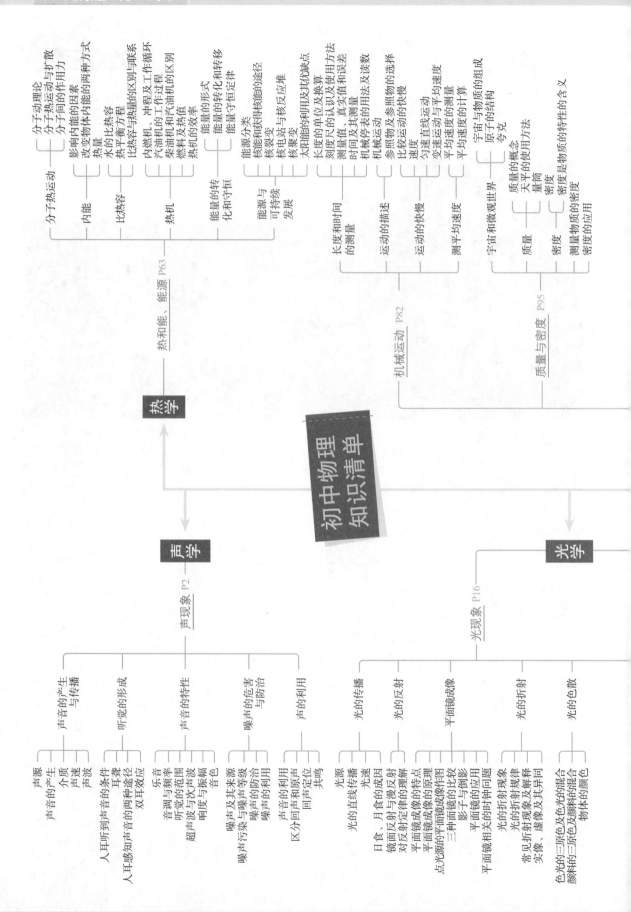

初中物理知识清单

热学

热和能、能源 P63

分子热运动 ── 分子动理论 / 分子热运动与扩散 / 分子间的作用力

内能 ── 影响内能的因素 / 改变物体内能的两种方式 / 热量

比热容 ── 水的比热容 / 热平衡方程 / 比热容与热量的区别与联系

热机 ── 内燃机、冲程及工作循环 / 汽油机和柴油机的区别 / 柴油机 / 燃料及热值 / 热机的效率

能量的转化和转移 ── 能源的形式 / 能量的转化和转移 / 能量守恒定律

能源与可持续发展 ── 能源分类 / 核能和获得核能的途径 / 核裂变 / 核能电站与核反应堆 / 核聚变 / 太阳能的利用及其应用

机械运动 P82

长度和时间的测量 ── 长度的单位及其换算 / 测量尺的认识及使用方法 / 时间及其测量 / 真实值与其测量值的用法及读数误差

运动的描述 ── 机械运动 / 参照物及参照物的选择

运动的快慢 ── 比较运动的快慢 / 速度

测平均速度 ── 匀速直线运动 / 变速运动与平均速度 / 平均速度的测量 / 平均速度的计算

质量与密度 P95

宇宙和微观世界 ── 宇宙与物质的组成 / 原子的结构 / 夸克

质量 ── 质量的概念 / 天平的使用方法 / 量筒

密度 ── 密度 / 密度是物质特性的含义 / 测量物质的密度 / 密度的应用

声学

声现象 P2

声音的产生与传播 ── 声源 / 介质 / 声速 / 声波

听觉的形成 ── 人耳听到声音的条件 / 耳聋 / 人耳感知声音的两种途径 / 双耳效应

声音的特性 ── 乐音 / 音调与频率 / 听觉的范围 / 超声波与次声波 / 响度与振幅 / 音色

噪声的危害与防治 ── 噪声及其来源 / 噪声污染与噪声的防治与利用 / 噪声的防治 / 噪声的利用

声的利用 ── 声音的利用 / 声音回声和原声 / 区分回声和原声 / 回声定位 / 共鸣

光学

光现象 P16

光的传播 ── 光源 / 光的直线传播 / 光速

光的反射 ── 光速 / 日食、月食的成因 / 镜面反射与漫反射 / 对反射定律的理解

平面镜成像 ── 平面镜成像的特点 / 平面镜成像的原理 / 点光源的平面镜成像作图 / 三种成像方式的比较 / 影子与倒影 / 平面镜的应用 / 平面镜相关的时钟问题

光的折射 ── 光的折射现象 / 光的折射规律 / 光的折射现象及解释 / 常见折射现象 / 实像、虚像及其异同

光的色散 ── 色光的三原色及色光的混合 / 颜料的三原色及颜料的混合 / 物体的颜色

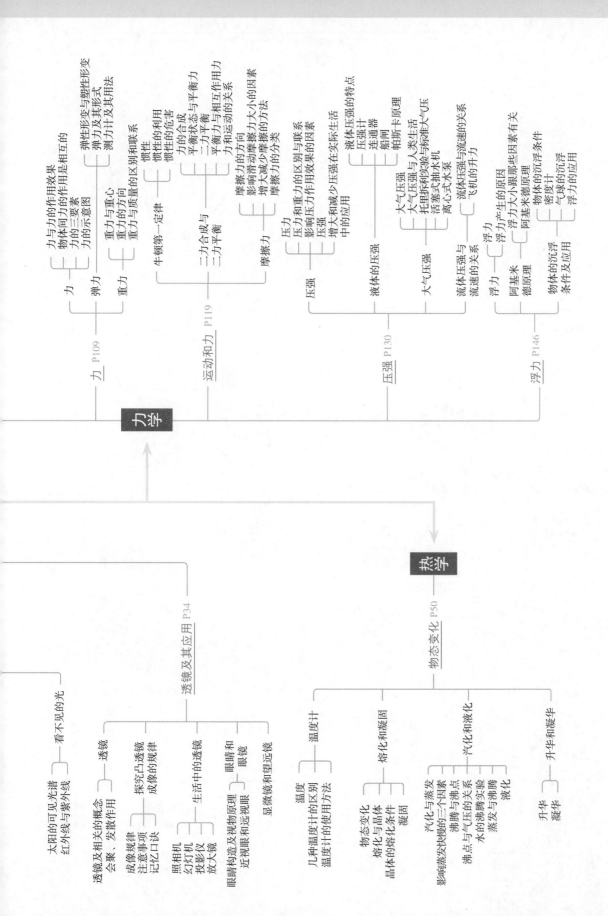

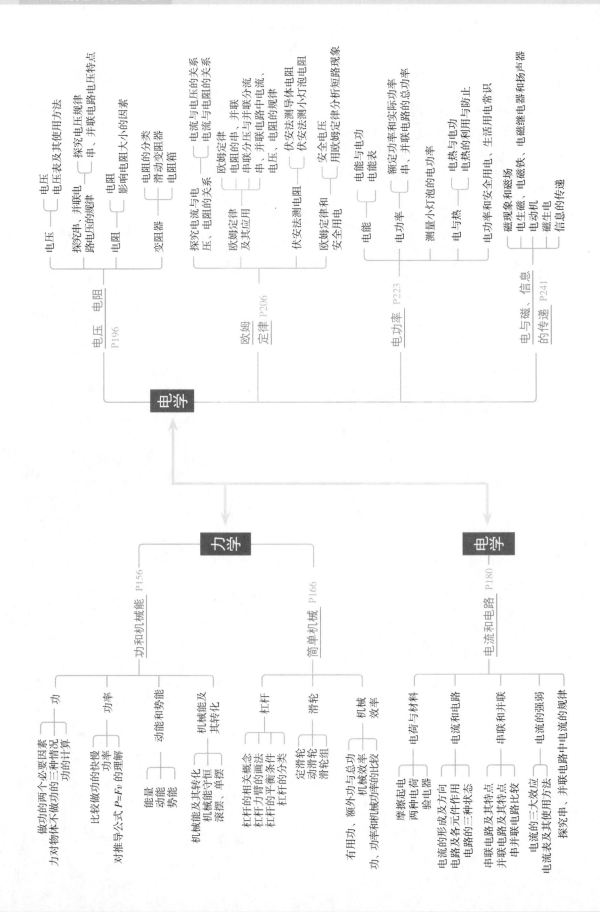

图文导引

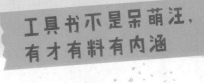
工具书不是呆萌汪，
有才有料有内涵

1 升华教材

升华教材知识
讲解更深更透

2 学科词典

学科知识应有尽有
考试内容尽在其中

3 超详目录、分类索引、结构框图，
速查便捷高效

实用工具

4 知识不理解，清单来解决
学习路漫漫，清单作陪伴

学习伴侣

---

1 紫色、蓝色、绿色
描绘知识点、方法重要性
（■<■<■）

工具书不是高冷范，淡妆浓抹总相宜

2 黄色荧光笔
标示必背知识、关键信息、重要结论

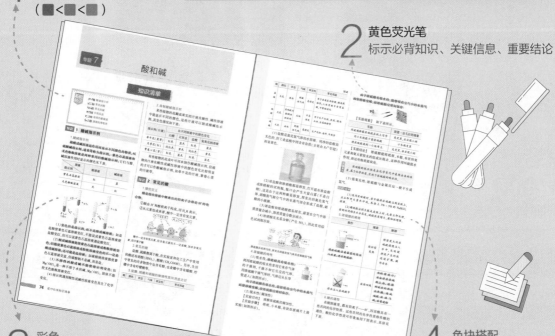

3 彩色
凸显重点、美化插图、标示实物颜色

4 色块搭配
温馨提示、拓展知识

目录

CONTENTS

分类索引

1

第①部分

声学

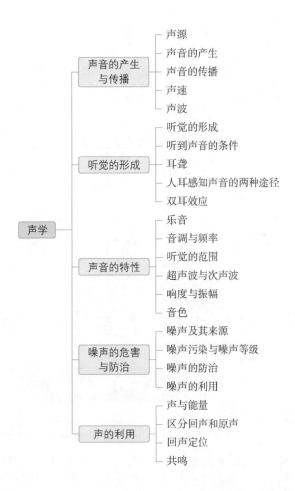

声学
- 声音的产生与传播
  - 声源
  - 声音的产生
  - 声音的传播
  - 声速
  - 声波
- 听觉的形成
  - 听觉的形成
  - 听到声音的条件
  - 耳聋
  - 人耳感知声音的两种途径
  - 双耳效应
- 声音的特性
  - 乐音
  - 音调与频率
  - 听觉的范围
  - 超声波与次声波
  - 响度与振幅
  - 音色
- 噪声的危害与防治
  - 噪声及其来源
  - 噪声污染与噪声等级
  - 噪声的防治
  - 噪声的利用
- 声的利用
  - 声与能量
  - 区分回声和原声
  - 回声定位
  - 共鸣

声现象

知识梳理

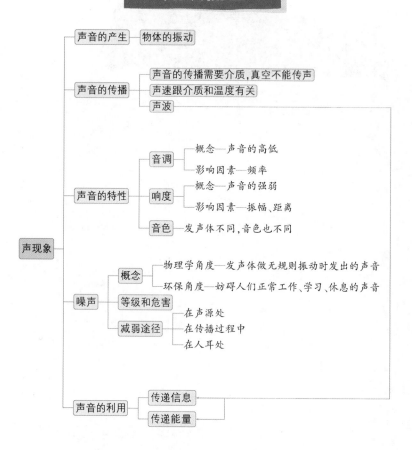

声现象
- 声音的产生 —— 物体的振动
- 声音的传播
  - 声音的传播需要介质,真空不能传声
  - 声速跟介质和温度有关
  - 声波
- 声音的特性
  - 音调
    - 概念——声音的高低
    - 影响因素——频率
  - 响度
    - 概念——声音的强弱
    - 影响因素——振幅、距离
  - 音色——发声体不同,音色也不同
- 噪声
  - 概念
    - 物理学角度——发声体做无规则振动时发出的声音
    - 环保角度——妨碍人们正常工作、学习、休息的声音
  - 等级和危害
  - 减弱途径
    - 在声源处
    - 在传播过程中
    - 在人耳处
- 声音的利用
  - 传递信息
  - 传递能量

第1节　声音的产生与传播

知识清单

基础知识
- 知识 1 声源
- 知识 2 声音的产生
- 知识 3 声音的传播
- 知识 4 声速

知识 1 声源

正在发声的物体叫做声源。固体、液体和气体都能发声,都可以是声源。

不同发声体的发声部位一般不同。①钢琴是靠琴弦振动发声;②笛子是靠空气柱振动发声;③人和其他哺乳动物是靠声带振动发声;④蝉靠胸部的两片鼓膜振动发声;⑤鸟靠鸣膜振动发声;⑥蟋蟀靠翅膀相互摩擦发声;⑦蜜蜂、蚊子、苍蝇在飞行时才有声音,是因为它们飞行时翅膀在振动,如图所示。

蟋蟀　　　　蜜蜂　　　　蝉

知识 2 声音的产生

声音的产生	是由于物体振动
声音的停止	振动停止,发声停止
发声体	是一切正在振动的固体、液体、气体

"振动停止,发声停止"不能叙述为"振动停止,声音消失",因为振动停止,只是不再发声,而原来发出的声音仍存在并会继续传播。

例 运动会上同学们敲锣打鼓,这锣声、鼓声是由于锣面和鼓面的_____产生的。用手按住锣面,_____停止,发声也停止。

解析 声音是由物体振动产生的,振动停止,发声停止。用手按住锣面,锣面的振动停止,发声也停止。

答案 振动　振动

知识 3 声音的传播

1.介质

能够传播声音的物质叫做声的介质。任何固体、液体和气体都是声音传播的介质。

2.声音的传播

声音的传播需要介质。

介质状态	实例
固体	隔墙有耳
液体	说话声吓跑游鱼
气体	人与人相互交谈

3.真空不能传声

在月球上面对面也不能直接交谈,因为月球上没有空气,真空不能传声。

例 如图所示为八年级(2)班物理活动小组成员在探究声音能否在固体、液体、气体、真空中传播时的一些场景。

甲　　　　乙　　　　丙

(1)甲图说明声音在_____中能传播。

(2)乙图中的声音是通过_____和_____介质传到耳朵里去的。

(3)丙图中当向外不断地抽气时,闹铃声在逐渐减弱,说明声音在_____中不能传播。

解析 甲图中传播声音的介质为固体;乙图中传播声音的介质为液体和气体;丙图中随着罩内的空气越来越少,听到的闹铃声越来越弱,可以推理出:罩内为真空时,将听不到闹铃声,说明真空不能传声。

答案 (1)固体　(2)液体　气体　(3)真空

知识 4 声速

定义	声音在介质中每秒传播的距离叫声速
计算公式	$v=s/t$, 其中 $\begin{cases} v:速度 & 单位:m/s \\ s:传播距离 & 单位:m \\ t:传播时间 & 单位:s \end{cases}$
常数	$v=340\ m/s(15\ ℃的空气中)$
影响因素	介质种类,一般情况下,$v_{固}>v_{液}>v_{气}$ 介质温度

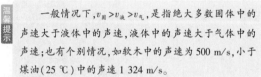

一般情况下,$v_{固}>v_{液}>v_{气}$,是指绝大多数固体中的声速大于液体中的声速,液体中的声速大于气体中的声速;也有个别情况,如软木中的声速为500 m/s,小于煤油(25 ℃)中的声速1 324 m/s。

例 甲同学在长铁管的一端轻轻敲击一下,乙同学会在另一端先后听到两次敲击声,为什么?

解析 这两次敲击声分别是经铁管和空气传播的结果,因为声音在铁管中比在空气中传得快,所以先听到经铁管传来的声音,然后听到经空气传来的声音。

答案 因为声音在铁管中比在空气中传得快,所以乙同学先后听到的两次敲击声,第一次是经铁管传来的,第二次是经空气传来的。

知识 1 声速与气温的关系

1.声速随温度的升高而增大。0 ℃时,声音在空气中的传播速度为 331 m/s。温度每升高 1 ℃,声音在空气中每秒传播的距离增加约 0.6 m。

2.当空气中不同区域的温度有区别时,声音的传播路线是向着低温方向的。如上方的温度低,声音就向上传播,此时,高处的人容易听到低处的声音。

例 烈日炎炎的沙漠或戈壁上,即使相距不太远的人也难以听清对方的大声叫喊,其中一个主要的原因是:声音在传播的过程中向_____拐弯,传入人耳的声音减少了。

知识 2 声波

声音在空气中以声波的形式向四周传播。如图甲所示,以击鼓为例,由于鼓面不断地振动,空气中会形成疏密相间的波,向远处传播,这与水波相似(如图乙),因此我们把这疏密相间的波叫做声波。声波是看不见、摸不到的,存在于发声体的四周。

甲　　　乙

解析 在沙漠或戈壁的上空,空气温度比地表温度低,声音会向上传播。
答案 上

方法清单
方法❶ 转换法探究声音是由物体振动产生的
方法❷ 理想实验法探究真空不能传声

方法 1 转换法探究声音是由物体振动产生的

1.在物理学中,对于一些看不见、摸不着的东西或不易直接测量的物理量,通常用一些非常直观的现象去认识或用易测量的物理量间接测量,这种研究方法称为转换法。

2.将纸屑放入发声的扬声器中,或将发声的音叉放入水中,通过纸屑跳动或溅起的水花反映出扬声器或音叉的振动,都用的是这种方法,如图。

纸屑在发声的扬声器中跳动　　　发声的音叉溅起水花

温馨提示 把扬声器或音叉的微小振动通过纸屑跳动或溅起的水花反映出来,这种将微小振动放大的方法也称为放大法。

例 如图所示,在探究"声音是由物体振动产生的"实验中,用正在发声的音叉紧靠悬线下的轻质小球,发现小球被多次弹开。这样做是为了 (　　)

A.使音叉的振动尽快停下来
B.把音叉的微小振动转换成小球的跳动,便于观察
C.把声音的振动时间延迟
D.使声波被多次反射形成回声

解析 发声体都在振动。音叉的振动幅度很小,不易觉察,可用悬线悬吊轻质小球靠近音叉,这样通过轻质小球的跳动,反映出音叉的振动,即把音叉微小的振动转换成轻质小球的跳动。
答案 B

易混对比 描述发声音叉弹开轻质小球的目的
本题中,若只强调"小球被弹开",目的是显示音叉的微小振动;若强调"音叉发声时小球被弹开,声音消失后小球不再跳动"这是为了证明声音是由物体振动产生的(或发声体在振动)。

方法 2 理想实验法探究真空不能传声

1.理想实验法是以大量可靠的事实为基础,通过真实的实验和合理的推理得出结论,深刻地揭示出物理规律的本质,是物理学研究问题的一种重要的思想方法。

2.在"探究真空不能传声"实验中,实验现象是:随着罩内空气不断抽出,听到的铃声越来越弱,由此推理得出:真空不能传声。

3.在实验中最后还是能听到声音,主要原因是抽气机总是很难将玻璃罩内抽成真空状态,以及周围的固体还能传声。

温馨提示　理想实验法也称推理法。

例　如图所示,将手机置于封闭的玻璃罩内,把罩内的空气用抽气机抽走,使之成为真空,再拨打该手机号码,发现手机屏幕上显示有来电,但却听不到来电提示音,这说明_____。

解析　声音的传播需要介质,在真空中不能传播。当罩内的空气用抽气机抽走后,声音不能传播,故听不到声音;而电磁波可以在真空中传播,所以能看见来电显示。

答案　声音在真空中不能传播,电磁波能在真空中传播

第2节　听觉的形成

知识清单

基础知识
知识 ① 听觉的形成
知识 ② 听到声音的条件
知识 ③ 耳聋
知识 ④ 人耳感知声音的两种途径

知识 1 听觉的形成

1.人耳的构造

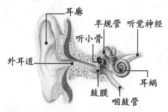

2.听觉的形成

耳廓把外界的声波收集起来,经外耳道传到鼓膜,引起鼓膜振动,鼓膜再将这种振动传给与它相连的听小骨,听小骨再将振动传给耳蜗和半规管,经处理后传至有关神经末梢,神经末梢再将声波信号传送到大脑产生听觉。

知识 2 听到声音的条件

人能听到声音需要四个条件:一是有声波到达人耳;二是人的听觉系统正常;三是声响达到一定的分贝数;四是声音的频率在人的听觉范围内。这四个条件必须同时满足,人才能听到声音。

知识 3 耳聋

类型	概念
传导性耳聋	一个人只有当外耳、中耳、内耳、大脑都完好无损时才会有正常的听力,否则,听力就会受到影响。有的人患过中耳炎,鼓膜穿孔,甚至听小骨也损坏了,导致听力不佳,这叫传导性耳聋
神经性耳聋	有的人鼓膜、听小骨、半规管、耳蜗以及外耳都没问题,但却听不到声音,医学上叫做神经性耳聋

知识 4 人耳感知声音的两种途径

1.空气传导

(1)定义:通过空气振动而引起鼓膜振动,这种振动经过听小骨及其他组织传给听觉神经,从而引起听觉,这种声音的传导方式叫做空气传导。

(2)原理:**气体可以传声**。

(3)途径:

2.骨传导

(1)定义:通过人的头骨、颌骨传到听觉神经,从而引起听觉,这种声音的传导方式叫做骨传导。

(2)原理:**固体可以传声**。

(3)途径:

声音 → （头骨、颌骨） 听觉神经 → 大脑

拓展知识　**知识** 双耳效应

知识 双耳效应

1.定义:声源到两只耳朵的距离一般不同,声音传到两只耳朵的时间、强弱及其他特征也就不同,这些

差异是判断声源方向的重要基础,这就是双耳效应(如图甲)。

甲　　　乙

2.原因:对同一声音,一是两只耳朵感到的强度不同;二是两只耳朵感受到的时间有先后;三是两只耳朵感受到的振动步调有差别。

3.应用:如果在声源四周多放几只话筒,在听众四周对应地多放几只扬声器,这样听众就会感到声音来自四面八方,立体效果就好(如图乙)。利用双耳效应还可判断声源所在的空间方位。

方法清单　**方法** 耳聋病人的听声法

方法 耳聋病人的听声法

如果只是由于传导障碍而失去听觉,想办法通过其他途径将振动传递给听觉神经,人也能够感知声音。

1.利用骨传导:通过人的头骨、颌骨将振动传到听觉神经。

2.利用助听器:助听器是利用增大响度来触动听觉的,它与骨传导助听方法不同。

例 音乐家贝多芬晚年失聪后,就用牙咬住木棒的一端,另一端顶在钢琴上,听自己演奏的琴声,这表明声音可以通过_____传播。

(解析) 贝多芬的耳聋属于传导性耳聋,当他演奏时,钢琴的振动通过木棒、牙齿、颌骨等固体传到听觉神经,从而感知声音。

(答案) 固体

第3节　声音的特性

知识清单

基础知识

知识1 乐音
知识2 音调与频率
知识3 听觉的范围
知识4 超声波与次声波
知识5 响度与振幅
知识6 音色

知识 1 乐音

1.悦耳的声音叫做乐音。从物理角度来看,乐音是发声体有规律的振动产生的。

2.乐音来源广泛,除乐器发出的乐音外,优美的歌声、潺潺的流水声等都是乐音。

知识 2 音调与频率

1.音调

(1)定义:声音的高低叫做音调。

(2)影响因素:音调是由发声体振动的频率决定的。

2.频率:是表示物体振动快慢的物理量。它等于物体 1 s 内振动的次数。频率的单位是赫兹,简称赫,符号为 Hz。如果物体在 1 s 内振动 100 次,那么频率就是 100 Hz。

3.音调与频率的关系:音调的高低取决于振动的频率。频率越高,音调也就越高;频率越低,音调也就越低。如图所示,齿轮的齿数越多,纸片发出声音的音调越高。

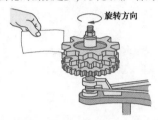

旋转方向

4.用波形比较频率:如图所示,甲、乙两个音叉的频率不同。在相同时间内,甲振动次数少,频率低,音调低;乙振动次数多,频率高,音调高。

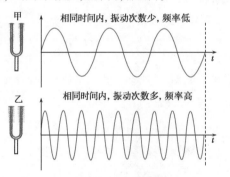

甲 相同时间内,振动次数少,频率低

乙 相同时间内,振动次数多,频率高

例 以下操作中,不能改变音调的是 ( )

改变杯内水量,再次用湿手摩擦杯口 A

改变用力大小,再次敲鼓面 B

改变钢尺伸出桌面长度,再次拨动钢尺 C

改变管内水量,再次对着试管吹气 D

解析 用湿手摩擦杯口,杯子壁振动发声,改变杯内水量,则杯子壁振动快慢会发生变化,所以音调会改变;改变用力大小,再次敲击鼓面,鼓面振动幅度发生变化,所以响度会改变,但不会改变音调;改变钢尺伸出桌面的长度会改变其振动的快慢,音调会改

变;改变管内水量,空气柱长短变化,振动快慢会发生改变,所以音调会改变。故本题选 B。

答案 B

知识 3 听觉的范围

人能感受到的声音的频率有一定范围,一般来说,人耳可以听见振动频率在 20~20 000 Hz 之间的声音。

例 根据图中所给信息,判断下列说法正确的是 ( )

人、蝙蝠的发声和听觉的频率范围/Hz

发声频率　　　　　听觉频率

人 85　1 100
20　　　　　20 000

蝙蝠 1 000
10 000　120 000
120 000

A.蝙蝠可以发出频率为 400 Hz 的声音

B.人能听到蝙蝠发出的所有频率的声音

C.人的听觉频率范围比人的发声频率范围要大

D.15 Hz 的声音只要振幅足够大,人耳是能听到的

解析 观察题图可获知:蝙蝠发声频率在 10 000 Hz 以上,A 项错;人的听觉范围没有包括蝙蝠发声频率的全部范围,B 项错;C 项表述与图中表达的信息相符,C 项正确;15 Hz 低于人耳听觉的最低频率,所以人耳是听不到的,D 项错。

答案 C

知识 4 超声波与次声波

	频率范围	特点	利用与危害
超声波	高于 20 000 Hz	定向性好,穿透能力强	利用:①超声探伤、测厚、测距、医学诊断和成像;②超声处理,如进行加工、清洗、焊接、乳化、粉碎、脱气、种子处理等
次声波	低于 20 Hz	传播过程中衰减少,波长较长,能绕过障碍物;传播距离远,强大的次声波破坏性很大	利用:检测核爆炸 危害:对建筑物有很大的破坏性,能震裂建筑物甚至使建筑物摆动;对人体有危害,当人处在 2~10 Hz 次声波环境中时,会产生失明、恶心、神经错乱等症状

例 2008 年 5 月 8 日,四川绵竹市西南镇檀木村制药厂附近突然出现大量蟾蜍(如图),12 日出现了地震。地震前也有"牛羊驴马不进圈,老鼠搬家往外逃"等现象,动物的这种异常表现是因为一些动物能听到人耳听不到的_____。

(解析) 地震往往伴随着次声波的产生,一些动物能听到次声波而会有与平常截然不同的表现。

(答案) 次声波

知识 5 响度与振幅

1.响度

(1)定义:声音的强弱(或大小)叫做响度。

(2)影响因素:响度是由发声体振动的幅度决定的。

①响度与振幅的关系:发声体的振幅越大,响度就越大;振幅越小,响度也越小。如敲鼓时,鼓声越响,鼓面上的纸屑跳得越高;发声的音叉越响,接触水面时溅起的水花越大。

②人听到声音是否响亮,除跟发声体发声时的响度有关外还与听者距发声体的远近有关,离发声体越近,响度越大。如两人说话时,离得越近,响度越大,听得越清楚。

③声音的响度跟声音发散程度有关,声音越集中,响度越大。如医生用听诊器看病,或把双手围成喇叭状向远处喊话时(如图),减小了声音的分散,增大响度。

④声音的响度还跟人的主观感觉和声音在传播途中是否遇到障碍物有关。

2.振幅:物体振动的幅度,也是物体离开原来位置的最大距离。

3.认识振幅

用较小的力敲击音叉

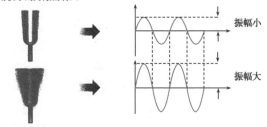

振幅小

振幅大

用较大的力敲击音叉

(易混对比)

乐器的音调与响度

各种乐器中,鼓锣等打击乐器,出厂时音调已经确定,用力打与轻打相比,只是声音的大小不一样,即响度不同;二胡、小提琴等弦乐器,音调由弦的粗细、长短和松紧程度决定,用力弹与轻弹相比,也只是响度发生变化;笛子等管乐器,每个孔对应的空气柱长度一定,音调不变,用力吹时,响度变大。

知识 6 音色

1.定义:音色又叫音品或音质,它反映了声音的品质与特色。

2.影响因素:发声体的材料、结构等。

(1)音色取决于发声体本身,不同发声体的振动情况不同,发出声音的音色就不同。如小白兔能分辨出门外不是自己的外婆(如图),主要是依据声音的音色来判断的。

乖乖快开门,我是外婆。

别开门! 他不是外婆,听声音就不对!

(2)音色是我们分辨各种声音的依据,不受音调、响度的影响,即使不同的乐器发出音调、响度相同的声音,我们也能够把它们区分开。

(拓展知识)
知识 1 示波器与波形图
知识 2 乐器的音调

知识 1 示波器与波形图

1.示波器是一种显示波形图的仪器。如图所示,先用麦克风接收声音,将声音信号转变为电信号输入到示波器中,通过示波器的处理就能在示波器的荧光屏上显示出与声波相对应的图形,即波形图。

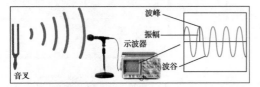

2.在波形图中,波峰(波谷)出现的个数的多少,表示声源振动频率的高低;振幅的大小,对应着声源振动幅度的大小。波形的具体形状反映了声源发声的特色(如图)。

音叉振动时,显示出的声波的波形

演员唱歌时,显示出的声波的波形

3.从物理学的角度看,乐音是声源有规则的振动产生的,其波形图也有规则;噪声是声源没有规则的振动产生的,其波形图杂乱无章,没有规则。

例 如图所示是声波的波形图,下列说法正确的是

( )

甲　　　乙　　　丙　　　丁

A.甲、乙的音调和响度相同
B.甲、丙的音调和音色相同
C.乙、丁的音调和音色相同
D.丙、丁的音色和响度相同

(解析) 甲、丙、丁三个声波的波形相同,其音色相同。甲、乙、丙三个声波振幅相同,故它们的响度相同,丁的振幅较小,响度较小。在相同的时间内,甲、乙、丁三个声波的振动次数相同,故它们的音调相同,丙的振动次数较少,故其音调较低。经以上分析可知,选项A正确,B、C、D错误。

(答案) A

知识 2 乐器的音调

各种乐器的音调

打击乐器	鼓、锣等乐器受到打击时发生振动,发出声音。以鼓为例,鼓皮绷得越紧,音调就越高
弦乐器	二胡、小提琴和琵琶等通过弦的振动发声。音调的高低取决于弦的粗细、长短和松紧程度。一般情况下,弦越细、越紧、越短,振动频率越高,音调越高
管乐器	长笛、箫、号等,音调的高低取决于所含空气柱的长短。一般来说,长空气柱的振动产生声音的音调低,短空气柱的振动产生声音的音调高

温馨提示 往暖瓶里灌开水,是根据音调不同来判断水位高低的。灌开水时,瓶内空气柱振动发出声音,随着瓶内水面上升,瓶内空气柱变短,振动频率变高,发出的声音音调变高。

例 如图所示,7个相同的水瓶中灌入不同高度的水,敲击它们,可以发出"1、2、3、4、5、6、7"的声音来。这些声音产生的原因和决定音调的因素分别是

( )

A.瓶子和水振动,水的高度
B.水振动,瓶内空气柱的高度
C.瓶内空气振动,水的高度
D.瓶内空气振动,瓶内空气柱的高度

(解析) 敲击瓶子时,主要是由于瓶子和水的振动产生声音。灌水少的瓶子,振动频率高,音调高。同理,灌水多的瓶子,振动频率低,音调低。故A正确。

(答案) A

易混对比 盛水不满的玻璃瓶发声时的音调变化问题
关于盛有部分水的玻璃瓶发声时的音调如何变化,首先要认清发声物体是瓶内空气柱还是瓶子。用嘴吹瓶口时,瓶内空气柱振动发声,空气柱越短,音调越高;敲击瓶口时,瓶子和水振动发声,水越少,音调越高。

方法 1　控制变量法探究音调高低与哪些因素有关

1.在研究物理问题时,某一物理量往往受几个不同因素的影响,为了确定该物理量与各个不同因素之间的关系,就需要控制某些因素,使其固定不变,只研究其中一个因素,看所研究的因素与该物理量之间的关系,这种研究问题的方法叫做控制变量法。

2.验证琴弦发声时音调高低与琴弦横截面积的关系时,需控制琴弦的材料、长度等因素相同。该实验运用了控制变量法。

例　在学习吉他演奏的过程中,小华发现琴弦发出声音的音调高低是受各种因素影响的,他决定对此进行研究。经过和同学们讨论,提出了以下猜想:

猜想一:琴弦发出声音的音调高低,可能与琴弦的横截面积有关。

猜想二:琴弦发出声音的音调高低,可能与琴弦的长短有关。

猜想三:琴弦发出声音的音调高低,可能与琴弦的材料有关。

为了验证上述猜想是否正确,他们找到了如表所示的 9 种规格的琴弦,因为音调的高低取决于声源振动的频率,于是借助一个能够测量振动频率的仪器进行实验。

编号	材料	长度(cm)	横截面积(mm^2)
A	铜	60	0.76
B	铜	60	0.89
C	铜	60	1.02
D	铜	80	0.76
E	铜		
F	铜	100	0.76
G	钢	80	1.02
H	尼龙	80	1.02
I	尼龙	100	1.02

(1)为了验证猜想一,应选用编号为＿＿＿的琴弦进行实验。为了验证猜想二,应选用编号为＿＿＿的琴弦进行实验。表中有的材料规格还没有填全,为了验证猜想三,必须知道该项内容。请在表中填上所缺数据。

(2)随着实验的进行,小华又觉得琴弦音调的高低,可能还与琴弦的松紧程度有关,为了验证这一猜想,必须进行的操作是:＿＿＿＿＿＿＿＿＿＿
＿＿＿＿＿＿＿＿＿＿＿＿＿＿＿＿＿＿＿＿＿
＿＿＿＿＿＿＿＿＿＿＿＿＿＿＿＿＿＿＿＿＿
＿＿＿＿＿＿＿＿＿＿＿＿＿＿＿＿＿＿。

解析　(1)因为音调高低取决于多个因素,在实验过程中就必须采用控制变量法,若验证猜想一,所选的琴弦就必须是长度、材料相同且横截面积不同的几根弦,所以应选 A、B、C 三根弦;同理可知,验证猜想二,要选 A、D、F 三根弦;要验证猜想三则长度、横截面积应相同。(2)若再研究音调与弦松紧程度的关系,必须用大小相同的力去拨松紧不同的弦,测出相应的频率,然后进行分析、比较。

答案　(1)ABC　ADF　80　1.02

(2)选取一根琴弦,拉紧琴弦,用一定大小的力拨动琴弦,测出此时振动的频率,然后改变琴弦的松紧,用同样大小的力拨动琴弦,测出此时的振动频率,进行分析、比较

方法 2　比较法判断民谚、俗语、古诗文中的声学知识

在日常生活中,我们经常会接触到一些民谚、俗语、古诗文,这其中蕴含着大量的声学知识。如"不敢高声语,恐惊天上人"中的"高声语"意为大声说话,指声音的响度大。通过分析其中的声学知识,然后与声音的三个特性比较,有助于提高我们分析问题、解决问题的能力。

例　下列关于声音的说法中不正确的是　　(　　)

A."响鼓也要重锤敲"说明声音是由振动产生的,且振幅越大响度越大

B."震耳欲聋"说明声音的音调高

C."闻其声而知其人"说明可以根据音色来判断说话者

D."隔墙有耳"说明固体能传声

解析　分析与声音有关的词语或句子,然后与声音的三个特性进行比较,最后判断出是与什么特性有关。"震耳欲聋"是指声音的响度大而不是音调高。

答案　B

第4节　噪声的危害与防治

知识❶ 噪声及其来源
知识❷ 噪声污染与噪声等级
知识❸ 噪声的防治

知识 1 噪声及其来源

1.噪声

噪声是使人烦躁不安的声音。可以从两个角度进行定义。(1)从物理学角度来看,噪声是由发声体杂乱无章、无规则的振动产生的,其波形图也是杂乱、无规则的(如图);(2)从环境保护的角度来看,凡是影响人们正常工作、学习和休息的声音都是噪声;如干扰其他同学听课的说话声。

2.噪声的来源

(1)交通噪声:交通工具的喇叭声、汽笛声、刹车声、排气声、机械运转声等。

(2)工业噪声:纺织厂、印刷厂、机械车间的噪声。

(3)建筑噪声:筑路、盖楼、打桩等建筑活动中的噪声。

(4)社会噪声:家庭噪声、娱乐噪声、商店和集贸市场里的喧哗声等。

易混对比

歌声是乐音还是噪声?

区分歌声是乐音还是噪声,需从两方面来判断。从物理角度看,悦耳动听的歌声属于乐音;从环境保护的角度来看,当歌声影响人的正常工作和休息时,就变为噪声了。

知识 2 噪声污染与噪声等级

1.噪声污染

当噪声对人及周围环境造成不良影响时,就形成了噪声污染。

噪声污染与水污染、大气污染、固体废弃物污染是当代社会的四大污染。

2.噪声的等级

噪声的等级	人的感觉	声音举例
0 dB	人们刚刚能听到的最弱声音	—
10 dB	相当于微风吹落叶声	钟表嘀嗒声
30~40 dB	较理想的安静环境	鸟鸣
>50 dB	影响睡眠和休息	轻声对话
>70 dB	会干扰说话,影响工作效率	大声呼喊
>90 dB	听力会受到严重影响,并产生神经衰弱、头疼、高血压等症状	重型载重汽车发出的声音
150 dB	鼓膜会破裂出血,双耳完全失去听力	喷气式飞机发出的声音

温馨提示 为了保护听力,控制噪声不超过90 dB;为了保证工作和学习,控制噪声不超过70 dB;为保证休息和睡眠,控制噪声不超过50 dB。

知识 3 噪声的防治

措施	实例
防止噪声产生(在声源处减弱)	改造噪声大的机器或换用噪声小的设备;给机器加橡皮垫来吸收它的振动;给汽车和摩托车安装消声器;手机调成静音等。
阻碍噪声传播(在传播过程中减弱)	在马路和住宅间设置屏障或植树造林;关闭门窗后教室外的吵闹声会小很多等。
防止噪声进入人耳(在人耳处减弱)	人在工作时佩戴耳塞、耳罩等。

拓展知识

知识 噪声的利用

知识 噪声的利用

1.噪声除草

实验发现,植物也会"听"声音。对于同样的声音,不同的植物有不同的反应。噪声能使杂草的种子提前发芽。据此,科学家们制造了噪声除草器。农作物播种后,向农田播放噪声,使杂草提前生长,在农作物生长之前,先把杂草除掉。

2.噪声除尘

高能量的噪声能使尘粒聚集在一起,尘粒变重而下沉。据此制成了新型除尘设备——噪声除尘器。

3.噪声诊病

利用声波反射原理,科技人员研制出一种听力诊断器。给人看病时,先让装置发出微弱短促的噪声波,使人的鼓膜振动,然后由装置中的微型电脑根据回声,把有关鼓膜功能的数据显示出来,供医师诊断。此法测试快速,对人体无害且不痛不痒,很适合儿童诊病。

4.噪声制冷

美国工程师设计了一种利用噪声制冷的冰箱。它不消耗电能,也不用化学制冷剂,既降低了成本又不会污染空气,很有发展前景。

5.噪声发电

英国剑桥大学的专家发现,声波碰到屏障时,声能会转化为机械能。据此,他们设计出一种鼓膜式声波接收器,跟一个共鸣器连在一起,可以大大提高会聚声能的能力,再通过声电转换装置,使声能转化为电能。

6.噪声武器

因为噪声有麻痹人体中枢神经系统的作用,科研人员已制造出一种"噪声弹",用它射击逃犯,能使逃犯立即昏迷,束手就擒。

7.以噪治噪

实验发现,两束频率相同、振幅相同、相位相反的声波相遇时,互相干涉的结果会使声波消失。为此科研人员制造出一种消声器,用来消除和减小工厂、车辆的噪声。

方法清单

> **方法** 减弱噪声的方法

方法 减弱噪声的方法

1.明确噪声的含义

(1)发声体无规则的振动产生。

(2)影响人们正常工作、学习和休息的声音。

2.减弱噪声的途径:在声源处、在传播过程中、在人耳处。

例 交通噪声是城市噪声的主要来源之一,如图所示,甲、乙两图分别表示在_____和_____控制了噪声。

禁止鸣笛
甲

高速路边隔音墙
乙

解析 禁止鸣笛是在声源处控制噪声;隔音墙是在传播过程中控制噪声。

答案 声源处 传播过程中

第5节 声的利用

知识清单

基础知识

知识1 声与信息
知识2 声与能量
知识3 区分回声和原声
知识4 回声定位

知识 1 声与信息

1.利用声传递信息。如:学生听到铃声进教室上课;医生利用听诊器,通过听到的声音判断人体内心脏、肺的健康状况;利用接收到台风产生的次声波来判断台风的风向及位置;利用地震、机器产生的次声波来判断地震的位置和机器的优劣。

2.利用回声测距离。如:古代在雾中航行的水手,利用听到号角的回声判断悬崖的远近;利用声呐系统探测海水深度(如图)、海中暗礁,还可用来探测鱼群、潜艇的位置。

我闭着眼睛都知道海水的深度。

3."B超"的原理:检查身体时,"B超"机向人体发射一定量的超声波,然后用移动的探头接收各器官反射回来的超声波信号,经过计算机对这些信号进行处理,在屏幕上呈现出内脏器官的图像,医生根据图像判断器官是否存在病变。

 利用回声测距离和"B超"原理实际上都是声音传递信息的应用。

知识 2 声与能量

声具有能量,也可以传递能量。

(1)声音是由物体振动产生的,传递声的过程就是传递振动的过程,有振动就有能量,利用振动就是利用能量。

(2)声波传递能量的应用:工业上可以利用超声波清洗精密仪器,利用超声波除尘器降低污染,美化环境;医学上可以利用超声波击碎人体内的结石;生活中有一种电子牙刷(如图),它能发出超声波,直达牙刷棕毛刷不到的地方,这样刷牙既干净又舒服。

 如图所示:若敲响右边的音叉,左边完全相同的音叉也会发声,并且把泡沫塑料球弹起。这一现象说明了:①发声体在振动,②空气可以传声,③声可以传递能量。

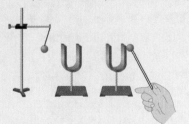

知识 3 区分回声和原声

回声的概念	如果声音在传播过程中遇到障碍物,一部分声音被反射回来形成回声
区分回声和原声的条件	若回声到达人耳比原声晚 0.1 s 以上,人耳就能把回声和原声区分开来,否则,回声与原声混在一起,使原声加强

 教室内听不到回声,是因为从教室墙壁反射回来的声音到达人耳时与原声的时间间隔小于 0.1 s,回声与原声混在一起,增加了声音的强度。

例 如果回声到达人耳的时间比原声晚 0.1 s 以上,人就可以把回声与原声分辨出来,那么障碍物到发声的人的距离至少是(声音在空气中的速度取 340 m/s)

( )

A.10 m   B.34 m   C.17 m   D.68 m

解析 距离最短时,回声与原声的时间间隔为 0.1 s,即声音传到障碍物再反射回到人耳所用时间为 0.1 s,人到障碍物的最短距离:$s=vt=340 \text{ m/s}×\dfrac{0.1 \text{ s}}{2}=17 \text{ m}$。

答案 C

知识 4 回声定位

蝙蝠在飞行时会发出超声波,这些超声波碰到墙壁或昆虫等物体时会反射回来,根据回声传来的方位和时间,蝙蝠可以确定目标的位置和距离。蝙蝠采用的这种方法叫做回声定位(如图所示)。

前方30米有食物!

 蝙蝠可用超声定位,也可以用超声进行导航,受蝙蝠超声导航的启示,人们制成了超声雷达,又叫声呐。

拓展知识 | **知识** 共鸣

知识 共鸣

将两个频率相同的音叉靠近放在桌上,用橡皮锤敲击其中一个,使其发声。然后用橡皮锤压在这个音叉上,使其停止发声。我们会听到未被敲击的音叉也在发声,这种现象称为共鸣。

温馨提示 | 能发生共鸣的两个物体具有相同的固有频率。

方法清单 | 方法❶ 比较法区分声传递的是信息还是能量
方法❷ 利用回声测距离

方法 1 比较法区分声传递的是信息还是能量

许多同学对声音传递的是信息还是能量区别不开。这里有一个小窍门:凡是声音能引起其他物体变化的例子,说明声音传递的是能量;声音未能引起其他物体的变化,而人们可以根据所听到的声音作出判断的例子,说明声音传递的是信息。

例 如图所示,医生正在用听诊器为病人诊病。听诊器运用了声音_____(选填"具有能量"或"传递信息")的道理;来自患者的声音通过橡皮管传送到医生的耳朵,这样可以提高声音的_____(选填"音调"或"响度")。

解析 听诊器就是运用了声音能传递信息的道理,听诊器将来自患者的声音通过橡皮管传送到医生的耳朵,减小了声音的分散,增大了响度。

答案 传递信息 响度

方法 2 利用回声测距离

利用回声测距的原理是 $s = \frac{1}{2} v_{声} t$,其中 t 为从发声到听到回声的时间,$v_{声}$ 为声音在不同介质中的传播速度,注意 $v_{声}$ 在不同介质中是不同的(如图)。

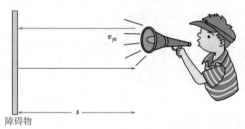

障碍物

例 汽车沿平直公路匀速驶向一座高山,汽车的速度为 10 m/s,声速为 340 m/s,途中司机按了一次喇叭,2 s 后听到回声,司机按喇叭时汽车距山脚多远?

解析 在声音传播并返回的过程中,汽车以 10 m/s 的速度向高山处行驶了 2 s。在这 2 s 的时间内,汽车前进的路程与声音在 2 s 内通过的路程之和,正是按喇叭时汽车与山脚距离的 2 倍,如图所示。汽车 2 s 内行驶的路程为 $s_1 = v_1 t = 10 \text{ m/s} \times 2 \text{ s} = 20 \text{ m}$,声音在 2 s 内传播的路程为 $s_1 + 2s_2 = v_2 t = 340 \text{ m/s} \times 2 \text{ s} = 680 \text{ m}$。

由上面分析可知,按喇叭时汽车距山脚的距离为

$$s = \frac{s_1 + s_1 + 2s_2}{2} = \frac{20 \text{ m} + 680 \text{ m}}{2} = 350 \text{ m}。$$

答案 350 m

点拨 (1)当声源不动时,声音从发出到返回通过的路程是声源到障碍物距离的两倍。

(2)当声源向障碍物运动时,发声的位置到障碍物的距离等于声音传播的路程与声源运动的路程总和的二分之一。

第❷部分

光学

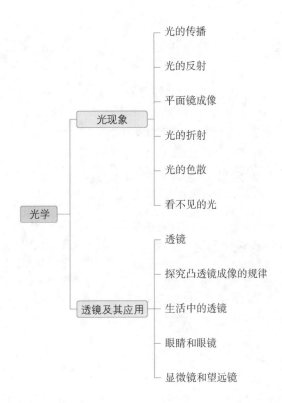

光学
- 光现象
  - 光的传播
  - 光的反射
  - 平面镜成像
  - 光的折射
  - 光的色散
  - 看不见的光
- 透镜及其应用
  - 透镜
  - 探究凸透镜成像的规律
  - 生活中的透镜
  - 眼睛和眼镜
  - 显微镜和望远镜

光现象

知识梳理

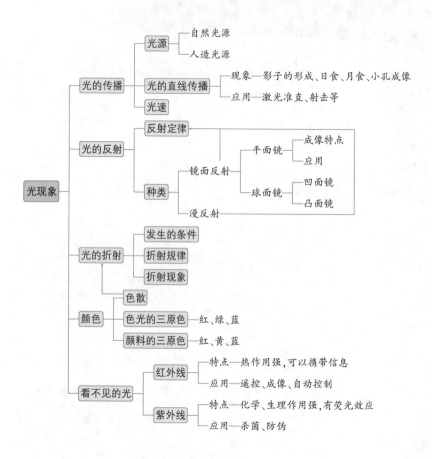

光现象
- 光的传播
  - 光源
    - 自然光源
    - 人造光源
  - 光的直线传播
    - 现象——影子的形成、日食、月食、小孔成像
    - 应用——激光准直、射击等
  - 光速
- 光的反射
  - 反射定律
  - 种类
    - 镜面反射
      - 平面镜
        - 成像特点
        - 应用
      - 球面镜
        - 凹面镜
        - 凸面镜
    - 漫反射
- 光的折射
  - 发生的条件
  - 折射规律
  - 折射现象
- 颜色
  - 色散
  - 色光的三原色——红、绿、蓝
  - 颜料的三原色——红、黄、蓝
- 看不见的光
  - 红外线
    - 特点——热作用强，可以携带信息
    - 应用——遥控、成像、自动控制
  - 紫外线
    - 特点——化学、生理作用强，有荧光效应
    - 应用——杀菌、防伪

第1节　光的传播

基础知识
知识**1** 光源
知识**2** 光的直线传播
知识**3** 光速

知识 **1** 光源

概念	正在发光的物体叫光源		
分类	按形成原因分	自然光源	如:太阳、萤火虫、水母等
		人造光源	如:点燃的蜡烛、发光的电灯等
	按发光原理分	热光源	如:太阳、点燃的火把、发光的电灯等
		冷光源	如:萤火虫、水母等
	按光束形状分	点光源	如:发光的电灯,点燃的蜡烛等
		平行光源	如:手电筒射出的光、太阳光等

温馨提示

光源指的是自身能发光且正在发光的物体,不包括反射光的情况。如月亮、自行车的尾灯、公路上的交通标志牌及放电影时的银幕都是靠反射射向它们的光才亮,它们本身不能发光,因此不是光源。

知识 **2** 光的直线传播

1.光沿直线传播的条件:**光在同种均匀介质中是沿直线传播的。**

易混对比

光在空气中的传播路径是直的还是弯曲的?

光在空气中是否沿直线传播关键在于空气是否均匀,由于地球表面的大气层不均匀,从大气层外射到地面的光线的传播路径会发生弯曲;生活中所说的光在空气中沿直线传播是因为地面附近均匀的空气是同种均匀介质。

2.光沿直线传播的现象

(1)如何看到光沿直线传播的路径。

在有雾的天气里,可以看到从汽车头灯射出的光束是直的;穿过森林的光束是直的(如图);用激光灯射出的光束紧贴整平的墙面传播,可看到直线光束。

茂密的树林挡不住阳光"直"的追求

温馨提示

我们能看见光的传播路径是利用了光照射到烟雾、灰尘或墙面时发生的漫反射现象。

(2)光沿直线传播形成的现象有:影子的形成,小孔成像,日食,月食等。

3.光线

(1)由于光在同种均匀介质中是沿直线传播的,所以经常用一条带箭头的直线来表示光的传播路线,箭头的方向表示光的传播方向,这样的直线叫做光线,如图所示。

光线

光束

(2)光线在几何作图中起着重要作用,在光的直线传播、反射与折射以及研究透镜成像中,都是必不可少且要反复用到的。

(3)应注意的是,光线不是实际存在的实物,而是在研究光的行进过程中对细窄光束的抽象。它是人们研究光现象的一种方法,即建立物理模型的方法。

知识 **3** 光速

1.光在各种介质中的传播速度

	传播速度/(m·s^{-1})
真空	$2.997\ 92\times10^8\approx3\times10^8$
空气	约为3×10^8
水	真空中光速的$\dfrac{3}{4}$
玻璃	真空中光速的$\dfrac{2}{3}$
其他介质	比真空中光速小

第②部分

2.光年:光年是长度的单位,1光年表示光在1年时间内所走的路程,1光年≈$9.46×10^{12}$ km。

知识 **1** 光沿直线传播的应用
知识 **2** 日食、月食的成因

知识 **1** 光沿直线传播的应用

1.激光准直:在开凿大山隧道时,工程师们常常用激光束引导掘进机,使掘进机沿直线前进,保证开凿隧道方向不出偏差,如图。

2.射击时利用"三点一线"进行瞄准,如图。

3.站队成直线:前面的人挡住了后面人的视线,使后面的人只能看到前面相邻人的后脑勺。

4.木工检测木料的表面是否平滑。

知识 **2** 日食、月食的成因

1.日食、月食是由于光的直线传播形成的。

2.当月球转到地球和太阳之间,并且三者在同一直线上时,月球就挡住了射向地球的阳光,由于光沿直线传播,在月球背后会形成长长的影子。

3.月球在地球的影子分为两部分,如图甲所示,中心的区域叫做本影区,外面的区域叫做半影区。位于半影区的人看到的是日偏食;位于本影区的人看到的是日全食;若地、月之间距离较远时,还会看到日环食。

4.当地球转到月球和太阳之间,并且三者在同一直线上时,地球就挡住了射向月球的阳光,就会形成月食,如图乙所示。

方法清单

方法 实验探究小孔成像的特点

方法 **实验探究小孔成像的特点**

1.小孔成像是由于光的直线传播形成的。

2.由于屏的阻碍,光源射出的光中,大部分被屏挡住,只有那些指向小孔的光,恰可沿直线通过小孔在光屏上形成光斑。

3.由于光的直线传播,烛焰上部发出的光线通过小孔后,射到了屏的下部;烛焰下部发出的光线通过小孔后,射到了屏的上部;形成了一个相对烛焰倒立的像(如图)。这个像由实际光线会聚而成,因此是实像。

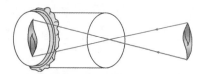

4.只有小孔足够小时才能成像。如果小孔太大,物体上任一点发出(或反射)的光透过小孔后在光屏上形成的光斑就比较大,物体上相邻点发出(或反射)

的光透过小孔后,在光屏上形成的光斑就比较大,光斑重叠较多,使像模糊不清,甚至不成像。

5.像倒立,像的形状与物体相似,与小孔的形状无关。

6.像的大小取决于光屏到小孔的距离和物体到小孔的距离的关系。

例 某兴趣小组在空易拉罐的底部中央戳个小圆孔,将顶部剪去后,蒙上一层塑料薄膜,制作成一个简易针孔照相机。如图所示,将其水平放置,在左侧固定一只与小孔等高的小灯泡,灯泡发光时,可在塑料薄膜上看到灯丝_____(选填"倒立"或"正立")的像。若水平向左移动易拉罐,像的大小_____(选填"变大""变小"或"不变")。若只将小圆孔改为三角形小孔,则像的形状_____(选填"改变"或"不变")。

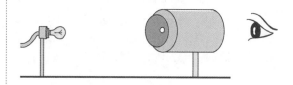

解析 小孔成像的原理是光的直线传播,小孔成像的特点是成一个倒立的实像,当光屏到小孔的距离一定时,像的大小与物体到小孔的距离有关,距离越小,所成的像越大,而与小孔的形状无关。

答案 倒立 变大 不变

第2节 光的反射

知识清单

基础知识
- 知识1 光的反射
- 知识2 光的反射定律
- 知识3 镜面反射和漫反射

知识1 光的反射

1.定义:当光射到物体表面时,被物体表面反射回去,这种现象叫做光的反射。

2.光的反射图中一点、二角、三线的认识

如图所示,要弄清一点、二角、三线的含义。

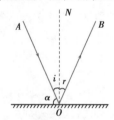

一点:指入射点,用字母 O 表示。

二角:指入射角 i 和反射角 r。

入射角是指入射光线和法线的夹角,反射角是指反射光线和法线的夹角。

三线:指入射光线 AO,反射光线 OB,法线 NO。

法线是通过入射点作的垂直于反射面的虚线,这是为了研究问题的方便而引入的,没有具体的物理含义,但在确定入射角、反射角时法线却是关键。因为反射角和入射角都是指光线与法线的夹角。

温馨提示 上图中,入射光线 AO 不能说成 OA,字母顺序应与光线的方向一致;同样,反射光线的字母顺序只能是 OB。

知识2 光的反射定律

1.反射定律:光发生反射时,反射光线、入射光线和法线在同一平面内,反射光线与入射光线分别位于法线的两侧,反射角等于入射角。

温馨提示 光的反射定律描述了"三线""两角"的关系,可简记为:"三线共面,法线居中(三线位置关系),两角相等(两角量值关系)"

2.光反射时光路是可逆的

如图甲所示,AO 是入射光线,OB 是反射光线。如果光线沿 BO 的方向入射,则反射光线一定沿 OA 的方向射出去,如图乙所示。

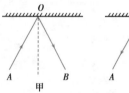

甲　　　　　　乙

例 如图所示,MM' 为平面镜,AO 为入射光线,NO 为法线,$\angle AON$ 等于 $60°$。已知 $\angle NOB$ 等于 $30°$,$\angle NOC$ 等于 $45°$,$\angle NOD$ 等于 $60°$。则入射光线 AO 的反射光线将沿着_____方向射出。(选填"OB"、"OC"或"OD")

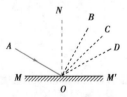

解析 根据反射角等于入射角,来确定反射光线。

答案 OD

第2部分 第2章 光现象 **19**

知识 3 镜面反射和漫反射

分类	定义	光路图	举例
镜面反射	平行光线照射到光滑平整的物体表面上,反射光线仍然是平行的		黑板反光、平面镜成像
漫反射	平行光线照射到凹凸不平的表面上,反射光线不再平行,而是射向各个方向		学生能在教室任何地方看清黑板上的字

易混对比

黑板反光是镜面反射还是漫反射

镜面反射和漫反射都遵守光的反射定律,只是反射面平整度不同;黑板反光现象是指当光线较强的时候,坐在教室前排靠墙的同学看不清离自己最近的部分黑板上的字的现象,这是因为光线射到黑板的某区域时发生了镜面反射,反射光线射向某个固定方向,没有进入该同学眼中;若强调在教室任何地方都能看清黑板上的字,说明光照在黑板上发生的是漫反射现象。

例 如图所示,晚上在桌面上铺一张白纸,把一块小平面镜放在白纸上(镜面朝上),让手电筒的光正对着白纸和平面镜照射,从侧面看上去 ( )

A.镜子比较亮,它发生了镜面反射

B.镜子比较暗,它发生了漫反射

C.白纸比较亮,它发生了漫反射

D.白纸比较暗,它发生了镜面反射

(解析) 镜子表面光滑,发生镜面反射,光线垂直入射到镜面,均垂直反射,所以在侧面看不到反射光,镜面比较暗。白纸表面粗糙,光射在上面发生漫反射,反射光线朝向各个方向,所以在侧面能看到白纸的反射光,白纸比较亮。

(答案) C

拓展知识　知识 对光的反射定律的理解

知识 对光的反射定律的理解

对于光的反射定律,应掌握以下五点:

(1)根据光的反射定律可知,任何一条反射光线都对应一条入射光线。

(2)定律的叙述有一定的逻辑因果关系:先有入射,后有反射。表达时不能把"反射角等于入射角"说成"入射角等于反射角",因为"反射角等于入射角"的意思是反射角随着入射角的变化而变化,若倒过来说意思就反了,不符合逻辑因果关系。

(3)两角量值关系的变化是相对应的,即反射角随着入射角的变化而变化。入射角增大时反射角也增大,入射角减小时反射角也减小,入射角变为0°,反射角也变为0°,此时,入射光线、反射光线、法线重合,"三线合一"。

(4)法线起"标准"的作用,是过入射点始终与反射面垂直的直线。当反射面转动一定角度时,法线仍与反射面垂直,也随之转过相同的角度。法线不仅过入射点与反射面垂直,而且还是入射光线与反射光线夹角的角平分线。

(5)在描述光的反射定律的光路图中,有两个重要的角度关系,即反射角等于入射角,入射角与入射光线和反射面的夹角互余。

方法清单
方法1 实验探究光的反射规律
方法2 光反射作图的方法

方法 1 实验探究光的反射规律

1.探究光的反射规律时,用一可沿法线 ON 折叠的硬纸板垂直放置在平面镜上(如图所示),使入射光紧贴硬纸板射向入射点 O,利用光在硬纸板上的漫反射,可看到光的路径。

2.改变入射角的大小,可探究反射角和入射角的大小关系。

3.向后沿法线 ON 弯折纸板,可研究"三线共面"这一规律。

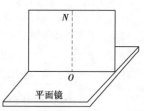

平面镜

例 如图是小明探究光的反射规律的实验装置，在平面镜上放置一块硬纸板，纸板由可以绕 ON 转折的 E、F 两部分组成。

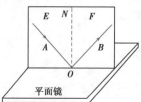

平面镜

（1）要使入射光和其反射光的径迹同时在纸板上出现，你认为纸板与平面镜的位置关系是 _____（选填"垂直"或"不垂直"）。实验时，从纸板前不同的方向都能看到光的径迹，这是因为光在纸板上发生了 _____ 反射。

实验次数	入射角	反射角
1	20°	70°
2	30°	60°
3	50°	40°

（2）小明让一束光沿着 AO 贴着纸板 E 射到平面镜上，在纸板 F 上会看到反射光 OB 的径迹。三次改变入射角的大小，实验所得数据如上表所示，他根据表中数据得出的结论和其他同学的结论并不一致。请你分析小明测量实验数据过程中出现的问题可能是 _____ _____。

（3）三次实验中，总能在纸板上观察到入射光和反射光的径迹。由此小明得出结论："在反射现象中，反射光线、入射光线和法线都在同一平面内"请你评估小明的做法是否合理并说明理由：_____ _____。

解析（1）探究光的反射规律时，纸板必须与平面镜垂直，才能同时在纸板上呈现入射光和反射光。能从不同的方向看到光的传播路径是因为光在纸板上发生了漫反射。

（2）表格中的数据虽然不相等，但总是互为余角，说明误把反射光线或入射光线与镜面的夹角当成了反射角或入射角。

（3）在实验时需要再将纸板前后折，发现不能在纸板上看到反射光，才能进一步证明反射光线、入射光线和法线在同一平面内，所以小明的做法不合理。

答案（1）垂直　漫
（2）把反射光线与平面镜的夹角当成了反射角（或把入射光线与平面镜的夹角当成了入射角）
（3）见解析

方法 **2** 光反射作图的方法

类型	作图方法
已知入射光线作反射光线	①先找出入射光线与反射面的交点（入射点），过入射点作垂直于界面的直线——法线。②将法线作为角的一边，以入射点作为角的顶点，在图中作一角等于入射角，所作角的另一条边就是反射光线。③标注光线方向
已知反射光线作入射光线	①先找出反射光线与反射面的交点（入射点），过入射点作垂直于界面的直线——法线。②将法线作为角的一边，以入射点作为角的顶点，在图中作一角等于反射角，所作角的另一条边就是入射光线。③标注光线方向
已知入射光线和反射光线确定平面镜的位置	①先作出入射光线和反射光线夹角的角平分线，此线为法线。②过入射光线与反射光线的交点（角的顶点或者说是入射点）作垂直法线的一条直线，该直线为平面镜的位置。③标注平面镜背面的短斜线

例 1 如图所示，入射光经平面镜反射后，反射光线与镜面的夹角是30°。请根据光的反射定律画出入射光线，并标出入射角的度数。

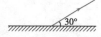

解析 反射光线与镜面的夹角是30°，则反射角为 90°−30°＝60°，先过入射点作法线，然后根据反射角等于入射角，作出入射光线。

答案 如图所示

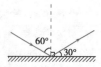

例 2 小明想利用一块平面镜使射向井口的太阳光竖直射入井中，如图所示。选项中的数字序号表示的是确定平面镜位置时作图的先后次序，其中作图过程正确的是　　　（　　）

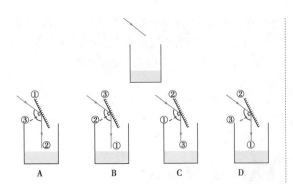

A   B   C   D

解析 图中已知入射光线,按要求先画出竖直射入井中的反射光线,根据反射角等于入射角可知,作反射光线与入射光线夹角的角平分线即法线,再过入射点作法线的垂线即平面镜位置,故作图的先后顺序正确的是 B。

答案 B

第 3 节　平面镜成像

知识清单

知识 **1** 平面镜成像的特点

1. 平面镜成像的特点:
(1) 物、像等大;
(2) 物、像到平面镜的距离相等;
(3) 物、像对应点的连线与平面镜垂直;
(4) 平面镜成虚像。
2. 用数学语言归纳:平面镜成的像与物关于镜面对称。

温馨提示
　　由于物体到镜面的距离和像到镜面的距离相等,则物体到镜面的距离变化了多少,像到镜面的距离也变化多少。因变化的时间相等,物体移动的速度和像移动的速度相等,像相对于物体的速度是物体速度的 2 倍。

例 小芳站在平面镜前 2 m 处,镜中的像与她相距_____m;当她走近平面镜时,她在镜中的像的大小_____(选填"变小"、"不变"或"变大")。

解析 根据平面镜成像特点,物体和像到镜面的距离相等,所以小芳和像之间的距离是小芳到镜面距离的 2 倍,即 4 m;因平面镜所成像的大小始终与物体等大,所以当小芳走近平面镜时,镜中的像的大小不变。

答案 4　不变

点拨 人离平面镜较远时,镜中的像看上去较小,这是因为距离远,视角小,感觉像较小,实际上像与人等大。

知识 **2** 平面镜成像的原理

1. 平面镜成像的原理是光的反射。
2. 像是物体发出(或反射)的光射到镜面上发生反射,由反射光线的反向延长线在镜后相交而形成的(如图)。

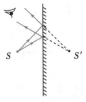

S S'

3. 点光源 S 在镜后的像 S' 并不是实际光线会聚形成的,而是由反射光线的反向延长线相交形成的,所以 S' 叫做 S 的虚像。
4. 如果把光屏放在 S' 处,是接收不到这个像的,所以虚像只能用眼睛看到,而不能呈现在屏上。

温馨提示
　　光线较暗时,我们要想看清自己在镜中的像,需把灯放在身前,这时灯光照在人身上,发生反射,经平面镜再次反射进入人眼。

例 关于平面镜成像,下列说法错误的是（　　）
A. 平面镜成的像是虚像
B. 平面镜成像原理是光的反射
C. 物体越靠近平面镜,像越大
D. 像与物体关于平面镜对称

（解析）由平面镜成像规律知,物体在平面镜里所成的像是正立、等大的虚像,像与物体关于平面镜对称,平面镜成像原理是光的反射,故 A、B、D 说法正确,选项 C 说法错误。

（答案）C

知识 3 点光源的平面镜成像作图

根据反射定律作图。

如图所示,步骤如下:

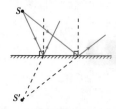

①从发光点 S 向平面镜引出两条入射光线;
②在入射点作出两条法线;
③根据反射定律,反射角等于入射角,作出反射光线;
④作两条反射光线的反向延长线,找出交点 S', S' 即 S 的像。

（例）如图所示,在平面镜右侧有一发光点 S,OB、$O'B'$ 分别是 S 发出的两条光线经平面镜后的反射光线,作出发光点 S 的位置。(要求保留必要的辅助线)

（解析）本题有两种解法:一是根据光的反射定律作图,需分别画法线,根据反射角等于入射角作出入射光线,两条入射光线的交点是发光点,如图甲;二是根据平面镜成像特点作图,反射光线反向延长线的交点即发光点 S 的像,根据物、像关于平面镜对称的特点,找到发光点,如图乙。

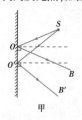 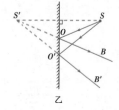

甲　　　　乙

（答案）见解析

拓展知识
知识1 三种面镜的比较
知识2 影子和倒影
知识3 平面镜的应用
知识4 平面镜相关的时钟问题

知识 1 三种面镜的比较

	平面镜	凸面镜	凹面镜
反射面	平面	凸面	凹面
示意图			
对平行光的反射特点	(1)既不会聚也不发散 (2)光路可逆 (3)遵守光的反射定律	(1)有发散作用 (2)F 是虚焦点 (3)光路可逆 (4)遵守光的反射定律	(1)有会聚作用 (2)F 是实焦点 (3)光路可逆 (4)遵守光的反射定律
成像	正立、等大虚像	正立、缩小虚像	—
应用	梳妆打扮用的镜子	汽车观后镜	太阳灶

知识 2 影子和倒影

1.影子(如图甲)是由于光在同种均匀介质中沿直线传播,若光被不透明物体所遮挡,在不透明物体的后面形成一个光达不到的区域,这就是所说的影子。

2.倒影(如图乙)是平面镜成的虚像,水面相当于平面镜,岸边的景物在水中成虚像,这就是所说的倒影。

甲 手影游戏　　　乙 水鸟倒影

知识 3　平面镜的应用

关于平面镜的应用有以下几方面：

①利用平面镜可以改变光的传播方向，起到控制光路的作用。如制作潜望镜，在挖井、掘山洞时，用平面镜把太阳光反射到作业区照明。

②利用平面镜成像。如制作各种镜子，商场和家庭装饰时，利用平面镜成像增强室内宽敞明亮的空间效果。

③利用平面镜反射光来使微小的形变放大，以便观测。

> **温馨提示** 潜望镜是指从海面下伸出海面或从低洼坑道伸出地面，用以窥探海面或地面上活动的装置。其构造与普通地上望远镜相同，但另加两个反射镜使物光经两次反射而折向眼中（如图所示）。潜望镜常用于潜水艇、坑道和坦克内，用以观察敌情。

知识 4　平面镜相关的时钟问题

1.根据平面镜成像特点——像与物左右对称，镜中"钟面"内的"指针"位置与实际钟面内的指针位置对称。

2.求解这类"镜中时钟"问题，只要由镜中"钟面"作出以上"12"、下"6"为对称轴的指针位置图形，再对作出的图形按实际钟面读出时间。如图所示虚线为镜中"指针"的左右对称图形，读得实际时间为 9:40。

例 如图甲所示是从平面镜中看到墙上的时钟的像，请在乙图上画出时钟的实际时间。

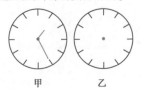

甲　　　　乙

解析 平面镜成的是正立、等大、左右对称的虚像。

答案 如图所示

点拨 解决此类问题时，还可以从试卷背面看时钟所示时间，即正面时钟所示时间关于平面镜对称的像。

方法清单
方法1　对称法作平面镜成像图
方法2　等效替代法探究平面镜的成像特点

方法 1　对称法作平面镜成像图

1.平面镜的成像特点：像和物的大小相等；它们到平面镜的距离相等；像和物的连线与平面镜垂直。**像和物关于平面镜是对称的**。利用这种对称性作物体在平面镜中所成像的方法称为对称法。

2.作图方法

（1）已知物体找像的位置

①在物体上找几个特殊点，从所选物点向镜面作垂线，过镜面延长等距离所找到的点即像点。

②将各个像点用虚线连接，即可得物体关于平面镜所成像的图。

（2）完成光路图

①利用对称法找到像点。

②根据像点在反射光线的反向延长线上这一特点，找到反射光线和入射点。

③完成光路图。

3.如图所示，是关于平面镜成像作图的几个变式。不管物体如何复杂，平面镜位置如何变化，还是考查角度如何变化，但有一条始终不变，那就是像和物的"对称性"。

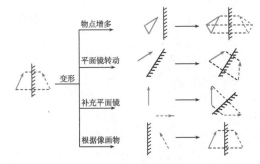

例 1 根据平面镜成像特点,在图中画出物体 AB 在平面镜中所成的像。

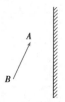

（解析）根据对称法找到物体上两个特殊点 A 和 B 的像 A' 和 B' 的位置,即从 $A(B)$ 向镜面作垂线过镜面延长等距离找到 $A'(B')$,用虚线连接 $A'B'$ 即物体 AB 的像,注意 AA' 和 BB' 连线也为虚线。

（答案）如图所示

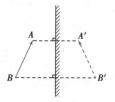

例 2 如图所示,从 S 点发出的一条光线,经平面镜 MN 反射后,其反射光线恰好通过 P 点。请你作出这条入射光线并完成光路图。

（解析）过镜面作出点 S 的对称点 S',即 S 点在平面镜中的像,连接 S'、P 与镜面交于 O 点,即入射点,连接 S、O 就得到了入射光线;标出入射光线 SO,反射光线 OP 的方向。注意 SS' 和 $S'O$ 都是虚线。

（答案）如图所示

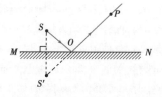

方法 2 等效替代法探究平面镜的成像特点

1.等效替代法就是在保证某一方面效果相同的前提下,用理想的、熟悉的、简单的物理对象、物理过程、物理现象替代实际的、陌生的、复杂的物理对象、物理过程、物理现象的思想方法。

2.常见的替代法主要有:物理模型的等效替代、物理过程的等效替代、作用效果的等效替代等形式。探究平面镜成像时,用玻璃板替代平面镜来进行实验。

例 在"探究平面镜成像特点"的实验中,如图所示。

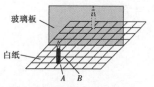

（1）现有厚度分别为 5 mm 和 2 mm 的两块玻璃板,应选择_____mm 厚的玻璃板做实验,目的是_____。

（2）用玻璃板代替平面镜的原因是_____,便于研究平面镜的成像特点。

（3）若白纸上每方格长度是 5 cm,将点燃的蜡烛由 A 点移至 B 点,此时它与移动后在玻璃板中所成的像的距离是_____cm。用光屏在玻璃板后面无论如何移动,在光屏上都_____(选填"能"或"不能")成像,说明平面镜所成的是_____像。

（4）用跳棋代替蜡烛,在方格上实验。你认为这样做有什么好处?_____(说出一点)。

（5）测量结果发现:蜡烛和它的像到玻璃板的距离不相等,请你找出造成距离不相等的可能原因(写出两点)_____

（6）移动点燃的蜡烛进行多次实验,目的是_____。

（解析）（1）玻璃板前后两面都相当于平面镜,前后两面的反射会成两个像,为了使重像不明显,应选薄的玻璃板。

（2）玻璃板容易透光,便于确定像的位置,且容易比较像与物的大小;平面镜不能确定像的位置,无法比较像与物的大小。

（3）像与物到平面镜的距离相等,B 点到玻璃板的距离是 10 cm,则点燃的蜡烛在 B 点时与它在玻璃板中所成的像的距离是 20 cm。平面镜成虚像,虚像不能用光屏承接。

（4）用方格纸方便研究像与物体到镜面距离的关系;用跳棋代替蜡烛,能更好地比较像与物的大小关系;用跳棋代替蜡烛,更环保(只要合理均可)。

（5）物、像到玻璃板距离不相等的原因有:①实验中玻璃板与水平桌面不垂直;②玻璃板有一定的厚度;③蜡烛没有竖直放置;④实验过程中玻璃板改变了位置。

（6）移动蜡烛进行多次实验,是为了避免偶然性,得到普遍规律。

答案 (1)2 使重像不明显
(2)容易找到镜中的像
(3)20 不能 虚
(4)见解析
(5)见解析

(6)避免实验结论的偶然性

点拨 对于探究规律的实验,多次实验是为了避免偶然性,得到普遍规律;对于测量类实验,多次实验可以减小误差。

第4节 光的折射

基础知识
知识 1 光的折射
知识 2 光的折射规律

知识 1 光的折射

1.光的折射

概念	说明
光从一种介质斜射入另一种介质时,传播的方向发生偏折,这种现象叫做光的折射。光从空气斜射入水或其他介质时,折射光线向法线方向偏折,如图所示	(1)入射光和折射光分别在两种不同的介质中,它们的传播速度不同,传播方向也往往发生改变 (2)通常在发生光的折射现象时,在界面上也同时发生光的反射现象 (3)光垂直射入界面时,将不会看到折射现象,即光的传播方向不发生变化

2.生活中的折射现象

斜插入水中的筷子在水下的部分看起来向上弯折;从厚玻璃砖后看到钢笔"错位";潜水员看岸边的树变高;池水变浅;渔民瞄准"鱼"的下方叉鱼。

例 如图所示光现象中,由于光的折射而形成的是 ( )

A.路边的影子

B.倒映在小河中的桥

C.水面"断笔"

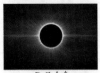
D.日全食

解析 路边的影子、日全食都是由光的直线传播

形成的。桥的倒影是由于光的反射形成的。水面"断笔"是由于光的折射形成的。

答案 C

知识 2 光的折射规律

1.基本概念

	意义	表示	图示
入射光线	射向界面的光线	AO	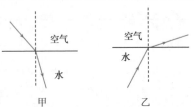
折射光线	进入另一种介质的光线	OB	
法线	与分界面垂直的虚线	MN	
入射角	入射光线与法线的夹角	∠AOM	
折射角	折射光线与法线的夹角	∠NOB	

2.内容:
光发生折射时,折射光线、入射光线和法线在同一平面内;折射光线与入射光线分别位于法线的两侧;当光从空气斜射入水或其他介质中时,折射角小于入射角,如图甲所示;当光从水或其他介质斜射入空气中时,折射角大于入射角,如图乙所示。

温馨提示 不论是光从空气斜射入水或其他介质,还是从水或其他介质斜射入空气,空气中的"角"总是大于水或其他介质中的"角"。

3.光路的可逆性

如果在原来折射光线的位置上换成入射光线,则新的折射光线的位置就在原来的入射光线的位置上，原来的折射角变成新的入射角，原来的入射角变成新的折射角；如图所示，A 点发出的光通过水面射向 B 点，光的传播路线为 AOB，如果一束激光要从 B 点射到 A 点，则激光的传播路线是 BOA，而不是 BCA 或 BDA。光路可逆可用原路返回来理解。

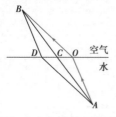

例 如图所示，一束光线从空气斜射入某种介质中，在分界面处发生反射和折射，则 AO 是_____光线，OB 是_____光线，OC 是_____光线，法线是_____，界面是_____。

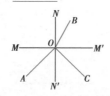

解析 由题图可知 MM′⊥NN′，可判断两者中一条表示法线，一条表示界面；再根据反射光线和折射光线都与入射光线分居法线两侧，反射角等于入射角，折射角小于入射角，可知 AO 是入射光线，OC 是反射光线，OB 是折射光线，MM′ 是界面，NN′ 是法线。

答案 入射 折射 反射 NN′ MM′

拓展知识 知识1 常见折射现象及解释
知识2 实像和虚像

知识 1 常见折射现象及解释

1.光的折射现象

由于光的折射会产生许多光学现象，如水池中的水看起来比实际的浅；一半斜插入水中的筷子变弯曲；鱼缸中的鱼看起来变大；海市蜃楼；看到地平线下的太阳等。要解释这些现象，首先要知道看见的并非实际物体，而是物体发出或反射的光经折射后形成的虚像。

2.举例分析光的折射现象

（1）池水看起来"变浅"，岸上物体看起来"变高"

我们能够看见物体是由于有光射入我们的眼睛里，假设从水池底的一点 A 射出的两条光线经折射后

射入人眼(如图甲)，眼睛根据光沿直线传播的经验(人的感觉总认为光沿直线传播)，逆着折射光线看过去，就会觉得光好像是从水中的 A′ 点射出并进入我们眼睛里的，因此我们会觉得 A′ 点所在位置就是池底，由于 A′ 比 A 高了，即看起来池底升高，池水"变浅"了。

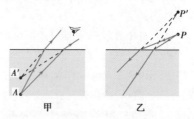

甲　　　　　乙

若从水中去观察岸上的物体 P，P 的位置将会升高(如图乙)。例如跳水运动员在水下观察 10 m 跳台，就会感到其高度超过 10 m。

因此可以得出结论：从岸上看水里和从水里看岸上相同，都是看到升高了的虚像。

（2）看到地平线下的太阳

光沿直线传播是有条件的，如果介质不均匀，光会发生弯曲。例如地球周围的大气层就是不均匀的，离地面越高，空气越稀薄，从大气层外射到地面的光就会发生弯曲。早晨，当太阳还在地平线以下时，我们就看见了它，就是不均匀的大气使光变弯了的缘故，如图所示。

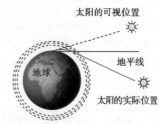

例 有经验的渔民都知道，只有瞄准鱼的下方才能叉到鱼，如图所示，下列四幅光路图中，能够正确说明叉到鱼的道理的是 (　　)

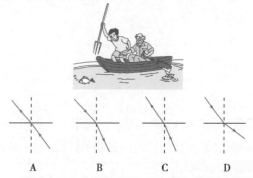

A　　B　　C　　D

解析 水中鱼反射的光，在水面处发生了折射，折射角大于入射角，人认为光是沿直线传播的，逆着折射光线看去，看到的是变浅的鱼的虚像，所以有经

验的渔民用鱼叉瞄准鱼的下方，才能将鱼叉到，故选C。

（答案）C

知识 2 实像和虚像

1.实像

物体上某点发出的光，经过反射或折射后的实际光线，如果是会聚的，其会聚点就是该点的实像点。物体可以看成是由许多点组成的，对应于物体上每一个物点都有一个像点，这些像点就组成了物体的实像。简单地说，实像是由实际光线会聚形成的像。实像既可以用肉眼看到，又能被光屏接收到。

2.虚像

物体上某点发出的光，经过反射或折射后的实际光线，如果是发散的，则它们不可能会聚，这时它们的

反向延长线的交点，就是虚像点。对应于物体上每一个物点都有一个虚像点，这些虚像点就组成了物体的虚像。简单地说，虚像是由实际光线的反向延长线会聚形成的像。虚像只能用肉眼看到，不能用光屏接收到。

易混对比

实像与虚像的异同

		实像	虚像
不同点	是否由实际光线会聚形成	是	不是
	是否能用光屏接收到	能	不能
	倒立还是正立	倒立	正立
相同点	都能用肉眼看到，都可以是放大、缩小或等大的		

方法清单

方法 利用光的折射规律作图

方法 利用光的折射规律作图

1.光的折射规律：光在发生折射时，折射光线、入射光线和法线在同一平面内；折射光线与入射光线分别位于法线的两侧；光从空气斜射入其他介质中时，折射光线向法线方向偏折（折射角小于入射角）；当入射角增大（或减小）时，折射角也增大（或减小）。

2.说明：（1）弄清一点（入射点）、二角（折射角、入射角）、三线（折射光线、入射光线、法线）的含义。（2）在光的折射中光路具有可逆性。

例1 请在图中画出反射光线，并画出折射光线的大致方向。

（解析）先作法线，根据反射角等于入射角，画出反射光线。作折射光线时需注意：光从水中斜射入空气中时，折射角大于入射角，即折射光线在原入射光线的方向上偏离法线一些。

（答案）如图所示

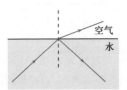

例2 如图所示，光线AB分别射向玻璃板和三棱镜，请分别作出光线在玻璃板左右界面处发生折射的光路图和光线通过三棱镜玻璃界面发生折射的光路图。

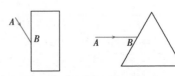

（解析）根据光的折射规律，光从空气斜射入玻璃中时，折射角小于入射角，光从玻璃斜射入空气中时，折射角大于入射角，可画出两条折射光线。

（答案）如图所示

 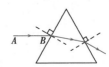

第5节 光的色散

知识清单

基础知识
- 知识1 光的色散
- 知识2 色光的三原色及色光的混合
- 知识3 颜料的三原色及颜料的混合
- 知识4 物体的颜色

知识 1 光的色散

1.色散:白光分解成多种色光的现象。

2.光的色散现象

(1)一束太阳光通过三棱镜,被分解成七种色光,这七种色光从上至下依次排列为红、橙、黄、绿、蓝、靛、紫(如图甲所示)。同理,被分解后的色光也可以混合在一起成为白光(如图乙所示)。

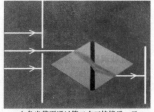

白光的色散
甲

七色光带再通过第二个三棱镜后,又混合成一束白光
乙

(2)由光的色散现象得出的两个结论:第一,白光不是单色光,而是由各种单色光组成的复色光;第二,不同的单色光通过棱镜时偏折的程度是不同的,红光的偏折程度最小,紫光的偏折程度最大。

温馨提示 太阳光可认为是"白光"。

知识 2 色光的三原色及色光的混合

1.色光的三原色

红、绿、蓝叫做色光的三原色。

2.色光的混合

(1)红、绿、蓝三种色光中,任何一种色光都不能由另外两种色光合成。但红、绿、蓝三种色光却能够合成出自然界绝大多数色光来,只要适当调配它们之间的比例即可。

(2)如图所示,适当的红光和绿光能合成黄光;适当的绿光和蓝光能合成青光;适当的蓝光和红光能合成品红色光;而相同比例的红、绿、蓝三色光能合成白光。因此红、绿、蓝三种色光被称为色光的"三原色"。

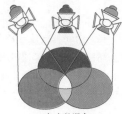

色光的混合

3.应用

色光的合成在科学技术中普遍应用,彩色电视机就是一例,它的荧光屏上出现的彩色画面,是由红、绿、蓝三种色光混合而成的。

温馨提示 不能简单地认为色光的混合是光的色散的逆过程。例如:红光和绿光能混合成黄光,但黄光仍为单色光,它通过三棱镜时并不能分散成红光和绿光。

知识 3 颜料的三原色及颜料的混合

1.颜料的三原色

颜料的三原色是红、黄、蓝,这三种颜料按一定比例混合,能调出各种不同的颜色。

第部分

第②部分 第2章 光现象 **29**

2.颜料的混合

（1）颜料与色光不同，颜料本身不发光，我们看到颜料的色彩是颜料所反射的色光，其他的色光被吸收掉了。颜料不同，所反射的色光不同。

（2）两种颜料混合后会反射第三种色光，而不是原来两种颜料反射色光的混合。所以，颜料的混合原理是：两种颜料的混合色是它们都能反射的色光，其余的色光都被这两种颜料吸收掉了。相同比例的颜料三原色混合后为黑色，如图所示。

颜料的混合

温馨提示 各种颜料主要反射与它颜色相同的色光，同时也反射光谱中跟它相邻的色光。

3.应用

在印刷行业，就是用红、黄、蓝三种颜料来调出各种色彩，在绘画上也是应用红、黄、蓝来调色的。

知识 4 物体的颜色

在光照到物体上时，不同物体对不同颜色的光反射、吸收和透过的情况不同，因此呈现不同的色彩。

物体的颜色由它所反射或透射的光的颜色所决定。

1.透明物体的颜色由通过它的色光决定

在光的色散实验中，如果在白屏前放置一块红玻璃，则白屏上的其他颜色的光消失，只留下红光，说明其他色光都被红玻璃吸收了，只能让红光通过（如图）。如果放置一块蓝玻璃，则白屏上呈现蓝色。

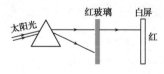

2.不透明物体的颜色由它反射的色光决定

在光的色散实验中，如果把一张红纸贴在白屏上，则红纸上看不到彩色光带，只有被红光照射的地方是亮的，其他地方是暗的；如果把绿纸贴在白屏上，则只有绿光照射的地方是亮的，其他地方是暗的（如图）。这表明不透明物体只反射与自身颜色相同的色光，吸收其他色光。

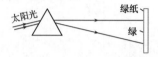

温馨提示 如果物体是不透明的，黑色的物体会吸收所有色光，白色物体会反射所有色光，其他颜色的物体只反射与它颜色相同的色光。如用白光照红苹果（如图 a），红苹果只反射红光，看到的苹果是红色。用绿光照红苹果（如图 b），红苹果只反射红光，绿光被吸收，没有光进入我们的眼睛，感觉苹果呈黑色；苹果后面的白色背景因反射的只有绿光而呈现绿色。

a   b

拓展知识   知识① 冷色与暖色
          知识② 大海为什么是蓝色的

知识 1 冷色与暖色

不同的色彩搭配，不仅给人美感，而且使人产生联想。如黄、橙、红属于暖色，让人想到火与太阳；绿、蓝、紫属于冷色，使人想到草地、水等。

知识 2 大海为什么是蓝色的

太阳光由红、橙、黄、绿、蓝、靛、紫七种色光组成，当太阳光照射到大海上时，蓝光、紫光大部分被反射，且蓝光部分多，所以大海看上去是碧蓝的。

方法 比较法探究透明物体和不透明物体的颜色

将透明物体和不透明物体的颜色进行对比,便于理解:

(1)透明物体的颜色是由它透过的色光颜色决定的;

(2)不透明物体的颜色是由它反射的色光颜色决定的;

(3)黑色物体吸收各种色光,不论什么色光照射黑纸,均呈现黑色。

(4)白色物体反射各种色光,红光照射白纸,白纸反射的只有红光而呈现红色;黄光照射白纸,白纸反射的只有黄光而呈现黄色;电影幕布为白色是因为它能反射各种色光。

例 某学校课外兴趣小组在黑暗的实验室里,对透明物体和不透明物体的颜色由什么决定进行了如下的探究。

实验一:先后用不同颜色的玻璃对着不同颜色的光进行观察,得到的结果如表一所示。

表一:透明物体的颜色

照射光的颜色	绿色	红色	红色	绿色	白色
玻璃的颜色	绿色	红色	蓝色	红色	黄色
观察到的颜色	绿色	红色	黑色	黑色	黄色

实验二:将不同颜色的光分别照射到不同颜色的纸上,观察纸的颜色,得到的结果如表二所示。

表二:不透明物体的颜色

照射光的颜色	绿色	红色	蓝色	红色	白色
纸的颜色	绿色	红色	红色	绿色	黄色
观察到的颜色	绿色	红色	黑色	黑色	黄色

(1)由表一可以得出:透明物体的颜色是由_____决定的;

(2)由表二可以得出:不透明物体的颜色是由_____决定的。

(3)请你由上述结论解释,为什么水果商卖西瓜(红瓤)时,总喜欢撑一顶红色的遮阳伞?

解析 白光由七种颜色的光混合而成,由表一分析可得,绿光照绿玻璃,有绿光透过,玻璃呈绿色;红光照红玻璃,有红光透过,玻璃呈红色;红光照蓝玻璃,红光被蓝玻璃吸收,没有光透过,玻璃呈黑色;绿光照红玻璃,绿光被红玻璃吸收,没有光透过,玻璃呈黑色;白光是复色光,照黄玻璃时,有黄光透过,玻璃呈黄色。所以透明物体的颜色由透过它的色光决定。表二的分析方法同表一。

答案 (1)透过它的色光

(2)它反射的色光

(3)因为透过红色遮阳伞的主要是红光,红光照射到西瓜的红瓤上后,反射的也主要是红光,红色就更突出,所以瓜瓤看上去就更红。

第6节　看不见的光

知识清单

基础知识
> 知识**1** 太阳的可见光谱
> 知识**2** 红外线与紫外线

知识 **1** 太阳的可见光谱

棱镜可以把太阳光分解成红、橙、黄、绿、蓝、靛、紫七种不同颜色的光。把它们按照一定的顺序排列（从上到下），就形成太阳的可见光谱。

知识 **2** 红外线与紫外线

	概念	特征	应用
红外线	在光谱的红光以外，有一种看不见的光，频率范围：10^{12} ~ $5×10^{14}$ Hz	一切物体都在不停地辐射红外线，物体的温度越高，辐射的红外线越强，红外线热作用越强	(1)诊断病情,拍摄"热谱图" (2)红外线夜视仪 (3)红外线遥控器 (4)红外线烤箱
紫外线	在光谱的紫光以外，有一种看不见的光，频率范围：$7.5×10^{14}$ ~ $5×10^{16}$ Hz	化学作用强,很容易使照相底片感光;生理作用强,能杀菌;有荧光效应	适当的紫外线照射有助于人体合成维生素D,促进身体对钙的吸收。紫外线能杀死微生物。在医院、饭店里,常用紫外线灯来灭菌。紫外线能使荧光物质发光,可用来制成验钞机

温馨提示
(1)全自动感应水龙头是利用人体发出的红外线进行自动控制的。

(2)红外线夜视仪利用了夜间人的体温比野外草木、岩石的温度高,人辐射的红外线比它们强的特点,人们根据这个道理制成了红外线夜视仪。

例 验钞机发出的"光"能使钞票上的荧光物质发光,遥控器发出的"光"能用来控制电视机、空调等家用电器。对于它们发出的"光",下列说法中正确的是 （　　）

A.验钞机和遥控器发出的"光"都是紫外线

B.验钞机和遥控器发出的"光"都是红外线

C.验钞机发出的"光"是紫外线,遥控器发出的"光"是红外线

D.验钞机发出的"光"是红外线,遥控器发出的"光"是紫外线

解析 紫外线能使荧光物质发光,钞票的某些部位用荧光物质印上了防伪标志,所以验钞机发出的是紫外线;遥控器利用红外线对家用电器进行控制。

答案 C

拓展知识
> 知识 生活中的紫外线

知识 生活中的紫外线

1.“紫外线是淡蓝色”这句话把紫外线与可见光混为一谈,认为凡是光都具有颜色,而事实上紫外线是在紫光之外人眼看不见的光。

2.验钞机的紫光灯发出的光中含有大量的紫外线,钞票的某些部位含有荧光物质,在紫外线的照射下,涂有荧光物质的地方发光。

3.过量的紫外线照射对人体十分有害,轻则使皮肤粗糙,重则引起皮肤癌。电焊的弧光中有强烈的紫外线,因此电焊工在工作时必须穿好工作服,并戴上防护面罩。

方法清单

方法 比较法区别紫外线与红外线

方法 比较法区别紫外线与红外线

对于红外线和紫外线可以从两方面进行比较:

①红外线和紫外线都是看不见的光,不能误认为红外线是红色的光,紫外线是紫色的光。紫外线灯看起来是淡蓝色的,那是因为紫外线灯除了辐射紫外线以外,它还发出少量的蓝光和紫光。

②红外线和紫外线这两种不可见光的应用十分广泛。利用红外线烧烤物体,制成夜视仪、遥控电视机、空调;利用紫外线促进人体合成维生素 D,治疗皮肤病、软骨症,灭菌消毒,验证钞票或古画的真伪。

温馨提示 遥控器是一个小功率的红外线发射器,它的前端有一个发光二极管,按下不同的键时,可以发出不同的红外线脉冲信号,受控器接收信号后进行相应的操作,实现对电器的遥控。

例 如图所示,将一束太阳光投射到玻璃三棱镜上,在棱镜后侧光屏上的 AB 范围内观察到了不同颜色的光,则　　　　　( )

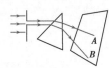

A.A 处应是紫光

B.只有 AB 范围内有光

C.将照相底片放到 AB 范围 B 处的外侧,底片不会感光

D.将温度计放到 AB 范围 A 处的外侧,会看到温度上升

(解析) 太阳光经三棱镜折射后,产生色散现象,从 A 到 B 依次是红、橙、黄、绿、蓝、靛、紫七种色光。在 A 的外侧是红外线。红外线最突出的性质就是热作用强,故 D 选项正确,A 选项错。在 B 的外侧是紫外线,紫外线的主要特点是化学作用强,可以使照相底片感光,故 C 选项是错误的。在 AB 外侧是红外线和紫外线,它们属于不可见光,故 B 选项错误。

(答案) D

知识梳理

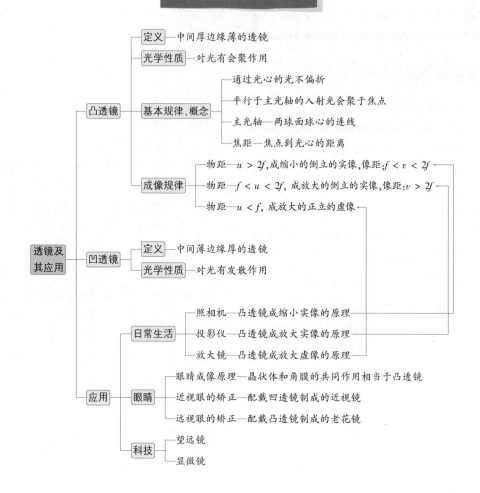

透镜及其应用

凸透镜
- 定义——中间厚边缘薄的透镜
- 光学性质——对光有会聚作用
- 基本规律、概念
  - 通过光心的光不偏折
  - 平行于主光轴的入射光会聚于焦点
  - 主光轴——两球面球心的连线
  - 焦距——焦点到光心的距离
- 成像规律
  - 物距—$u > 2f$,成缩小的倒立的实像,像距:$f < v < 2f$
  - 物距—$f < u < 2f$,成放大的倒立的实像,像距:$v > 2f$
  - 物距—$u < f$,成放大的正立的虚像

凹透镜
- 定义——中间薄边缘厚的透镜
- 光学性质——对光有发散作用

应用
- 日常生活
  - 照相机——凸透镜成缩小实像的原理
  - 投影仪——凸透镜成放大实像的原理
  - 放大镜——凸透镜成放大虚像的原理
- 眼睛
  - 眼睛成像原理——晶状体和角膜的共同作用相当于凸透镜
  - 近视眼的矫正——配戴凹透镜制成的近视镜
  - 远视眼的矫正——配戴凸透镜制成的老花镜
- 科技
  - 望远镜
  - 显微镜

第1节　透镜

知识 1　透镜

名称	概念	说明
透镜	(1)透镜是利用光的折射来工作的光学元件,它是由透明物质(如玻璃、塑料、水晶等)制成的,至少一个表面是球面的一部分 (2)中间厚、边缘薄的透镜叫凸透镜;边缘厚、中间薄的透镜叫凹透镜	按其厚薄的形状可分为两类:凸透镜和凹透镜
主光轴	通过透镜两个球面球心的直线叫主光轴,如图所示 光心 主光轴 ─── O ─── 光心 主光轴 ─── O ───	每个透镜都有一条主光轴
光心	主光轴上有个特殊的点,通过它的光传播方向不改变,这个点叫做镜的光心,如上图所示	用字母"O"表示,可以认为薄透镜的光心就在透镜的中心
焦点	(1)凸透镜能使跟主光轴平行的光通过凸透镜后会聚在主光轴上的一点,这一点叫凸透镜的焦点,如图甲所示 (2)凹透镜能使跟主光轴平行的光通过凹透镜后变得发散,且这些发散光线的反向延长线相交在主光轴上一点,这一点不是实际光线的会聚点,所以叫凹透镜的虚焦点,如图乙所示 F O F f f 甲 F F 乙	透镜两侧各有一焦点,且对称,用字母"F"表示

续表

名称	概念	说明
焦距	焦点到透镜光心的距离叫焦距,如上图甲所示	透镜两侧焦距相等,用字母"f"表示

知识 2　会聚、发散作用

1.会聚作用

让一束跟主光轴平行的光射向凸透镜,观察到折射光线为会聚光束(如图甲),即凸透镜对光有会聚作用。

甲　　　　乙

2.发散作用

让一束跟主光轴平行的光射向凹透镜,观察到折射光线为发散光束(如图乙),即凹透镜对光有发散作用。

例　如图所示,玻璃瓶内有一细棉线,细线下端系有一个泡沫塑料小球。请你设计一个实验,在不打开瓶盖和不损坏玻璃瓶的情况下,使瓶内的细棉线断掉。(器材可根据需要自选)

实验方法	
实验原理	

解析　根据题目要求,"不打开瓶盖和不损坏玻璃瓶",只能通过一个无形的东西进入玻璃瓶内去弄断细棉线。可从光的角度去考虑(图上方有太阳),利用凸透镜对光有会聚作用来解决。

答案　实验方法:用凸透镜将太阳光会聚到瓶中棉线上

实验原理:凸透镜对光有会聚作用

知识 1　对会聚和发散作用的理解

1.会聚作用是指凸透镜对光的作用。通过凸透镜的折射光线相对于入射光线而言,是会聚了一些或发散程度减小了一些,如图甲。**凸透镜不仅对平行光束有会聚作用,对发散光束也有会聚作用。**

2.发散作用是指凹透镜对光的作用。通过凹透镜的折射光线相对于入射光线而言,是发散了一些或会聚程度减小了一些,如上图乙。**凹透镜不仅对平行光束、发散光束有发散作用,对会聚光束也有发散作用。**

3."会聚作用"并不等同于通过凸透镜后的折射光线都是会聚光束(如上图甲);"发散作用"并不等同于通过凹透镜后的折射光线都是发散光束(如上图乙)。

4.凸透镜和凹透镜对光的作用原理可以用棱镜对光的偏折作用来说明。透镜可以被看做是由许多个小棱镜组成的(如图甲、乙所示),由光经过棱镜后向底面偏折的知识可知,凸透镜使光会聚,凹透镜使光发散。

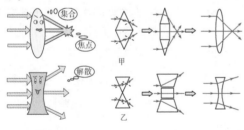

知识 2　对光学黑箱子的理解

如图,每个方框中放着一个光学元件,请在方框内填入合适的"镜"。

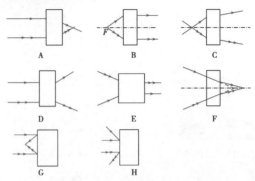

(1)从光路图上观察所用"镜"是让光线发生反射还是折射,以此为依据判断是面镜还是透镜,上述八个图中,图G、H中的镜让光线发生了反射,应填面镜;其余图中光线均发生折射,光透过了镜,应填透镜。

(2)确定了是面镜还是透镜后,再观察所用镜对光起何种作用:会聚、发散还是镜面反射。

(3)具体分析:A、B、C三个图中通过透镜的折射光线相对入射光线都发生了会聚,所以方框内应填凸透镜;D、E、F三个图中通过透镜的折射光线相对入射光线都发散,方框内都填凹透镜;凹面镜反射光线,起会聚作用,G图中方框内填凹面镜;凸面镜反射光线,起发散作用,H图中方框内填凸面镜。

(4)总结镜的类型与作用:
镜面反射(平行射入,平行射出)——平面镜;
反射后起会聚作用——凹面镜;
反射后起发散作用——凸面镜;
折射后起会聚作用——凸透镜;
折射后起发散作用——凹透镜。

方法清单

方法 根据透镜三条特殊光线作图

方法 根据透镜三条特殊光线作图

内容种类 \ 项目	入射光线	光路图	折射光线
凸透镜	平行于主光轴		会聚于焦点
	经过焦点的或从焦点发出的光线		平行于主光轴
	经过光心		传播方向不变

内容种类 \ 项目	入射光线	光路图	折射光线
凹透镜	平行于主光轴		折射光线的反向延长线经过入射侧虚焦点
	延长线经过凹透镜对侧虚焦点的光线		平行于主光轴
	经过光心		传播方向不变

例 请在图中画出入射光线或折射光线。

解析 过光心的光线经过凹透镜后,传播方向不改变;过焦点的光线经过凸透镜后平行于主光轴射出。

答案 如图所示

第2节 探究凸透镜成像的规律

知识清单

基础知识
知识**1** 物距、焦距及物与像的关系
知识**2** 凸透镜成像的规律
知识**3** 凸透镜成像时光路可逆的理解

知识 1 物距、焦距及物与像的关系

名称	概念	说明
物距	物体到凸透镜的距离	用 u 来表示
像距	像到凸透镜的距离	用 v 来表示
焦距	焦点到凸透镜光心的距离	用 f 来表示

续表

名称	概念	说明
正立或倒立	像和物体上下、左右均一致为正立的像;像和物体上下颠倒、左右互换为倒立的像	相对于物体而言,虚像总是正立的,实像总是倒立的
放大或缩小	像的大小大于物体大小的为放大的像;等于物体大小的为等大的像;小于物体大小的为缩小的像	可以通过比较像距和物距来判断:若像距大于物距,则是放大的像;若像距等于物距,则是等大的像;若像距小于物距,则是缩小的像
实像或虚像	实像是由实际光线相交而成的像,虚像是由实际光线的反向延长线相交而成的像	实像既能用光屏承接,又可以用眼睛看到,虚像只能用眼睛看到,不能用光屏承接

知识 2 凸透镜成像的规律

物的位置	像的位置	像的性质	应用举例
$u=\infty$（平行光）	$v=f$	成一点	测定焦距
$u>2f$	$2f>v>f$	像与物异侧 缩小、倒立的实像	照相机、眼睛
$u=2f$	$v=2f$	等大、倒立的实像	—
$2f>u>f$	$v>2f$	放大、倒立的实像	幻灯机
$u=f$	$v=\infty$	不成像	探照灯
$u<f$	—	像与物同侧 放大、正立的虚像	放大镜

成像图

易混对比

两种放大像的理解

在探究凸透镜成像的规律时，某同学用凸透镜观察手指的像（如图）。他先看到一个正立、放大的手指的像；逐渐将凸透镜远离手指，向自己眼睛的方向移动，又看到一个倒立、放大的手指的像；第一次是放大的虚像，像正立且满足 $u<f$；第二次是放大的实像，像倒立且满足 $f<u<2f$；注意将这两种放大的像识别清楚。

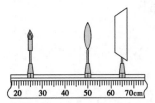

例 在探究凸透镜成像规律时，将点燃的蜡烛、凸透镜和光屏放置在光具座上，调整后的位置如图，此时在光屏上得到烛焰清晰的像。对于该次实验下列描述正确的是 （ ）

A.光屏上成倒立、缩小的实像
B.光屏上成倒立、放大的实像
C.照相机应用了该次实验的成像规律
D.投影仪应用了该次实验的成像规律

解析 由题图可知，物距大于像距，此时成倒立、缩小的实像，A 正确，B 错误；照相机成倒立、缩小的实像，投影仪成倒立、放大的实像，C 正确，D 错误。故选 A、C。

答案 AC

知识 3 凸透镜成像时光路可逆的理解

（1）凸透镜成实像时，根据光路图（如图）可知：A 点发出的光线经透镜折射后会聚于 A' 点，即 A' 点为 A 点的像，$A'B'$ 为物体 AB 的像。

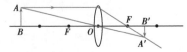

（2）由于光路具有可逆性，若 $A'B'$ 为物体，A' 点发出的光线经透镜折射后成像在 A 点，即 AB 为物体 $A'B'$ 的像。

（3）由上图可知：当物距为 OB 时，像距为 OB'；当物距为 OB' 时，像距为 OB。

（4）因此，若保持物体 AB 和 $A'B'$ 处光屏的位置不动，把透镜向左移动，当透镜移到物距等于原来的像距 OB' 时，光屏上会呈现物体 AB 倒立、放大的实像。

例 某同学利用图示装置来研究凸透镜成像。

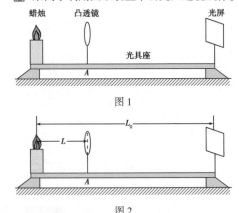

图 1

图 2

（1）实验前，应调整烛焰、凸透镜和光屏三者的中心在_____；

（2）如图 1 所示，当凸透镜位于光具座上 A 处时，恰好在光屏上成清晰的像，成的是_____（选填"正立"或"倒立"）的像。蜡烛燃烧一段时间后，烛焰的像将位于光屏中心的_____方；

（3）在保持（2）中蜡烛和光屏位置不变的情况下，将凸透镜向右移到 B 处（图中未标出），光屏上再次成清晰的像，成的是_____（选填"放大"、"缩小"或"等大"）的像；

（4）在上述探究活动中，若已知蜡烛与光屏间的距离为 L_0，与凸透镜第一次所在位置 A 间的距离为 L，如图 2 所示。则该透镜焦距 f_____L（选填">"、"<"或"="），透镜先后两次所在位置 A、B 之间的距离 $s=$_____（用 L_0、L 表示）。

（解析）（1）凸透镜成像时,烛焰、凸透镜和光屏三者的中心在同一高度是为了使像成在光屏的中央。

（2）能呈现在光屏上的像是实像,凸透镜所成的实像是倒立的。燃烧一段时间,蜡烛变短,烛焰下移,像则上移,位于光屏中心的上方。

（3）由光路的可逆原理可知:当物距为 $u_A = L$,像距为 v_A,成放大的实像,当物距为 $u_B = v_A$,像距为 $v_B = u_A = L$ 时,成的是缩小的实像。

（4）当凸透镜位于光具座上 A 处时所成的是实像,物距 u_A 应大于焦距 f,即 $f < u_A = L$,由（3）的分析可知,$A、B$ 之间的距离 $s = L_0 - u_A - v_B = L_0 - L - L = L_0 - 2L$。

（答案）（1）同一高度　（2）倒立　上　（3）缩小
（4）< 　$L_0 - 2L$

拓展知识
知识1 对凸透镜成像的理解
知识2 凸透镜成像实验中要注意的几个问题
知识3 口诀记忆凸透镜成像规律

知识 1 对凸透镜成像的理解

1.凸透镜所成的实像必倒立,且物与像分居透镜的两侧,可以是放大的、等大的或缩小的;所成虚像必正立,且物与像位于透镜的同侧,一定是放大的。

2.物体沿主光轴移动,像也沿主光轴移动。对于实像来说,物体向靠近透镜的方向移,像向远离透镜的方向移,且像越来越大(如图)。对虚像来说,物向透镜移,像也向透镜移,且像越来越小。

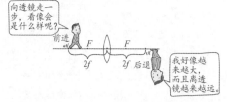

3.物距一定,物体垂直主光轴向上、向下或向左、向右移动时,虚像的移动方向跟物体移动方向是一致的;实像的移动方向跟物体移动方向恰好相反,即物向上移,像要向下移,物向左移,像要向右移。

4.透镜一部分被遮挡,这部分不透光,其余部分仍透光,仍能成完整的像,只不过像变暗些。透镜破裂后去掉一部分,就相当于遮挡了一部分,像的大小、位置不变,只是变暗些。

5.当把蜡烛放在凸透镜的焦点上时,由于烛焰有一定的宽度,它的某些部分到凸透镜的距离小于焦距,所以在另一侧透过凸透镜看到了正立、放大的像。

（例）某物理实验小组用光具座研究凸透镜成像时,调节器材后光屏上出现蜡烛清晰的像,如果用遮光板挡住透镜的上半部分,我们会在光屏上看到
（　　）
A.蜡烛像的下半部分
B.蜡烛像的上半部分
C.蜡烛完整的像,像的亮度变暗
D.蜡烛完整的像,像的亮度不变

（解析）透镜一部分被遮挡,其余部分仍透光,仍能成完整的像,像的大小、位置不变;只不过光线少了一部分,像的亮度会变暗一些,所以选 C。

（答案）C

知识 2 凸透镜成像实验中要注意的几个问题

1.实验中蜡烛、凸透镜、光屏应依次放置

这是能在光屏上观察到像的前提。能在光屏上显示的像是实像,而凸透镜成实像时,像与物体在透镜的异侧,因此必须使蜡烛和光屏分居凸透镜的两侧。

2.实验中蜡烛、凸透镜、光屏应该在同一直线上

这是像能成在光屏上的前提。如果做这个实验时用的是光具座,在调节时只要按程序操作,很容易完成共线调节。如果在做这个实验时没有用光具座,就要特别注意这个问题。

3.实验中凸透镜的镜面、光屏面应大致平行

这是保证像成在光屏上的条件。因为若镜面和光屏面不平行,镜面倾斜,像将不会成在光屏上。

4.实验中烛焰、凸透镜、光屏三者的中心应该大致在同一高度

这是保证像成在光屏中央的条件。有些同学认为,只要这三者的中心在一条直线上就可以了。事实上,如果三者的高度不同,则在光屏上所成的像不是在光屏的上方,就是在光屏的下方,不利于对像的观察。

5.实验中要注意凸透镜的定位

由于物体在 2 倍焦距之外时像在 1 倍焦距和 2 倍焦距之间,而物体在 1 倍焦距和 2 倍焦距之间时像在 2 倍焦距之外。所以实验时应给物距和像距留大致相同的调节空间,即凸透镜应该固定在光具座的中间。

6.像位置的确定

一般情况下,凸透镜成像时,若光屏在一定的范围内移动,屏上都能够得到像,但是我们要找到最清晰的像的位置。如果将光屏向任何一个方向移动,像都比最先得到的像模糊,则那个位置的像就是最清晰的像了。

7.要注意物距适当

在观察物体在 1 倍焦距与 2 倍焦距之间的成像时,要注意物距适当,不能使物体靠近焦点,否则像离凸透镜太远,像也太大,光屏可能接收不到。

 温馨提示　在做"探究凸透镜成像规律"实验时,为了使像成在光屏中央,应调节烛焰、凸透镜、光屏三者的中心在同一高度。

知识 **3** 口诀记忆凸透镜成像规律

1.口诀一:一倍焦距分虚实,二倍焦距分大小;虚像同侧正,实像异侧倒;成实像,物近像远像变大;成虚像,物近像近像变小。

口诀二:三物距、三界限,成像随着物距变;物远实像小而近,物远虚像大而远。

口诀三:凸透镜,本领大,照相、幻灯和放大;二倍焦外倒实小,二倍焦内倒实大;若是物放焦点内,像物同侧虚像大;物远实像近又小,物远虚像远又大。

2.对口诀中内容的理解:"物近像远像变大"、"一倍焦距分虚实,二倍焦距分大小",我们可以结合图加深理解。

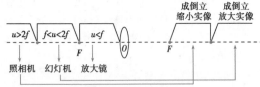

 温馨提示　放大的像指所成的像比物体大。像变大指物体到透镜的距离发生变化时,相对于原来的像变大。像变大不等于所成的像是放大的。

例 如图是"探究凸透镜成像"实验的装置,实验时,先调节烛焰、凸透镜、光屏三者的中心大致在同一高度上,然后不断改变蜡烛到凸透镜的距离,并移动光屏的位置,得到的实验数据如下表。

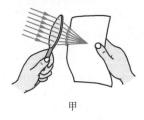

甲

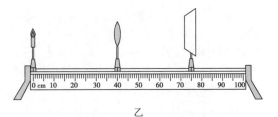

乙

实验序号	物距(cm)	像距(cm)	像的性质		
			正倒	大小	虚实
1	40	13.3	倒立	缩小	实像
2	30	15	倒立	缩小	实像
3	20	20	倒立	等大	实像
4	15	30	倒立	放大	实像
5	12	60	倒立	放大	实像
6	10		不成像		
7	8		正立	放大	虚像
8	4		正立	放大	虚像

(1)图甲所示的实验操作目的是什么?

(2)实验过程中,观察到随着蜡烛位置的变化,像的变化有两个转折点,分析表中数据你认为这两个转折点的位置在何处? 它们分别是像的哪种变化过程的转折点?

解析 (1)平行光经过凸透镜折射后会聚于一点,该点就是凸透镜的焦点,焦点到凸透镜光心的距离为焦距,则题图甲中所示的实验操作目的是粗略测量凸透镜的焦距。

(2)由表中数据可知,物距在不断减小的过程中,成像性质发生改变的两个转折点是一倍焦距处和二倍焦距处。其中,一倍焦距处是虚像和实像的分界点,二倍焦距处是放大的像和缩小的像的分界点。

答案 (1)粗略测量凸透镜的焦距
(2)见解析

方法 1 归纳凸透镜焦距的测量方法

1.太阳光聚集法：把凸透镜正对着太阳光，在凸透镜的另一侧放一张白纸，调节凸透镜到白纸之间的距离，使白纸上出现最小最亮的光斑，这个光斑的位置就是焦点的位置。用直尺测出凸透镜到焦点的距离，即焦距。

2.平行光源法：将几束平行光沿主光轴射到凸透镜上，在光屏上得到折射光线相交的一点，量出这点到凸透镜的距离，即焦距。

3.二倍焦距法：在光具座上依次放置蜡烛、凸透镜和光屏，点燃蜡烛并使烛焰、凸透镜和光屏的中心在同一高度，调节烛焰到凸透镜的距离和光屏到凸透镜的距离，直到光屏上的像与烛焰等大为止。此时烛焰到凸透镜的距离和光屏到凸透镜的距离均为 2 倍焦距。

4.焦点不成像法：透过凸透镜看物体，调节物体到凸透镜的距离，从看得见像到刚好看不见时，测出物体到凸透镜的距离即焦距。

5.焦点入射法：在凸透镜的一侧放一光屏，另一侧放一个发光的小灯泡，沿主光轴移动，直到光屏上得到一个与透镜直径相等的圆形光斑为止，测出小灯泡到凸透镜的距离即焦距。

例 某同学在做"探究凸透镜成像规律"实验时，需要知道凸透镜的焦距。

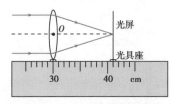

(1)在实验室常用如图所示的实验测量焦距。由图可知凸透镜对光有_____作用，此凸透镜的焦距为_____cm。

(2)知识和经验告诉我们也可用_____法测量焦距。

解析 平行光经过凸透镜，在光屏上出现光斑，说明凸透镜对光有会聚作用。光会聚在焦点处，即光斑到透镜的距离就是凸透镜的焦距。

答案 (1)会聚 11.0 (2)太阳光聚集

方法 2 图像法理解透镜成像

1.三条特殊光线：①经过光心的光线传播方向不改变；②平行于主光轴的光线经折射后过焦点(对于凹透镜，它的焦点是虚焦点，是折射光线的反向延长线经过的点)；③过焦点的光线经折射后平行于主光轴(对于凹透镜来说是虚焦点，是入射光线的正向延长线经过的点)。

2.可利用三条特殊光线作图找到像的位置，进一步理解凸透镜的成像规律。

(1)物体处于 2 倍焦距以外时，如图所示。

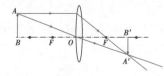

(2)物体处于 1 倍焦距和 2 倍焦距之间时，如图所示。

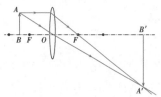

(3)物体处于焦点以内时，如图所示。

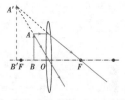

例 图中 O 为凸透镜的光心，F 为焦点，请画出烛焰上的 S 点发出的三条光线(中间一条光线平行于主光轴)经凸透镜后的出射光线，并确定其像的位置 S'。

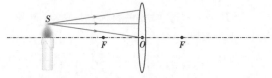

解析 根据凸透镜的成像规律，先作出两条特殊光线的出射光线，确定像的位置，再连接像与最上面一条光线的出射点。

答案 如图所示

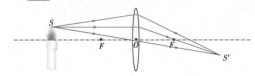

第3节 生活中的透镜

知识清单

知识 1 照相机

1.照相机是利用"凸透镜能成倒立、缩小的实像"这个原理制成的(如图)。

要想效果好，倒立得练好!

温馨提示 现在的照相机利用电子技术,把倒立的像转正,便于观察。

2.照相机的镜头相当于一个凸透镜,胶片相当于光屏,来自物体的光经镜头后会聚在胶片上,形成被照物体的像。

3.胶片上涂着一层对光敏感的物质,它在曝光后发生化学变化,物体的像就被记录在胶片上,经过显影、定影后成为底片,再用底片洗印就可以得到相片。

知识 2 幻灯机

1.幻灯机是利用"凸透镜能成倒立、放大的实像"这个原理制成的(如图所示)。

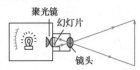

聚光镜　幻灯片　镜头

2.镜头相当于一个凸透镜,幻灯片相当于"探究凸透镜成像规律"实验中的蜡烛(物体),屏幕相当于光屏。

3.幻灯机构造:镜头、画片框、聚光镜、光源和反光镜、机箱等。

温馨提示 反光镜用凹面镜,聚光镜为一组凸透镜,光源发出光经反光镜和聚光镜作用后集中射向幻灯片。把幻灯片放在距镜头稍大于焦距的位置,在强光的照射下,就能在屏幕上成放大的像。

例 如图所示是幻灯机的工作原理图。幻灯机的镜头相当于一个_____镜。为了使观众看到正立的像,幻灯片要_____(选填"顺着"或"倒着")插入架上,用强光照射幻灯片,幻灯片上的画面在屏幕上形成_____像(选填"实"或"虚")。

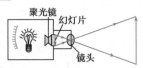

聚光镜　幻灯片　镜头

解析 幻灯机的镜头相当于一个凸透镜,幻灯机的工作原理是当物体距离凸透镜大于1倍焦距且小于2倍焦距时,成倒立、放大的实像。为了使观众看到正立的像,幻灯片要倒着插入架上。

答案 凸透　倒着　实

知识 3 投影仪

1.投影仪是利用"凸透镜能成倒立、放大的实像"这个原理制成的(如图所示)。

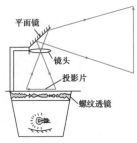

平面镜　镜头　投影片　螺纹透镜

2.镜头相当于一个凸透镜,投影片相当于"探究凸透镜成像规律"实验中的蜡烛(物体),屏幕相当于光屏。

3.投影仪的结构与幻灯机相似,主要区别是投影仪用两块大的螺纹透镜作聚光器,同时用一块平面镜把光反射到屏幕上。

例 如图所示是上课经常使用的投影仪,请按要求回答。

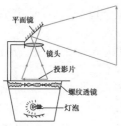

(1)平面镜的作用是:_____。
(2)灯泡的作用是:_____。
(3)若在屏幕上的像比较模糊(与投影片无关),调整方法是:_____。

解析 (1)平面镜对光有反射作用,能改变光的传播方向,使凸透镜所成的像成在屏幕上。(2)投影仪中的灯泡正好位于下方凹面镜的焦点处,当灯泡发光时,将发散光变为平行光,照亮投影片,使凸透镜所成的像更加清晰。(3)据凸透镜成像规律可知,应适当调整镜头与投影片的距离或屏幕与投影仪的距离,可使模糊的像变清晰。

答案 (1)改变光的传播方向,使像成在屏幕上
(2)充当光源,照亮投影片,使成的像更清晰
(3)适当调整镜头与投影片的距离(或屏幕与投影仪的距离)

知识 4 放大镜

1.放大镜实际上就是一个短焦距的凸透镜。当物体位于凸透镜焦点以内,即物距小于焦距时,对着凸透镜观察,就可以看到正立、放大的虚像(如图)。像和物位于凸透镜的同侧。

2.当物体越靠近凸透镜的焦点时,所成的虚像越大。放大镜可以将小的、眼睛不易辨清的物体"放大",以便人们能看得更清楚。放大镜放大的倍数一般只有几倍,最多不超过 20 倍,要想进一步提高放大倍数,就要用显微镜。

放大镜成虚像时,像的大小变化问题

当物体位于凸透镜的焦点以内时,我们在透镜的另一侧可以看到物体正立、放大的虚像;物体越靠近焦点(或离透镜越远),所成的虚像越大;物体越远离焦点(或离透镜越近),所成虚像越小(如下图)。

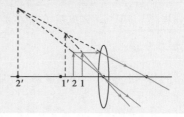

知识 照相机的构造及各部分作用

知识 照相机的构造及各部分作用

1.照相机的主要构造:镜头、调焦环、光圈环、快门、取景器、胶片。如图所示。

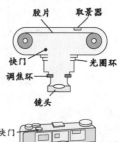

2.作用:(1)照相机调物距是通过调整照相机与物体间的距离来实现的。调焦距(胶片与镜头的距离)则是通过调镜头的位置来实现的,调整时旋转调焦环,拍摄近的景物时,镜头往前伸,离胶片远一些;拍摄远的景物时,镜头往后缩,离胶片近一些。调焦环上刻有数字,表示拍摄的景物到镜头的距离。适当调整调焦环能使景物在胶片上成清晰的像。

(2)光圈和快门的作用:光圈控制进入镜头的光的多少,快门控制曝光时间,选择合适的光圈和快门可以拍出亮度适当的照片。

方法 **照相时调节像大小的方法**

1.照相机是利用凸透镜成倒立、缩小实像的原理工作的。

2.若使胶片上的像变大,需缩小物距,增大像距;应将相机离物体近一些,同时调整镜头往前伸,离胶片远一些。

3.若使胶片上的像变小,需增大物距,缩小像距;应将相机离物体远一些,同时调整镜头往后缩,离胶片近一些。

例 用一架焦距不变的照相机,给一个人照了一张全身像,若要再给这个人照一张半身像,应该 (   )

A.使照相机的镜头离人远些,并减小镜头到底片的距离

B.使照相机的镜头离人远些,并增大镜头到底片的距离

C.使照相机的镜头离人近些,并增大镜头到底片的距离

D.使照相机的镜头离人近些,并减小镜头到底片的距离

解析 底片大小不变,从全身像到半身像,实际上是人的像变大了,根据照相机的调节方法,要想使底片上的像变大,人离镜头要近一些,像离镜头要远一些。因此照相机的镜头应离人近一些,同时镜头往前伸,使暗箱长一些,增大镜头到底片的距离。

答案 C

点拨 此题可以用"物近像远像变大"这句话来帮助理解。

第 4 节　眼睛和眼镜

知识清单

知识 1 **眼睛构造及视物原理**

1.眼睛的构造

如图是眼睛构造的示意图。

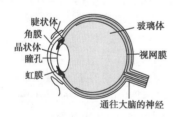

眼睛的构造

2.各部位作用:角膜和晶状体的共同作用相当于一个凸透镜,它把来自物体的光会聚在视网膜上,形成物体的像;虹膜能调节瞳孔的大小,控制进入眼睛的光的多少;睫状体起到改变晶状体的形状,从而改变晶状体焦距的作用;视网膜相当于凸透镜成像用的光屏。

3.眼睛的视物原理

正常人的眼睛具有很强的自我调节本领,可以使远处的物体和近处的物体都成像在视网膜上。因此,正常人的眼睛既可以看清远处的物体,又可以看清近处的物体,其成像原理如图所示。

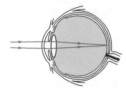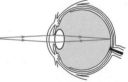

甲:正常眼看远处物体　　乙:正常眼看近处物体

易混对比 *眼睛视物时,晶状体的薄厚变化问题*

眼睛具有很强的自我调节能力,看远处物体时(如上图甲),相当于平行光通过晶状体(凸透镜)会聚在视网膜处,此时晶状体较薄;看近处物体时,相当于一束发散光通过晶状体折射后会聚于视网膜处,这时晶状体变厚(如上图乙),会聚能力增强。

知识 2 近视眼和远视眼

	近视眼	远视眼
特点	近视眼只能看清近处的物体,看不清远处的物体	远视眼只能看清远处的物体,看不清近处的物体
形成原因	晶状体太厚,折光能力太强,或者眼球在前后方向上太长,使来自远处某点的光会聚在视网膜前,到达视网膜时已经不是一点,而是一个模糊的光斑	晶状体太薄,折光能力太弱,或者眼球在前后方向上太短,使来自近处一点的光还没有会聚成一点就到达视网膜了,在视网膜上形成一个模糊的光斑
矫正	配戴凹透镜,利用凹透镜对光的发散作用	配戴凸透镜,利用凸透镜对光的会聚作用
近点	比正常眼近	比正常眼远
远点	有限远处	无限远处

例 如图所示,一直以来,小强总是用这样的姿势看书或电视,近几天他发现自己看不清远处的物体,小强的眼睛是_____(选填"远视眼"或"近视眼")。

解析 近视眼的特点是只能看清近处的物体,看不清远处的物体。青少年近视的原因有:看书、写字姿势不正确,平时用眼过度,以及周围环境的光污染等。

答案 近视眼

方法清单

方法 近、远视眼的识别及其矫正

方法 近、远视眼的识别及其矫正

1.近视眼的识别及其矫正

(1)特点:看远处的物体很吃力,只有把物体拿到离眼睛较近处才能看清楚,这种眼睛叫"近视眼"。其特点是"怕远不怕近"。

拓展知识 知识 视角

知识 视角

观察物体时,从物体两端(上、下或左、右)引出的光线在人眼光心处所成的夹角(如图所示)。

温馨提示 物体对眼睛所成的视角不仅和物体大小有关,还和物体与眼睛的距离有关。物体的尺寸越小,离观察者越远,则视角越小。

例 (1)从图中可以看出,眼睛以一定视角观察某一物体时,物体在视网膜上所成的像大,眼睛所看到的物体就大,下面四种情况,眼睛感到最长的物体是 ( )

A.20 m 远的 1.6 m 高的人

B.18 m 远的 1.7 m 高的小树

C.20 m 远的 1.7 m 高的栏杆

D.40 m 远的 1.6 m 高的竹竿

(2)一个同学站在平面镜前,当他逐渐远离镜子时,由于像对他的眼睛所成的视角逐渐_____,所以产生一种"像在变小"的错觉,其实所成的像的大小_____。

解析 (1)同一高度的物体距离眼睛越近,视角越大,眼睛感到该物体越长,综合比较四个选项,B 项符合题意。(2)当该同学远离平面镜时,他与像之间的距离增大,视角逐渐减小,看起来像在变小,实际上根据平面镜成像的特点知像与物的大小相等,故像的大小不变。

答案 (1)B (2)减小 不变

---

(2)矫正:配戴凹透镜,使入射的平行光经凹透镜发散后再射入眼睛,会聚点就能成到视网膜上(如图)。

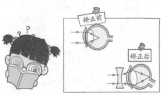

近视眼及其矫正

2.远视眼的识别及其矫正

(1)特点:看近处的物体很吃力,只有把物体拿到离眼睛较远处才能看清楚,这种眼睛叫"远视眼",老花眼就是远视眼,其特点是"怕近不怕远"。

(2)矫正:配戴凸透镜,使入射的光经凸透镜会聚后再射入眼睛,会聚点就能成到视网膜上(如图)。

远视眼及其矫正

例 在探究"近视眼的矫正"课外实验中:

(1)调整烛焰(模拟远处所视物)、水凸透镜(模拟人眼晶状体,并与注射器相连,其凸起程度可通过注射器注入或吸取水量来调节)、光屏(模拟人眼视网膜)在光具座上的位置,如图所示,此时在光屏上得到了烛焰清晰的像,该像是倒立、_____的_____像。

(2)向水凸透镜内_____(填"注入"或"吸取")适量水来模拟近视眼,发现光屏上原来清晰的像变模糊了。①将光屏向靠近透镜的方向移动适当距离,再次得到清晰的像。说明近视眼将远处的物体成像在视网膜_____(填"前"或"后")。②若光屏不移动,在烛焰和水凸透镜间加一个焦距合适的凹透镜,光屏上也能得到清晰的像。说明近视眼镜是_____透镜。

解析 (1)由题图可知,物距大于像距,此时在光屏上成倒立、缩小的实像。(2)近视眼的晶状体厚度变大,折光能力增强,故应向水凸透镜内注入适量水来模拟近视眼;光屏向靠近透镜方向移动适当距离后,再次得到清晰的像,说明近视眼将远处物体的像成在了视网膜前;若在烛焰和水凸透镜间加一个合适的凹透镜,则光屏上也能得到清晰的像,说明近视眼可以用凹透镜来矫正,故近视眼镜是凹透镜。

答案 (1)缩小 实 (2)注入 ①前 ②凹

第 5 节　显微镜和望远镜

知识清单

基础知识
知识 1 显微镜与望远镜
知识 2 显微镜和望远镜看到的像都是放大的吗

知识 1　显微镜与望远镜

	显微镜	望远镜
主要构造	两组凸透镜组合 目镜 粗准焦螺旋 细准焦螺旋 镜臂 镜柱 镜筒 转换器 物镜 通光孔 载物台 遮光器 压片夹 反光镜 镜座	开普勒望远镜是由两组凸透镜组成的 开普勒望远镜

	显微镜	望远镜
原理	显微镜就是利用两组透镜的放大作用组合制成的。利用这一结构，来看被观察物体的光先通过物镜使物体成一倒立、放大的实像，然后用目镜把这个实像再放大（成正立、放大的虚像），就能看清很微小的物体了	开普勒望远镜是由物镜和目镜这两组凸透镜组成的，不同的是物镜的焦距长，而目镜的焦距短，如图甲所示。利用这一结构，来看被观察物体的光先通过物镜使物体成一倒立、缩小的实像，然后用目镜把这个实像再放大（成正立、放大的虚像），就能看清很远处的物体了，这就是望远镜的原理（见图乙）。通过望远镜看远处的物体时，并不是成放大的像，而是使视角变大了，所以才看清远处的物体
目镜	靠近眼睛的一组透镜，成正立、放大的虚像，其作用相当于一个普通的放大镜	靠近眼睛的透镜叫目镜，它的作用就是把物镜所成的像放大
物镜	靠近被观察物体的一组透镜，成倒立、放大的实像，其作用相当于一个幻灯机镜头	靠近被观察物体的透镜叫物镜，它的作用是使远处的物体在焦点附近成倒立、缩小的实像，相当于一架照相机
目镜与物镜间的距离	显微镜的物镜要成放大的实像，物体处于物镜的一倍焦距与二倍焦距之间，则像将大于二倍焦距。实像在目镜中需要成放大的虚像，则实像应处在目镜的焦距以内。由此可知，两透镜间的距离大约为 $2f_物+f_目$	用开普勒望远镜观察较远的物体，物镜使远处的物体所成的像在物镜的焦点处附近。这一实像又要在目镜中成放大的虚像，实像就必须落在目镜的焦距以内。因此，望远镜的物镜与目镜间的距离应不大于两透镜的焦距之和。实际望远镜物镜的前焦点和目镜的后焦点重合在一起
调节	物镜成倒立的实像，目镜成正立的虚像。因此，眼睛看到的像相对于原像是倒着的。当从显微镜中观察到物体偏上时，应向上移动载物片，才能使被观察的物体处于视野的中央	物镜成倒立的实像，目镜成正立的虚像。因此，眼睛看到的像相对于原物是倒着的。当从望远镜中看到物体偏下时，应将物镜镜头上移，才能使被观察的物体处于视野的中央

例 如图，有一种望远镜由两组凸透镜组成。靠近眼睛的叫做目镜，靠近物体的叫做物镜。物镜的作用是使远处的物体在焦点附近成缩小的实像，它相当于一架 （　　）

A.幻灯机　　　　　　B.投影仪
C.放大镜　　　　　　D.照相机

解析 远处物体的位置在 2 倍焦距以外，经过物镜成一个倒立、缩小的实像，相当于一架照相机。

答案 D

知识 2 显微镜和望远镜看到的像都是放大的吗

1.用显微镜观察物体时，要将被观察物体放在物镜一倍焦距和二倍焦距之间，经过物镜得到一个倒立、放大的实像，实像的位置在目镜一倍焦距内，再经其放大，最后得到比原物体大许多倍的虚像。该虚像和物体比较是倒立的，为便于观察，需将物体倒放。

2.天文望远镜距离被观察物体（如天体）很远，物体和物镜的距离远大于物镜的二倍焦距，经过物镜成一倒立、缩小的实像，其作用相当于将被观察物体移近，再经目镜将得到的实像放大，最后得到的虚像比原物体小得多，该虚像和物体比较是倒立的。

例 用显微镜和由两组凸透镜组成的天文望远镜观察物体时,下列关于它们的成像和使用的说法中正确的是　　　　　　　　　　(　　)

A.通过显微镜和望远镜所观察到的像与物体比较都是放大的

B.显微镜和望远镜的物镜作用相同,都能得到物体倒立、放大的实像

C.显微镜和望远镜的目镜作用相同,都能将物镜成的像放大

D.用显微镜和望远镜观察物体时,为得到正立的像,都应先将物体倒放

(解析) 通过显微镜所观察到的像比原物体大得多,通过望远镜所观察到的像比原物体小得多,A 不正确。经过显微镜的物镜得到倒立、放大的实像,经过望远镜的物镜得到倒立、缩小的实像,B 不正确。用望远镜观察天体时,天体不能倒放,D 不正确。应选 C。

(答案) C

方法 显微镜的调节方法

方法 显微镜的调节方法

1.在显微镜中,物镜和目镜都使物体的像放大,其中物镜成倒立、放大的实像,相当于幻灯机;目镜成正立、放大的虚像,相当于放大镜。

2.经显微镜的物镜和目镜两次放大后的像相对于被观察物体而言是倒立的,既上下互换,也左右互换。

3.在调节显微镜时,要把像移到视野的中央,像偏向哪个方向,载物片(物体)就朝哪个方向移动。

例1 用显微镜观察载物片上的物体时,发现被观察物体的像在视野的右下方,要把像移到视野的中央,应　　　　　　　　　　(　　)

A.使载物片向右下方移动

B.使载物片向左上方移动

C.使载物片向右上方移动

D.使载物片向左下方移动

(解析) 用显微镜观察到物体的像相对于物体是倒立的。如像在视野的右下方,要把像移到视野中央,像应向左上方移动,因为像相对于物体倒立,即上下左右都颠倒,所以物体应向完全相反的方向移动,即物体应向右下方移动,而物体在载物片上,故选 A。

(答案) A

例2 李洋用显微镜观察上皮细胞时,通过调节被观察的物体使之处于视野中央,但发现像太小,观察不清楚,这时他应该　　　　　　　(　　)

A.使物镜远离物体,目镜位置不变

B.使物镜靠近物体,目镜远离物镜一些

C.使物镜远离物体,目镜靠近物镜一些

D.使物镜位置不变,目镜靠近物镜一些

(解析) 要想使观察到的物体的像再大些。首先,第一次成的像应变大,对物镜来说,像变大,被观察的物体必须靠近物镜。如果物镜靠近被观察物体,第一次成的像是变大了,但第一次成的像将向目镜靠近。如目镜不动,这时目镜的放大倍数变小,所以目镜应远离物体。

(答案) B

第3部分

热学

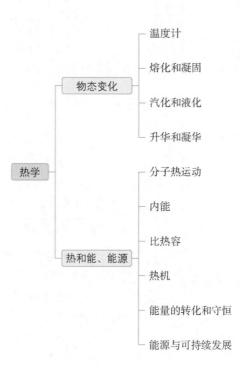

热学
├─ 物态变化
│   ├─ 温度计
│   ├─ 熔化和凝固
│   ├─ 汽化和液化
│   └─ 升华和凝华
└─ 热和能、能源
     ├─ 分子热运动
     ├─ 内能
     ├─ 比热容
     ├─ 热机
     ├─ 能量的转化和守恒
     └─ 能源与可持续发展

第4章　物态变化

知识梳理

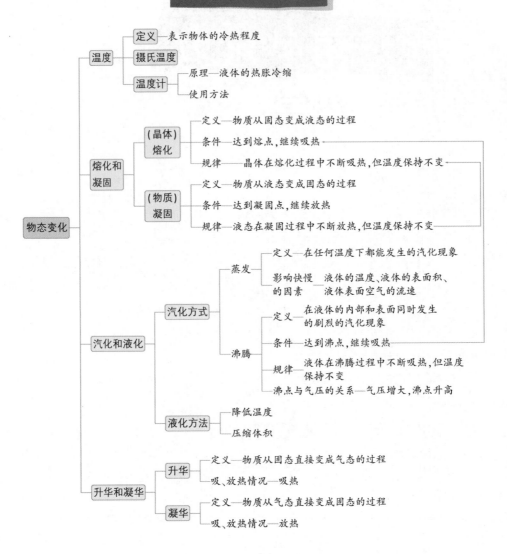

物态变化
- 温度
  - 定义——表示物体的冷热程度
  - 摄氏温度
  - 温度计
    - 原理——液体的热胀冷缩
    - 使用方法
- 熔化和凝固
  - (晶体)熔化
    - 定义——物质从固态变成液态的过程
    - 条件——达到熔点,继续吸热
    - 规律——晶体在熔化过程中不断吸热,但温度保持不变
  - (物质)凝固
    - 定义——物质从液态变成固态的过程
    - 条件——达到凝固点,继续放热
    - 规律——液态在凝固过程中不断放热,但温度保持不变
- 汽化和液化
  - 汽化方式
    - 蒸发
      - 定义——在任何温度下都能发生的汽化现象
      - 影响快慢的因素——液体的温度、液体的表面积、液体表面空气的流速
    - 沸腾
      - 定义——在液体的内部和表面同时发生的剧烈的汽化现象
      - 条件——达到沸点,继续吸热
      - 规律——液体在沸腾过程中不断吸热,但温度保持不变
      - 沸点与气压的关系——气压增大,沸点升高
  - 液化方法
    - 降低温度
    - 压缩体积
- 升华和凝华
  - 升华
    - 定义——物质从固态直接变成气态的过程
    - 吸、放热情况——吸热
  - 凝华
    - 定义——物质从气态直接变成固态的过程
    - 吸、放热情况——放热

第1节　温度计

知识清单

知识 1 温度

1.温度的概念及单位

（1）定义:表示物体的冷热程度。

（2）单位:温度的国际单位是开尔文,符号是 K。常用单位是摄氏度,符号是℃。

2.摄氏温度

（1）摄氏温度的表示符号为 t,它的单位是摄氏度(℃),

（2）摄氏温度的规定:在标准大气压下,把冰水混合物的温度规定为 0 ℃,把沸水的温度规定为100 ℃,在 0 ℃ 和100 ℃之间分成 100 等份,每一等份就是摄氏温度的一个单位,叫做 1 摄氏度。

知识 2 实验室用温度计、体温计、寒暑表的主要区别

	实验室用温度计	体温计	寒暑表
原理	液体的热胀冷缩	液体的热胀冷缩	液体的热胀冷缩
玻璃泡内液体	煤油、酒精等	水银	煤油、酒精等
测量范围	−20~110 ℃	35~42 ℃	−30~50 ℃
分度值	1 ℃	0.1 ℃	1 ℃
构造	玻璃泡上部是均匀细管	玻璃泡上部有一段细而弯的"缩口"	玻璃泡上部是均匀细管
使用方法	不能离开被测物体读数,不能甩	可以离开人体读数,使用前要甩几下	放在被测环境中直接读数,不能甩

温馨提示　体温计缩口的作用是防止体温计离开人体后,玻璃泡内的水银柱冷却收缩,退回玻璃泡内。

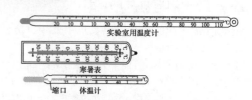

实验室用温度计

寒暑表

缩口　体温计

知识 3 温度计的使用方法

估测	根据被测物体的温度选择合适的温度计
观察	看清温度计的量程和分度值
放置	温度计的玻璃泡要全部浸入被测的物体当中,不能接触容器底或容器壁
读数	①让温度计在物体当中稍待一会儿,等示数稳定后再读数;②在读数时温度计不能离开被测的物体;③视线要与液柱的上表面相平

例　图甲所示为测量冰的温度的操作,其中正确的是图_____,此时温度计的示数如图乙所示,则冰的温度是_____ ℃。

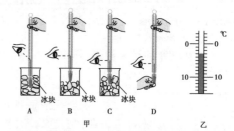

甲　　　乙

解析　使用温度计测量物体温度时,使温度计的玻璃泡和被测物体充分接触,读数时温度计的玻璃泡不能离开被测物体,故 B、D 错;读数时视线要和液柱的上表面保持相平,故 A 错;温度计上标有0 ℃,在 0 ℃ 和−10 ℃ 之间被分成 10 个小格,说明此温度计每一小格代表 1 ℃,因此温度计的示数是−3 ℃。

答案　C　−3

知识 1 热力学温度

1.以宇宙温度的下限——绝对零度(约−273 ℃)为起点的温度,叫做热力学温度。

2.冰水混合物的热力学温度是 273 K。热力学温度(T)和摄氏温度(t)的换算关系是:$T=273+t$。

3.研究表明,无论人类如何改进低温技术,0 K 的温度都是达不到的。在微观粒子和天体研究方面都采用热力学温度。

知识 2　不准确温度计的读数

不准确温度计的读数可用数学中的比例方法求解。

例 有一支刻度均匀,但实际测量不准确的温度计,把它放在冰水混合物中,示数是 4 ℃;把它放在 1 个标准大气压下的沸水中,示数是 94 ℃。把它放在某液体中时,示数是 22 ℃,则该液体的实际温度是_____。当把该温度计放入实际温度为 40 ℃ 的温水中时,温度计的示数为_____。

解析 根据摄氏温度的规定,1 个标准大气压下冰水混合物的温度是 0 ℃,沸水的温度为 100 ℃,并由已知条件画出线段图,如图所示,按比例计算如下:

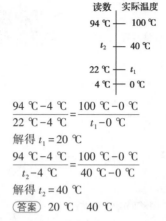

$$\frac{94 \text{ ℃}-4 \text{ ℃}}{22 \text{ ℃}-4 \text{ ℃}}=\frac{100 \text{ ℃}-0 \text{ ℃}}{t_1-0 \text{ ℃}}$$

解得 $t_1=20$ ℃

$$\frac{94 \text{ ℃}-4 \text{ ℃}}{t_2-4 \text{ ℃}}=\frac{100 \text{ ℃}-0 \text{ ℃}}{40 \text{ ℃}-0 \text{ ℃}}$$

解得 $t_2=40$ ℃

答案 20 ℃　40 ℃

方法清单　方法 体温计的使用与读数方法

方法　体温计的使用与读数方法

1.由于细小缩口的作用,缩口上方的水银柱不能退回玻璃泡。当体温计离开人体时,它表示的仍然是人体的温度;每次使用前,都要将水银甩下去。

2.体温计读数时,眼睛通过一条棱看过去,圆弧形的棱相当于一个放大镜,可以观察到放大了的较粗的水银柱,便于观察和读数。

3.明确体温计的量程为 35～42 ℃,分度值为 0.1 ℃。

例 2008 年 4 月,常德市出现了首例"手足口"病例之后,引起了市政府的高度重视,要求各地学校每天对学生进行晨检、晚检,并报告检查情况,其中就用到了体温计。图甲是一支常见体温计的示意图,它的量程是_____℃,它的分度值为_____℃。

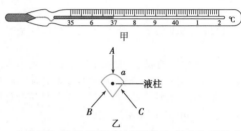

由此可知体温计的测量结果比实验室用温度计更精确,但因液柱太细难以读数,所以体温计具有特殊构造,其横截面如图乙所示,a 为向外凸起的弧形玻璃面,要看清体温计中液柱的位置就应沿_____方向观察(选填"A"、"B"或"C"),这是利用_____
_____。

解析 观察题图可知量程和分度值;体温计液柱太细难以读数,根据放大镜的特征和工作原理,应从 A 方向观察。

答案 35～42　0.1　A　凸透镜成正立放大的虚像(或放大镜原理)

第 2 节　熔化和凝固

知识清单

基础知识　知识1 物态变化　　知识2 熔化与晶体
知识3 晶体的熔化条件　知识4 凝固

知识 1　物态变化

1.定义:物质由一种状态变为另一种状态的过程叫物态变化。

2.物态变化及吸、放热关系图

物质存在着三种状态,而三种状态之间又存在着六种变化,物态变化现象与人们生活、生产关系密切。可以通过下图加强记忆。

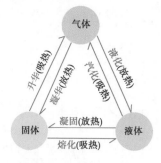

知识 **2** **熔化与晶体**

1.熔化

(1)定义:物质从固态变成液态的过程叫做熔化。在熔化过程中需要吸收热量(如图)。

固体　＋　热　＝　液体
熔化吸热

(2)应用:超市利用冰熔化吸热使荔枝和海虾保鲜。

(3)熔点:<u>晶体熔化时的温度叫做熔点。</u>

2.晶体与非晶体

固体分为晶体和非晶体两类。

(1)晶体

①定义:分子整齐规则排列的固体叫做晶体。

②特性:a.晶体在熔化时,温度不变;b.晶体有一定的熔点;c.不同晶体的熔点不同;d.同一种晶体的凝固点跟它的熔点相同。

③常见晶体:海波(如图)、冰、萘、石英、水晶、金刚石、食盐、明矾、金属。

海波

(2)非晶体

①定义:分子杂乱无章排列的固体叫做非晶体。

②特性:a.非晶体在熔化吸热时,温度不断地升高;b.非晶体没有熔点。

③常见非晶体:松香、玻璃、石蜡(如图)、沥青。

石蜡

例 在探究海波和石蜡熔化规律时,小琴记录的实验数据如表所示。请根据表中的实验数据解答下列问题。

时间/min	0	1	2	3	4	5	6	7	8	9	10	11	12
海波的温度/℃	40	42	44	46	48	48	48	48	48	48	50	53	56
石蜡的温度/℃	40	41	42	44	46	47	48	49	51	52	54	56	59

(1)在海波和石蜡这两种物质中,属于晶体的是_____;

(2)该晶体的熔点是_____℃;

(3)当该晶体的温度为42 ℃时,它处于_____态。(选填"固"或"液")

解析 因晶体熔化时吸热,温度不升高,故海波是晶体;它在4~9 min的过程中吸热,温度保持48 ℃不变,则它的熔点是48 ℃;海波在温度为42 ℃时是固态。

答案 (1)海波 (2)48 (3)固

知识 **3** **晶体的熔化条件**

1.晶体的熔化有温度达到熔点和继续吸热两个条件,两者缺一不可。

2.如果晶体的温度达到熔点但不能继续吸热,晶体就不能熔化,仍然处在固态。如果可以从外界继续吸收热量,则晶体开始熔化,进入由固态变为液态的过程。

3.当冰的温度升高到冰的熔点(也叫冰点)时,并继续吸热,冰便从固态逐渐变为液态。<u>温度等于熔点时,物质的状态可能是固态,可能是液态,也可能是固液共存状态。</u>

例 把盛有碎冰块的大试管插入烧杯里的碎冰块中,用酒精灯对烧杯底部慢慢加热,当烧杯中的冰块有大半熔化时,如图所示,试管中的冰　　　( )

A.熔化一部分　　　B.全部熔化
C.一点也不熔化　　D.无法判断

（解析）冰是晶体,冰熔化的条件是:①温度达到熔点0 ℃,②能够继续吸热。由题意知:烧杯中是冰水混合物,温度是 0 ℃,试管中的冰达到 0 ℃后无法从周围吸热,即试管中的冰只满足冰熔化的第一个条件,不满足冰熔化的第二个条件,所以试管中的冰不会熔化。正确答案是 C。

（答案）C

知识 **4** 凝固

1.定义:物质从液态变成固态的过程叫做凝固。凝固是熔化的逆过程。凝固放热(如图)。水结成冰,由液态变成固态属于凝固现象。

凝固放热

2.凝固点:液体凝固成固体时的温度称为凝固点;同种物质的凝固点等于熔点。

3.凝固条件:(1)温度达到凝固点;(2)**不断放出热量**。

（例）深秋,为避免树上的橘子在夜间气温骤降时被冻坏,果农经常在傍晚给橘子树喷水。如图所示,虽然水在夜间结了冰,但橘子却没被冻坏,这是为什么?

（答案）夜间气温骤降时,水降温直至凝固成冰,放出热量,使橘子温度不会降得太低,所以没有冻坏橘子。

拓展知识 **知识** 压强对熔点的影响

知识 **压强对熔点的影响**

晶体的熔点并不是固定不变的,压强对物质的熔点会产生一定的影响。

(1)大部分晶体熔化时,体积增大,其熔点随压强的增大而升高。

(2)冰熔化过程中体积变小,当压强增大时,冰的熔点降低。

如图所示:将一根两端挂有重物的细金属丝挂在冰块上,金属丝下的冰块熔化,说明增大压强可以使冰熔化。金属丝通过后,冰的熔点又升高了,熔化成的水又凝固成冰,这样,金属丝就可以轻松穿过冰块而不留缝隙。

温馨提示 掺加杂质也会影响晶体的熔点:如下雪天,向积雪的公路上撒盐,盐水在-20 ℃以下才结冰,方便交通;但盐水会腐蚀车辆、道路,应慎用盐熔雪的方法。

（例）如图所示,王濛在 2007~2008 年国际短道速滑世界杯的比赛中收获了两枚金牌。滑冰时,冰面在冰刀压力作用下,稍有熔化,由此,你能猜想到冰的熔点可能与_____有关,这层水的作用跟润滑油的作用一样,减小了_____。

（解析）冰刀与冰面的接触面积小,对冰面的压强大,由此可猜想冰的熔点可能与压强有关;这层水的作用是减小摩擦。

（答案）压强 摩擦力(摩擦、阻力)

方法清单
方法 **1** 图像法描述物质熔化和凝固过程
方法 **2** 水浴法加热在晶体熔化实验中的运用

方法 **1** 图像法描述物质熔化和凝固过程

1.图像法具有直观、形象和概括力强的独特优点;它能将物理情景、物理过程、物理状态以直观的方式

呈现在我们面前;描述熔化和凝固时,常用温度-时间图像描述其特点。

2.物质的熔化、凝固图像

	晶体	非晶体
熔点和凝固点	有	无
熔化图像	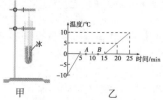温度/℃ 图像(D、B、C、A)O 时间/min AB段:物质为固态 BC段:熔化过程,物质为固液共存状态,吸收热量,温度不变(此温度为熔点) CD段:物质为液态	温度/℃ 图像 O 时间/min 熔化过程中,物质吸收热量,温度升高
凝固图像	温度/℃ 图像(E、F、G、H)O 时间/min EF段:物质为液态 FG段:凝固过程,物质为固液共存状态,放出热量,温度不变(此温度为凝固点) GH段:物质为固态	温度/℃ 图像 O 时间/min 凝固过程中,物质放出热量,温度降低

例1 小明利用如图甲所示装置探究冰的熔化特点,他每隔相同时间记录一次温度计的示数,并观察物质的状态。

甲   乙

(1)应选用颗粒_____(选填"较大"或"较小")的冰块做实验。

(2)图乙是他根据记录的数据绘制的"温度-时间"图像。由图像可知:冰属于_____(选填"晶体"或"非晶体"),这样判断的依据是_____。

(3)图乙中第3 min时,物质处于_____态。

(4)图乙中,物体在A点时具有的内能_____(选填"大于"、"小于"或"等于")在B点时的内能。

解析 (1)较小的冰块易受热均匀;

(2)由图像知,冰在熔化过程中温度保持不变,所以冰是晶体;

(3)由图像知,冰从第5 min时开始熔化,则第3 min时处于固态;

(4)在A点和B点时虽温度相同,但冰不断吸热,内能增加,故在A点时具有的内能小于在B点时的内能。

答案 (1)较小 (2)晶体 冰在熔化过程中,温度不变 (3)固 (4)小于

例2 如图所示为蜡油和水在凝固时的温度-时间图像,则图_____表示水的凝固图像。甲图中该物质在t_1至t_2时间段内的状态是_____,内能_____(增加/不变/减少)。

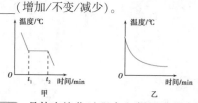

甲   乙

解析 晶体在熔化过程中和凝固过程中温度不变,而非晶体熔化过程温度一直上升,凝固过程温度一直下降。冰是晶体,水凝固成冰的过程应该是甲图所示过程;$t_1 \sim t_2$这段时间内水正在凝固,处于固液共存态;凝固过程放热,所以内能减少。

答案 甲 固液共存 减少

方法 2 水浴法加热在晶体熔化实验中的运用

熔化实验中采用水浴加热(如图)的方法,利用水的对流,使受热更均匀,测量更科学。

观察熔化现象的实验装置

例 (1)如图所示是小明同学设计的"探究晶体萘熔化规律"的实验装置图,你认为这个实验装置如何?请作出评价。

第③部分

(2) 下表是小兵同学利用合理的实验装置, 测得的该物质熔化时温度随时间变化的数据, 你认为他测得的数据可靠吗?

时间/min	2	4	6	8	10	12	14	16	18	20	22	24
温度/℃	65	70	74	78	80	80	80	78	80	80	82	85

解析 (1) 为了均匀加热晶体, 要把晶体研碎, 要把试管浸在烧杯的水中均匀加热, 同时让温度计的玻璃泡与晶体粉末充分接触。装置错误: 一是温度计玻璃泡碰到试管底; 二是用酒精灯直接加热试管, 不能使萘均匀受热。应加一个石棉网和一个烧杯, 采用水浴加热法, 如图所示。

(2) 由题表中的数据可知萘的熔点是80 ℃, 在其熔化过程中虽然吸热, 但温度却保持不变, 不会升高, 更不会降低, 加热到第 16 min 测得的温度是 78 ℃, 这个数据不可靠。

答案 见解析

第3节　汽化和液化

知识清单

知识 1　汽化与蒸发

1. 汽化

(1) 定义: 物质从液态变为气态的过程叫做汽化。

(2) 特点: 汽化吸热(如图)。

液体　　＋　　热　　＝　　气体
汽化吸热

(3) 方式: 蒸发和沸腾。

2. 蒸发

(1) 定义: 在任何温度下都能发生的汽化现象叫做蒸发。

(2) 特点: 蒸发只发生在液体的表面。液体在蒸发过程中吸热, 致使和它接触的物体温度下降。例如, 吹电扇感到凉快, 是因为汗液蒸发吸热; 从游泳池中上岸后感觉冷(如图), 是因为体表水分蒸发吸热。

知识 2　影响蒸发快慢的三个因素

1. 液体的温度

温度越高, 蒸发越快。无论在什么温度下, 液体中总有一些速度很大的分子能够飞出液面而成为气体分子, 因此液体在任何温度下都能蒸发。如果液体的温度升高, 分子的平均动能增大, 从液面飞出去的分子数就会增多, 所以液体的温度越高, 蒸发得就越快。如晾衣服时, 要晾在有阳光的地方。

2. 液体的表面积

如果液体表面积增大, 处于液体表面附近的分子数目增加, 因而在相同的时间里, 从液面飞出的分子数就增多, 所以液体表面积增大, 蒸发就加快。如晒粮食时, 要把粮食摊开; 晾衣服时, 要展开衣服。

3. 空气流速

当从液体飞入空气里的分子和空气中的分子或其他气体分子发生碰撞时, 有可能被碰回到液体中来。如果液面上方空气流动快, 通风好, 分子重新返回液体中的机会就小, 蒸发就快。晾晒衣服时要展开衣服, 选有阳光的地方, 还要选有风的地方, 如图所示。

例 下列措施中,为了减慢蒸发的是 ( )

A.将地面上的积水向周围扫开

B.将湿手放在干手器下吹干

C.将湿衣服晾在通风的地方

D.将新鲜蔬菜装入保鲜袋

解析 A是增大液体的表面积,B是提高液体的温度与加快液体表面空气的流动,C是加快液体表面空气的流动,都是属于加快蒸发的措施;D是减慢液体表面空气的流动,从而减慢蒸发。

答案 D

知识 3 沸腾与沸点

1.沸腾

(1)定义:沸腾是液体内部和表面同时发生的剧烈的汽化现象。

(2)特点:沸腾吸热,但温度保持不变。

2.沸点:各种液体沸腾时都有确定的温度,这个温度叫做沸点。不同液体的沸点不同。水的沸点在1标准大气压下是100 ℃;食用油的沸点约为250 ℃。

3.液体沸腾的条件:要使液体沸腾,必须同时满足两个条件:第一,要达到一定的温度(即液体的沸点);第二,要继续吸热。达到沸点的液体,如果不能继续吸热,那它就不能沸腾。

易混对比	汽化方式 异同点	蒸发	沸腾
	相同点	都是从液态变成气态,都要吸热	
不同点	发生部位	只在液体表面进行	液体内部和表面同时发生
	剧烈程度	缓慢平和	剧烈
	温度条件	在任何温度下	在一定温度下(沸点)

例 如图所示,大锅 B 内和小铝管 A 内装的均为水,把大锅 B 放在炉火上加热,使大锅 B 内的水沸腾,若外界为1个标准大气压,则小铝管 A 中的水 ( )

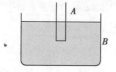

A.温度等于100 ℃,沸腾

B.温度低于100 ℃,不沸腾

C.温度等于100 ℃,不沸腾

D.温度低于100 ℃,沸腾

解析 水在1个标准大气压下的沸点是100 ℃,当大锅 B 内的水沸腾时,温度就保持在100 ℃不再升高,由于热传递,小铝管 A 中的水温最终也会升到100 ℃,但当 A 中的水和 B 中的水温度相等时,由于没有温度差而不再发生热传递,小铝管 A 中的水不能从外界得到热量,因此 A 中的水就不会沸腾,故正确选项应为 C。

答案 C

知识 4 沸点与气压的关系

1.沸点与液体表面处的气压有关。气压增大,沸点升高(高压锅原理);气压减小,沸点降低。

2.高压锅内水面上的蒸汽气压较高,大于1个标准大气压,所以沸点就超过100 ℃,食物容易煮熟。在高海拔处,因为气压比较低,水的沸点低于100 ℃,食物不容易煮熟,这时可利用高压锅(如图)。

例 如图所示,小烧杯和小试管中都盛有水,将烧杯口进行密封处理,小试管口敞开。用酒精灯给小烧杯加热,当小烧杯中的水沸腾时,小试管中的水将(在1个标准大气压下) ( )

A.达到沸点,能沸腾

B.达到沸点,不沸腾

C.不能达到沸点,不沸腾

D.条件不足,无法判断

解析 由于烧杯口被密封,在加热过程中,小烧杯中气压升高,水的沸点大于100 ℃,所以当烧杯中的水沸腾时,烧杯中水的温度大于100 ℃。小试管口是敞开的,小试管中水的沸点是100 ℃,对小试管中的水,由于满足沸腾的条件,因此能够沸腾,可见,正确选项为 A。

答案 A

第3部分

知识 5 水的沸腾实验

实验目的	观察沸腾现象和沸腾时的温度情况
实验器材	烧杯、水、温度计、铁架台、酒精灯、石棉网、火柴、中心有孔的纸板、钟表
实验装置图	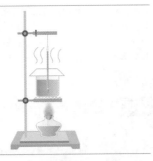
实验步骤	(1)把水倒进烧杯中,按实验装置图将各器材安装好 (2)用酒精灯给盛了水的烧杯加热,并注意观察温度计的示数 (3)当水温升到90 ℃左右时,每隔1 min(或2 min)记录1次水的温度,直到水沸腾后5 min为止,并注意观察水的沸腾现象 (4)根据记录的温度值,作出水的沸腾图像
实验现象	(1)沸腾前,在水中出现小的气泡,上升过程中温度降低,体积收缩变小,未到液面就消失了,同时,水温持续上升 (2)沸腾时,水中形成大量的气泡,上升、变大,到水面破裂开来,里面的水蒸气散发到空气中 (3)沸腾后,水继续吸收热量但温度始终保持不变,用下漫画形象表示 沸腾前　　　　沸腾时
注意事项	(1)点燃酒精灯时,应用火柴点燃,绝对禁止用一只酒精灯点燃另一只酒精灯 (2)用完酒精灯必须用灯帽盖灭,不得用嘴吹灭 (3)应该用酒精灯的外焰部分加热 (4)实验中尽可能取质量较少、初温较高的水进行实验,且最好在烧杯上加一个盖,这样可以减少加热时间 (5)实验中若测出水的沸点不是100 ℃,可能是受大气压影响或温度计存在质量问题

例 徐老师和同学们在实验室做探究【水沸腾时温度变化特点】的实验时,观察到水沸腾时温度计示数如图所示,则所测水的沸点为_____℃,出现这一结果的原因可能是这处大气压_____1标准大气压(选填"大于"、"小于"或"等于");开始实验时烧杯内最好装入热水,这样做的好处是_____。

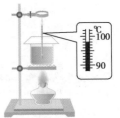

解析 水沸腾时的温度叫作沸点,由温度计的示数可知沸点为98 ℃;沸点与气压有关,气压增大沸点升高,气压减小沸点降低,1标准大气压下水的沸点是100 ℃,因此,该处大气压小于1标准大气压;一定质量的水,升高的温度越少,吸收的热量越少,需要加热的时间越短,所以,实验时用热水,好处是缩短实验时间。

答案 98　小于　缩短实验时间

知识 6 液化

1.**定义**:物质从气态变为液态的过程叫液化。
2.**特点**:液化放热(如图)。

我要变形!　　放热放热!　　变形成功!
气体　　　　　热　　　　　液体
液化放热

3.**液化方法**:(1)降低温度。当气体的温度降低到足够低的时候,所有的气体都可以液化,其中温度降到足够低是指气体的温度下降至沸点或沸点以下。不同的气体液化的温度不同,利用这种性质可以分离物质。(2)压缩体积。用压缩体积的方法可以使大多数的气体液化,如日常生活中使用的液化石油气就是用压缩体积的方法液化的。有些气体单靠压缩不能使它们液化,必须同时降低温度才行。

4.**液化放热在生活中的应用**

冬天手感到冷时,可向手哈气,是因为呼出的水蒸气液化放热。被锅内喷出的水蒸气烫伤比被开水烫伤还严重,是因为水蒸气液化时要放热。通常用管道把高温水蒸气送入浴池,使池中的水温升高,这是利用液化放热来完成的。

例 如图所示的物态变化过程中,放出热量的是
(　　)

A.冬天哈出的"白气"　B.正在消融的冰凌　C.夏天湿衣服晒干　D.放入衣箱中的樟脑球变小

解析 冬天哈出的"白气"是水蒸气发生液化(放热)变成的小水滴;冰凌消融是熔化(吸热)过程;夏天湿衣服晒干是汽化(吸热)过程;樟脑球变小属于升华(吸热)现象。故选A。

答案 A

拓展知识 知识 "白气"

知识 "白气"

1. 水蒸气:我们赖以生存的空气中含有水蒸气;水蒸气是一种无色透明的气体,是一种看不见、摸不着的气体。

2. 白气:我们看到的"白气"是水蒸气遇冷液化形成的小水滴。例如:冬天口中呼出的"白气";水烧开时从壶嘴喷出的"白气"等。

易混对比

冷物体与热物体冒"白气"的区别		
现象及来源 异同点	现象	水蒸气来源
不同点 热物体	冬天口中呼出"白气"	呼出温度较高的水蒸气遇冷液化形成的小水滴
	烧开水时壶嘴喷出"白气"	开水冒出高温水蒸气遇冷液化形成的小水滴
冷物体	冰棒冒"白气"	空气中的水蒸气遇冷液化形成的小水滴
	冰箱门打开时冒"白气"	冰箱外的空气中的水蒸气遇冷液化形成的小水滴
相同点	都是水蒸气遇冷液化形成的小水滴	

方法清单
- 方法❶ 控制变量法研究液体蒸发的快慢
- 方法❷ 图像法描述水沸腾现象

方法 1 控制变量法研究液体蒸发的快慢

研究液体蒸发快慢与哪些因素有关时,需控制变量:

(1)研究蒸发快慢与液体表面积的关系时,需控制液体温度和液体上方空气流速相同;

(2)研究蒸发快慢与液体温度的关系时,需控制液体表面积和液体上方空气流速相同;

(3)研究蒸发快慢与液体上方空气流速的关系时,需控制液体温度和液体表面积相同。

例 小凡同学在4块相同的玻璃板上各滴一滴质量相同的水,进行如图所示的实验探究,得出水蒸发快慢与水的温度、水的表面积和水面上方空气流动快慢有关。

例 生活中我们常看到"白气",下列有关"白气"形成的说法中正确的是 （ ）

A.文艺演出时舞台上经常施放"白气",这是干冰在常温下的升华现象

B.夏天从冰箱取出的冰棍周围冒"白气",这是空气中水蒸气的凝华现象

C.深秋清晨的河面上经常出现"白气",这是河面上水蒸气的汽化现象

D.冬天水烧开后壶嘴处喷出"白气",这是壶嘴喷出水蒸气的液化现象

解析 生活中看到的"白气"通常都不是气体,是由悬浮在空气中的小水滴形成的。干冰升华过程中变成二氧化碳气体,二氧化碳气体是看不见的,不会形成"白气"。舞台上施放的"白气"的正确解释是干冰升华过程中从周围吸收大量的热量,空气中的水蒸气遇冷液化形成小水滴,A项错。冰棍周围冒的"白气"是空气中的水蒸气遇冷液化成的小水滴,B项错。河面上的水蒸气在深秋清晨温度降低时发生液化形成小水滴,出现"白气",所以C项错。壶中水蒸气温度较高,喷到温度较低的空气中会发生液化现象,形成"白气",D项正确。

答案 D

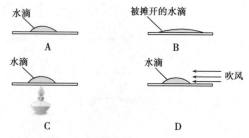

（1）通过 A、B 两图的对比,可以得出水蒸发快慢与水的_____有关。

（2）通过_____两图的对比,可以得出水蒸发快慢与水的温度有关。

（3）小凡同学猜想水蒸发快慢还可能与水的质量有关,于是继续进行了如下探究。在相同环境下的两块相同的玻璃板上分别滴上一滴和两滴水（如图）。结果发现甲图中水先蒸发完,于是他得出结论:水蒸发快慢与水的质量有关,水的质量越小蒸发越快。从实验设计环节看,他没有控制水的_____(选填"质

量"或"表面积")相同。

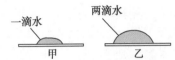

一滴水　两滴水

甲　　　　乙

（解析）（1）A、B两图控制水的温度和水面上方空气流速相同,研究水蒸发快慢与水的表面积的关系。

（2）研究水蒸发快慢与水的温度的关系,需控制水的表面积和水面上方空气流速相同。

（3）通过甲、乙两图可知,只控制了水的温度和水面上方空气流速相同,没有控制表面积相同。

（答案）（1）表面积　（2）A、C　（3）表面积

方法2　图像法描述水沸腾现象

描述水沸腾现象时,作温度–时间图像如下:

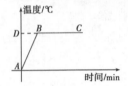

A 点表示水的初温是多少;

AB 段表示水的升温阶段;

BC段表示水的沸腾阶段,是一条水平直线,表示水沸腾时温度不变;

D 点对应的是水的沸点,若该温度低于100 ℃,则表示此地气压小于 1 个标准大气压。

（例）小明用图甲的装置,探究水沸腾时温度变化的特点,得到如下一组实验数据

时间/min	0	2	4	6	8	10	12	…
温度/℃	90	92.6	94.6	96.2	97	97	97	

甲

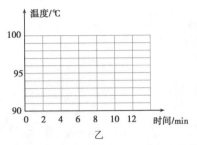

（1）该实验器材装配的合理顺序是(填序号) _____（①烧杯;②酒精灯;③温度计;④铁圈及石棉网）。

（2）请根据表中数据,在图乙中描点画出水沸腾时温度变化的图像。分析图像可知水在沸腾时温度的特点是_____。

（3）实验中水加热时间过长,其原因可能是_____（写出一种即可）。

（4）实验之后,小明产生了一个困惑:水的沸点怎么不是100 ℃? 要解决小明的困惑,可提出进一步探究的问题是_____。

（解析）（1）器材装配的合理顺序应为从下到上逐步安装。

（2）见答案。由图像可知,沸腾时温度保持不变。

（3）加热时间过长是由于水的初温太低或水的质量太大等。

（4）影响水的沸点的因素有哪些?
大气压对水的沸点有影响吗?
水的纯度对水的沸点有影响吗?
(答案合理均可)

（答案）（1）②④①③

（2）如图所示　(温度保持)不变

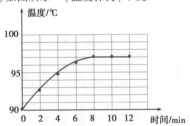

（3）水的质量太大(其他答案合理即可)

（4）见解析

第4节　升华和凝华

知识清单

基础知识
知识1 升华
知识2 凝华

知识 1 升华

1.定义:物质从固态直接变成气态的过程叫升华。

2.特点:物质在升华时要吸收热量(如图)。例如,碘升华时要对它加热。

升华吸热

3.(1)常见易升华的物质:干冰、碘、冰、萘、金属钨等。

(2)常见升华的现象:结冰的衣服变干,衣柜里的樟脑丸变小。

4.应用:物质在升华时吸热,具有致冷作用。生产和生活中可以利用物质的升华吸热来降低温度。如干冰就是一种常见的制冷剂,在生活中常有下列两个方面的应用。

(1)人工降雨:将干冰发射到云层附近,干冰迅速升华并从周围空气中吸收大量的热,使空气温度急剧下降,高空中的水蒸气液化成小水滴或凝华成小冰晶。当这些小水滴和小冰晶逐渐增大时,就从空中掉下来,小冰晶在下落时熔化,就形成了雨。

(2)制作舞台烟雾:舞台烟雾是利用干冰升华吸热致冷,使空气中的水蒸气液化形成的(如图)。

例 现在有一种叫"固体清新剂"的商品,把它放置在厕所、汽车、饭店内,能有效地清新空气等,"固体清新剂"发生的物态变化是　　　　　(　　)

A.熔化　　　　　　B.凝华

C.汽化　　　　　　D.升华

解析 由题意可知,"固体清新剂"本来是固态的,使用时并没有液体出现,但空气中弥漫着它的气味,同时它变得越来越小,说明使用时它是由固态直接变为气态,是升华现象。

答案 D

知识 2 凝华

1.定义:物质从气态直接变成固态的过程叫凝华。

2.特点:凝华是升华的逆过程,物质在凝华时要放出热量(如图)。

凝华放热

3.(1)常见易凝华的物质:气态碘、水蒸气、气态钨、气态萘等。

(2)常见的凝华现象

①霜和雾凇:是空气中的水蒸气遇冷凝华成小冰晶黏附在物体上形成的。如图:

②云:是空气中的水蒸气遇冷,液化成的小水滴和凝华成的小冰晶悬浮在高空中形成的。

③灯泡用久发黑:钨丝高温升华成钨蒸气,钨蒸气遇冷凝华成固态钨附着在灯泡内壁。

温馨提示　冬天窗户玻璃上的冰花是由于室内水蒸气液化形成的小水珠附着在玻璃上,再凝固成冰,或者是水蒸气直接凝华成冰附着在玻璃上形成冰花。

例 如图所示,将盛有少量冷水的烧瓶放在装有少量碘颗粒的烧杯口处,并将烧杯放在盛有热水的水槽中。不久会观察到烧杯内固态碘减少且出现紫红色的碘蒸气,这是　　　　　现象;过一会儿还可观察到烧瓶底部附着少量针状的碘晶体,这是　　　　　现象,在此物态变化过程中　　　　　热量。

温度计

(解析) 固态碘减少,出现碘蒸气,这是升华现象,烧瓶底部出现的碘晶体,是碘蒸气凝华形成的。碘蒸气凝华时要放出热量。

(答案) 升华 凝华 放出

拓展知识

知识 用物态变化解释雨、雪、云、雾、露、霜、冰雹的成因

知识 用物态变化解释雨、雪、云、雾、露、霜、冰雹的成因

自然现象	成因	物态变化名称
雨	①云层中的水蒸气液化形成小水珠后再合并成大水珠落下来 ②水蒸气凝华成小冰晶下落过程中熔化成水滴落下来	液化 凝华 熔化
云	太阳照到地面上,温度升高,含有水蒸气的高温空气上升到空中,在上升过程中,空气逐渐冷却,水蒸气液化成小水珠或凝华成小冰晶,便形成云	液化 凝华
雾	水蒸气在空气中遇到冷空气液化成小水珠,这些小水珠悬浮在空气中,在地面附近称为雾	液化

自然现象	成因	物态变化名称
露	在天气较热的早晨,空气中的水蒸气遇到温度较低的树叶、花草等,液化成为小水珠附着在它们的表面上	液化
霜、雪	霜是水蒸气在地表遇到 0 ℃ 以下的物体时,直接凝华为小冰晶。如果高空的温度为 0 ℃ 以下,水蒸气直接凝华成小冰晶,这些冰晶聚集起来,便以雪的形式降回地面	凝华
冰雹	冰雹是体积较大的冰球,云中的水珠被上升气流带到气温低于 0 ℃ 的高空,凝固成小冰珠。小冰珠在下落时,其外层受热熔化成水,并彼此结合,使冰珠越来越大。如果上升气流很强,就会再升入高空,在其表面形成一层冰壳,经过多次上下翻腾,结合成较大的冰珠。当上升气流托不住它时,冰珠就落到地面上,形成冰雹	熔化 凝固

例 如图是水循环示意图。图中过程①发生的物态变化是汽化,同时伴随着_____热;过程②发生的物态变化是凝华和_____,同时伴随着放热。

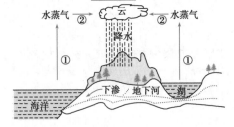

(解析) 汽化是吸热过程,在空中由于温度降低,水蒸气会液化为小水珠或凝华为小冰晶,形成云。

(答案) 吸 液化

方法清单

方法 概念法识别物态变化的类型

方法 概念法识别物态变化的类型

识别方法:①明确物质的初状态和末状态;②根据物态变化的概念进行分析判断。

例 从冰箱中取出的冻鱼在空气中放置一会儿,冻鱼身上出现一层白霜,又过一段时间冻鱼身上的霜变成了水。此过程经历的物态变化是先_____后_____。

(解析) 冻鱼身上出现的白霜,是空气中的水蒸气遇冷形成的小冰晶,水蒸气由气态变成固态,属于凝华现象;固态的霜变成水属于熔化现象。

(答案) 凝华 熔化

第5章

热和能、能源

知识梳理

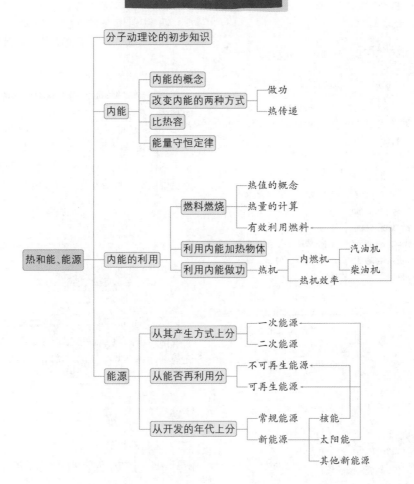

第③部分

第1节 分子热运动

知识清单

基础知识　知识**1** 分子动理论
　　　　　知识**2** 分子热运动与扩散

知识 **1** 分子动理论

内容	扩展	实例
常见的物质是由大量的分子、原子组成的	分子间存在着空隙	①食盐能溶于水中 ②酒精与水混合总体积变小 ③气体极易被压缩
物质内的分子在不停地做热运动	温度越高,分子无规则运动越剧烈,扩散现象就是由分子的无规则运动引起的	①墙内开花墙外香 ②把硫酸铜水溶液注入水底,过一段时间全部水都变蓝 ③把铅块与金块紧压在一起,5年后它们相互渗入约1 mm
分子之间存在引力和斥力	引力和斥力同时存在,不过有时以引力为主,有时以斥力为主	①固体和液体很难被压缩,固体不易被拉断 ②把两个铅块的底部刮干净,紧压一下,两个铅块就会连在一块,下面再吊一个重物,两铅块也不分开

例 如图所示,这个实验表明 （ ）

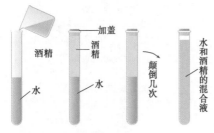

A.物体是由大量分子组成的
B.分子在不停地运动
C.分子间有间隙
D.分子间存在引力

（**解析**）酒精和水混合后,总体积小于水和酒精的体积之和,表明分子间有间隙,故选C。

（**答案**）C

知识 **2** 分子热运动与扩散

1.分子热运动

物质中大量分子的无规则运动叫做分子热运动。分子的运动用肉眼是看不见的。扩散现象是分子热运动的宏观体现。

2.扩散及影响扩散的因素

(1)不同的物质互相接触时彼此进入对方的现象叫扩散。扩散现象的实质是分子的相互渗入。

(2)扩散现象表明一切物质的分子都在不停地做无规则的运动,例如:"酒香不怕巷子深"说明酒精分子在不停地做无规则运动;很远就能闻到臭豆腐的味道也说明臭豆腐分子在不停地做无规则运动(如图)。

扩散现象

(3)影响扩散的因素:温度越高,扩散越快。分子无规则运动的剧烈程度跟温度有关,温度越高,分子无规则运动越剧烈,故扩散越快。

拓展知识　知识**1** 扩散现象的认识和理解
　　　　　知识**2** 分子间的作用力

知识 **1** 扩散现象的认识和理解

1.扩散现象只能发生在不同的物质之间,同种物质之间不能发生扩散现象。

2.不同物质只有相互接触时,才能发生扩散现象,没有相互接触的物质之间是不会发生扩散现象的。

3.扩散现象是两种物质的分子彼此进入对方,而不是单一的某种物质的分子进入另一种物质。

4.气体、液体或固体之间都可以发生扩散现象,不同状态的物质之间也可以发生。

例 在装着红棕色二氧化氮气体(二氧化氮的密度大于空气密度)的瓶子上面倒扣一个空瓶子,使两个瓶口相对,两瓶口之间用一块玻璃板隔开(图甲)。抽掉玻璃板后,最终发现两瓶内气体颜色基本相同(图乙)。

空气
玻璃板
二氧化氮

甲　　乙

(1)这是一种什么现象？

(2)它说明了什么？

解析 相互接触的不同物质彼此进入对方的现象叫做扩散，扩散现象说明分子在不停地做无规则的运动。

答案 见解析

知识 2 分子间的作用力

1.分子间的引力和斥力是同时存在、同时消失的，是不会相互抵消的。

(1)当分子间的距离 $r = 10^{-10}$ m 时，引力等于斥力，分子之间作用力为零。

(2)当分子间的距离 $r < 10^{-10}$ m 时，分子之间的斥力大于引力，分子之间作用力表现为斥力，如图甲。

(3)当分子间的距离 $r > 10^{-10}$ m 时，分子之间的引力大于斥力，分子之间作用力表现为引力，如图乙。

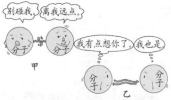

(4)当分子间的距离大于 10^{-10} m 的 10 倍时，分子之间作用力变得十分微弱，可以忽略；破镜难圆就是由于断裂处的距离已经超出分子间引力作用的最大距离。

2.从分子间作用力的角度理解固体、液体、气体的特征。

(1)固体中分子之间的距离小，相互作用力很大，分子只能在一定的位置附近振动，所以既有一定的体积，又有一定的形状。

(2)液体中分子之间的距离较小，相互作用力较大，以分子群的形态存在，分子可在某个位置附近振动，分子群却可以相互滑过，所以液体有一定的体积，但有流动性，形状随容器而变化。

(3)气体中分子之间的距离很大，相互作用力很小，每一个分子几乎都可以自由运动，所以气体既没有固定的体积，也没有固定的形状，可以充满能够达到的整个空间。

(4)固体很难被拉伸，是因为分子间存在着引力。固体和液体很难被压缩，是因为分子间存在着斥力。固体和液体能保持一定的体积是因为分子间存在着引力。

例 液体和空气接触的表面存在一个薄层——表面层，如图所示。由于液体分子做无规则运动，表面层中就存在一些具有较大能量的分子，它们可以克服分子间相互作用的_____力，脱离液体跑到空气中去。其宏观表现就是液体的_____(填物态变化名称)。

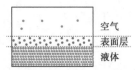

空气
表面层
液体

解析 分子间的引力对分子脱离液体有阻碍作用。物体由液态变为气态是汽化现象。

答案 引　汽化

方法清单

方法 比较法判断分子热运动和物体机械运动

方法 比较法判断分子热运动和物体机械运动

1.从概念上判断。分子热运动是物体内部大量分子的无规则运动，而机械运动则是一个物体相对于另一个物体位置的改变。

2.从引起运动因素上判断。分子热运动是自发的，永不停息的，不受外界影响的，而物体的机械运动则要受到外力的影响。例如，秋天，桂花飘香是由于分子热运动而形成的扩散现象，而冬天，雪花飘扬属

于雪花在重力和风力作用下的机械运动，它不属于扩散现象。

例 下列现象中属于扩散现象的是　　　(　　)

A.擦黑板时，粉笔灰在空中飞舞

B.打开一盒香皂，很快就会闻到香味

C.粉笔蹭到衣服上，在衣服上留下粉笔痕迹

D.冬天，雪花漫天飞舞

解析 扩散现象是由于分子无规则运动形成的，我们用肉眼不可能直接看到分子的运动，A、C、D 都不属于扩散现象；只有 B 选项中的"闻到香味"是分子做无规则运动的结果，属于扩散现象。

答案 B

第2节 内能

知识清单

知识 1 内能

	定义	微观	宏观	量值
分子的动能	运动着的分子所具有的能量	分子永不停息地做无规则运动	与温度有关	永远不等于零
分子的势能	由分子之间的相对位置所决定的能量	分子间存在着相互作用的引力和斥力	与物体的体积有关	可能等于零
物体的内能	物体内所有分子动能和分子势能的总和	分子永远在运动和分子间存在作用力	与质量及温度、体积有关	永远不等于零

温馨提示 理解物体内能时，要注意以下三点：
(1)内能是指物体的内能，不是分子的内能，不能说内能是个别分子和少数分子所具有的。内能是物体内部所有分子具有的动能和势能的总和，所以，单纯考虑一个分子的动能和势能是没有现实意义的。(2)任何物体在任何情况下都有内能。(3)内能具有不可测性。只能比较物体内能的大小，不能确定这个物体具有的内能究竟是多少。因为内能是物体的所有分子具有的总能量，宏观量度比较困难。

例 下列说法正确的是 （ ）
A.物体的内能增加，则一定是外界对物体做了功
B.物体的温度升高，则一定是从外界吸收了热量
C.物体的温度越高，含有的热量越多
D.内能是物体内所有分子动能和势能的总和

解析 物体温度升高，内能增加，改变物体的内能有做功和热传递两种途径，所以A、B两项错。热量是热传递过程中的物理量，它是个过程量，所以不能说含有热量，C项错。D项表述正确。

答案 D

知识 2 影响内能的因素

1.温度是影响物体内能最主要的因素，同一个物体，温度越高，它具有的内能就越大。

2.物体的内能还受质量、体积、状态等因素的影响。如冰熔化过程中，虽然温度没有变化，但物体吸热后，其状态由固态变成了液态，内能增加。

例 桶的容积大，杯的容积小，当它们均装满水时，下列说法正确的是 （ ）
A.一桶开水的内能一定比一杯开水的内能多
B.一桶开水的内能一定比一桶凉水的内能少
C.一桶开水的热量一定比一杯开水的热量多
D.一桶开水的热量一定比一桶凉水的热量少

解析 内能大小与质量、温度等因素有关系。对于同一物质，在温度一定时，质量越大，具有的内能越多；对于同一物体，质量一定，温度越高，具有的内能越多。因此，一桶开水一定比一杯开水内能多，A项正确；一桶开水一定比一桶凉水内能多，B项错误。不能说物体含有或具有多少热量，只能说吸收或放出多少热量，C、D项错误。

答案 A

知识 3 改变物体内能的两种方式

1.热传递可以改变物体的内能

(1)热传递：温度不同的物体互相接触，低温物体温度升高、高温物体温度降低的过程叫做热传递。如图所示。

铁锅烫手是由于热传递使铁锅内能增加，温度升高

序号	公式	应用	各物理量及单位			
1	$v=\dfrac{s}{t}$	可求物体的速度、路程和时间	物理量	速度(v)	路程(s)	时间(t)
			主单位	m/s	m	s
			常用单位	km/h	km	h
2	$\rho=\dfrac{m}{V}$	可求物体的密度、质量和体积	物理量	密度(ρ)	质量(m)	体积(V)
			主单位	kg/m³	kg	m³
			常用单位	g/cm³	g	cm³
3	$G=mg$	可求物体的重力和质量	物理量	重力(G)	质量(m)	重力与质量的比值(g)
			主单位	N	kg	N/kg
4	方向相同 $F_合=F_1+F_2$ 方向相反 $F_合=F_1-F_2$	可求同一直线上的合力和分力	物理量	合力、分力($F_合$、F)		
			主单位	N		
5	$F_浮=G_排=\rho_液gV_排$	可求物体受到的浮力、液体密度和物体排开液体的体积	物理量	浮力($F_浮$) / 排开液体受到的重力($G_排$) / 液体密度($\rho_液$) / 排开液体的体积($V_排$)		
			主单位	N / N / kg/m³ / m³		
6	$p=\rho gh$	可求液体的压强、密度和深度	物理量	压强(p)	液体密度(ρ)	深度(h)
			主单位	Pa	kg/m³	m
7	$p=\dfrac{F}{S}$	可求物体的压强、压力和受力面积	物理量	压强(p)	压力(F)	受力面积(S)
			主单位	Pa	N	m²
8	$F_1L_1=F_2L_2$	可求作用在杠杆上的力和力臂	物理量	动力、阻力(F_1、F_2)	动力臂、阻力臂(L_1、L_2)	
			主单位	N	m	
9	$W=Fs$	可求做功的多少、力和力的方向上通过的距离	物理量	功(W)	作用在物体上的力(F)	在力的方向上通过的距离(s)
			主单位	J	N	m
10	$P=\dfrac{W}{t}$	可求功率、功和做功时间	物理量	功率(P)	功(W)	时间(t)
			主单位	W	J	s
			常用单位	kW	kW·h	h
11	$\eta=\dfrac{W_有}{W_总}\times100\%$	可求机械效率、有用功和总功	物理量	机械效率(η)	有用功($W_有$)	总功($W_总$)
			主单位	无单位	J	J
12	$I=\dfrac{Q}{t}$	可求导体中的电流、电荷量和时间	物理量	电流(I)	电荷量(Q)	时间(t)
			主单位	A	C	s
13	$I=\dfrac{U}{R}$	可求电路中的电流、电压和电阻	物理量	电流(I)	电压(U)	电阻(R)
			主单位	A	V	Ω
14	$R_串=R_1+R_2+\cdots+R_n$	可求串联电路的总电阻和各部分电阻	物理量	电阻(R)		
			主单位	Ω		
15	$\dfrac{1}{R_并}=\dfrac{1}{R_1}+\dfrac{1}{R_2}+\cdots+\dfrac{1}{R_n}$ $R_并=\dfrac{R_1R_2}{R_1+R_2}$	可求并联电路的总电阻和各支路电阻	物理量	电阻(R)		
			主单位	Ω		
16	$W=UIt$	可求电功、电压、电流和时间	物理量	电功(W)	电压(U) / 电流(I)	时间(t)
			主单位	J	V / A	s
17	$P=UI$	可求电功率、电压和电流	物理量	电功率(P)	电压(U)	电流(I)
			主单位	W	V	A
18	$Q=I^2Rt$	可求电热、电阻、电流和时间	物理量	电热(Q)	电流(I)	电阻(R) / 时间(t)
			主单位	J	A	Ω / s
19	$Q=mq$	可求燃料完全燃烧放出的热量、燃料质量和热值	物理量	热量(Q)	质量(m)	热值(q)
			主单位	J	kg	J/kg
20	$Q=cm\Delta t$	可求物体吸收或放出的热量、比热容、质量和温度变化量	物理量	热量(Q)	比热容(c) / 质量(m)	温度变化量(Δt)
			主单位	J	J/(kg·℃) / kg	℃
21	$c=\lambda f$	可求真空中电磁波的速度、波长和频率	物理量	真空中电磁波的速度(c)	波长(λ)	频率(f)
			主单位	m/s	m	Hz

物理量	常见物体	数值
长度	分子直径	约 10^{-10} m
	头发直径	约 70 μm
	成年人腿长	约 1 m
	课桌高	约 0.8 m
	普通教室长	约 10 m
	住宅楼一层楼高	约 3 m
	1光年	约 9.46×10^{15} m
速度	人步行	约 1.1 m/s
	中学生长跑	约 5 m/s
	自行车	约 5 m/s
	小汽车正常行驶	约 20 m/s
	通常情况下空气中的声速	340 m/s
	真空中光和电磁波的速度	3×10^{8} m/s
时间	人耳能够把回声跟原声区分开的时间	大于0.1 s
	1 小时	3 600 s
面积	成人单只脚底面积	约250 cm²
质量	一元硬币	6 g
	一个鸡蛋	约 50 g
	一瓶矿泉水	约 600 g
	一位中学生	约 50 kg
密度	水	1.0×10^{3} kg/m³
	人体	约1×10^{3} kg/m³
	空气	1.29 kg/m³
	冰	0.9×10^{3} kg/m³
	汞(水银)	13.6×10^{3} kg/m³
体积	人	约 0.05 m³
	教室	约 180 m³
力	2个鸡蛋的重力	约 1 N
	一位中学生的重力	约 500 N

物理量	常见物体	数值
压强	一张报纸平放时对桌面的压强	约为0.5 Pa
	人站立时对地面的压强	约为10^4 Pa
	大气压强	10^5 Pa
	标准大气压	1.013×10^5 Pa
电荷量	一个电子带的电荷量	1.6×10^{-19}C
电流	计算器	约100 μA
	普通照明白炽灯	约 0.2 A
	空调	约5 A
电压	1节干电池的电压	1.5 V
	一节蓄电池的电压	2 V
	人体安全电压	不高于36 V
	我国家庭电路电压	220 V
	我国工业动力电压	380 V
电功率	计算器	约0.5 mW
	日常用节能灯	20W左右
	电冰箱平均功率	约 100 W
	洗衣机	约 500 W
	空调	约1 000 W
	电热水器	约 3 000 W
比热容	水	4.2×10^3 J/(kg·℃)
温度	人体正常温度	约37 ℃
	体温计的刻度范围	35~42 ℃
	标准大气压下冰水混合物的温度	0 ℃
	标准大气压下水的沸点	100 ℃
频率	人耳听觉范围	20 ~20 000 Hz
	我国交流电频率	50 Hz
声音响度	保证休息和睡眠	不超过50 dB
	保证正常工作和学习	不超过70 dB

单位换算

- 时间 1 h = 60 min, 1 min = 60 s
- 长度 1 m = 10^3 mm = 10^6 μm（微米）= 10^9 nm（纳米）
- 面积 1 m² = 10^2 dm² = 10^4 cm² = 10^6 mm²
- 体积 1 m³ = 10^3 dm³(升L) = 10^6 cm³（毫升mL）= 10^9 mm³
- 密度 1×10^3 kg/m³ = 1 g/cm³
- 速度 1 m/s = 3.6 km/h
- 电能 1度(电) = 1 kW·h = 3.6×10^6 J

丙

丁

棉被晒热是由于热传递使棉被内能增加,温度升高

（2）热传递的条件:物体之间存在着温度差。

（3）热传递的方向:内能从高温物体传递到低温物体。

（4）热传递的结果:高温物体内能减少,低温物体内能增加,直至物体的温度相同为止。

> **易混对比**
>
> **热传递过程中传递的是温度还是内能**
>
> （1）热传递中传递的是内能,而不是传递温度,更不是传递某种热的物质。
>
> （2）热传递是把内能由温度高的物体传给温度低的物体,不是由内能多的物体传给内能少的物体。
>
> （3）同一物体的不同部分之间若存在温度差,也可以进行热传递。

2.做功可以改变物体的内能

（1）对物体做功,物体的内能会增加。

（2）物体对外做功,物体的内能会减少。

（3）做功改变物体内能的实例

①向下压活塞时(图甲),活塞压缩玻璃筒内空气,对筒内空气做了功。棉花燃烧表明筒内空气的温度升高了,也就是说,筒内空气的内能增加了。在压缩活塞的过程中,机械能转化为内能。

②将一根铁丝快速反复弯折数十次(图乙),铁丝弯折处就会发热,表明铁丝弯折处的温度升高,铁丝的内能增大,铁丝内能的增大是由于人对铁丝做了功。

③小孩从滑梯上滑下时(图丙),感觉臀部发烫是因为人与滑梯间存在摩擦,克服摩擦做功,人的内能增加,温度升高。

④用气筒向装有少量水的瓶里打气(图丁),瓶塞跳出时,瓶内气体对外做功,内能减少,温度降低,水蒸气液化,瓶口出现白雾。

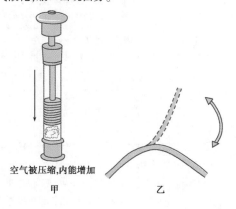

空气被压缩,内能增加

甲　　　　　乙

> **温馨提示**
>
> （1）做功和热传递是改变物体内能的两种方式;做功是其他形式的能和内能的相互转化,热传递是内能的转移;两种方式对改变物体内能是等效的。
>
> （2）做功不一定会使物体的内能发生变化。如举高物体时,做功所消耗的能量转化为物体的势能,而不是转化为物体的内能,所以物体的内能就没有改变。

知识 4　热量

定义	在热传递过程中,传递能量的多少叫做热量
单位	焦耳(J)
符号	Q
表达方式	吸收热量、放出热量

> **温馨提示**
>
> （1）热量是指热传递过程中所改变的内能,热量是一个过程量,是一个变化量(如图)。我们不能说一个物体"具有多少热量"、"含有多少热量",而只能说一个物体"放出了多少热量"或"吸收了多少热量"。
>
> （2）热量的多少与物体内能的多少、物体温度的高低无关,而与热传递过程中传递内能的多少有关。

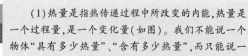

> **例** 下列关于热量的说法中,正确的是　　（　）
>
> A.温度高的物体比温度低的物体含有的热量多
>
> B.温度从高温物体转移到低温物体
>
> C.热量总是从内能大的物体传向内能小的物体
>
> D.热量从高温物体传递到低温物体
>
> **（解析）** 热量是表示热传递过程中传递内能多少的物理量,是个过程量,不能说含有热量,A错;热传递中传递的是热量,而不是温度,B错;热传递的方向是从高温物体传向低温物体,而不是从内能大的物体传到内能小的物体,C错误,D正确。
>
> **（答案）** D

拓展知识 **知识** "热"字的含义

知识 "热"字的含义

1.温度、热量和内能是热学中三个基本的物理量,在日常生活中都用"热"来表示,但三者的实质又有不同,十分容易混淆。温度描述了物体的冷热程度,热量描述了热传递过程中物体内能的变化量,内能描述了物体内所有分子所具有能量的多少。

2.理解多变的"热"字

(1)"天气热"表示气温高,这里的"热"指温度。

(2)"摩擦生热"表示用摩擦做功的方式消耗了机械能,增加了内能,这里的"热"指内能。

(3)"热运动"是指大量分子的无规则运动,这里的"热"跟温度有关。

(4)"热膨胀"指温度升高时体积增大,这里的"热"跟温度有关。

例 夏天中午天气真热,这个"热"字表示_____;摩擦生热,这个"热"字表示_____;煤燃烧时,向外放热,这个"热"字表示_____。

解析 日常生活中的"热"与物理学中的"热"区别很大,"热"字用在不同的地方其含义也不同。温度是表示物体冷热程度的物理量,天气的冷热,当然也就是温度的高低;摩擦时是克服阻力做功,机械能转化为内能,因此摩擦生热的"生"字指的是转化,而"热"字表示的是内能;煤燃烧时向外放热,放热指的是内能的转移,所以这里"热"字是指热量。

答案 温度 内能 热量

方法清单
方法1 比较法区别对物体做功和物体对外做功
方法2 概念法区别温度、内能和热量

方法 1 比较法区别对物体做功和物体对外做功

1.做功改变物体内能的实质是能量的转化,即内能的变化是由于内能与机械能之间的相互转化引起的。

2.对物体做功时机械能转化为内能,则物体内能增加;物体对外做功时内能转化为机械能,则物体内能减少。

例 如图所示,对于图片中所描述的物理过程,下列分析中正确的是 ( )

A.图甲:厚玻璃筒内的空气被压缩时,空气的内能减少

B.图乙:瓶子内的空气推动塞子跳起时,空气的内能增大

C.图丙:试管内的水蒸气推动塞子冲出时,水蒸气的内能减少

D.图丁:汽缸内的气体使活塞向下运动时,气体的内能增大

解析 甲图厚玻璃筒内的空气被压缩时,其内能增大,温度升高,A项错误;乙图瓶内气体推动塞子跳起时,对塞子做功,瓶内气体的内能减少,温度降低,B项错误;丙图试管内水蒸气推动塞子冲出时,对塞子

做功,水蒸气内能减少,温度降低,C项正确;同理D项错误。故选C。

答案 C

方法 2 概念法区别温度、内能和热量

	温度	内能	热量
定义	宏观上:表示物体的冷热程度;微观上:反映物体中大量分子无规则运动的剧烈程度	物体内所有分子动能和分子势能的总和	热传递过程中传递能量的多少
性质	状态量	状态量	过程量
表述	降低(到)、升高(到)	具有、改变、增加、减少	放出、吸收
单位	℃	J	J
关系	①一个物体温度升高了,内能一定增加,可能是吸收了热量,也可能是外界对物体做了功。②一个物体内能增加了,它的温度不一定升高,如0 ℃的冰变成0 ℃的水		

例 有关温度、热量、内能的说法,正确的是 ( )

A.物体吸收热量,内能一定增加,同时温度一定升高

B.物体温度升高,不一定吸收热量,但内能一定增加

C.物体温度升高,内能不一定增加,但一定吸收热量

D.发生热传递时,热量总是从内能大的物体传递到内能小的物体

解析 物体吸收热量,内能一定增加,但温度并不一定升高,如晶体熔化吸热,内能增加,但温度不变,故A项错误;物体温度升高,不一定吸收热量,可能是外界对它做了功,但内能一定增加,故B项正确;

物体温度升高,内能一定增加,C 项错误;发生热传递时,热量总是从温度高的物体传递给温度低的物体,但温度高的物体内能不一定大,D 项错误。

第3节　比热容

知识清单

基础知识 | 知识**1** 比热容　　知识**2** 水的比热容
知识**3** 热平衡方程

知识 **1** 比热容

1.定义:一定质量的某种物质,在温度升高(或降低)时吸收(或放出)的热量与它的质量和升高(或降低)的温度乘积之比,叫做这种物质的比热容。

2.公式及单位:公式: $c = \dfrac{Q}{m \cdot \Delta t}$;单位:J/(kg·℃)。

3.比热容的理解

(1)比热容是物质的一种特性:a.质量相等的不同物质,在升高(或降低)的温度相同时,吸收(或放出)的热量一般是不同的;b.不同的物质,比热容一般不同。

(2)比热容是物质的一种属性:a.比热容不随质量改变而改变;b.比热容与温度及温度变化无关;c.比热容与物质吸热或放热的多少无关。

(3)比热容与状态有关:状态改变,比热容改变。

(4)比热容是反映物质吸热或放热能力大小的物理量:在同样受热或冷却的情况下,质量相同的不同物质,当吸收或放出同样热量时,比热容较大的物质温度变化较小,比热容较小的物质温度变化较大(如图)。

好烫!

水里凉快

吸收相同的热量,由于沙子的比热容较小,故升高的温度高

例　下表列出由实验测定的几种物质的比热容[× 10^3 J/(kg·℃)]:

物质	比热容	物质	比热容
水	4.2	干泥土	0.84
酒精	2.4	铜	0.39
冰	2.1	铝	0.88

续表

物质	比热容	物质	比热容
煤油	2.1	铅	0.13
水银	0.14	沙石	约 0.92

认真阅读上表,你一定能有所发现。请填出其中的任意 4 条。

(1)_____;
(2)_____;
(3)_____;
(4)_____。

(解析) 由表可看出,不同物质的比热容一般不同,说明比热容是物质的一种特性;其中水的比热容最大;比较冰和煤油可知,不同物质,比热容也可能相同;比较水和冰可知,同种物质,状态不同,比热容不同。

(答案) (1)比热容是物质的一种特性,每种物质都有自己的比热容

(2)同种物质的不同状态,比热容不同

(3)水的比热容最大

(4)不同物质比热容可能相同

知识 **2** 水的比热容

1.水的比热容表示的意义

水的比热容为 4.2×10^3 J/(kg·℃),表示的意义:1 千克水温度升高(或降低)1 摄氏度所吸收(或放出)的热量是 4.2×10^3 焦耳。

2.水的比热容的应用

水的比热容对人们的日常生活和生产具有重要意义,主要表现在两个方面。

(1)冷却或取暖。由于水的比热容较大,在一般情况下,一定质量的水升高(或降低)一定的温度而吸收(或放出)的热量比相同质量的其他物质升高(或降低)相同的温度而吸收(或放出)的热量多,所以我们利用水作为冷却剂或利用水来取暖(如图)。作为冷却剂时,是让水吸收更多的热量;用来取暖时,是让水放出更多的热量。

用冷水冷却汽车发动机　　用热水取暖

（2）调节气温。由于水的比热容较大，一定质量的水吸收（或放出）较多的热量而自身的温度却改变不多，这一点有利于调节气温。夏天，太阳照在海面上，海水在温度升高的过程中吸收大量的热量，所以住在海边的人们并不觉得特别热；冬天，气温降低了，海水由于温度降低而放出大量的热量，使沿海气温不致降得太低，所以沿海地区比内陆地区昼夜温差小。

知识 3　热平衡方程

两个温度不同的物体放在一起，高温物体放出热量，低温物体吸收热量，当两个物体温度达到相同时，如果没有热量损失，则有 $Q_{吸}=Q_{放}$，称为热平衡方程。在热量计算题中，常采用此等式。

例 一质量为 2 kg 的金属块，被加热到 500 ℃ 后放入 1 kg、20 ℃ 的水中，不计热量损失，达到热平衡后，水和金属块的温度均为 80 ℃，求水吸收的热量和金属块的比热容各是多少？

解析 $Q_{吸}=c_{水}\,m_{水}(t-t_1)$
$\quad=4.2\times10^3\ \text{J}/(\text{kg}\cdot℃)\times1\ \text{kg}\times(80\ ℃-20\ ℃)$
$\quad=2.52\times10^5\ \text{J}$

$Q_{放}=Q_{吸}$

$c_{金}=\dfrac{Q_{放}}{m_{金}(t_2-t)}=0.3\times10^3\ \text{J}/(\text{kg}\cdot℃)$

答案 2.52×10^5 J　0.3×10^3 J/(kg·℃)

拓展知识　知识 比热容和热量的区别与联系

知识　比热容和热量的区别与联系

	比热容	热量
概念	一定质量的某种物质，在温度升高时吸收的热量与它的质量和升高的温度乘积之比	在热传递过程中，传递内能的多少
单位	J/(kg·℃)	J
有关因素	只与物质的种类、状态有关，而与质量、温度、热量无关	与比热容、质量、温度的改变量有关
联系	$Q=cm\Delta t$	

例 由公式 $Q=cm\Delta t$，可得：$c=\dfrac{Q}{m\Delta t}$。下列有关此表达式意义的说法中正确的是（　　）

A.物质的比热容大小与吸收或放出的热量成正比

B.物质的比热容大小与它的质量大小成反比

C.物质的比热容大小与它的温度改变量成反比

D.物质的比热容大小可以用此表达式来量度，但与物质吸收或放出热量的多少、质量的大小和温度改变的多少（或是否改变）无关

解析 表达式 $c=\dfrac{Q}{m\Delta t}$ 是比热容的定义式，比热容在数值上等于单位质量的某种物质温度升高（或降低）1 ℃ 所吸收（或放出）的热量。因此，此表达式可以用来量度物质比热容的大小，但比热容是物质本身的一种属性，在物质的种类和状态一定时，比热容 c 的大小与 Q、m、Δt 无关，它总是一个确定的数值。故选项 D 是正确的。

答案 D

方法清单

方法1　控制变量法探究物质吸热与哪些因素有关
方法2　公式法计算物体吸收或放出的热量
方法3　比热容相关比值问题的求法

方法 1　控制变量法探究物质吸热与哪些因素有关

1.物质吸收热量的多少与质量、升高的温度和物质种类都有关系，因此应用控制变量法进行探究，只让其中一个因素改变而其他因素保持不变，这样可使研究的问题简单化。

2.在探究物质吸收热量的多少与质量关系时，需控制物质种类相同，升高的温度相同；探究物质吸收热量的多少与升高的温度的关系时，需控制物质种类和质量相同；探究物质吸收热量的多少与物质种类的关系时，需控制质量和升高的温度相同。

例 如图所示是"比较不同物质的吸热情况"的实验装置，烧杯中装有质量相同、初温相同的两种液体 A 和 B，将规格相同的电加热器分别浸没在两种液体中，同时加热。用停表测出液体加热到相同温度时所用的时间。下表是小明记录的实验数据。

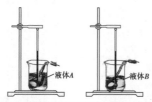

液体	质量/g	初温/℃	加热时间/s	末温/℃
A	60	20	80	45
B	60	20	120	45

（1）上述实验中,加热时间较长的液体,其比热容较_____（填"大"或"小"）。

（2）小红想用与小明不同的方法进行实验,则她在实验中应控制_____（填"加热时间"或"升高温度"）相同。

（解析）（1）在该实验中,A、B两种液体的温度变化相同,质量相同,加热时间较长的液体吸收的热量较多,根据 $c=\dfrac{Q}{m\Delta t}$,$m\Delta t$ 相同时,Q 越大,该物质的比热容越大。

（2）本实验应采用控制变量法,小明控制了质量和温度的变化相同,通过加热时间（吸收的热量）的长短来比较吸热能力;小红想用与小明不同的方法进行实验,所以小红应控制质量和加热时间（吸收的热量）相同,通过比较温度的变化来比较吸热能力。

（答案）（1）大 （2）加热时间

（点拨） 题中通过比较加热时间长短来判断物质吸热多少,用到了转换法。

方法 2 公式法计算物体吸收或放出的热量

1.热量计算公式（在没有发生状态变化的情况下）

（1）当物体的温度升高时,吸收的热量是:
$Q_{吸}=cm(t-t_0)$。

（2）当物体的温度降低时,放出的热量是:
$Q_{放}=cm(t_0-t)$。

公式中 c 表示物质的比热容,m 表示物体的质量,t_0 表示物体的初温,t 表示物体的末温,$t-t_0$ 表示物体吸热时升高的温度,t_0-t 表示物体放热时降低的温度。

（3）若温度的变化量用 Δt 表示,那么吸、放热公式可统一表示为:$Q=cm\Delta t$。

2.热量公式的变形式

利用热量的计算公式,不仅可以计算物体吸收（或放出）热量的多少,还可以计算物质的比热容、质量、温度变化等。计算式为:$c=\dfrac{Q}{m\Delta t}$,$m=\dfrac{Q}{c\Delta t}$,$\Delta t=\dfrac{Q}{mc}$。

（例） 水稻是喜温植物,春季育秧时,农民通常在傍晚向秧田灌水,早晨再将水放出,以防霜冻,这是因为水的_____较大,当气温降低时,水能放出较多的热量。如果某秧田中水的温度降低了2 ℃,放出了3.36×10^7 J的热量,则该秧田内的水的质量为_____kg。［已知 $c_{水}=4.2\times10^3$ J/(kg·℃)］

（解析） 由于水的比热容较大,在质量相同的条件下,当气温降低时,水能放出较多的热量,可以防止秧田温度下降过多而霜冻;由 $Q_{放}=cm\Delta t$ 得,水的质量

$m=\dfrac{Q_{放}}{c\Delta t}=\dfrac{3.36\times10^7\ \text{J}}{4.2\times10^3\ \text{J/(kg·℃)}\times2\ \text{℃}}=4\times10^3$ kg。

（答案） 比热容 4×10^3

方法 3 比热容相关比值问题的求法

求某些物理量之比的问题常以填空或选择题的形式出现,解题时,如能正确应用比例关系,即可快速求出正确答案。

（例） 有甲、乙两物体,质量之比 $m_{甲}:m_{乙}=5:3$,比热容之比 $c_{甲}:c_{乙}=2:1$,如果它们放出相同的热量,则它们降低的温度之比 $\Delta t_{甲}:\Delta t_{乙}=$_____。

（解析）方法一:由 $Q=cm\Delta t$ 得 $\Delta t=\dfrac{Q}{cm}$,

所以 $\dfrac{\Delta t_{甲}}{\Delta t_{乙}}=\dfrac{Q_{甲}/c_{甲}\ m_{甲}}{Q_{乙}/c_{乙}\ m_{乙}}=\dfrac{Q_{甲}}{Q_{乙}}\cdot\dfrac{c_{乙}}{c_{甲}}\dfrac{m_{乙}}{m_{甲}}=\dfrac{3}{10}$。

方法二:

$\Delta t_{比}=\dfrac{\Delta t_{甲}}{\Delta t_{乙}}=\dfrac{Q_{甲}/Q_{乙}}{(m_{甲}/m_{乙})\cdot(c_{甲}/c_{乙})}=\dfrac{Q_{比}}{m_{比}\cdot c_{比}}$

$m_{比}=\dfrac{5}{3}$,$c_{比}=\dfrac{2}{1}$,$Q_{比}=\dfrac{1}{1}$

$\Delta t_{比}=\dfrac{Q_{比}}{c_{比}\cdot m_{比}}=\dfrac{3}{10}$。

方法三:设 $m_{甲}=5$,$m_{乙}=3$,$c_{甲}=2$,$c_{乙}=1$,$Q_{甲}=Q_{乙}=Q$

则 $\Delta t_{甲}=\dfrac{Q_{甲}}{c_{甲}\ m_{甲}}=\dfrac{Q}{5\times2}=\dfrac{Q}{10}$

$\Delta t_{乙}=\dfrac{Q_{乙}}{c_{乙}\ m_{乙}}=\dfrac{Q}{1\times3}=\dfrac{Q}{3}$

$\dfrac{\Delta t_{甲}}{\Delta t_{乙}}=\dfrac{Q/10}{Q/3}=\dfrac{3}{10}$

（答案） 3:10

第4节 热机

知识清单

知识 **1** 热机

1.内能的利用:一是直接用来加热物体,如烧水、做饭等;二是用来做功,如水烧开后,壶内水蒸气将壶盖顶起来。

2.热机

(1)热机定义:利用内能做功的机械。

(2)热机原理:

化学能 $\xrightarrow{\text{燃料燃烧}}$ 内能 $\xrightarrow{\text{做功}}$ 机械能

(3)热机种类:蒸汽机、内燃机、汽轮机、喷气发动机等。

知识 **2** 内燃机、冲程及工作循环

1.内燃机:燃料直接在发动机汽缸内燃烧产生动力的热机叫内燃机,内燃机分为汽油机和柴油机。它们的特点是让燃料在汽缸内燃烧,从而使燃烧更充分,热损失更小,热效率较高,内能利用率较大。

2.冲程:活塞在汽缸内往复运动时,从汽缸的一端运动到另一端的过程,叫做一个冲程。

3.工作原理:四冲程内燃机的工作过程是由吸气、压缩、做功、排气四个冲程组成的。四个冲程为一个工作循环,在一个工作循环中,活塞往复两次,曲轴转动两周。四个冲程中,只有做功冲程燃气对外做功,其他三个冲程靠安装在曲轴上的飞轮的惯性来完成。

知识 **3** 汽油机的工作过程

	进气门开关	排气门开关	活塞运动	曲轴运动	冲程的作用	能量的转化
吸气冲程	开	关	向下	半周	吸入汽油和空气的混合物	—
压缩冲程	关	关	向上	半周	燃料混合物被压缩,温度升高,压强增大	机械能→内能
做功冲程	关	关	向下	半周	燃料剧烈燃烧产生的高温高压的气体推动活塞向下运动,通过连杆带动曲轴转动,对外做功	内能→机械能
排气冲程	关	开	向上	半周	排出废气	—
说明	一个工作循环中,有两次内能与机械能的转化:压缩冲程中机械能转化为内能,做功冲程中内能转化为机械能					

例 如图所示,图 A、B、C、D 是四冲程汽油机的工作示意图,图 E、F 是演示实验的示意图,C 图是_____冲程,与它原理相同的是_____图所示的演示实验。汽油机的工作示意图中机械能转化为内能的冲程是_____图。(后两空选填字母)

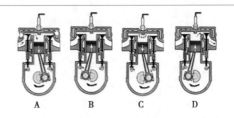

A B C D

E   F

解析 图 A、B、C、D 所示的四个冲程分别是:吸气冲程、压缩冲程、做功冲程和排气冲程。E 图所示的演示实验中空气被压缩时内能增大,与压缩冲程 B 的原理相同,压缩冲程中机械能转化为内能;F 图所示的演示实验中水蒸气的内能转化为活塞的机械能,与做功冲程 C 的原理相同。

答案 做功 F B

知识 4 柴油机和汽油机的区别

内燃机 项目	汽油机	柴油机
构造	汽缸顶部有火花塞	汽缸顶部有喷油嘴
燃料	汽油	柴油
吸气冲程	吸入的是汽油和空气的混合物	只吸入空气
点火方式	压缩冲程结束时,火花塞产生电火花点燃燃料,称为点燃式	压缩冲程结束时,喷油嘴向汽缸内喷出的雾状柴油遇到温度超过柴油燃点的空气便立刻燃烧,称为压燃式
效率	效率低 20%~30%	效率高 30%~45%
应用	轻便,主要用于汽车、飞机、摩托车等	机体笨重,主要用于载重汽车、火车、轮船等

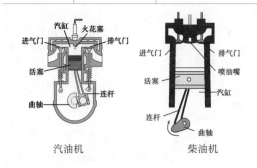

汽油机   柴油机

知识 5 燃料及热值

1.燃料

(1)定义:能够燃烧并且在燃烧时放出光和热的物质,叫做燃料。

燃料的燃烧是一种化学变化,在燃烧的过程中,燃料的化学能转化为内能,然后,内能转移到其他物体上或转化为其他形式的能量供人们使用。

(2)分类:按照状态,燃料可分为固体燃料(如煤炭、木材等)、液体燃料(如汽油、煤油、石油等)和气体燃料(如天然气、煤气、沼气等)。

2.燃料的热值

定义	某种燃料完全燃烧放出的热量与其质量之比
单位	J/kg 或 J/m³(气体)
意义	例:干木柴热值为 $1.2×10^7$ J/kg 表示 1 kg 干木柴完全燃烧放出的热量是 $1.2×10^7$ J
燃料燃烧放热公式	$Q_{放}=mq$ 或 $Q_{放}=V·q$ m 代表质量,单位 kg V 代表体积,单位 m³ q 代表热值,单位 J/kg $Q_{放}$ 代表放出的热量,单位 J

(1)燃料的热值与燃料的种类有关,热值反映的是所有能燃烧的物质的一种性质,反映了不同燃料在燃烧过程中,化学能转化为内能本领的大小。燃料的热值只与燃料的种类有关,与燃料的形态、质量、体积以及是否完全燃烧无关。

同样烧开一壶水,需要不同质量的燃料,说明不同种类的燃料热值不同。

(2)"完全燃烧"的含义是烧完、烧尽,若该燃料在燃烧时没有完全燃烧,放出的热量就比对应的热值小。

例 一个成年人参加一次长跑,身体消耗的能量为 $6.6×10^6$ J,这些能量相当于完全燃烧0.55 kg的干木柴才能得到,则干木柴的热值为_____J/kg。干木柴用掉一半后,剩余干木柴的热值将_____(选填"变大"、"变小"或"不变")。

解析 干木柴的热值 $q=\dfrac{Q}{m}=\dfrac{6.6×10^6 \text{ J}}{0.55 \text{ kg}}=1.2×10^7$ J/kg。热值是燃料的特性,它的大小只与燃料的种类有关,不受质量改变的影响。

答案 $1.2×10^7$ 不变

知识 6 热机的效率

1.燃料的有效利用

(1)燃料的利用率:有效利用的热量与燃料完全燃烧释放的总能量的比值,叫燃料的利用率;计算公式为 $\eta = \dfrac{Q_{利用}}{Q_{放}}$。

(2)影响燃料利用率的因素:

①未燃烧完全的部分;②高温烟气带走的热量;③被容器、炉具、周围的空气等吸收的热量。

(3)提高燃料利用率的途径:

①让燃料充分燃烧,如将煤炭磨成粉状,吹入炉内燃烧;②要减少热量的散失,如加大受热面积等。

2.热机的效率

(1)热机中燃料燃烧能量走向示意图:

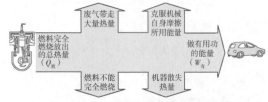

(2)热机的效率:用来做有用功的那部分能量与燃料完全燃烧放出的能量之比,叫热机的效率;计算公式为 $\eta = \dfrac{W_{有}}{Q_{放}}$。

(3)提高热机效率的途径:

①使燃料完全燃烧;②保证良好润滑,减小机械摩擦;③采用先进技术,改变机械结构;④减少各种热量散失。

例 某家庭用燃气热水器将质量为 100 kg、温度为 20 ℃的自来水加热到 50 ℃,消耗的天然气体积为 1 m³(假设天然气完全燃烧)。已知水的比热容为 $4.2×10^3$ J/(kg·℃),天然气的热值为 $3.2×10^7$ J/m³。求:

(1)天然气完全燃烧放出的热量;

(2)水吸收的热量;

(3)该热水器工作时的效率。

解析 (1)天然气完全燃烧放出的热量:

$Q_{放} = qV = 3.2×10^7×1 \text{ J} = 3.2×10^7 \text{ J}$

(2)水吸收的热量:

$Q_{吸} = cm\Delta t = 4.2×10^3×100×(50-20) \text{ J} = 1.26×10^7 \text{ J}$

(3)热水器工作时的效率:

$\eta = \dfrac{Q_{吸}}{Q_{放}}×100\% = \dfrac{1.26×10^7}{3.2×10^7}×100\% ≈ 39\%$

答案 见解析

拓展知识 知识 温室效应和热岛效应

知识 温室效应和热岛效应

1.温室效应

温室效应指的是地球表面大气中二氧化碳含量增加,吸收部分的太阳辐射能量后,转化成内能释放到地球表面而不能散去,于是造成地表温度升高的效应。

2.热岛效应

(1)热岛效应是由于人们改变城市地表而引起气候变化的综合现象,是城市气候最明显特征之一。

(2)引起城市"热岛效应"的主要原因有:①工厂、交通工具等排放出大量的热量;②城市的建筑物、马路上的砂石的比热容小,相同日照条件下升温快;③城市中水少,使热量不能被充分吸收;④楼群林立,难以形成空气对流。

(3)主要的改善措施有:植树造林,建绿地和人工湖等。

例 城市中的气温通常比郊区的气温高一些,这种现象叫做城市的"热岛效应"。形成热岛效应的主要原因是人类的活动。

(1)举出两个例子,说明人类的一些活动可以引起热岛效应。

(2)提出两点切实可行的建议,用于改善热岛效应。

解析 人类活动对气候的影响,在城市中表现最为突出。城市人口密集,高楼密集,高速公路密集,工厂、汽车、家用电器等大量消耗能源,除造成大气污染外,释放出的废热进入大气,使城市年平均气温比郊区高出 1 ℃,甚至更多,在温度的空间分布上,城市犹如一个温暖的岛屿。城市中密集、高大的建筑物,是气流通行的障碍物,使城市中风速减小,由于城市的热岛效应,市区与郊区形成了一个昼夜相反的热力环流。近年来,由于城市建设的飞速发展,城市热岛效应越来越明显。扩大绿地面积,增加城市的人工湖面积等能改善热岛效应。

答案 (1)①汽车的普及导致汽车尾气的排放越来越多。

②工厂排放的大量废热进入大气。

(2)①扩大城市绿地面积。

②对工厂排放废气进行环保处理。

③设立无汽车日。

④减少家电的使用频率。(只要答出合理的两点即可)

方法　比较法区分汽油机、柴油机的工作过程

1.区分汽油机和柴油机时,要从构造上区别,有喷油嘴的是柴油机,有火花塞的是汽油机。

2.判断四个冲程的关键是看两个气门的开关情况和活塞的运动方向,具体情况如下表所示:

冲程	进气门	排气门	活塞运动方向
吸气冲程	打开	关闭	向下运动
压缩冲程	关闭	关闭	向上运动
做功冲程	关闭	关闭	向下运动
排气冲程	关闭	打开	向上运动

例 单缸四冲程内燃机的四个冲程的示意图如图所示,下列关于这种内燃机一个工作循环中四个冲程的顺序排列正确的是　　　(　　)

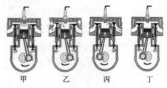

甲　　乙　　丙　　丁

A.丙、丁、乙、甲　　　B.乙、丁、甲、丙
C.乙、甲、丁、丙　　　D.甲、乙、丙、丁

解析 题图甲两气门关闭,活塞向下运动,火花塞点火,是做功冲程;题图乙进气门打开,排气门关闭,活塞向下运动,是吸气冲程;题图丙,进气门关闭,排气门打开,活塞向上运动,是排气冲程;题图丁两气门关闭,活塞向上运动,是压缩冲程。正确的排列顺序是:乙、丁、甲、丙,故选 B。

答案 B

第5节　能量的转化和守恒

知识清单

基础 知识	知识**1** 能量的形式 知识**2** 能量的转化和转移 知识**3** 能量守恒定律

知识 **1** 能量的形式

在自然界中,能量以多种形式存在,主要有机械能、内能、电磁能、化学能、核能等。

1.机械能:分动能和势能两类,机械能是物体所具有的动能和势能的和。

2.内能:物体内所有分子的动能和势能的和叫内能,与物体的温度、质量等因素有关。

3.电磁能:指的是储存在特定物体或空间中的能量。比如说,两个带电体相互靠近时会相互影响;通电导体在磁场中会受到力的作用;两块磁铁相互靠近,也会相互影响,其中都有电磁能。

4.化学能:是指由于化学反应,物质的分子结构发生变化而产生的能量。燃料燃烧产生的光和热以及蓄电池产生的电都是来源于燃料和蓄电池里储存的化学能。食物也具有化学能。

5.核能:是指由于核反应,物质的原子核结构发生变化而产生的能量。

知识 **2** 能量的转化和转移

1.能量转化和转移的比较

	解释	实例
能量的转化	能量由一种形式转变为另一种形式	①电灯发光:电能转化为光能和内能;②摩擦生热:机械能转化为内能;③光合作用:太阳能转化为化学能;④燃料燃烧:化学能转化为内能;⑤摩擦起电:机械能转化为电能
能量的转移	能量不经过变化直接由一个物体转移到另一个物体上	①碰撞时:动能从一个物体转移到另一个物体;②围着火炉烤火:内能从火炉转移到人体

2.能量转化和转移的方向性

能量的转化和能量的转移,都是有方向性的。①温度不同的两个物体接触后,一部分内能从高温物体转移到低温物体上,并不能自发地由低温物体转移到高温物体上;②燃料燃烧,化学能转化为内能,但此时得到的内能并不能自发地转化为燃料的化学能;③电流通过灯泡发光,电能转化为内能和光能,但是

这些内能和光能并不能自发地重新转化为电能；④汽车制动时，由于摩擦，机械能转化为内能，但这些内能并不能自发地转化为机械能并用来再次开动汽车。

例 如图所示，在试管内装一些水，用软木塞塞住，拿到酒精灯上加热，使水沸腾起来，水蒸气会使木塞冲出去，从能量转化和转移的角度，可用下面的三句话来概括：①水和水蒸气吸热，内能增大；②酒精的化学能转化为内能，传给水和水蒸气；③水蒸气对木塞做功，内能转化为木塞的机械能。以上三句话正确的顺序是 （ ）

A.①②③　　　　　　B.②③①
C.②①③　　　　　　D.③②①

解析 在这个实验中，酒精的燃烧过程是酒精的化学能转化为内能的过程，内能传给水和水蒸气使其温度升高，内能增大，当水蒸气使木塞冲出去时，水蒸气的内能转化为木塞的机械能，所以正确的顺序应是：②①③。

答案 C

知识 3 能量守恒定律

1.能量既不会凭空消灭，也不会凭空产生，它只会从一种形式转化为其他形式，或者从一个物体转移到其他物体，而在转化和转移的过程中，能量的总量保持不变。这就是能量守恒定律。

温馨提示 "能量不会凭空产生，也不会凭空消灭"，是指一个物体所具有的总能量发生了变化，必有另一个物体所具有的总能量同时发生了变化。自然界中能量的总量保持不变。

2.能量守恒定律是自然界中最基本的定律之一，不管是在哪里，也不管是什么物体，微观世界也好，宏观世界也好，能量守恒定律总是适用的。

例 如图所示，金属筒固定在桌子上，里面放些乙醚，用塞子塞紧，拿一根皮带在筒外绕一圈后迅速地来回拉皮带，此时金属筒的内能会增加，温度会升高，这时_____能转化为_____能。同时筒内乙醚的温度升高，内能增加，这是_____的结果。一会儿，筒口的塞子被气体推出，此时_____能转化成_____能，在此过程中_____保持不变。

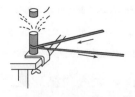

解析 来回拉皮带对筒壁做功，机械能转化为筒壁的内能。筒内的乙醚内能增加，这是筒壁的能量转移给乙醚的结果。气体膨胀做功把塞子推出，乙醚的内能转化为机械能，在此过程中能的总量保持不变。

答案 机械　内　能量转移　内　机械　能的总量

拓展知识　**知识** 单摆、滚摆的能量守恒

知识 单摆、滚摆的能量守恒

1.单摆

小球摆动时，势能与动能不断地相互转化着；小球在摆动过程中能量应该守恒，似乎小球应该永远运动下去，可事实上，小球的机械能不断减少，最终会停下来。这是为什么呢？原来，小球在运动过程中还要产生热。如果将内能一并计算进去，总的能量则是守恒的。

2.滚摆

与单摆类似，摆盘上下旋转过程中，势能和动能不断相互转化；摆盘运动过程中也产生热，机械能不断减少，最终会停下来，但总的能量是守恒的。

易混对比 能量守恒与机械能守恒
能量守恒定律是自然界的基本定律之一，宏观世界和微观世界都适用。
机械能守恒是指只有动能和势能相互转化的过程中，机械能总和保持不变。
对于单摆，理想情况下认为只有动能和势能相互转化。小球的机械能守恒；事实上，小球每次摆动到的高度都比上一次低一些，这是因为小球运动过程中还要产生热，有一部分机械能转化成了内能，机械能不断减少，但从能量守恒的角度讲，小球的机械能和转化成的内能总量是不变的。

方法　比较法判断能量的转化和转移

1.发生能量转移时,能量的形式不变;而发生能量转化时,能量的形式要发生改变。

2.在确定能量转化的方向时,可通过对消耗什么能和得到什么能进行比较来确定。

例　下面关于能量转化或转移的说法中,错误的是　　　　　　　　　　　　　　　　　（　　）

A.摩擦起电是将电能转化为机械能的过程

B.冬天将手放在炉旁烤火感到暖和,是内能从一个物体转移到另一个物体的过程

C.木柴燃烧是将化学能转化为内能的过程

D.打桩机的重锤下落的过程,是将重力势能转化为动能的过程

解析　摩擦起电是消耗了机械能,最终获得电能,因而是机械能转化为电能;烤火是将燃料燃烧后获得的内能转移给手,是内能的转移;木柴燃烧消耗了储存在木柴中的化学能,获得了内能,因而是化学能转化为内能;打桩机的重锤下落时,高度减小,重力势能减小,转化为重锤的动能。故 A 选项错误。

答案　A

第 6 节　能源与可持续发展

知识清单

基础知识

知识1 能源分类

知识2 核能和获得核能的途径

知识3 核裂变

知识4 核电站与核反应堆

知识5 核聚变(热核反应)

知识6 太阳能的利用及其优、缺点

知识7 能源与可持续发展

知识 1　能源分类

1.能源

凡是能够提供能量的物质资源都叫做能源。石油、天然气在燃烧时可以提供能量,它们是能源。水流和风可以提供能量,它们也是能源。

温馨提示　能源的利用过程,实质上是能量的转化或转移过程,但不能说能源就是能量。

2.能源分类

分类标准	类别	定义	举例
能否从自然界直接获取	一次能源	可以从自然界中直接获取的能源	水能、风能、太阳能、地热能、潮汐能、煤、石油、天然气等
	二次能源	无法从自然界中直接获取的能源	电能、汽油、柴油等

续表

分类标准	类别	定义	举例
是否可以再生	可再生能源	可以从自然界中源源不断地得到的能源	太阳能、水能、风能、生物质能等
	不可再生能源	短期内不可能从自然界得到补充的能源	煤、石油、天然气、核能等
利用的早晚	常规能源	人类已经利用了多年的能源	煤、石油、天然气等
	新能源	人类近期利用的能源	太阳能、地热能、潮汐能、风能、核能等

温馨提示　同一种能源可属于不同的能源类型,例如,水能既属于一次能源,也属于可再生能源。

例　下列说法正确的是　　　　　　　　　　　（　　）

A.电能是一次能源

B.风能是可再生能源

C.我国的煤炭取之不尽,用之也无污染

D.能量是守恒的,故不会有能源危机

解析　电能是由其他形式的能转化来的二次能源,A 错误;风能可以在短期内从自然界得到补充,是可再生能源,B 正确;煤炭是一种化石能源,化石能源会越用越少,且大量使用会造成环境污染,C 错误;能

量是守恒的,但可利用的能源是有限的,故 D 错误。
故选 B。

（答案）B

知识 2 核能和获得核能的途径

1.原子结构

2.核能:质子、中子依靠强大的核力紧密地结合在一起,一旦使原子核分裂或聚合,就可能释放出惊人的能量,这就是核能。

3.目前获得核能有两条途径:核裂变、核聚变。

4.核污染:核燃料产生核辐射,使用不当会对地球上的生物造成伤害。

知识 3 核裂变

1.核裂变:重核分裂成质量较小的核,释放出核能的反应称为核裂变。

2.链式反应:原子核持续裂变,并释放出大量的核能。如图。

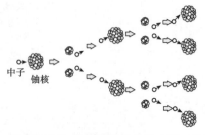

3.应用:原子弹、核电站的能量都来源于核裂变。如图为我国第一颗原子弹爆炸图。

我国第一颗原子弹爆炸

知识 4 核电站与核反应堆

1.核反应堆

核反应堆是产生核反应的装置,是核电站的核心。核反应堆一般由铀棒(核材料)、减速剂、控制棒和屏蔽物(水泥)等组成(如图)。用石墨或其他材料制成的减速剂使核反应产生的中子减速以提高核裂变的效率;控制棒的下部为阻挡中子的材料,用来控制链式反应的速度,如果希望加快反应速度就把控制棒拉出来一点,希望降低反应速度则推进控制棒。

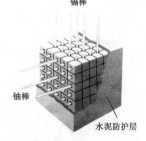

2.核电站工作原理

基本工作原理是这样的:核材料在反应堆内部发生核反应产生热量;冷却剂在反应堆中循环并将热量带入热交换器;水在热交换器中被加热成为蒸汽并输出用于推动蒸汽轮机,再带动发电机发电。核电站工作流程如图。

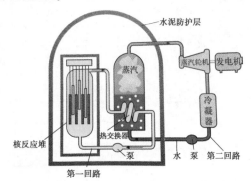

3.能量转化过程

核能──→水和水蒸气的内能──→蒸汽轮机的机械能──→电能。

温馨提示 原子弹和核反应堆中发生的都是核裂变,它们的区别是:原子弹爆炸时发生的链式反应是不加控制的;而通过核反应堆,可将链式反应的速度加以控制,使其平稳地释放出大量核能。

知识 5 核聚变(热核反应)

1.核聚变是产生核能的另一种方式。核聚变是较轻的原子核结合成为较重的原子核的一种反应。

**2.如图所示的是氘核和氚核结合成为氦核的聚变过程。这种核反应也会释放出巨大的能量。

3.利用核聚变反应也能制造核武器。氢弹就是利用核聚变原理制造的一种威力比原子弹还要大的核武器(如图)。

利用核聚变原理制造的氢弹
爆炸时产生巨大的蘑菇云

4.核聚变需要超高温度,因此核聚变也被称做热核反应。太阳内部发生的就是热核反应。

例 如图所示是太阳能 LED 照明路灯。它主要由太阳能电池板、LED 灯头等部分构成。LED 是一种发光二极管,通过电流能够发光,可以把电能直接转化成_____能。太阳能是_____能源(填"一次"或"二次"),清洁无污染,它是在太阳内部的氢原子核发生_____(选填"裂变"或"聚变")时释放出的核能。

(解析) 发光二极管通电发光,将电能转化为光能。太阳能是一次能源,在太阳内部每时每刻都发生着核聚变,释放大量的核能。

(答案) 光　一次　聚变

知识 6　太阳能的利用及其优、缺点

利用太阳能的三种方式	太阳能转化为内能	太阳能热水器
	太阳能转化为电能	太阳能电池
	太阳能转化为化学能	植物进行光合作用
太阳能的优点	完全清洁、无污染,并且取之不尽,用之不竭	
太阳能的缺点	太阳能太分散,收集和转换系统过于庞大,因而造价高;随气候、季节变化,不稳定,转换效率低	

知识 7　能源与可持续发展

1.21 世纪的能源趋势:虽然能量是守恒的,但能量的转化和转移是有方向的。随着能源消耗的迅速增长,化石能源将会枯竭。必须提高能源的利用率,节约能源,同时不断开发新能源,才能解决能源危机。

2.能源的消耗对环境的影响:利用化石能源会造成空气污染,加剧温室效应,形成酸雨,对植物、建筑物、金属构件造成危害;核泄漏会对人类和其他生物造成伤害。

3.解决能源问题的出路:一是提高能源的利用率;二是开发和利用新能源,特别是开发和利用太阳能和核能。

4.未来的理想能源必须满足如下条件:
①足够丰富,可以保证长期使用;
②足够便宜,可以保证多数人用得起;
③相关技术成熟,可以保证大规模使用;
④足够安全、清洁,可以保证不会严重影响环境。

拓展知识　知识❶ 能源之母——太阳能
　　　　　知识❷ 其他新能源

知识 1　能源之母——太阳能

1.太阳主要由最轻的元素——氢构成,其表面的温度高达 6 000 ℃,核心的温度高达 1 500 万摄氏度。

2.数十亿年来,太阳一直不知疲倦地向太空辐射着光和热,在它内部不停地进行着核聚变反应。氢不断地发生核聚变反应,生成氦,同时释放出巨大的核能,发出光和热。

3.太阳不断地向宇宙空间辐射能量,到达地球上的光和热不过是辐射出总能量的 20 亿分之一。这个数字相当于目前全世界能源总消费量的几万倍。现在,太阳已经"燃烧"了近 50 亿年,地球在太阳的照耀下积累的太阳能是我们所用大部分能量的源泉。

4.地球上的能量除地热能、潮汐能和核能外,绝大多数能源都是直接或间接地来源于太阳,因此太阳能也被誉为人类的能源之母。

知识 2　其他新能源

1.地热能:地球内部蕴藏着大量的热,可以直接用来发电。

2.潮汐能:发生潮汐时,大量水流动,具有巨大的能量。可利用流水带动水轮机转动,继而带动发电机发电。每天潮涨和潮落可以发两次电。

3.风能:在风力资源丰富的地方,可利用风车带动发电机发电。另外,帆船也可以利用风能来前进。

4.氢能:氢气作为一种可燃的气体,燃烧时可放出热,而且由于产物只有水一种,是一种绝对清洁的新能源。

方法清单

方法 比较法计算能源利用效率

方法 比较法计算能源利用效率

能源利用效率包括能源热效率和热机效率两类。

1.能源热效率:$\eta = \dfrac{Q_{有用}}{E} \times 100\%$,$Q_{有用}$是有效利用的热量,$E$指总能量。如果是炉子,则$E$为燃料完全燃烧放出的能量($E = Q_{总} = mq$);如果是太阳能热水器,则$E$为接收到的太阳能;如果是电热器,则$E$为电流做功放出的热量。

2.热机效率:$\eta = \dfrac{W_{有用}}{Q_{总}} \times 100\%$,其中$W_{有用}$是指输出的有用功($W_{有用} = Pt$),$Q_{总}$为燃料完全燃烧放出的总能量($Q_{总} = mq$)。

解决能源利用的效率问题,关键是分清有效利用的能量和总能量。一般来说,转化成的能量是有效利用的能量,消耗的能量为总能量。

例 某学习小组同学想研究酒精灯烧水时的热效率。他们用酒精灯给100 g的水加热,经过一段时间测得水温升高了60 ℃,消耗了4.2 g酒精。已知:水的比热容为4.2×10^3 J/(kg·℃),酒精的热值为3×10^7 J/kg。求:

(1)此过程中水吸收的热量;

(2)4.2 g酒精完全燃烧放出的热量;

(3)酒精灯烧水时的热效率。

(解析) (1)水吸收的热量:

$Q_{吸} = cm_{水}\Delta t = 4.2 \times 10^3$ J/(kg·℃)$\times 0.1$ kg$\times 60$ ℃ $= 2.52 \times 10^4$ J

(2)4.2 g酒精完全燃烧放出的热量:

$Q_{放} = m_{酒精}q = 4.2 \times 10^{-3}$ kg$\times 3 \times 10^7$ J/kg $= 1.26 \times 10^5$ J

(3)酒精灯烧水时的热效率:

$\eta = \dfrac{Q_{吸}}{Q_{放}} \times 100\% = \dfrac{2.52 \times 10^4 \text{ J}}{1.26 \times 10^5 \text{ J}} \times 100\% = 20\%$

(答案) (1)2.52×10^4 J   (2)1.26×10^5 J   (3)20%

第 4 部分

力学

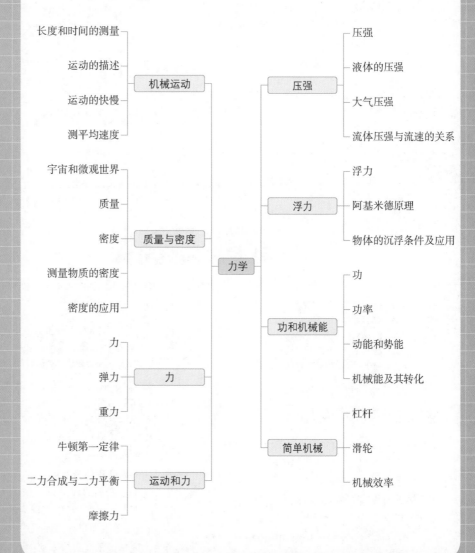

长度和时间的测量 ── 机械运动
运动的描述
运动的快慢
测平均速度

宇宙和微观世界 ── 质量与密度
质量
密度
测量物质的密度
密度的应用

力 ── 力
弹力
重力

牛顿第一定律 ── 运动和力
二力合成与二力平衡
摩擦力

力学

压强 ── 压强
液体的压强
大气压强
流体压强与流速的关系

浮力 ── 浮力
阿基米德原理
物体的沉浮条件及应用

功 ── 功和机械能
功率
动能和势能
机械能及其转化

杠杆 ── 简单机械
滑轮
机械效率

机械运动

知识梳理

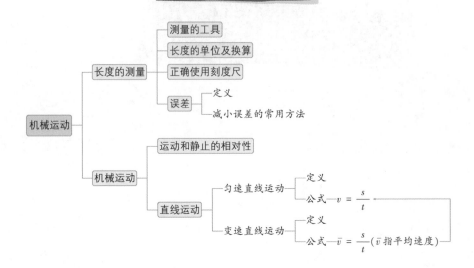

第1节　长度和时间的测量

知识清单

基础知识

知识1 长度的单位及换算

知识2 刻度尺的认识及使用方法

知识3 测量值、真实值与误差

知识4 时间及其测量

知识5 机械停表的用法及读数

知识 1 长度的单位及换算

1.在国际单位制中,长度的基本单位为米(m),比米大的单位有千米(km),比米小的单位有分米(dm)、厘米(cm)、毫米(mm)、微米(μm)、纳米(nm)等。

2.各单位之间的换算关系为:

$1 \text{ km} = 10^3 \text{ m}$;

$1 \text{ m} = 10 \text{ dm} = 10^2 \text{ cm} = 10^3 \text{ mm} = 10^6 \text{ μm} = 10^9 \text{ nm}$;

$1 \text{ mm} = 10^{-3} \text{ m}$; $1 \text{ μm} = 10^{-6} \text{ m}$; $1 \text{ nm} = 10^{-9} \text{ m}$。

3.对生活中常见的一些长度,要求学生有一定的估测能力,如一支铅笔的长度约为 18 cm,中学生的身高约为 1.72 m 等。

> **温馨提示** PM2.5是指空气中直径很小的颗粒,其直径还不到人的头发丝粗细的二十分之一。PM2.5中的"2.5"是表示颗粒直径的数字,它的单位是微米。

例 对于我们教室里一张单人课桌的下列估测,最接近实际值的是 （　　）

A.课桌高度约为 0.8 m

B.课桌质量约为 50 kg

C.桌面面积约为 4 m²

D.书箱容积约为 0.8 m³

解析 我们的教室里一张单人课桌高度大约为 0.8 m,故 A 正确;一张单人课桌的质量约 10 kg,故 B 错误;一张单人课桌桌面面积约 20 dm²,故 C 错误;一张单人课桌书箱容积约为 30 dm³,故 D 错误。

答案 A

知识 **2** 刻度尺的认识及使用方法

1.认识刻度尺

要做到"三看"(如图):

(1)看刻度尺的零刻度线是否磨损。如已磨损应从其他清晰刻度线量起。

(2)看刻度尺的量程(测量范围)。

(3)看刻度尺的分度值。分度值反映了刻度尺的精确程度。

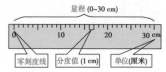

量程(0~30 cm)

零刻度线 分度值(1 cm) 单位(厘米)

2.使用方法

(1)会"选"。根据实际情况及所需要求选择刻度尺。测量对象不同,所需刻度尺的量程可能不同,分度值可能不同。

(2)会"放"。如图所示,尺要沿着所测的物体,不利用磨损的零刻度线。所谓沿着,一是指放正,不歪斜;二是指要尽可能地贴近被测物体。若零刻度线磨损,应以其他清晰刻度线为"零点",读数时要注意减去"零点"所对应的刻度值。

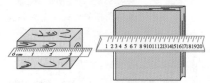

(3)会"看"。如图所示,读数时,视线要与刻度尺的刻度线垂直,不要斜视。

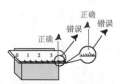

正确 错误 错误

正确

(4)会"读"。精确的测量需要估读,指在读数时,除准确读出准确值外,还要估读到分度值的下一位;如果被测物体的长度刚好到某一刻度线,则估读值为0,记录数据时估读值0不能省略。

(5)会"记"。记录测量结果时,除了正确无误地记下所读出的数字外,还要标明单位。只写了数字但未标明单位的记录是没有意义的。

知识 **3** 测量值、真实值与误差

1.测量值

用测量仪器测定待测物理量所得到的值。

2.真实值

任何一个物理量都有它的客观大小,这个客观值称为真实值。

最理想的测量就是能够测得其真实值,但由于测量是利用仪器在一定条件下通过人来完成的,受仪器的灵敏度和分辨能力、环境和人的精神状态等因素的影响,使得待测量的真实值是不可测得的。

3.误差

(1)测量值和真实值之间总会存在或多或少的偏差,这种偏差叫误差。

(2)减小误差的途径:选用精密的测量仪器,改进实验方法,熟练掌握实验技能等。在一般实验中,减小误差的有效途径是取多次测量的平均值(这种方法对减小偶然误差有效)。

易混对比	误差与错误	
	误差	错误
产生原因	仪器精密度不够或实验方法不完善;估读时的偏差及环境对仪器的影响	不遵守测量仪器的规则,或记录结果时粗心大意
可否避免	不可避免	可以避免
如何判断	有误差的实验数据比较接近真实值	错误的数据远远偏离了真实值

例 如图所示,用刻度尺测量铅笔的长度,读数为_____cm,一次测量可能误差较大,为了减小误差,应当_____。

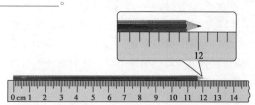

12

0 cm 1 2 3 4 5 6 7 8 9 10 11 12 13 14

解析 测量铅笔长度时需估读,由题图可看出刻度尺的分度值为 1 mm,题目中的长度单位是 cm,可采用以下两种方法读数:①准确值 12.0 cm,估读值 0.02 cm,铅笔长度为 12.02 cm;②准确值 120 mm,估读值 0.2 mm,铅笔长度为 120.2 mm,即 12.02 cm。

多次测量求平均值可以减小误差。

答案 12.02 多次测量求平均值

知识 **4** 时间及其测量

1.在国际单位制中,时间的基本单位为秒(s)。

比秒大的单位有时(h)、分(min),比秒小的单位有毫秒(ms)、微秒(μs)等。它们之间的换算关系为:

1 h = 60 min;1 min = 60 s;1 s = 10^3 ms;1 ms = 10^3 μs。

2.测量工具

时间的测量工具主要有停表、手表、钟表以及古代用的日晷、沙漏等，如图所示。

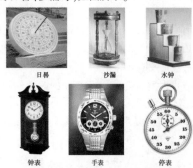

日晷　　　沙漏　　　水钟

钟表　　　手表　　　停表

在一些要求不太严格的时间测量中，我们也可以用自己的脉搏（或心率）来测量时间，知道自己心脏每分钟的跳动次数，再数出做某件事时自己脉搏的总次数，就可以求出做这件事所用的时间了[注意:必须是在脉搏（或心率）稳定的情况下]。

知识 5 机械停表的用法及读数

1.机械停表的使用方法

（1）使用前先上好发条，测量时用手握住停表，大拇指按下"开始/停止"按钮，停表指针立即走动，计时开始；

（2）再次按下"开始/停止"按钮，停表指针停止走动，指针指示出两次按压之间的时间间隔；

（3）测量完成，按动"复位"按钮，秒针和分针都弹回原点（零刻度线处）。

2.使用机械停表进行读数与记录数据

（1）所测时间超过 0.5 min 时，0.5 min 的整数倍部分由小圆刻度盘内分针所指示的刻度读出，不足 0.5 min 的部分由大圆刻度盘中秒针所指示的刻度读出，所测的时间为两次读数之和。

（2）停表读数时一般不估读，这是因为机械停表为机械表，其表针的运行是靠齿轮转动的，指针不可能停在两刻度线之间，一定停在刻度线上。

3.使用机械停表时的注意事项

（1）使用停表前应检查停表指针是否与零刻度线对齐，如果没有对齐，应记下此时指针所指示数，并对读数进行修正；

（2）不同的停表表盘示数有所不同，在测量前要认真观察；

（3）实验中切勿摔碰停表，以免损坏；

（4）测量完毕，应让停表继续走动，让发条完全放松，恢复到松弛状态。

例 如图所示，机械停表的示数是_____s。

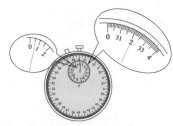

（**解析**）停表表盘的分针所指示数大于半分钟，由题图可知此时指针所指示数为 32 s。

（**答案**）32

拓展知识　　**知识** 长度测量的特殊方法

知识 长度测量的特殊方法

曲直互化法	①借助于一些辅助器材把不能直接测量的曲线变为直线，再用刻度尺测量，这就是"化曲为直"法 ②要测某段曲线长，可用不易被拉长的软线，先使它与待测曲线完全重合，并在始末端做上记号，然后把软线拉直，用刻度尺测出始末端记号间的长度即曲线的长度。例如测地图上某段公路线的长度 ③用已知周长的滚轮在较长的曲线上滚动，记下滚过的圈数，再用滚过的圈数乘以滚轮的周长，就得到曲线的长度。汽车、摩托车上的里程表就是根据这一原理制作的 ④还可将圆规两脚分开（分开的距离视曲线弯曲程度而定，越弯曲，间距就越小些），再用圆规两脚连续分割曲线，记下分割的总段数，测出圆规两脚间的距离，此距离乘以两脚在曲线上连续画出的总段数，便得到曲线的大约长度 ⑤用自行车测一段马路的长度时，可先测出车轮的周长，再推动自行车通过这段马路，并数出车轮转的圈数，则圈数乘以周长即得这段马路的长度
平移法	借助于一些简单的辅助器材（如三角板、直尺）把不可直接测量的长度"平移"到刻度尺上，从而可直接测出该长度，这种方法叫"平移法"。例如借助于三角板、直尺便可测出硬币、乒乓球的直径及圆锥体的高
公式法	测圆的周长时，可先测出圆的直径，再利用公式求出周长。像这样先测出相关量，再利用公式求出被测量的方法叫"公式法"
化暗为明法	有些待测物体，不是明显地露在外面，而是隐含在其他物体的内部，刻度尺不能直接测量。如测玻璃管的内径，可以选择大小合适的钢针插入管内，在管口处给钢针做上记号，然后再测钢针记号处的直径即可（常用千分尺测量）。如图所示 

例 1 利用_____和_____能够测出图中曲线的长度。

(解析) 用"化曲为直"法可测图示曲线长度。

(答案) 弹性很小的软线　刻度尺

例 2 小亮在"长度的测量"实验中：

(1)图中圆的直径是_____cm。

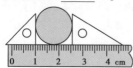

(2)一条纸带厚薄均匀,他把纸带紧密地环绕在圆柱形铅笔上,直至恰好能套进一个圆环内,如图所示,纸带环绕了 n 圈,则纸带的厚度是_____(选填"A"或"B")。

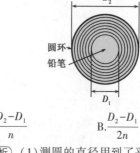

A. $\dfrac{D_2 - D_1}{n}$ 　　　　 B. $\dfrac{D_2 - D_1}{2n}$

(解析) (1)测圆的直径用到了平移法;由题图可知,所用刻度尺的分度值为 1 mm,圆的直径为两三角板直角边所对刻度值之差,且读数时要估读到分度值的下一位,故为 1.55 cm;(2)题中运用累积法测量了纸带的厚度,n 层纸的厚度为 $\dfrac{D_2 - D_1}{2}$,故纸带的厚度为 $\dfrac{D_2 - D_1}{2n}$,选择 B。

(答案) (1)1.55 (2)B

方法清单

方法1 选用合适刻度尺的方法
方法2 利用多次测量求平均值减小误差
方法3 累积法测微小长度
方法4 对位法判断刻度尺的分度值
方法5 用拉长的刻度尺测物体长度

方法 1 选用合适刻度尺的方法

长度测量的精确程度是由刻度尺的分度值决定的。

1.根据所要达到的精确度和被测物体的特点,要选择分度值和量程都合适的刻度尺。

2.用精确度很高的刻度尺去测量一个精确度要求不是很高的物体长度,增加了测量的麻烦,也是不可取的。

3.测量时要尽量选择量程大于所测物体长度的刻度尺,这样可避免多次测量的累加,减小误差。

例 现有以下几种刻度尺:①量程为 0~3 m 的毫米刻度尺;②量程为 0~3 m 的厘米刻度尺;③量程为 0~15 m 的厘米刻度尺;④量程为 0~30 m 的厘米刻度尺。

安装门窗玻璃时应选用刻度尺_____;量衣服长度时应选用刻度尺_____;运动会上测跳远成绩时应选用刻度尺_____;测量教室长和宽时应选用刻度尺_____。(填序号)

(解析) 此题联系实际,长度测量与我们生活紧密相关,如何选择适当的测量工具,是我们必须掌握的。如主要从测量所需的精确度考虑,选择刻度尺的分度值:安装门窗玻璃、量衣服分别选用分度值为 1 mm 与 1 cm 的刻度尺;从实际测量的范围考虑,选择刻度尺的量程:测跳远成绩选量程 0~15 m 即可,而测量

教室长必须用量程为 0~30 m 的刻度尺才够用。

(答案) ①　②　③　④

方法 2 利用多次测量求平均值减小误差

1.测物体长度时,测量误差要尽量减小。

2.减小误差的措施有:

(1)采用较精密的刻度尺;(2)采用科学的测量方法测量;(3)多次测量取平均值。

3.在计算平均值时,应先计算到分度值的下两位,然后再对最后一位数字进行四舍五入,最后的记录结果一定要和每次测量的记录值的精确度相同。

例 某同学在课本的不同位置测得课本的宽度值分别为 12.89 cm、12.88 cm、12.87 cm、12.87 cm,那么课本的宽度应该是 (　　)

A.12.89 cm 　　　　　 B.12.88 cm

C.12.87 cm 　　　　　 D.12.877 5 cm

(解析) 多次测量求平均值可以减小误差。在求平均值时要计算到分度值的下两位,对最后一位数字进行四舍五入,使结果仍与测量的精确度相同。因为记录值要能反映出刻度尺的分度值。

所以,12.89 cm+12.88 cm+12.87 cm+12.87 cm = 51.51 cm

$\dfrac{51.51 \text{ cm}}{4} \approx 12.878 \text{ cm} \approx 12.88 \text{ cm}$

由于所用刻度尺的分度值是 1 mm,因而记录应准确到毫米位,估读到毫米的下一位,只有四位有效数字。所以,应按四舍五入的方法保留四位有效数字。

(答案) B

方法 3 累积法测微小长度

1.把若干个相同的微小量"累积"起来,变得可直接测量,将测出的总量除以累积的个数,便得到微小量,这种方法叫"累积法"。

2.这种方法用于长度测量就是把多个相同的微小长度的物体叠放在一起,测出叠放后的总长度,用总长度除以叠放物体的个数,得到单个物体的微小长度。

(1)测一张纸的厚度时,我们可以先用毫米刻度尺测出课本正文(除去封面)的总厚度,根据页数确定纸的张数,用总厚度除以张数算出一张纸的平均厚度。

(2)测细铜丝的直径时,可以把细铜丝在圆铅笔上紧密排绕若干圈,测出总长度,用总长度除以所绕的圈数,便可得到铜丝的直径。

例 用普通刻度尺来测金属丝直径,可采用如图所示的办法,根据图示情况,该金属丝的直径是_____mm。

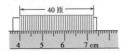

解析 累积法测量物体的长度,40匝金属丝的总长度为3.30 cm=33.0 mm,所以一根金属丝的直径应该是33.0 mm/40=0.825 mm,因为测量所用的刻度尺的分度值为1 mm,所以应该四舍五入,即金属丝直径为0.8 mm。

答案 0.8

方法 4 对位法判断刻度尺的分度值

1.对位法是根据测量值所带的单位,将测量值的每个数位与长度单位一一对应。

2.步骤:

①看所给测量结果的单位;

②从小数点的前一位开始,逐级缩小单位,并同时在各个数位上标出对应的单位,直到倒数第二位为止;

③看标出的最后一级的单位(即倒数第二位数字所对应的单位)是什么,就可以确定此刻度尺的分度值。

例 新铅笔的长度是 0.175 3 m,则测量时所用刻度尺的分度值是_____。

解析 此题中 0.175 3 m 的个位"0"对应的单位是 m,"1"对应的单位是 dm,"7"对应的单位是 cm,"5"对应的单位是 mm。在物理实验中,测量长度要估读到分度值的下一位,题中的"3"是估读的,而"5"是准确读数,即分度值就是 1 mm。

答案 1 mm

方法 5 用拉长的刻度尺测物体长度

1.测量结果偏大还是偏小指的是测量值比真实值大还是小。

2.将刻度尺拉长后,相邻两刻度线之间的距离变大,导致测量值比真实值小。

例 小明不慎将钢卷尺掉入沸水中煮了一段时间后,从水中取出后垫上纱布立即测量课桌的长度,他测得的长度比课桌的真实长度 ( )

A.稍大   B.不变

C.稍小   D.上述答案都不对

解析 钢卷尺在沸水中煮了一段时间,由于热胀冷缩,钢卷尺也相当于被拉长。测得的长度比课桌真实长度偏小。

答案 C

第 2 节 运动的描述

知识清单

基础知识

知识 1 机械运动
知识 2 参照物及参照物的选择

知识 1 机械运动

1.运动是宇宙中的普遍现象。宇宙中的一切物体都是运动的,没有绝对静止的物体,宇宙中的万物都在以各种不同的形式运动着。

2.机械运动:在物理学里,把物体位置的变化(一个物体相对于另一个物体位置的改变)叫机械运动。通常简称运动。

3.判断机械运动的方法:看这个物体相对于另一个物体有没有位置变化。如果有,我们就说这个物体相对于另一个物体在做机械运动。

如图,小明认为小狗动了,是因为小狗相对于车的位置发生了变化。

4.一个物体相对于另一个物体的位置没有改变，我们就说它是静止的。

知识 2 参照物及参照物的选择

1.参照物:要描述一个物体是运动的还是静止的，要先选定一个物体作为标准，这个选定的作为标准的物体叫参照物。

2.参照物的理解

(1)参照物的选定是为了研究机械运动中物体的运动或静止。

(2)所选定的参照物是一个假定不动的物体，有了它作为标准，再看被研究的物体跟它之间的位置是否发生了变化就比较方便了。

3.参照物的选择

(1)参照物的选择是任意的，既可以选相对地面静止的物体，也可以选相对地面运动的物体。

(2)研究地面上物体的运动，通常选取地面或相对于地面静止的物体作为参照物。

(3)被研究的物体本身不能选作参照物，因为以此研究对象为参照物，研究对象永远都是静止的。

(4)研究对象为多个时，应选取同一个参照物。

例 举世瞩目的第 29 届奥林匹克运动会在北京开幕，当时全世界电视观众均可通过卫星传输的信号在家里收看开幕式盛况，这种卫星称为地球同步通信卫星，这里的"同步"是指卫星 (   )

A.相对太阳静止　　　　B.相对地球静止
C.相对月球静止　　　　D.相对火星静止

(解析) 地球同步卫星是指与地球相对静止的卫星，它绕地球公转的周期与地球的自转周期相同，所以从地球上看卫星总是静止在空中某一个地方。地球同步卫星相对太阳、火星和月亮都是运动的。

(答案) B

知识 运动和静止的相对性

知识 运动和静止的相对性

1.运动是绝对的

一切物体都在运动，绝对不动的物体是没有的；如果说一个物体在运动，是指它相对于参照物有了位置的变化。

2.静止是相对的

我们平常说某物体静止，是指它相对于所选的参照物位置没有发生变化。例如，卡车和联合收割机，同样快慢，向同一方向前进，以其中一个为参照物，另一个是静止的，属于相对静止，如图所示。实际上这个被选作参照物的物体也在运动(因为一切物体都在运动)，所以绝对静止的物体是不存在的。

卡车和联合收割机相对静止

3.对运动状态的描述是相对的

研究同一物体的运动状态，如果选择不同的参照物，得出的结论可能不同，但都是正确的结论。总之，不事先选定参照物，就无法对某个物体的运动状态作出肯定的判断，说这个物体运动或静止是毫无意义的。

例 如图是小明同学所拍摄的一幅海边风景照片。由照片所示的情景，可以分析判断出甲船的运动状态是＿＿＿＿＿＿＿＿＿，乙船的运动状态可能是＿＿＿＿＿＿＿＿＿。

(解析) 由题图可知，山上的小旗向左飘，则风从右往左吹，若乙船静止，则小旗向左飘，若乙船向右行驶，则小旗也向左飘，若乙船向右行驶，且速度小于风速，小旗也向左飘，若乙船向左行驶，且速度大于风速，小旗向右飘，故乙船的运动状态可能是:静止、向右行驶、向左行驶但船速小于风速。同理，甲船的运动状态是向左行驶，且速度大于风速。

(答案) 向左运动且船速大于风速　静止、向右运动、向左运动但船速小于风速(答出两种情况即可)

方法 1　判断物体是否运动的方法

1.判断一个物体是否运动,要看它相对于参照物的位置是否在改变。

2.具体步骤是:

①选定一个参照物;

②观察比较物体与参照物之间位置有无变化以及怎样变化;

③作出判断,若位置发生了变化,则说明该物体相对于参照物在运动;若位置没有变化,则说明该物体相对于参照物是静止的。

3.同一个物体相对于不同的参照物,运动状态一般是不同的。如图,若选出租车为参照物,乘客是静止的;若选地面为参照物,乘客则是运动的。

例 "神舟十号"飞船与"天宫一号"成功对接后,以下列哪一个作为参照物,"天宫一号"是静止的

( )

A.西昌卫星中心的发射塔架

B."神舟十号"飞船

C.海面上行驶的远洋观测船

D.在"天宫一号"内穿行的航天员

解析 "天宫一号"与"神舟十号"飞船对接后,它们之间没有位置变化,相对静止。

答案 B

方法 2　参照物的判断方法

方法指南:①要明确研究对象;②明确物体的运动情况;③如果说研究对象是运动的,哪个物体相对于它的位置发生了改变,那个物体就是参照物;如果说研究对象是静止的,哪个物体相对于它的位置没有改变,那个物体就是参照物。

例 2012 年 11 月 23 日,国产歼-15 舰载机首次在航空母舰"辽宁号"上成功起降。如图所示,飞机起飞时,若说该飞机上的飞行员是静止的,所选的参照物是

( )

A.航母

B.该飞行员驾驶的飞机

C.海水

D.航母上的工作人员

解析 飞机起飞时,以航母、海水和航母上的工作人员为参照物,飞行员的位置在发生变化,是运动的;以他驾驶的飞机为参照物,飞行员的位置保持不变,所以是静止的。

答案 B

第 3 节　运动的快慢

知识清单

基础
知识　知识**1** 比较运动的快慢
　　　知识**2** 速度
　　　知识**3** 匀速直线运动
　　　知识**4** 变速运动与平均速度

知识 1　比较运动的快慢

1.通过相同的路程比较时间

如图甲,通过相同的路程,谁用的时间少,谁就

快;谁用的时间多,谁就慢。在体育比赛中,裁判员就是根据这种方法比较运动员运动的快慢。

2.经过相同的时间比较路程

如图乙,经过相同的时间,谁通过的路程长,谁就快;谁通过的路程短,谁就慢。在观看体育比赛时,观众就是根据这种方法比较运动员运动的快慢。

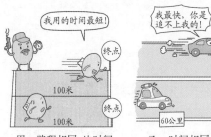

甲 路程相同，比时间　　　乙 时间相同，比路程

例 如图，龟兔赛跑的故事中，比赛开始后，"观众"通过比较_____认为跑在前面的兔子运动得快；由于兔子轻敌，中途睡了一觉，"裁判员"通过比较_____判定最先到达终点的乌龟运动得快。

(解析) 比赛刚开始阶段，相同时间内，兔子通过的路程长，兔子快；比较全程，路程相同的情况下，乌龟用时短，乌龟快。

(答案) 相同时间内通过路程的长短　通过相同的路程所用时间的长短

知识 **2** 速度

1.定义

在物理学中，将物体在一段时间内通过的路程与通过这段路程所用时间的比称为速度。速度是表示物体运动快慢的物理量。

2.公式：$v=\dfrac{s}{t}$。其中 v 表示速度，s 表示路程，t 表示时间。

3.单位

(1)在国际单位制中，速度的单位是 m/s；交通运输中常用单位是 km/h。

(2)m/s 与 km/h 的换算关系为 1 m/s=3.6 km/h。以 5 m/s 为例，具体的换算方法是：5 m/s = 5×3.6 km/h=18 km/h，18 km/h=18×$\dfrac{1}{3.6}$ m/s=5 m/s。

(3)常见的换算关系有：

1 m/s=3.6 km/h，5 m/s=18 km/h

10 m/s=36 km/h，15 m/s=54 km/h

20 m/s=72 km/h，25 m/s=90 km/h

30 m/s=108 km/h

温馨提示 ①应用 $v=\dfrac{s}{t}$ 计算时，单位要统一。s 用 m，t 用 s 作单位时，速度 v 的单位为 m/s；当 s 用 km，t 用 h 作单位时，速度 v 的单位为 km/h。

②公式 $v=\dfrac{s}{t}$ 中的三个物理量必须对应于同一物体。

4.意义：速度等于单位时间内通过的路程。某汽车匀速直线运动的速度是 15 m/s，则表示的意义是：每秒钟汽车通过的路程为 15 米。

例 某飞机在 5 s 内飞行了 1 000 m，则它飞行的速度为_____m/s，合_____km/h，初中学生步行的速度大约为_____m/s。

(解析) $v=\dfrac{s}{t}=\dfrac{1\ 000\ \text{m}}{5\ \text{s}}=200\ \text{m/s}=200×3.6\ \text{km/h}=720\ \text{km/h}$。初中生步行速度大约为 1 m/s。

(答案) 200　720　1

知识 **3** 匀速直线运动

1.定义：我们把物体运动速度保持不变的直线运动称为匀速直线运动。

2.匀速直线运动是运动状态不变的运动，是最简单的机械运动。

3.匀速直线运动的特征：一是运动的路径是直线；二是运动的快慢及方向保持不变，即它的速度是一个恒量，任一时刻都相同。

例 下列有关匀速直线运动的说法中，正确的是　　　　　　　　　　　　　　　　（ ）

A.物体做匀速直线运动的速度大小，由运动时间决定

B.汽车沿平直公路每分钟行驶的路程均为 1 000 m，则汽车一定做匀速直线运动

C.根据 $v=\dfrac{s}{t}$ 可知，物体做匀速直线运动的速度与通过的路程成正比

D.根据 $v=\dfrac{s}{t}$ 可知，物体做匀速直线运动通过的路程与时间成正比

(解析) 速度是路程与时间的比值，不是只由时间决定，故 A 选项错误。在平直公路上行驶意在说明是直线运动，每分钟行驶的路程均为 1 000 m，并不能说明该汽车做匀速运动，有可能在 1 分钟之中，前半分钟行驶 800 m，后半分钟行驶 200 m，故 B 选项错误。匀速直线运动速度保持不变，与路程、时间无关，故 C 选项错误。据 $v=\dfrac{s}{t}$，v 不变，则 s 与 t 成正比，故 D 正确。

(答案) D

知识 **4** 变速运动与平均速度

1.变速运动亦称"非匀速运动"。物体的速度随时间而变化，可能是速度大小发生变化，也可能是速度方向发生变化，还可能是速度大小和方向同时发生变化。它是最常见的一种机械运动。例如火车、汽车从车站或轮船从码头开出时的运动，都是变速运动。

2.按其运动的轨迹来分，有直线运动和曲线运动。

3.物体沿着直线且速度变化的运动叫变速直线运动。

4.通常用平均速度来表示变速运动的快慢程度。它等于物体通过的路程和通过这段路程所用时间的比值，计算公式为 $\bar{v}=\dfrac{s}{t}$。

例 如图是一个水滴下落过程的示意图，水滴通过 AB 和 BC 所用时间均为 0.1 s。水滴由 A 位置下落到 C 位置运动的距离是_____cm，则这个过程中水滴下落的平均速度是_____ m/s。该水滴下落过程是_____运动。(选填"匀速直线"或"变速直线")

解析 $s=20$ cm-0 cm$=20$ cm；$\bar{v}=\dfrac{s}{t}=$ $\dfrac{0.2\ \text{m}}{0.2\ \text{s}}=1$ m/s；相同时间内通过的路程不同，故水滴下落过程是变速直线运动。

答案 20 1 变速直线

拓展知识 **知识** 巧选参照物简化速度的计算

知识 **巧选参照物简化速度的计算**

对于生活中的某些运动，例如超车、错车、漂流物等问题，在选取参照物时，我们首先想到的是地面，这时物体都在运动，问题很复杂，如果我们选取其中一个运动的物体为参照物，问题会简单很多。

例 在一列以 18 m/s 的速度匀速行驶的火车上，某乘客以 2 m/s 的速度在车厢内行走(车厢长20 m)，下列说法正确的是（　　）

A.乘客用 1 s 的时间从车厢头走到车厢尾
B.乘客用 11 s 的时间从车厢头走到车厢尾
C.乘客用 10 s 的时间从车厢头走到车厢尾
D.乘客用 1.25 s 的时间从车厢头走到车厢尾

解析 选取匀速行驶的火车为参照物，只剩下一个相对于参照物运动的物体——乘客，无论乘客从车厢头走到车厢尾，或从车厢尾走到车厢头，相对于车厢走过的路程都是车厢长 20 m，相对于车的速度为 2 m/s，由速度公式的变形式，可求出时间 $t=\dfrac{s}{v}=$ $\dfrac{20\ \text{m}}{2\ \text{m/s}}=10$ s，乘客从车厢头走到车厢尾与从车厢尾走到车厢头所需时间相等，故正确选项为 C。

答案 C

方法清单

方法**1** 图像法解决匀速直线运动相关的问题
方法**2** 速度比值问题的解决方法
方法**3** 火车过桥(隧道)问题的解法
方法**4** 公式法计算火车、汽车的平均速度

方法 **1** 图像法解决匀速直线运动相关的问题

1.匀速直线运动的路程-时间图像，如图所示：

(1)该图线是过原点的直线，它说明做匀速直线运动的物体通过的路程与时间成正比。

(2)该图像的纵坐标表示路程，横坐标表示运动时间，利用一组对应的时间和路程值，可求出该物体运动速度的大小。

(3)可以通过图像得出某段时间内通过的路程。

(4)可以通过图像得出该物体通过某段路程需要的时间。

(5)如果是两条图线在同一个图中，可以比较两个物体运动速度的大小。

(6)如果路程-时间图像中某段时间内图线是水平的(如图 AB 段所示)，说明这段时间内物体是静止的。

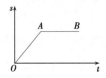

2.匀速直线运动的速度-时间(v-t)图像如图所示，它是与时间轴平行的直线，可以直接得出物体的速度。同一匀速直线运动的 s-t 图像和 v-t 图像形状不同。

匀速直线运动的 $s\text{-}t$ 图像与 $t\text{-}s$ 图像中速度大小的比较

在匀速直线运动的 $s\text{-}t$ 图像中(如图甲),要想比较 v_1 与 v_2 的大小,一般采用"相同时间比路程"的方法,当时间均为 t_0 时,路程 $s_1 > s_2$,所以 $v_1 > v_2$。

甲

若图中横坐标表示 s,纵坐标表示 t(如图乙),由图可知当时间相同时,路程 $s_1 < s_2$,所以有 $v_1 < v_2$。

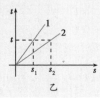

乙

例 如图(a)是小车甲运动的 $s\text{-}t$ 图像,图(b)是小车乙运动的 $v\text{-}t$ 图像,由图像可知 ( )

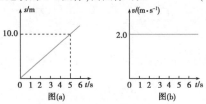

图(a)   图(b)

A.甲、乙都由静止开始运动
B.甲、乙都以 2 m/s 的速度做匀速运动
C.甲、乙两车经过 5 s 一定相遇
D.甲车速度越来越大,乙车速度不变

解析 由题图可知,乙车开始计时时的速度为 2 m/s,不是从静止开始运动,A 错误;小车甲运动的 $s\text{-}t$ 图线是一条过原点的直线,表示随着时间的增加,甲的路程均匀变大,所以甲做匀速直线运动,速度为 $v = \dfrac{s}{t} = \dfrac{10.0 \text{ m}}{5 \text{ s}} = 2 \text{ m/s}$,小车乙运动的 $v\text{-}t$ 图线是一条平行于横轴的直线,表示随着时间的增加,乙的速度不变,所以乙做匀速直线运动,速度为 2 m/s,B 正确,D 错误;甲、乙都以 2 m/s 的速度做匀速运动,如果两车从不同的位置开始同向运动,则两车不能相遇,C 错误。故选 B。

答案 B

方法 2 速度比值问题的解决方法

对于求比值的问题,把所给条件写成比的形式后,根据速度公式或者其变形公式,把所要求的量用比值表示出来,化简,代入数据,计算得出结果。

例 甲、乙两个运动物体,所用时间之比 $t_{甲} : t_{乙} = 4 : 3$,通过路程之比 $s_{甲} : s_{乙} = 5 : 2$,则甲、乙速度之比 $v_{甲} : v_{乙}$ 为 ( )

A.6 : 5   B.5 : 6
C.15 : 8   D.8 : 15

解析 解答本题有两种方法:

方法一:$v_{甲} = \dfrac{s_{甲}}{t_{甲}}$,$v_{乙} = \dfrac{s_{乙}}{t_{乙}}$,$\dfrac{v_{甲}}{v_{乙}} = \dfrac{s_{甲}/t_{甲}}{s_{乙}/t_{乙}} = \dfrac{s_{甲}}{s_{乙}} \times \dfrac{t_{乙}}{t_{甲}}$

$= \dfrac{s_{甲}}{s_{乙}} \times \dfrac{t_{乙}}{t_{甲}} = \dfrac{5}{2} \times \dfrac{3}{4} = \dfrac{15}{8}$;

方法二:速度比 $= \dfrac{\text{路程比}}{\text{时间比}}$,得 $\dfrac{v_{甲}}{v_{乙}} = \dfrac{5/2}{4/3} = \dfrac{5}{2} \times \dfrac{3}{4} = \dfrac{15}{8}$;

方法三:设 $t_{甲} = 4$,$t_{乙} = 3$,$s_{甲} = 5$,$s_{乙} = 2$;则 $v_{甲} = \dfrac{s_{甲}}{t_{甲}} = \dfrac{5}{4}$,

$v_{乙} = \dfrac{s_{乙}}{t_{乙}} = \dfrac{2}{3}$;$\dfrac{v_{甲}}{v_{乙}} = \dfrac{5/4}{2/3} = \dfrac{15}{8}$,故 C 正确。

答案 C

方法 3 火车过桥(隧道)问题的解法

1.对火车过隧道问题,从火车头进入隧道就开始算起,直到火车尾离开隧道才叫做火车通过了隧道,所以火车通过隧道经过的路程应该等于隧道长度与车身长度的和。

2.对火车过桥问题也类似,火车通过桥经过的路程等于桥长加车长。

3.对于本身有长度的物体过桥(隧道)问题小结如下:物体通过的路程等于桥(隧道)长与物体本身长度的和。

例 一座大桥长 1.6 km,一列长 200 m 的火车以 10 m/s 的速度通过此桥,则所需时间为 ( )

A.120 s   B.140 s   C.160 s   D.180 s

解析 设桥长为 L,火车长为 l,由图可知,火车要全部通过大桥,就要从车头上桥开始,到车尾离开桥为止,这样,火车的车头通过的路程就是 $L+l$,由公式 $s = L+l = vt$,可得 $t = \dfrac{L+l}{v} = \dfrac{1\,600 \text{ m} + 200 \text{ m}}{10 \text{ m/s}} = 180 \text{ s}$。

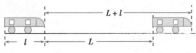

答案 D

点拨 过桥问题可以分为两种情况:一种是车全部通过桥所用的时间,公式为 $t = \dfrac{L+l}{v}$;另一种情况是车全部在桥上(如图)所用的时间,公式为 $t = \dfrac{L-l}{v}$。

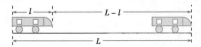

第 4 部分

方法 4 公式法计算火车、汽车的平均速度

1.根据火车的时刻表求火车从甲地到乙地的平均速度时,总时间等于火车到达乙地的时间减去离开甲地的时间,包括中间站停车所占用的时间;然后用 $v=\dfrac{s}{t}$ 进行计算。

2.根据汽车的车速里程表求汽车的平均速度时,要从表盘中读出汽车行驶的路程,并知道行驶这段路程所用的时间,用 $v=\dfrac{s}{t}$ 进行计算即可。

例1 便捷的交通与互联网给人们出行带来极大的方便。某天,王爷爷带小孙子驾车到南昌西站,然后乘高铁去上海迪士尼乐园游玩。9:35 开车出发,并看到路边如图甲所示交通标志牌,此刻吩咐小孙子通过铁路 12306 网站查询列车时刻表,如图表乙所示。求:

甲

车次	南昌西开	上海虹桥到	运行距离
G1346	09:43	13:18	780 km
G1386	10:05	13:59	780 km
G1348	10:26	13:41	780 km

乙

(1)在交通正常情况下,依据以上信息并通过计算,爷孙俩最快能赶乘上哪一车次?

(2)该趟高铁运行的平均速度为多少 km/h?

解析 (1) $t=\dfrac{s}{v}=\dfrac{30\ km}{60\ km/h}=0.5\ h$

即 10:05 到达车站,最快能赶上 G1348 车次

(2)列车运行时间 $t'=13:41-10:26=3\ h\ 15\ min=3.25\ h$

$v'=\dfrac{s'}{t'}=\dfrac{780\ km}{3.25\ h}=240\ km/h$

答案 (1)见解析 (2)240 km/h

例2 善于观察的小黄坐在行驶在平直公路上的汽车中,看到汽车上有一个显示速度和路程的表盘,示数如图甲所示,汽车行驶了 45 分钟后,表盘示数变为图乙所示,汽车行驶的路程为_____ km,这段时间内的平均速度为_____ km/h。

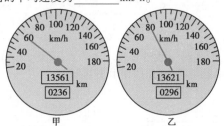

甲   乙

解析 从表盘上可以看出,汽车行驶的路程为 60 km,时间为 $t=45\ min=0.75\ h$,平均速度 $v=\dfrac{s}{t}=\dfrac{60\ km}{0.75\ h}=80\ km/h$。

答案 60 80

第4节 测平均速度

知识清单

基础知识
知识 **1** 平均速度的测量
知识 **2** 平均速度的计算

知识 **1** 平均速度的测量

1.我们可以通过测量物体运动所经过的路程、时间,然后应用公式 $v=\dfrac{s}{t}$ 计算物体运动的平均速度。

2.借助光电计时器(如图)测量小车通过一段距离的时间,从而计算出小车的运动速度。

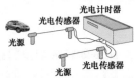

3.用速度仪等仪器(如图)直接测量物体运动的速度。

汽车速度仪

利用超声波测速仪直接测量速度

例 重庆高速路网全面推行区间测速以来,车辆超速行驶得到了一定遏制。一辆小汽车进入测速路段后,乘客发现测速提示牌往后退,他是以_____为参照物。测速设备测得小汽车在通过 9.45 km 的测速区间用时 270 s,其平均速度为_____ km/h。根据该路段限速 100 km/h 的规定,该车驾驶员受到了相应处罚。

解析 当以小汽车(或乘客自己)为参照物时,测速提示牌的位置不断向后发生改变,所以他会感觉测速提示牌在往后退;$t = 270 \text{ s} = 0.075 \text{ h}$,该车的平均速度为:$v = \dfrac{s}{t} = \dfrac{9.45 \text{ km}}{0.075 \text{ h}} = 126 \text{ km/h}$。

答案 小汽车(或乘客自己) 126

知识 2 平均速度的计算

1.计算平均速度时,必须指明是哪一段路程上或哪一段时间内的平均速度。因为不同路程上或不同时间内的平均速度通常情况下是不同的。

2.平均速度不是速度的算术平均值,全程的平均速度也不是各段平均速度的算术平均值,应该根据公式用总路程除以总时间去求得。

温馨提示

计算平均速度有三种解法:

第一种是用公式法,$\bar{v} = \dfrac{s}{t}$。

第二种是路程分半,前一半路程的速度为 v_1,后一半路程的速度为 v_2,平均速度 $\bar{v} = \dfrac{2v_1v_2}{v_1+v_2}$。

第三种是时间分半,前一半时间速度为 v_1,后一半时间速度为 v_2,平均速度 $\bar{v} = \dfrac{v_1+v_2}{2}$。

方法清单

方法 实验探究速度的变化

方法 实验探究速度的变化

1.猜想:做变速直线运动的物体的速度大小在不同时间段(或路程段)内是变化的。

例 晓燕在学校春季运动会百米赛跑中以 16 s 的成绩获得冠军,测得她在 50 m 处的速度是 6 m/s,到终点时的速度为 7.5 m/s,则全程内的平均速度是 ( )

A.6 m/s B.6.25 m/s

C.6.75 m/s D.7.5 m/s

解析 $\bar{v} = \dfrac{s_{总}}{t_{总}} = \dfrac{100 \text{ m}}{16 \text{ s}} = 6.25 \text{ m/s}$,平均速度表示全程的平均快慢程度,与 50 m 处的速度 6 m/s 和终点时的速度 7.5 m/s 无关。

答案 B

拓展知识

知识 估测平均速度

知识 估测平均速度

1.估测骑自行车的平均速度

方法:利用学校操场上跑道的长度来测量。

学校操场上的跑道长是已知的,如 400 m 的跑道。用手表测出骑自行车通过 400 m 跑道所用的时间,则可计算出骑自行车的平均速度。

2.估测汽车的平均速度

方法:利用路边的里程碑来测量。

公路边上都设置有里程碑,它是公路长度的标记。从某一里程碑,如 10 km 处开始计时,当汽车通过 40 km 的里程碑时结束计时,则汽车通过的路程 $s = 40 \text{ km} - 10 \text{ km} = 30 \text{ km}$。再根据汽车通过这段路程所用的时间,即可计算出汽车的平均速度。

3.估测火车的平均速度

方法:利用火车经过铁轨接口时发出的撞击声来测量。

我国的铁轨每根长为 12.5 m。乘火车时总能听到有节奏的声响,这是火车经过铁轨接口时发出的撞击声。用手表测量时间,从听到某组声响开始计时,并同时从零开始数听到声响的次数:0、1、2、3…如在 1 min 内数得火车发出 80 组声响,则火车在 1 min 内通过的路程 $s = 12.5 \times 80 \text{ m} = 1\,000 \text{ m}$。根据路程和时间即可计算出火车在这 1 min 内的平均速度 $v = 60 \text{ km/h}$。

2.设计实验:要探究物体运动速度的变化,可以将物体运动所经历的时间或路程分解成若干段,用刻度尺测出该段路程的长度,用钟表测出物体通过该段路程所用时间,再根据公式 $\bar{v} = \dfrac{s}{t}$ 计算出不同时间段(或路程段)中物体的运动速度。根据测量结果判断自己的猜想是否正确。

第 4 部分

3.进行实验

（1）实验目的：测出小车在斜面上半段、下半段以及全程运动中的平均速度。

（2）实验器材：小车、斜面、刻度尺、钟表等。

（3）实验原理：测出运动物体在时间 t 内通过的路程 s，可利用 $\bar{v}=\dfrac{s}{t}$ 求得该物体在这段时间内（或这段路程内）的平均速度。

（4）实验步骤：

①使斜面保持较小的坡度，将小车放于顶端，金属片放于斜面底端，测小车通过的路程 s。

②测小车从斜面顶端滑到底端撞击金属片的时间，重复多测几次。

③据 s 和 t 求得全过程的平均速度。

④将金属片移到斜面的中点，测得小车从顶端滑过斜面上半段路程 s_1，所用时间 t_1，算出小车通过上半段路程的平均速度 v_1。

⑤利用全程所用时间 t 减去上半段所用时间 t_1，求出下半段所用时间 t_2，算出小车在下半段的平均速度 v_2。

4.处理数据： 公式 $\bar{v}=\dfrac{s}{t}$ 中，s 和 t 应一一对应，s 一定是 t 时间内通过的路程，t 一定是通过路程 s 所用的时间。

5.得出结论： 下半段运动速度比上半段运动速度大。

温馨提示

"测量平均速度"的实验中（如下图）：

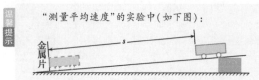

斜面的作用是使小车获得动力而做变速运动；金属片的作用是使小车在同一位置停下，便于计时和多次测量。

例 某物理兴趣小组利用带有刻度尺的斜面、小车和电子钟"测量小车的平均速度"，如图所示，图中显示的是他们测量过程中小车在甲、乙、丙三个位置及其对应时间的情形，显示时间的格式是"时:分:秒"

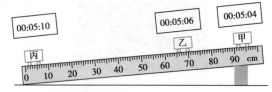

（1）该实验的原理是：_____。

（2）实验中为了方便计时，应使斜面的坡度较____（选填"大"或"小"）。

（3）请你根据图示完成下表：

	小车由甲至乙	小车由乙至丙	小车由甲至丙
路程 s/cm	26		
时间 t/s		4	
平均速度 v/(cm/s)			15

（4）分析表中的数据，小车全程是在做匀速运动吗？为什么？

解析 （1）该实验的实验原理是计算平均速度的公式 $v=\dfrac{s}{t}$；（2）实验中斜面的坡度越大，小车运动到底端所用的时间越短，越不容易计时，因此应使斜面的坡度较小；（3）通过读图得出各段通过的路程和各段所用的时间，分别运用实验原理 $v=\dfrac{s}{t}$，计算出每段的平均速度；（4）通过比较发现小车在前段路程运动得慢，后段路程运动得快，所以小车在全程不是做匀速运动。

答案 （1）$v=\dfrac{s}{t}$　　（2）小

（3）如表所示

	小车由甲至乙	小车由乙至丙	小车由甲至丙
路程 s/cm		64	90
时间 t/s	2		6
平均速度 v/(cm/s)	13	16	

（4）见解析

质量与密度

知识梳理

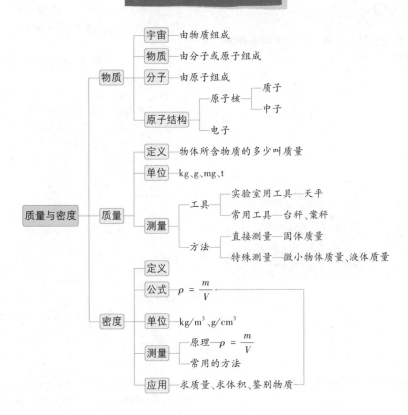

第1节 宇宙和微观世界

知识清单

基础知识
- 知识 1 宇宙与物质的组成
- 知识 2 原子的结构

知识 1 宇宙与物质的组成

1.宇宙中拥有数十亿个星系,银河系只是其中之一;银河系有几千亿颗恒星,太阳只是其中之一;地球是太阳周围八大行星之一,地球和其他星体都是由物质组成的。

2.物质

（1）物质是由分子或原子组成的,分子是保持物质化学性质的最小粒子,分子由原子构成。由单个原子组成的是单原子分子,绝大多数分子是多原子分子。

（2）原子又是由原子核和绕核运动的带负电的电子组成的,其中原子核包括质子和中子两种粒子,后来科学家发现质子和中子都是由称为夸克的更小的粒子组成的。

第 4 部分

（3）随着人类对微观世界的探索不断深入，在 20 世纪中叶，科学工作者相继发现了 400 余种粒子，它们是比原子核更深一个层次的物质存在形式。人类对微观世界的探索还在继续，这种探索是永无止境的。

易混对比

物体与物质

物体是指具有一定形状，占据一定空间，有体积和质量的实物；如桌子、铝锅、铁钉、塑料尺等均是物体。而构成物体的材料——木材、铝、铁、塑料等是物质。

知识 **2** **原子的结构**

1.卢瑟福在成功地进行了 α 粒子的散射实验后，提出了原子核式结构模型。原子的中心有一个原子核，占很小的体积，但其密度很大，几乎集中了原子的全部质量。带负电的电子在不同的轨道上绕原子核运动，就像地球绕太阳运动一样，如图甲。

2.20 世纪初，科学家们在探索物质结构的历程中，相继发现了原子核可以释放出质子和中子，质子带正电，中子不带电。由此知道了原子核是由质子和中子组成的，如图乙。

 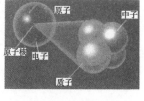

甲 原子核式结构模型　　乙 原子核结构示意图

方法清单

方法 概念法认识分子

方法 **概念法认识分子**

①物质是由分子组成的；②分子是保持物质化学性质的最小微粒；③分子的直径很小，用肉眼和一般显微镜根本观察不到。凡是用肉眼直接看到的一定不是分子。

例 下列关于分子的说法正确的是 （ 　 ）

3.质子和中子是由夸克组成的。
原子的组成可表示为：

例 关于粒子和宇宙，下列认识中正确的是

（ 　 ）

A.分子间仅存在吸引力，不存在排斥力

B.在质子、电子和原子中，尺度最小的是质子

C.根据银河系的直径大约为 8 万光年，可知光年是时间单位

D.科学家在研究物质内部结构时，常应用建立"模型"的方法

(解析) 分子间同时存在着引力和斥力，A 项错误；原子是由原子核和核外电子组成的，原子核是由质子和中子组成的，在质子、电子和原子中，尺度最小的是电子，B 项错误；光年是光在 1 年中通过的路程，故光年是长度单位，C 项错误；科学家研究物质内部结构时，常应用建立模型的方法，D 项正确。

(答案) D

拓展知识

知识 夸克

知识 **夸克**

现代科学研究发现，质子和中子等微粒也有内部结构，它们是由一种叫做夸克的更小的微粒组成的。

A.分子是微观世界中的最小微粒

B.将一块糖进行若干次对分，但要保持其甜味，可分为的最小微粒是分子

C.蛋白质是一种大分子，它的大小大约有几十微米

D.以上说法都不对

(解析) 分子是人们认识微观世界的一道大门，它是保持物质化学性质的最小微粒，而分子则由更小的微粒——原子组成，原子还可以再分，因此选项 A 错，B 对；1 μm＝ 10^{-6} m，蛋白质的分子比较大，但用微米显然不合理，因此 C 选项错。

(答案) B

第 2 节　质量

知识清单

基础知识

知识 **1** 质量的概念
知识 **2** 天平的使用方法
知识 **3** 量筒

知识 1　质量的概念

定义	单位	说明
物体所含物质的多少叫质量	千克（kg）、克（g）、毫克（mg）、吨（t），1 t = 10^3 kg= 10^6 g= 10^9 mg	质量是物体本身的一种属性,物体的质量不随它的形状、状态、位置的改变而改变

温馨提示

"质量是物体本身的一种属性"理解为:

①物体的质量只与物体所含物质的多少有关(如图)。

我含木料少,我的质量小!

我含木料多,我的质量大!

②物体的质量与物体的形状、状态、位置等无关。如一个玻璃杯,打碎后玻璃碎片的质量与玻璃杯的质量相同;一杯水结成冰后,冰的质量与水的质量相同;一个玻璃杯,从北京带到上海,其质量不变,就是带到月球上,其质量也不变。

知识 2　天平的使用方法

在物理实验中,测物体质量的工具是天平,为正确使用天平,需注意以下事项。

1.使用天平前须知

（1）了解天平的构造。天平由底座、分度盘、横梁、平衡螺母、托盘、标尺、游码、指针及砝码组成。

（2）知道天平的称量和感量。

2.天平的使用方法

天平的使用方法可归纳为:放、移、调、称、读、收。

放	将天平放在水平台上
移	使用前将游码移至标尺左端的"0"刻度线处
调	调节横梁上的平衡螺母,使指针指在分度盘的中央刻度线处,这时横梁平衡。调节平衡螺母的方法有两种:①"螺母反指针"法:也就是当指针向右偏时,应将横梁上的平衡螺母向左调(如图),即螺母调的方向与指针偏转的方向相反;②"左高左调,右高右调"法:即横梁左端高,平衡螺母向左调;横梁右端高,平衡螺母向右调  向左调节螺母才会平衡哟!
称	称量时,把被测物体放在左盘,估计一下被测物体的质量后,用镊子夹取砝码,并按"先大后小"的顺序向右盘中依次试加砝码(如图),如果添加最小的砝码偏多,而取出这个最小的砝码又偏小,这时应取出最小的砝码,再调节游码在标尺上的位置,直到天平指针指在分度盘的中央刻度线处。特别注意:被测物体和砝码的位置是"左物右码" 先来个大的。  添加砝码应"先大后小"
读	右盘里砝码的总质量加上标尺上游码的示数,就是被测物体的质量(如图),即:$m_{物} = m_{砝} + m_{游}$;游码的示数以与游码的左侧对齐的示数为准 一起去计算质量 走了  等等我!
收	测量完毕,把被测物体取下,砝码放回盒中,游码拨回标尺零刻度线处,即"取下物体,砝码回盒,游码归零"

第 4 部分

第 4 部分　第 7 章　质量与密度　**97**

例 学过天平使用的知识后,好奇的小明想用家中的一架旧天平称一个鸡蛋的质量。在调节横梁平衡时,先将砝码移至零刻度线处,此时指针偏向分度盘右侧,则应将平衡螺母向_____调节。他发现无论怎样调节平衡螺母,指针总略偏向分度盘右侧,于是他在天平的左盘中放入几粒米后重新调节平衡并进行了测量,如图所示。则鸡蛋的质量_____61 g(大于/等于/小于)。

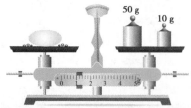

(解析) 调节天平时,哪边高将平衡螺母向哪边调,所以应向左调节;天平左盘放上几粒米,使天平平衡,道理和调节平衡螺母相同;调平后鸡蛋的质量等于砝码质量加上游码对应的示数,所以鸡蛋的质量等于61 g。

(答案) 左　等于

知识 3　量筒

1.量筒是用来测量液体体积的工具,一般由玻璃制成,使用时注意轻拿轻放。

2.量筒的使用方法

(1)使用前要先观察量筒的量程和分度值(每小格表示的体积值)。实验室中常用的量筒的量程有:0~50 mL、0~100 mL、0~250 mL、0~500 mL、0~1 000 mL等。不同的量筒的分度值通常是不同的。测量时,要根据测量精度的要求和被测物体的体积等因素来选择合适的量筒。

(2)用量筒测量液体的体积。测量时,要把量筒放在水平桌面上,**读数时视线要与量筒中液面的凹面底部(或凸面顶部)相平**(如图所示)。

(3)用量筒测量形状不规则的固体体积是利用排水法,即把固体浸没在液体中,固体的体积等于被它排开的液体体积。

(4)如果是测量糖块等在水中溶解的固体体积时可用"排沙法"(用细沙代替水)。

例1 实验室里有四种规格的量筒,下列每组选项中的前一个数据是量筒的量程,后一个数据是它的分度值,想要尽可能精确地一次量出 125 cm³ 的酒精,应选用的合适量筒是　　　　　　　( )

A.0~500 mL,50 mL　　　　B.0~100 mL,2 mL
C.0~250 mL,5 mL　　　　D.0~400 mL,10 mL

(解析) 量筒的选择应根据测量精度的要求和被测物体的体积。本题中 125 cm³ = 125 mL,所选量筒量程应大于 125 mL,分度值尽可能小些,所以选 C。

(答案) C

例2 如图是小亮用漫画的方式描绘了"迷糊教授"的实验操作,其中正确的是　　　　( )

A　　　　B　　　　C　　　　D

(解析) 用温度计测量水温,读数时温度计的液泡不能离开被测液体,故 A 错误;用量筒测液体体积,读数时量筒应放在水平桌面上,视线与凹液面底部相平,故 B 正确,D 错误;用刻度尺测量长度时,刻度尺有刻度的一边应紧贴被测物体,若物体的一端没与 0 刻度线对齐,读数时应将末端所对刻度值减去起始端所对准的刻度值,故 C 错误。

(答案) B

拓展知识 ○○○○○○○○○
知识 天平使用时的几个为什么

知识　天平使用时的几个为什么

1.观察天平是否平衡,为什么要采用"摆动法"?

答:无论是称量前的调平,还是称量过程中观察天平是否平衡,一般都采用"摆动法",这主要是针对天平的摆动惯性。尽管指针在分度盘上左右摆动的幅度会依次递减,但只要指针左右摆动的幅度基本相等,便可认为天平达到平衡。

2.为什么使用天平称物体的质量时,被测物体的质量不能超过天平的称量?

答:每一种测量工具都有一个测量范围,天平也一样。天平的称量就是它所能称的最大质量。如果被测物体的质量超过了这个称量,显然天平不可能平衡,因而测不出结果。仔细观察天平横梁的支点,就会发现它是一个十分锋利的刀口。如果被测物体的质量超过了天平的称量,就会损伤刀口,使天平摆动不灵活,影响测量的准确性。因而使用天平时,不能测质量超过它称量的物体。用镊子加减砝码时要轻拿轻放,也是为了避免损坏刀口及其他部件。

方法清单
方法❶ 累积法测微小质量
方法❷ 归纳法解决天平使用时常见的问题

方法 1 累积法测微小质量

质量较小物体的称量用累积法,即取 n 个物体称出其质量 M,则每个物体质量 $m = \dfrac{M}{n}$。

例 为了测量一张邮票的质量,小东设计了以下几种方案,其中可行的是 （ ）

A.用天平直接测一张邮票的质量

B.用天平测出 10 张相同邮票的质量,再将结果除以 10

C.用天平测出一张邮票和一个砝码的总质量,再减去一个砝码的质量

D.用天平测出 100 张相同邮票的质量,再将结果除以 100

解析 因为天平的感量是天平测量质量时的最小允许值。如果被测物体的质量小于天平的感量,将无法用天平测出物体的质量。因为一张邮票的质量远小于天平的感量,所以 A 是错误的。通过测 10 张相同邮票的质量来求单张邮票的质量时,尽管考虑到了累积法,但由于累积的质量仍然小于天平的感量,所以 B 是错误的。(如果用天平测一张邮票和一个砝码的总质量,用减差法也无法测出来,因为一张邮票的质量和一个砝码的质量相差太大,)所以 C 错误。取 100 张邮票时,它们的总质量大于天平的感量,可以用天平测出 100 张相同邮票的质量,除以 100 算出一张邮票的质量,故选 D。

答案 D

方法 2 归纳法解决天平使用时常见的问题

使用天平时,常见问题归纳如下:

1.游码未归零问题

题型特征:游码未置于标尺左端的零刻度线处就将天平调节平衡了,而在称量的过程中又移动了游码的位置。

在正常使用情况下,将游码向右移动,相当于在右盘中添加砝码;同理,若将游码向左移动,则相当于在左盘中添加砝码(或者相当于在右盘中减去砝码)。

2.物码错位问题

题型特征:称量时误将被测物体和砝码位置放反。

正常情况下,物体(质量为 $m_物$)放在天平左盘,砝码(质量为 $m_码$)放在天平右盘,且游码(其示数值表示质量为 $m_游$)是作为小砝码在使用的,有 $m_左 = m_右$,即 $m_物 = m_砝 + m_游$;若物码错位放置,则有 $m_砝 = m_物 + m_游$,即被测物体的质量 $m_物 = m_砝 - m_游$。

3.砝码不规范问题

如果砝码磨损,其质量减小,用它来平衡与它示数所对应质量相同的物体,必须向右移动游码,因此,读出的数值比物体的实际质量大。如果砝码上粘有其他物质,砝码的质量比它所示的质量大,称量时,导致游码向右移动较少,读出的数值比物体的实际质量小。

例1 某同学使用天平时,游码固定在 4 g 处,将天平调平衡。在测量物体质量时,右盘加上 18 g 砝码,再把游码移到零刻度线处,天平横梁再次平衡。则所称物体质量为 （ ）

A.10 g　　B.22 g　　C.14 g　　D.26 g

解析 解法一:使用天平时,游码固定在 4 g 处,相当于从右盘中拿去砝码,所以物体的质量 $m_物 = m_砝 - m_游 = 18$ g-4 g$=14$ g;解法二:游码固定在 4 g 处,相当于在左盘中添加砝码,则有:$m_物 + 4$ g$= 18$ g,$m_物 = 14$ g。C 项正确。

答案 C

例2 小明利用天平测一块小石块的质量。

(1)他测量小石块质量时的情形如图所示,其中违反操作规定的是＿＿＿＿＿＿＿。

(2)图中小石块的实际质量是＿＿＿＿＿g。

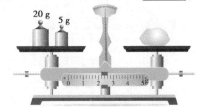

解析 (1)使用天平测质量时,物体应放在左盘,砝码放在右盘。(2)若物体和砝码放错位置,砝码的总质量减去游码的示数就是被测物体的实际质量。本题中小石块的质量是 25 g-2.2 g$= 22.8$ g。

答案 (1)被测物体放在右盘,砝码放在左盘
(2)22.8

例3 用天平称量物体质量时,如果砝码磨损了,则测得的质量比真实值 （ ）

A.偏小　　　　　　B.偏大

C.相同　　　　　　D.无法确定

解析 砝码磨损,本身质量减小,测质量时,游码需向右多移一些,测量值偏大。

答案 B

第3节 密度

基础知识 | 知识① 密度
知识② "密度是物质的特性"的含义

知识 1 密度

定义	某种物质组成的物体的质量与它的体积之比叫做这种物质的密度
单位	密度的国际单位是 kg/m^3，常用单位还有 g/cm^3。这两个单位的换算关系是 $10^3\ kg/m^3 = 1\ g/cm^3$。如水的密度是 $1.0×10^3\ kg/m^3$，表示的意思是 $1\ m^3$ 的水的质量是 1 000 kg
公式	密度的计算公式为 $\rho = m/V$，由此可得两个变形公式为 $m = \rho V$、$V = m/\rho$
作用	密度是物质的一种特性，不同物质的密度通常是不同的，因此可用密度来粗略地鉴别物质(如图) 

例 为了研究物质的某种特性，某同学测得四组数据，并填入表中。

实验序号	物体	m/g	V/cm³	$\frac{m}{V}$/(g·cm⁻³)
①	铝块1	54	20	2.7
②	铝块2	108	40	2.7
③	松木1	108	216	
④	松木2	10	20	0.5

(1)将表中的空格补全；

(2)比较①、②两次数据得出结论:同一种物质，它的质量跟它的体积成_____比；

(3)比较②、③两次数据得出结论:_____(填条件)，体积大的，密度小；

(4)比较①、④两次数据得出结论:_____(填条件)，质量大的，密度大；

(5)分析全部数据发现，对不同物质来说，质量与体积的比值不同，我们把物质的这种特性叫做物质的_____。

解析 (1)$\frac{m}{V} = \frac{108\ g}{216\ cm^3} = 0.5\ g/cm^3$。

(2)由表中数据分析，同一种物质，它的质量与体积的比值为一定值，质量跟体积成正比。

(3)由②、③数据知，质量相同的不同物质，体积不同。

(4)由①、④数据知，体积相同的不同物质，质量不同。

(5)通过分析可知此特性为物质的密度

答案 (1)0.5 (2)正 (3)质量相同的不同物质 (4)体积相同的不同物质 (5)密度

知识 2 "密度是物质的特性"的含义

1.当状态不变(气体除外)时，对于同种物质来说，密度是不变的，它的质量与体积成正比。例如铝制品，不论它体积多大，质量多少，质量跟体积的比值是不变的。

2.不同的物质，其密度一般不同，平时习惯上讲"水比油重"就是指水的密度大于油的密度，在相同体积的情况下，水的质量大于油的质量。

拓展知识 | 知识① 影响密度的因素
方法② 瓶装气体的密度

知识 1 影响密度的因素

1.温度:一般来说，物体受热膨胀，遇冷收缩，即温度变化时体积改变，因此物质的密度在温度升高时会变小，在温度降低时会变大。(水例外，它在 4 ℃时密度最大)

2.状态:物体发生物态变化时，物质的密度也会随之发生改变。在通常情况下，同种物质组成的物体固态时密度最大，液态次之，气态时密度最小。(水例外，冰比水的密度小)

3.气压:气体的密度随压强的增大而增大，随压强的减小而减小。因为质量不变时，压强增大则体积减小，导致密度增大，反之亦然。

4.浓度:液体的浓度变大时，密度增大;浓度减小时，密度减小。

例 某研究性学习小组做"水的体积随温度变化"的研究，得到如图所示的图像。从图中可知，水温从 8 ℃降到 2 ℃的过程中，其密度 (　　)

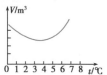

A.先变大后变小　　　B.先变小后变大
C.一直变大　　　　　D.保持不变

(解析) 由图像知,水的体积先变小后变大,据 $\rho = \dfrac{m}{V}$ 知,其密度先变大后变小,选 A。

(答案) A

知识 2 瓶装气体的密度

对于瓶装气体,由于气体始终充满整个容器,瓶内气体的体积保持不变;但用掉一部分后,气体的质量会变小;根据 $\rho = \dfrac{m}{V}$ 可知,瓶内气体的密度会变小;也可以理解为瓶内气体变"稀"了一些。

(例) 某瓶氧气的密度是 5 kg/m³,给人供氧用去了氧气质量的一半,则瓶内剩余氧气的密度是 _____;容积是 10 L 的瓶子装满了煤油,已知煤油的密度

是 0.8×10^3 kg/m³,则瓶内煤油的质量是 _____,将煤油倒去 4 kg 后,瓶内剩余煤油的密度是 _____。

(解析) 气体的分子间作用力非常微弱,可忽略不计,它总是充满盛它的整个容器,氧气用去一半后,其质量变为原来的一半,而体积不变,由密度公式 $\rho = \dfrac{m}{V}$ 可知,密度变为原来的一半;煤油的质量 $m = \rho V = 0.8 \times 10^3$ kg/m³×10×10^{-3}m³ = 8 kg,液体的密度与质量无关,故煤油倒去 4 kg 后密度仍为 0.8×10^3 kg/m³。

(答案) 2.5 kg/m³　8 kg　0.8×10^3 kg/m³

点拨 密度是物质的一种特性,对于同一种物质(其状态不变)密度不变,但是对于气体来说,由于气体的体积始终充满整个容器,所以同一种气体的密度也是不稳定的。气体在容器中用去一部分,体积是不变的,质量变小,密度变小;而固体、液体去掉一部分后,密度是不变的。

方法清单

方法 1　图像法判断物质的密度
方法 2　密度比值类问题的解法
方法 3　隐含"体积、密度、质量"不变问题的解法
方法 4　合金物体密度的计算方法

方法 1　图像法判断物质的密度

1.此类问题一般是给出质量-体积图像,判断或比较物质密度。

2.解答时可在横轴(或纵轴)上任选一数值,然后在纵轴(或横轴)上找到对应的数值,进行分析比较。

(例 1) 甲、乙两种物质的质量 m 与体积 V 的关系图像如图所示。由图像可知　　　　(　　)

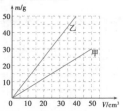

A.体积相等时,甲的质量大
B.质量相等时,乙的体积大
C.甲的密度比乙的大
D.乙的密度为 1.25×10^3 kg/m³

(解析) 由图可知,体积相等时,甲的质量小,乙的质量大;质量相等时,乙的体积小,甲的体积大,故选项 A、B 错误。质量相等时,乙的体积小,甲的体积大,由密度公式可知,甲的密度比乙的小,故选项 C 错误。$m = 50$ g 时,乙的体积为 $V = 40$ cm³,故乙的密度为 $\rho = \dfrac{m}{V} = \dfrac{50\ \text{g}}{40\ \text{cm}^3} = 1.25$ g/cm³ = 1.25×10^3 kg/m³,故 D 正确。

(答案) D

(例 2) 为测量某种液体的密度,小明利用天平和量杯测量了液体和量杯的总质量 m 及液体的体积 V,得到了几组数据并绘出了 m-V 图像,如图所示。下列说法正确的是　　　　　　(　　)

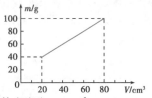

A.该液体密度为 2 g/cm³
B.该液体密度为 1.25 g/cm³
C.量杯质量为 40 g
D.60 cm³ 的该液体质量为 60 g

(解析) 由题图可知,横坐标表示液体的体积,纵坐标表示液体和量杯的总质量,当液体体积由 20 mL 增大到 80 mL 时,总质量由 40 g 增大到了 100 g,所以液体密度 $\rho = \dfrac{m}{V} = \dfrac{100\ \text{g}-40\ \text{g}}{80\ \text{cm}^3-20\ \text{cm}^3} = 1$ g/cm³,故 A、B 项错误;20 mL 液体质量为 20 g,所以量杯质量为 40 g-20 g = 20 g,C 项错误;60 cm³ 液体质量是 $m = \rho V = 1$ g/cm³×60 cm³ = 60 g,D 项正确。

(答案) D

方法 2　密度比值类问题的解法

对于求比值的问题,把所给条件写成比的形式后,根据密度公式或者其变形公式,把所要求的量用比值表示出来,化简,代入数据,计算得出结果。

(例) 甲、乙两个物体的质量之比为 3∶2,体积之比为 1∶3,那么它们的密度之比为　　(　　)

A.1∶2　　B.2∶1　　C.2∶9　　D.9∶2

(解析) 此类问题的解法很多,一般有下列几种方法。

第4部分　第 7 章　质量与密度　**101**

解法一:写出所求物理量的表达式 $\rho_甲 = \dfrac{m_甲}{V_甲}$, $\rho_乙 = \dfrac{m_乙}{V_乙}$;

写出该物理量比的表达式

$$\dfrac{\rho_甲}{\rho_乙} = \dfrac{\dfrac{m_甲}{V_甲}}{\dfrac{m_乙}{V_乙}} = \dfrac{m_甲}{V_甲} \cdot \dfrac{V_乙}{m_乙} = \dfrac{m_甲}{m_乙} \cdot \dfrac{V_乙}{V_甲};$$

代入已知比值求解

$$\dfrac{\rho_甲}{\rho_乙} = \dfrac{3}{2} \times \dfrac{3}{1} = \dfrac{9}{2}.$$

解法二:由公式 $\rho = \dfrac{m}{V}$ 得到 $m = \rho V$, $V = \dfrac{m}{\rho}$, 我们可以直接利用下面的公式求出密度比、体积比或质量比。

密度比 $= \dfrac{质量比}{体积比}$, 质量比 $=$ 密度比 × 体积比,

体积比 $= \dfrac{质量比}{密度比}$;

即 $\dfrac{\rho_甲}{\rho_乙} = \dfrac{m_甲/m_乙}{V_甲/V_乙} = \dfrac{3/2}{1/3} = \dfrac{9}{2}.$

解法三:已知两个物体的质量和体积的关系,可以用一个物体的质量和体积表示出另一个物体的密度,再求出两个物体的密度比(求体积比或质量比也可以用此方法)。

由 $\dfrac{m_甲}{m_乙} = \dfrac{3}{2}$ 得 $m_甲 = \dfrac{3}{2} m_乙$; 由 $\dfrac{V_甲}{V_乙} = \dfrac{1}{3}$ 得 $V_甲 = \dfrac{1}{3} V_乙$, 因为 $\rho_甲 = \dfrac{m_甲}{V_甲} = \dfrac{\frac{3}{2} m_乙}{\frac{1}{3} V_乙} = \dfrac{9}{2} \rho_乙$, 所以 $\dfrac{\rho_甲}{\rho_乙} = \dfrac{9}{2}.$

解法四:设 $m_甲 = 3, m_乙 = 2, V_甲 = 1, V_乙 = 3$, 则 $\rho_甲 = \dfrac{m_甲}{V_甲} = \dfrac{3}{1} = 3, \rho_2 = \dfrac{m_乙}{V_乙} = \dfrac{2}{3}$, $\dfrac{\rho_甲}{\rho_乙} = \dfrac{3}{2/3} = \dfrac{9}{2}.$

(答案) D

方法 3 隐含"体积、密度、质量"不变问题的解法

物理问题中的有些条件需要仔细审题才能确定,这类条件称为隐含条件;寻找隐含条件是解决这类问题的关键。

密度计算题形式多样,变化灵活,但其中有一些题具有这样的特点:即质量、体积、密度中的某个量在其他量发生变化时保持不变。抓住这一特点,就掌握了求解这类题的规律。

1.隐含体积不变

例1 飞机设计师为减轻飞机自重,将一钢制零件改为铝制零件,使其质量减少 104 kg,则所需铝的质量是($\rho_钢 = 7.9$ g/cm³, $\rho_铝 = 2.7$ g/cm³)　( )

A.35.5 kg　　　　　　B.54 kg

C.104 kg　　　　　　D.158 kg

(解析) 解此题的关键是抓住隐含条件——零件的体积不变。$m_钢 = \rho_钢 V$, $m_铝 = \rho_铝 V$, $m_钢 - m_铝 = \rho_钢 V - \rho_铝 V = (\rho_钢 - \rho_铝) V$, $V = \dfrac{m_钢 - m_铝}{\rho_钢 - \rho_铝} = \dfrac{104 \text{ kg}}{7.9 \times 10^3 \text{ kg/m}^3 - 2.7 \times 10^3 \text{ kg/m}^3} = 20 \times 10^{-3} \text{ m}^3$, $m_铝 = \rho_铝 V = 2.7 \times 10^3 \text{ kg/m}^3 \times 20 \times 10^{-3} \text{ m}^3 = 54 \text{ kg}$。应选 B。

(答案) B

2.隐含密度不变

例2 一块石碑的体积为 $V_碑 = 30$ m³, 为测石碑的质量,先取了一块刻制石碑时剔下来的小石块作为样品,其质量是 $m_样 = 140$ g, 将它放入 $V_1 = 100$ cm³ 的水中后水面升高,总体积增大到 $V_2 = 150$ cm³, 求这块石碑的质量 $m_碑$。

(解析) 此题中隐含的条件是石碑和样品属于同种物质,密度相同,而不同的是它们的体积和质量。依题意可知,样品体积为:

$V_样 = V_2 - V_1 = 150 \text{ cm}^3 - 100 \text{ cm}^3 = 50 \text{ cm}^3$

$V_样 = 5.0 \times 10^{-5} \text{ m}^3$

由密度的计算式和密度不变的条件有 $\dfrac{m_碑}{V_碑} = \dfrac{m_样}{V_样}$

得 $m_碑 = \dfrac{m_样 V_碑}{V_样} = \dfrac{140 \times 10^{-3} \times 30}{5.0 \times 10^{-5}}$ kg $= 8.4 \times 10^4$ kg $= 84$ t。

(答案) 84 t

3.隐含质量不变

例3 规格相同的瓶装了不同的液体,放在横梁已平衡的天平上,如图所示。则　( )

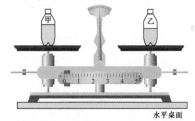

水平桌面

A.甲瓶液体质量较大

B.乙瓶液体质量较大

C.乙瓶液体密度较大

D.两瓶液体密度相等

(解析) 天平两边平衡,说明两瓶内液体质量相同,乙瓶内液体体积较小,由 $\rho = \dfrac{m}{V}$ 知乙瓶中液体密度较大,所以 A、B、D 项错误,C 项正确。

(答案) C

方法 4 合金物体密度的计算方法

首先要抓住合金物体的总质量与总体积分别等于各种物质的质量之和与体积之和这一特征,然后根据具体问题,灵活求解。

例 两种不同的金属,密度分别为 ρ_1、ρ_2。

(1)若取质量相等的金属混合后制成合金,则合金的密度为_____。

(2)若取体积相等的金属混合后制成合金,则合金的密度为_____。

解析 解这道题的关键是抓住"两总"不变,即总质量和总体积不变。

(1)两种金属的质量相等,设为 $m_1 = m_2 = m$,合金的质量 $m_总 = 2m$,密度为 ρ_1 的金属的体积 $V_1 = \dfrac{m}{\rho_1}$,密度为 ρ_2 的金属的体积 $V_2 = \dfrac{m}{\rho_2}$,合金的体积 $V_总 = V_1 + V_2 = \dfrac{m}{\rho_1} + \dfrac{m}{\rho_2}$,则合金的密度 $\rho = \dfrac{m_总}{V_总} = \dfrac{2\rho_1\rho_2}{\rho_1 + \rho_2}$。

(2)两种金属的体积相等,设为 $V_1 = V_2 = V$,合金的体积 $V_总 = 2V$,密度为 ρ_1 的金属的质量 $m_1 = \rho_1 V$,密度为 ρ_2 的金属的质量 $m_2 = \rho_2 V$,合金的质量 $m_总 = (\rho_1 + \rho_2)V$,合金的密度 $\rho = \dfrac{m_总}{V_总} = \dfrac{\rho_1 + \rho_2}{2}$。

答案 (1)$\dfrac{2\rho_1\rho_2}{\rho_1 + \rho_2}$ (2)$\dfrac{\rho_1 + \rho_2}{2}$

点拨 求合金密度与求平均速度类似,计算方法分别为:$\rho = \dfrac{m_总}{V_总}$,$\bar{v} = \dfrac{s_总}{t_总}$;质量分半和路程分半时分别为:$\rho = \dfrac{2\rho_1\rho_2}{\rho_1 + \rho_2}$,$\bar{v} = \dfrac{2v_1v_2}{v_1 + v_2}$;体积分半和时间分半时分别为:$\rho = \dfrac{\rho_1 + \rho_2}{2}$,$\bar{v} = \dfrac{v_1 + v_2}{2}$。

第 4 节　测量物质的密度

知识清单

基础知识

知识 密度的测量

知识　密度的测量

1.原理:由密度公式 $\rho = \dfrac{m}{V}$ 可知,要测量某种物质的密度,需要测量由这种物质构成的物体的质量和体积。

2.密度的测量

物体特征	测量方法
液体	用天平测烧杯和液体的总质量 m_1,将烧杯中的液体倒入量筒中一部分,读出示数 V,再测剩下的液体与烧杯的总质量 m_2,则液体的密度 $\rho = \dfrac{m}{V} = \dfrac{m_1 - m_2}{V}$
形状规则的固体	质量可用天平测量,体积可直接用刻度尺测量,并利用体积公式算出,如正方体体积 $V = a^3$,圆柱体体积 $V = \pi r^2 h$,长方体体积 $V = abc$,根据 $\rho = \dfrac{m}{V}$ 求得密度(a、b、c 均为边长)

续表

物体特征	测量方法	
形状不规则的固体(不溶于水)	质量可用天平测量	
	体积可用"排水法"间接地测出	①先在量筒中倒入适量水,读出水的体积 V_1(水的多少以刚好淹没固体为宜。水过多,放入固体后液面会超过量程;水过少,不能淹没固体) ②将固体用细线拴住慢慢放入量筒内水中,并使其全部浸入,此时读出水与固体的总体积 V_2 ③由 $V = V_2 - V_1$,可得出固体体积
	根据 $\rho = \dfrac{m}{V}$ 求得密度	

物体特征	测量方法
漂浮的固体	质量可用天平测量
	体积可用"助沉法"测出 ①将固体和能沉入水中的重物用细线拴在一起,先用手提固体端的细线,只将能沉入水中的重物浸没在量筒内的水中,读出体积 V_1(如图甲) ②然后使拴在一起的固体完全浸入水中,读出体积 V_2(如图乙)  ③被测固体体积 $V=V_2-V_1$
	体积也可用"针压法"测出: 用一细长针刺入被测物体并用力将其压入量筒内的水中,使其浸没,测固体的体积
	根据 $\rho=\dfrac{m}{V}$ 求得密度
较大固体	质量可用天平测量
	体积可用"溢水法"测出: 把大烧杯装满水,以水刚好溢出为准,此时把较大固体浸没在烧杯内的水中,同时用另一容器承接从烧杯中溢出的水,再用量筒测溢出水的体积 V, V 就是较大固体的体积
	根据 $\rho=\dfrac{m}{V}$ 求得密度

易混对比 对助沉法求漂浮固体体积的理解

对于漂浮的固体,用排水法测体积时,需用重物将待测物体坠入水中,我们称为"助沉法"。下面以蜡块为例。

由图可知:量筒内盛水的体积为 V_0(图甲);重物浸入水中后,水和重物的体积和为 V_1,即 $V_0+V_重=V_1$(图乙);重物和蜡块都浸入水中后,水、重物与蜡块的体积和为 V_2,即 $V_0+V_重+V_蜡=V_2$(图丙)。

所以,由图乙和图丙可知: $V_蜡=V_2-V_1$;有些同学理解时受水的体积 V_0 的影响,我们换个角度理解:由图甲、图乙可知: $V_重=V_1-V_0$;由图甲、图丙可知 $V_蜡+V_重=V_2-V_0$;则 $V_蜡=V_2-V_0-(V_1-V_0)=V_2-V_1$。

拓展知识 知识 巧测密度

知识 巧测密度

1.天平、溢水法测固体的密度

用天平测出固体的质量,若没有量筒,无法直接测体积,可用"溢水法"换算出体积,然后由密度公式 $\rho=\dfrac{m}{V}$ 求解密度。例如:给你一串钥匙、烧杯、足量的水、天平(带砝码)、细线,要求测出钥匙的密度。可以这样测量:

(1)用天平测出钥匙的质量 m;

(2)在烧杯中装满水,用天平测出总质量 m_1;

(3)用细线拴住钥匙放入水中浸没,溢出部分水,取出钥匙,再用天平测出此时烧杯和剩余水的总质量 m_2。

则钥匙的体积 $V=V_溢水=\dfrac{m_溢水}{\rho_水}=\dfrac{m_1-m_2}{\rho_水}$,

钥匙的密度 $\rho=\dfrac{m}{V}=\dfrac{m}{m_1-m_2}\cdot\rho_水$。

2.天平、满容器法测液体的密度

(1)用天平测出空容器的质量 m_1;

(2)在容器中装满水,用天平测出容器和水的总质量 m_2;

(3)倒出容器中的水并擦干容器,在容器中装满待测液体,用天平测出容器和待测液体的总质量 m_3。

则待测液体的密度 $\rho=\dfrac{m_3-m_1}{m_2-m_1}\cdot\rho_水$。

3.标记法(等容转换)测液体的密度

(1)用天平测出空烧杯的质量 m;

(2)在烧杯中装入适量的水,用细线或笔在水面处做上标记,用天平测出烧杯和水的总质量 m_1;

(3)倒出水擦干烧杯,再向烧杯内倒入待测液体至标记处,用天平测出烧杯和待测液体的总质量 m_2。

待测液体的密度 $\rho=\dfrac{m_2-m}{m_1-m}\cdot\rho_水$。

例1 已知一个空瓶子装满水后的总质量为300 g,在装满水的瓶子中放入一个小石块,溢出水后其总质量为320 g,取出石块后,剩余的水和瓶子的总质量为290 g。(不计取出石块的过程中带走的水)则石块的质量为_____g,石块的密度为_____ g/cm^3。($\rho_水=1\times10^3\ kg/m^3$)

解析 $m_石=320\ g-290\ g=30\ g$

$V_石=V_溢=\dfrac{m_溢}{\rho_水}=\dfrac{300\ g-290\ g}{1.0\ g/cm^3}=10\ cm^3$

$\rho_石=\dfrac{m_石}{V_石}=\dfrac{30\ g}{10\ cm^3}=3\ g/cm^3$

答案 30 3

例2 某中学环保小组在长江边取适量江水样品,进行了江水密度的测量:

小亮把样品带回家,用家里的一台电子秤(如图所示)和没喝完的半瓶纯净水,做了如下实验:

①用电子秤测出半瓶纯净水的总质量为 m_1,并用笔在瓶身水面位置标记为 A;

②把瓶中的水全部用来浇花,然后吹干,用电子秤测出空瓶的质量为 m_2;

③把江水慢慢倒入空瓶中,直至液面与_____相平,再用电子秤测出瓶的总质量为 m_3;

④则江水的密度表达式 $\rho =$ _____(纯净水的密度用 $\rho_{水}$ 表示)。

⑤小亮测算江水的体积使用了下列 3 种物理方法中的_____。

A.控制变量法　　B.等量替代法　　C.类比法

(解析) 在无量筒的情况下,取相同体积的样品和纯净水计算密度,运用了等量替代法,根据水的密度可求出江水的密度:

$$\rho = \frac{m}{V} = \frac{m_3 - m_2}{(m_1 - m_2)/\rho_{水}} = \frac{m_3 - m_2}{m_1 - m_2}\rho_{水}。$$

(答案) ③标记 A　④$\dfrac{m_3 - m_2}{m_1 - m_2}\rho_{水}$　⑤B

方法清单

方法 1 比较法测液体的密度
方法 2 排水法测固体密度

方法 1 比较法测液体的密度

1.测液体密度时,实验误差要尽可能小。

2.两种实验方法的比较

	步骤	误差
实验一	①用天平测出烧杯和液体的总质量 m_1;②将烧杯中的液体向量筒中倒入一部分,读出示数 V;③测出剩下的液体与烧杯的总质量 m_2;④计算液体的密度 $\rho = \dfrac{m}{V} = \dfrac{m_1 - m_2}{V}$ 测总质量m_1　测倒出液体体积V　测剩余质量m_2	较小
实验二	①用天平测空烧杯质量 m_1;②将液体倒入空烧杯,测烧杯和液体的总质量 m_2;③将烧杯中的液体倒入量筒,读出示数 V;④计算液体密度 $\rho = \dfrac{m}{V} = \dfrac{m_2 - m_1}{V}$ 测烧杯质量m_1　测总质量m_2　测杯内液体体积V	将液体由烧杯倒入量筒时,烧杯壁上会粘有少量液体,所测液体体积偏小,所求密度值偏大;误差较大

例 1 某同学按照以下步骤测量盐水的密度:

①在烧杯中倒入适量盐水,用天平测出烧杯和盐水的总质量 m_1;

②将烧杯中的一部分盐水倒入量筒,测出烧杯和剩余盐水的总质量 m_2;

③_____;

④把测得的数据填入表格,计算出盐水的密度。

(1)请补充步骤③的内容。

(2)为了记录相关数据,他设计了如下表格,请将表格中第一行所缺的项目补充完整。

烧杯和盐水的总质量/g	烧杯和剩余盐水的总质量/g	量筒内盐水的质量/g	盐水的密度/(g·cm⁻³)

(3)盐水密度的表达式为 $\rho =$ _____。(用测量的物理量符号表示)

(解析) (1)将烧杯中的一部分盐水倒入量筒,利用量筒测出倒出盐水的体积,所以步骤③应是读出量筒内盐水的体积 V;(2)表格中应记录下量筒内盐水的体积,并附上其记录数值的单位;(3)由题中的操作步骤可知,量筒中盐水的质量为 $m_1 - m_2$,故盐水的密度 $\rho = \dfrac{m_1 - m_2}{V}$。

(答案) (1)读出量筒内盐水的体积 V

(2)量筒内盐水的体积/mL

(3)$\dfrac{m_1 - m_2}{V}$

例 2 某中学环保小组在长江边取适量江水样品,进行了江水密度的测量:

小薇把样品带回学校,用天平和量筒做了如下实验:

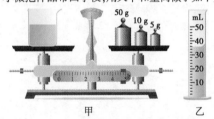

甲　　　　　乙

①用天平测出空烧杯的质量为 30 g，在烧杯中倒入适量的江水样品，测出烧杯和江水的总质量如图甲所示，则烧杯中江水的质量为_____g，将烧杯中的江水全部倒入量筒中，江水的体积如图乙所示，则江水的密度为_____g/cm³。

②小微用这种方法测出的江水密度比真实值_____（选填"偏大"或"偏小"）。

(解析) ①烧杯和江水的总质量为69.6 g，再减去烧杯质量30 g，则江水质量为39.6 g，量筒中江水的体积为36 cm³，则密度$\rho = \dfrac{m}{V} = \dfrac{39.6\ \text{g}}{36\ \text{cm}^3} = 1.1\ \text{g/cm}^3$；②由于从烧杯向量筒中倒入江水时会有残留，这样体积的测量值会偏小，则测出的江水密度会偏大。

(答案) ①39.6　1.1　②偏大

方法 2　排水法测固体密度

1.测量固体密度

(1)用天平测量固体的质量 m；

(2)用量筒测量固体的体积 V(排水法)；

(3)计算固体的密度 $\rho = \dfrac{m}{V}$。

2.注意：实验中不能改变实验步骤的顺序，应该先测量固体的质量，再测量固体的体积。因为测量固体的体积后，固体变得潮湿，不宜直接放在托盘上，而且这样测量的固体质量也会偏大，使固体密度的测量值偏大。

(例) 小王用天平和量筒测量矿石的密度。

(1)有如下一些实验步骤：

①用调节好的天平测出矿石的质量 m；

②向量筒中倒进适量的水，测出这些水的体积 V_1；

③根据密度的公式，求出矿石的密度 ρ；

④将矿石浸没在量筒内的水中，测出矿石和水的总体积 V_2。

他应采用的正确的实验步骤顺序为 (　　)

A.①②③④　　　　　　B.①②④③

C.②③①④　　　　　　D.②③④①

(2)由图可知，矿石的质量为_____g，矿石的体积为_____cm³，矿石的密度为_____g/cm³。

(解析) 在用天平和量筒测矿石的密度时，为减小误差应先测矿石质量后测体积。用量筒测矿石的体积时，要用到排水法，先在量筒中倒入一定量的水，记下量筒内水的体积 V_1，再将矿石用细线悬吊，小心地放入量筒内的水中，记下矿石没入水中后量筒内水和矿石的体积 V_2。根据排水法可计算出矿石的体积为 $V = V_2 - V_1 = 40\ \text{mL} - 30\ \text{mL} = 10\ \text{mL} = 10\ \text{cm}^3$；根据天平平衡时所加的砝码及游码的位置可读出矿石的质量为 $m = 20\ \text{g} + 5\ \text{g} + 2.2\ \text{g} = 27.2\ \text{g}$，再根据密度公式 $\rho = m/V$ 求得矿石的密度。

(答案) (1)B　(2)27.2　10　2.72

第 5 节　密度的应用

知识清单

 基础知识　**知识** 密度知识的应用

知识　密度知识的应用

应用	适用范围	方法
求物体的质量	不便于直接称量质量的物体	(1)查出组成该物体物质的密度 ρ，测出体积 V (2)根据 $\rho = \dfrac{m}{V}$ 的变形公式 $m = \rho V$ 求出质量

续表

应用	适用范围	方法
求物体的体积(实心)	形状不规则或不便于直接测量体积的物体	(1)查出组成该物体物质的密度 ρ，测出质量 m (2)根据 $\rho = \dfrac{m}{V}$ 的变形公式 $V = \dfrac{m}{\rho}$ 求出体积
求物质的密度	鉴别物质(选材料)	(1)根据 $\rho = \dfrac{m}{V}$ 算出物质的密度 (2)对照密度表，鉴别是什么物质

例 密度知识与生活联系非常紧密,下列关于密度的一些说法中正确的是（　　）

A.1 kg 冰与 1 kg 水的密度相等

B.乒乓球不慎被挤瘪但无破损,球内气体密度变大

C.为减轻质量,比赛用自行车采用强度高、密度大的材料制造

D.节日放飞的气球可以飘在空中,是因为气球内部气体的密度比空气大

解析 1 kg 的冰与 1 kg 的水,虽然质量相等,但体积不相等,由 $\rho=\dfrac{m}{V}$ 知,它们的密度不相等,A 项错误;乒乓球被挤瘪后,球内气体质量不变,但体积变小,则密度变大,B 项正确;比赛用的自行车,其体积是一定的,为减轻质量,应采用强度高、密度小的材料制造,C 项错误;气球可以飘在空中,气球内部气体的密度不大于空气的密度,D 项错。故选 B。

答案 B

拓展知识 知识 密度的特殊用途

知识 **密度的特殊用途**

根据需要选取不同密度的物质作为产品的原材料。

（1）铅用来制作网坠,铸铁用来制作落地扇的底座、塔式起重机的压铁等,都是因为它们的密度比较大。

（2）铝合金用来制造飞机,玻璃钢用来制造汽车的外壳,泡沫塑料用来制作救生器件等,都是因为它们的密度比较小。

方法清单

方法1 归纳法理解密度知识的应用

方法2 比较法判断物体是否空心

方法 1 归纳法理解密度知识的应用

密度知识的应用主要有三个方面:①求质量;②求体积;③鉴别物质或选择材料。

1.利用公式 $m=\rho V$,可以计算出庞大物体的质量,或者是在不使用天平的情况下,测出物体的质量。

例如:知道了人民英雄纪念碑的体积和花岗岩的密度,就可以大概计算出人民英雄纪念碑的质量。

例 1 一块石碑的体积为 5 m^3,取一小块作为这块石碑的样品,测得它的质量是 130 g,用量筒装入 100 cm^3 的水,再把石碑样品完全浸入水中,水面升高到 150 cm^3 处,请你根据以上数据,计算出整块石碑的质量为_____kg。

解析 石碑密度 $\rho_石=\dfrac{130\ g}{150\ cm^3-100\ cm^3}=2.6\ g/cm^3=2.6\times10^3\ kg/m^3$,所以石碑总质量 $m_石=\rho_石 V_石=2.6\times10^3\ kg/m^3\times5\ m^3=1.3\times10^4\ kg$。

答案 1.3×10^4

2.利用公式 $V=\dfrac{m}{\rho}$,可以计算出形状不规则的或不便于直接测量的较大物体的体积,或者在不方便用量筒的条件下,间接测出物体的体积。

例如:形状不规则石块的体积或一卷细铜丝的体积等。

例 2 有一捆质量为 8.9 kg,横截面积为 $2\times10^{-5}\ m^2$,粗细均匀的金属丝。小红想知道这捆金属丝的长度,她选择了一条同规格、同材料的短金属丝来间接测量这捆金属丝的长度,经测量得知短金属丝的长为 1 m,质量为 0.178 kg,求:

（1）这捆金属丝的总长 L;

（2）此金属丝的密度 ρ。

解析 （1）当金属丝的长度 $l=1$ m 时,其质量 $m=0.178$ kg,总质量为 $m_总=8.9$ kg,根据 $\dfrac{l}{L}=\dfrac{m}{m_总}$ 可计算出这捆金属丝的总长度 L。金属丝的总长度 $L=\dfrac{m_总\ l}{m}=8.9\ kg\times\dfrac{1\ m}{0.178\ kg}=50$ m。（2）已知金属丝的长度和横截面积,根据公式 $V=SL$ 可求出金属丝的体积,再根据公式 $\rho=\dfrac{m}{V}$ 可求出金属丝的密度。金属丝的总体积 $V=SL=2\times10^{-5}\ m^2\times50\ m=1\times10^{-3}\ m^3$,则金属丝的密度 $\rho=\dfrac{m_总}{V}=\dfrac{8.9\ kg}{1\times10^{-3}\ m^3}=8.9\times10^3\ kg/m^3$。

答案 （1）50 m （2）$8.9\times10^3\ kg/m^3$

3.鉴别物质或选择材料

（1）根据密度的大小可以鉴别物质。

例如:市面上卖的金、银首饰是否由纯金、银制成,我们只要把它们的密度大小计算出来,再跟纯金、银的密度比较,就可以鉴别出它们的真假,相等则可能为真,不等则为镀金、银。

例 3 莹莹的爸爸在商店里买了一件实心懒羊羊摆设如图,莹莹很想知道它是由什么物质制成的。通过实验,她测得其质量为 534 g,体积为 60 cm^3,则这件摆设的密度是_____g/cm^3,由下面的密度表可知,它可能是由_____制成的。

物质	密度ρ/(kg·m⁻³)
金	$19.3×10^3$
银	$10.5×10^3$
铜	$8.9×10^3$
钢、铁	$7.9×10^3$
铝	$2.7×10^3$

(解析) $\rho = \dfrac{m}{V} = \dfrac{534\ g}{60\ cm^3} = 8.9\ g/cm^3 = 8.9×10^3\ kg/m^3$,对照密度表可知该物质可能是铜。

(答案) 8.9 铜

（2）根据实际的需要,利用密度知识可以帮助选择材料。

例如:制造飞机的材料要求硬度大且"轻",因此就要选择密度小的合金材料。拍摄电影、电视剧时用的房屋等一些道具,要用密度小的材料来制造,这样即使人被压在下面,也不会有任何危险。

(例)4 制造战斗机,质量越_____越灵活,据此,选用_____较小且硬度较大的铝合金;落地式电风扇底座质量越_____越稳,所以,应选用_____较大且成本又低的铸铁较合理。

(解析) 战斗机的质量越小越灵活,应选密度较小且硬度较大的材料;落地式电风扇底座质量越大越稳定,应选密度较大的材料。

(答案) 小 密度 大 密度

方法 2 比较法判断物体是否空心

判断物体是实心还是空心,解决此类问题的方法很多,实质上都是根据密度的定义式,比较实际物体与实心物体的质量、体积或密度之间是否存在差异,即可采用比较质量法、比较体积法或比较密度法。如果存在差异,则实际物体为空心物体。

1.假设物体是实心的,则该物体的密度应该和组成物体的物质的密度相同。因此可用"比较密度法"比较,即可确定该物体是否空心。

2.假设物体是实心的,可以由 $V = \dfrac{m}{\rho}$ 求得等质量的实心物体的体积是多少,再跟该物体的真实体积相比较,即可确定该物体是否空心,这种方法称为"比较体积法"。

3.假设物体是实心的,可以由 $m = \rho V$ 求得等体积的实心物体的质量是多少,再跟该物体的真实质量相比较,即可确定该物体是否空心,这种方法称为"比较质量法"。

(例)1 一个边长为 0.1 m,质量为 4.45 kg 的正方体铜块,平放在水平桌面上。请用两种方法计算并说明铜块是空心的还是实心的。($\rho_{铜} = 8.9×10^3$ kg/m³, $\rho_{水} = 1.0×10^3$ kg/m³,g 取 10 N/kg)

(解析) 方法一:假设铜块是实心的,则:

$\rho = m/V = 4.45$ kg/$(0.1$ m$)^3 = 4.45×10^3$ kg/m³ < $8.9×10^3$ kg/m³

所以是空心的;

方法二:假设铜块是实心的,则:

$m = \rho V = 8.9×10^3$ kg/m³ × $(0.1$ m$)^3 = 8.9$ kg > 4.45 kg

所以是空心的;

方法三:假设铜块是实心的,则:

$V = \dfrac{m}{\rho} = \dfrac{4.45\ kg}{8.9×10^3\ kg/m^3} = 0.5×10^{-3}$ m³

$V_{铜块} = (0.1$ m$)^3 = 1×10^{-3}$ m³

$V < V_{铜块}$,所以是空心的。

(答案) 见解析

(例)2 体积、质量都相等的空心铜球、铁球和铝球三个球中,空心部分体积最大的是($\rho_{铜} > \rho_{铁} > \rho_{铝}$)

( )

A.铝球　　　　　　　　B.铁球

C.铜球　　　　　　　　D.无法判断

(解析) 由于空心部分体积等于球体体积减去实心部分体积,即 $V_{空} = V_{球} - V_{实}$,而三球体积相等,只需比较实心部分体积 $V_{实}$ 即可,$V_{实} = \dfrac{m}{\rho}$,质量相等,密度大的实心部分体积小,空心大。因为 $\rho_{铜} > \rho_{铁} > \rho_{铝}$,所以铜球空心部分体积最大。故选 C。

(答案) C

第8章 力

知识梳理

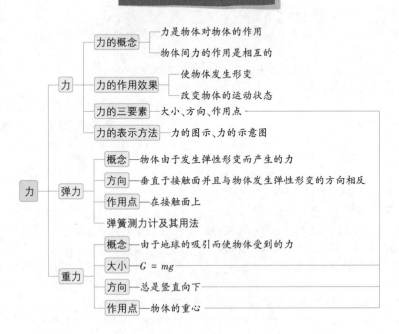

力
- 力
  - 力的概念 — 力是物体对物体的作用 / 物体间力的作用是相互的
  - 力的作用效果 — 使物体发生形变 / 改变物体的运动状态
  - 力的三要素 — 大小、方向、作用点
  - 力的表示方法 — 力的图示、力的示意图
- 弹力
  - 概念 — 物体由于发生弹性形变而产生的力
  - 方向 — 垂直于接触面并且与物体发生弹性形变的方向相反
  - 作用点 — 在接触面上
  - 弹簧测力计及其用法
- 重力
  - 概念 — 由于地球的吸引而使物体受到的力
  - 大小 — $G = mg$
  - 方向 — 总是竖直向下
  - 作用点 — 物体的重心

第1节 力

知识清单

基础知识
- 知识① 力与力的作用效果
- 知识② 物体间力的作用是相互的
- 知识③ 力的三要素
- 知识④ 力的示意图

知识 1 力与力的作用效果

1.力

(1)定义:力是物体对物体的作用。

(2)单位:在国际单位制中,力的单位是牛顿,简称为牛,符号是 N。

2.力的作用效果

(1)力可以改变物体的运动状态(如图)

①物体运动状态的改变分为三种情况:一是物体运动方向不变,速度大小发生改变,如物体从快到慢、从慢到快、从静止到运动和从运动到静止都是速度大小在改变;二是物体速度大小不变,运动方向发生改变,如左转弯、右转弯等都是说明其运动方向在改变;三是物体速度大小和运动方向同时发生了改变。

②力可以改变物体的运动状态,并不是说物体只要受力,其运动状态就一定要改变。如放在水平面上的物理课本,受到重力和支持力的作用处于静止状态。

（2）力能使物体发生形变

揉面时,面团形状不断变化(如图甲);射箭时,拉弯了的弓(如图乙);用手拉弹簧使弹簧变长了等,这些都表明力能使物体发生形变。

甲　　　　乙

温馨提示 （1）一个物体只要发生了运动状态的改变或发生了形变,这个物体就一定受到力的作用;（2）一个物体若受到了力的作用,则物体要么发生了形变,要么运动状态发生了改变,要么两者都发生了变化。要根据题意判断是哪一种情况,不能盲目地下结论。

例 踢足球是学生们喜欢的运动之一。小明用脚踢静止的足球,足球向前滚动,说明力可以改变物体的_____;但最终足球会停下来,是因为_____。

解析 足球由静止变为运动,其运动状态发生改变,说明可以改变物体的运动状态;足球停下来,是因为受到阻力作用,阻力改变了足球的运动状态。

答案 运动状态　足球受到阻力的作用

知识 2 物体间力的作用是相互的

1.一个物体对另一个物体施加作用力的同时,这个物体也同时受到来自对方的作用力;游泳时,人向后拨水,水同时向前推人(如图)。也就是说,物体间力的作用是相互的,施力物体同时也是受力物体。

手往后拨水才能向前游。

2.物体间力的作用是相互的,相互作用的两个力互为作用力和反作用力。

作用力和反作用力具有以下特点:

（1）大小相等、方向相反、在同一直线上,但作用在两个物体上。

温馨提示 鸡蛋撞石头时,作用力与反作用力大小相等,因为石头比蛋壳坚硬,在相等的力的作用下,石头毫发无损,鸡蛋却粉身碎骨,如图。

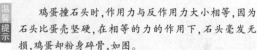

你随便来,我不怕。　我顶　糟糕

（2）同时产生,同时消失,同时增大,同时减小。

（3）性质相同,如小孩推墙时,对墙的作用力为弹力,则墙对小孩的反作用力也一定是弹力,绝不会是其他性质的力。

例 质量相等的甲、乙两同学站在滑板上,在旱冰场上相对而立,如果甲用 60 N 的力推乙,如图所示,以下分析正确的是 　　　（　　　）

甲　　乙

A.同时乙对甲的推力小于 60 N

B.甲静止不动,乙向后退

C.乙后退的过程中,始终受到 60 N 推力的作用

D.乙由静止变为后退,说明力可以改变物体的运动状态

解析 物体间力的作用是相互的。甲对乙的作用力与乙对甲的作用力,大小相等,都是 60 N;方向相反,甲、乙都会后退。当甲、乙分开后,甲、乙之间无相互作用。力可以改变物体的运动状态,D 选项正确。

答案 D

知识 3 力的三要素

在物理学中,把力的大小、方向、作用点称为力的三要素(如图)。这三个因素都能影响力的作用效果,当其中一个因素改变时,力的作用效果也会随之改变。

我们是力的三要素!

大小　方向　作用点

1.力的三要素中有一个因素变化,力的作用效果也将发生变化。例如:在开门时,手推门的部位(即作用点)不同时,推力的效果也不同;人拉车前进时,拉力的方向不同,拉力的效果也不同;将钢尺压弯时,压力的大小不同,钢尺弯曲的程度也不同。

2.两个完全相同的力必须是三要素完全相同。

3.力的三要素都影响力的作用效果,因此表述一个力必须把这个力的三要素都指明。

4.在探究力的三要素影响力的作用效果时,用控制变量法。

例 如图所示,分别用大小相等的力拉和压同一弹簧。该实验表明,弹簧受力产生的效果与力的　　（　　）

A.大小有关

B.作用点有关

C.方向有关

D.大小、方向、作用点都有关

解析 影响力的作用效果的因素有力的大小、方向和作用点;本题中控制力的大小和作用点相同,探究力的作用效果与力的方向的关系,故选 C。

答案 C

知识 **4** 力的示意图

1.力的三要素在示意图中的表示方法

力的三要素	力的示意图
力的大小	用线段的长短粗略表示力的大小
力的方向	箭头所指的方向表示力的方向
力的作用点	力的作用点画在线段的起点或箭头处

2.画法

(1)在受力物体上画出力的作用点;

(2)确定力的方向,然后沿力的方向画一条线段;

(3)在线段的末端标上箭头,并在箭头旁标出所画力的符号;

(4)在同一个图上画几个力的示意图时,力越大,线段应越长,大小相同的力,线段长度应相等。

如图所示为茶杯对桌面的压力的示意图。

温馨提示 力的作用点一定要画在受力物体上,重力要画在物体的重心上,压力要画在被压物体的表面上。当一个物体受多个力作用时,这几个力的作用点都要画在物体的重心上。(共用一个作用点)。

例 如图所示,小车在水平面上运动,受到作用于 *A* 点的与水平面成30°角的斜向右上方 100 N 的拉力,用力的示意图表示出小车受到的拉力。

解析 由题意可知,力的作用点在 *A* 处,经过 *A* 点作一条与地面平行的水平虚线,从 *A* 点出发画出一条与水平虚线成30°角斜向右上方的线段,在线段的末端画上箭头来表示力的方向,若力的大小是具体数值,可在其附近标注上。

答案 如图所示

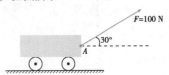

拓展知识 知识**1** 对力的三点认识
知识**2** 力的图示

知识 **1** 对力的三点认识

施力物体与受力物体	一个物体对另一个物体施加拉、推、提、压等作用力时,另一个物体就会受到这种作用。施加这种作用的物体叫施力物体,受到这种作用的物体叫受力物体
力不能离开物体而单独存在	一对作用力总是与两个物体有关(一个是施力物体,一个是受力物体),单独一个物体不能产生力的作用,如果离开物体就更不可能有力的作用,即力是物体对物体的作用
力的存在与是否接触无关	相互接触的物体不一定有力的作用,没有接触的物体之间也不一定无力的作用(如磁铁吸引小钢球),所以力的有无与是否接触无关

知识 **2** 力的图示

1.为了形象、直观地表示力,我们可用一根带箭头的线段来表示力的大小、方向和作用点(即力的三要素)。这种表示力的方法叫做力的图示,如图所示。力的方向所沿的直线叫力的作用线。

2.画力的图示的步骤:(1)选定标度;(2)从作用点开始沿力的方向画一条线段,根据选定的标度和力的大小按比例确定线段的长度,并在线段上加上刻度;(3)在线段的末端加箭头表示力的方向;(4)在箭头旁标出所画力的符号及大小。

第**4**部分

<table>
<tr><td>易混
对比</td><td colspan="2" style="text-align:center">力的示意图与力的图示</td></tr>
</table>

（1）力的示意图侧重于表示力的方向和作用点；力的图示更直观地描述力的三要素。

（2）二者的主要区别是在表示力的大小时不一样：

力的示意图用线段长短粗略地表示物体受力的大小；如水平方向加速运动的物块（如图），画物块在水平方向所受拉力 F 与摩擦力 f 的示意图时，其大小通过线段长度表示出来；

而力的图示表示力的大小需选定标度，然后根据标度和力的大小，按比例确定线段的长度，并在线段上加上刻度。

例1 重为6牛的物体静止在水平地面上，用力的图示法在图中画出它受到的重力 G。

解析 先选定标度，然后以物体的几何中心为作用点，竖直向下作出相应长度的线段表示重力大小，最后标上箭头。

答案 如图所示

例2 如图，水平地面上有一辆小车，甲水平向左推车，用力6 N，乙向左上方与水平方向成30°角拉车，用力9 N，作出这两个力的图示。

解析 作力的图示，应按要求标明角度大小，在一个图上，不管有几个力，标度都应统一，线段的长度最好是标度的整数倍。

答案 如图所示

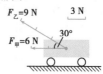

<table>
<tr><td>方法
清单</td><td>方法 控制变量法探究力的作用效果与哪些因素有关</td></tr>
</table>

方法 控制变量法探究力的作用效果与哪些因素有关

在探究力的作用效果与哪些因素有关时就用到了控制变量法。

（1）探究力的作用效果与力的大小的关系时，需控制力的方向、作用点相同；

（2）探究力的作用效果与力的方向的关系时，需控制力的大小、作用点相同；

（3）探究力的作用效果与力的作用点的关系时，需控制力的大小、方向相同。

例1 如图所示，将一根弹簧挂在天花板上，某人用方向相同的两个力作用于弹簧，已知 $F_1 < F_2$。观察比较（a）、（b）、（c）三图，可知力的作用效果与力的_____有关。

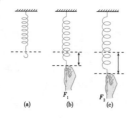

解析 根据题意可知，控制力的方向、作用点相同，探究的是力的作用效果与力的大小的关系。

答案 大小

例2 如图所示，使一薄钢条的下端固定，现分别用不同的力去推它，使其发生（1）、（2）、（3）、（4）各图所示的形变，如果 $F_1 = F_3 = F_4 > F_2$，那么能说明力的作用效果跟力的作用点有关的是 （ ）

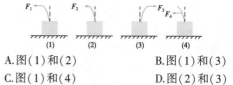

A.图（1）和（2）　　　　　　B.图（1）和（3）

C.图（1）和（4）　　　　　　D.图（2）和（3）

解析 力的作用效果跟力的大小、方向、作用点有关。当力的方向和作用点相同时，力的作用效果跟力的大小有关，见图（1）和（2）；当力的大小和作用点相同时，力的作用效果跟力的方向有关，见图（1）和（3）；当力的大小和方向相同时，力的作用效果跟力的作用点有关，见图（1）和（4），因此本题选 C。

答案 C

第2节 弹力

基础知识
知识1 弹性形变与塑性形变
知识2 弹力
知识3 测力计

知识 1 弹性形变与塑性形变

1.弹性形变

（1）物体在力的作用下发生形变，当力撤去后，物体又恢复原状，这样的形变叫弹性形变。

（2）物体在外力消失后能自动恢复原来形状的性质叫弹性。

2.塑性形变

（1）也有一些物体发生了形变，当力撤去后，不能恢复原状，我们把这样的形变叫塑性形变，如面团、橡皮泥受力后发生的形变为塑性形变。

（2）物体变形后不能自动恢复原来形状的性质叫做塑性。

知识 2 弹力

1.弹力

（1）定义：物体发生弹性形变后，由于要恢复原状，对与它接触的物体会产生力的作用，这种力叫做弹力。

（2）弹力方向总是与物体发生弹性形变的方向相反。如图中跳板发生形变向下弯曲，弹力的方向向上。

跳板的弹力把运动员弹起

（3）弹力的大小与物体的弹性强弱、形变大小有关，形变越大，弹力越大；形变消失，弹力也随之消失。

温馨提示 弹力产生在直接接触并发生弹性形变的物体之间，任何物体只要发生弹性形变就一定会产生弹力。

2.弹力的形式

（1）因物体的形变有多种多样，所以产生的弹力也有各种不同的形式。

①把一重物放在塑料板上，被压弯的塑料板要恢复原状，产生向上的弹力，这就是它对重物的支持力。

②将一物体挂在弹簧上，物体把弹簧拉长，被拉长的弹簧要恢复原状，产生向上的弹力，这就是它对物体的拉力。

（2）不仅塑料板、弹簧能够发生形变，许多物体都能够发生形变，对与它接触的物体产生弹力。我们通常所说的压力、支持力、绳子的拉力等，其实质就是弹力。

例 下列关于弹力的说法中，正确的是 （ ）

A.相互接触的物体之间一定存在弹力作用

B.只有受弹簧作用的物体才受到弹力作用

C.只有相互接触并发生弹性形变的物体间才存在弹力作用

D.弹簧的弹力总是跟弹簧的长度成正比

解析 两物体相互接触且发生了弹性形变，才能产生弹力，故 A 错；发生弹性形变的物体，由于要恢复原状，对跟它接触的物体会产生弹力，所以不一定只有受弹簧作用的物体才受到弹力作用，故 B 错；在弹性限度内，弹簧的弹力总是跟弹簧长度的变化量成正比，故 D 错。故选 C。

答案 C

知识 3 测力计

1.测力计及其构造

（1）测量力的大小的工具，称为测力计。有握力计、拉力计、弹簧测力计等。（如图所示）

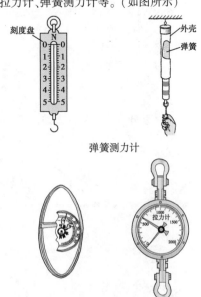

弹簧测力计

握力计　　　　拉力计

(2)测力计有各种不同的构造,但它们的主要部分都是弯曲而有弹性的钢片或螺旋形弹簧。

(3)当外力使弹性钢片或弹簧发生形变时,通过杠杆等传动装置带动指针转动,根据指针停在刻度盘上的位置,即可读出外力的大小。

2.弹簧测力计

作用	测量力的大小(主要测量物体的重力、拉力)
结构	主要是一根弹簧
测力原理	在弹簧的弹性限度内,弹簧的伸长量与受到的拉力成正比。也可表达为:在弹簧的弹性限度内,弹簧受到的拉力越大,弹簧的伸长量越长。
使用方法	①首先看清它的量程,加在弹簧测力计上的力不允许超过它的量程;②认清它的分度值,以便读数时快速准确;③观察指针是否指在零刻度线处,若没有,需要校零;④使用前,最好轻轻拉几次它的挂钩,可以避免弹簧被外壳卡住;⑤使用时,拉力方向应与弹簧轴线方向一致,确保测量准确

易混对比 弹簧的伸长量与弹簧的长度

弹簧的伸长量不是指弹簧被拉长后的长度,而是指受到力的作用后,弹簧形变的长度,即"伸长了"的长度;若弹簧原长为 L_0,受力后弹簧的长度为 L,则弹簧的伸长量 $\Delta L = L - L_0$。与拉力成正比的是弹簧的伸长量,而不是弹簧的长度。

例1 如图所示,弹簧测力计的量程是_____,分度值是_____,该弹簧测力计_____(选填"能"或"不能")直接用来测力的大小,需先_____,否则会使测得的值比真实值偏_____(选填"大"或"小")。

解析 使用弹簧测力计前首先应观察它的量程是 0~5 N,再观察分度值是 0.2 N。由于弹簧测力计未受拉力时,指针已指在0.6 N的位置,所以该弹簧测力计不能直接用来测力的大小,需先校零(移动指针,使指针对准零刻度线),否则会使测得的结果比真实值偏大。

答案 0~5 N 0.2 N 不能 校零 大

例2 如图所示几种使用弹簧测力计的方法,错误的是 ( )

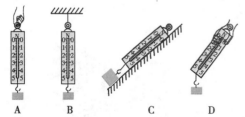

A B C D

解析 D图中拉力方向与弹簧轴线方向不一致而且不应用手直接握住测力计外壳。

答案 D

知识 **量程与弹性限度**

1.弹簧的伸长量与拉力成正比的规律是有一定限度的,即加在弹簧上的拉力不能太大,拉力超出弹簧的弹性限度后,弹簧的伸长量就不再与拉力成正比,甚至形变后无法恢复原状。

2.弹簧测力计的量程就是弹簧测力计允许测量的力的范围。

例 某实验小组的同学对 A、B 两根长度相同粗细不同的橡皮筋进行研究,并做成橡皮筋测力计。将橡皮筋的一端固定,另一端悬挂钩码(图甲所示),记录橡皮筋受到的拉力大小 F 和橡皮筋的伸长量 Δx,根据多组测量数据作出的图线如图乙所示。

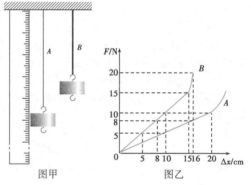

图甲 图乙

(1)当在两根橡皮筋上都悬挂重力为 8 N 的物体时,橡皮筋 A 的伸长量为_____cm,橡皮筋 B 的伸长量为_____cm。

(2)分别用这两根橡皮筋制成的测力计代替弹簧测力计,则用橡皮筋_____制成的测力计量程大,用橡皮筋_____制成的测力计测量的精确程度高(均选填"A"或"B")。

(3)将与本实验中相同的两根细的橡皮筋并联起来代替弹簧测力计,能够测量力的最大值为_____N。

解析 (1)由图乙可知,当 $F = 8$ N,$\Delta x_A = 16$ cm,$\Delta x_B = 8$ cm。

(2)在伸长量相同的情况下,B 橡皮筋所需的拉力大,故用 B 制成的测力计量程大;在相同的拉力下,A 橡皮筋伸长量大,故用 A 橡皮筋做成的测力计分度值更小,精确程度更高。

(3)A 的最大伸长量为 20 cm,拉力为 10 N,则两根细的橡皮筋并联使用时所受拉力相同,能够测量力的最大值为 20 N。

答案 (1)16 8 (2)B A (3)20

方法 图像法研究弹簧伸长量与所受拉力的关系

方法 图像法研究弹簧伸长量与所受拉力的关系

1.弹簧测力计的原理:在弹性限度内,弹簧的伸长量跟所受拉力成正比,即 $\dfrac{F_1}{F_2}=\dfrac{\Delta l_1}{\Delta l_2}$。

2.实验过程中数据的分析与处理:分析数据,作出弹簧长度 l 随拉力 F 变化的关系图像,可以得出结论。

例 某同学在探究弹簧的特点时,得出了弹簧受到的拉力与弹簧的长度的关系如图,请回答下列问题:

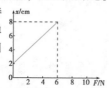

(1)这根弹簧的原长是_____cm。

(2)弹簧在受到 6 N 的拉力时,弹簧比原来伸长了_____cm,此时弹簧发生了_____形变,它具有弹力。

(3)分析图像中有关数据,你可以得出的结论是_____。

(解析) (1)从图中可以看出,当拉力 $F=0$ 时,弹簧的长度 $x=2$ cm。

(2)拉力 $F=6$ N 时,弹簧的长度 $x=8$ cm,弹簧比原来伸长了 $\Delta x=8$ cm-2 cm$=6$ cm,弹簧发生了弹性形变。

(3)分析图像中数据可知:在一定范围内,拉力与弹簧的伸长量成正比。(或在一定范围内,拉力越大,弹簧的长度越大。)

(答案) (1)2 (2)6 弹性 (3)见解析

第 3 节 重力

知识清单

基础知识
- 知识1 重力与重心
- 知识2 重力的方向
- 知识3 重力与质量的区别和联系

知识 1 重力与重心

1.重力

定义	由于地球的吸引而使物体受到的力
大小	$G=mg$
方向	竖直向下
作用点	物体的重心
施力物体	地球
重力方向的应用	重垂线(铅垂线)

2.重心

(1)重力在物体上的等效作用点叫做重心。物体重心的位置和物体的形状、质量分布有关。

(2)质量分布均匀、形状规则的物体,它的重心在它的几何中心上(如图)。

(3)物体的重心可能不在物体上,如一个质量分布均匀的金属环的重心在环所形成圆的圆心上。

温馨提示 重心的位置并不是固定不变的。它随质量分布的变化而变化。如将一块质量分布均匀的圆铁饼偏离圆心的地方去掉一小块,则铁饼的重心就要发生变化。

例 忽略空气阻力,抛出后的小球在空中运动轨迹如图所示,抛出后的小球由于 ( )

A.不受力,运动状态发生改变
B.不受力,运动状态不发生改变
C.受到重力作用,运动状态发生改变
D.受到推力作用,运动状态发生改变

(解析) 抛出去的小球在空中只受重力作用,由题图可知球在空中的运动方向在改变,即运动状态在改变。

(答案) C

知识 2 重力的方向

1.重力的方向

重力的方向总是竖直向下的,如图甲所示。应注意"竖直向下"与"垂直向下"是有区别的,如图乙所示,"垂直向下"是指垂直于某个平面向下。

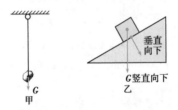

甲

乙

易混对比

"竖直向下"的理解

"竖直向下"也可理解为"垂直水平面向下"。水平面上的物体对水平面的压力方向也是"垂直水平面向下"。这种情况下物体所受重力与水平面所受压力方向重合,但重力的作用点在重心,压力的作用点在水平面上,二者是不同的两个力(如图)。

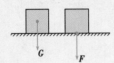

2.重垂线的应用

人们在一根线下吊一个重物,做成重垂线,重垂线可以显示重力的方向——竖直向下。利用重垂线可以检查桌面是否水平,相框是否挂正,如图所示。

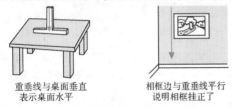

重垂线与桌面垂直
表示桌面水平

相框边与重垂线平行
说明相框挂正了

知识 3 重力与质量的区别和联系

		质量	重力
区别	概念	物体所含物质的多少	由于地球吸引而使物体受到的力
	符号	m	G
	大小方向	只有大小,没有方向	既有大小,又有方向
	单位	千克(kg)	牛顿(N)
	与地理位置的关系	无关	有关
	公式	$m=\rho V$	$G=mg$
	测量工具	天平	测力计
联系		重力与质量的关系是$G=mg$ ($g=9.8$ N/kg)	

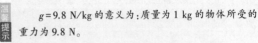

温馨提示 $g=9.8$ N/kg的意义为:质量为1 kg的物体所受的重力为9.8 N。

例 已知物体在月球上受到的重力为地球上的六分之一,一位宇航员的体重为 686 N,当他登上月球时,其质量为 ( )

A.70 kg   B.11.7 kg

C.114.3 kg   D.686 kg

(解析) 本题中的"体重"是指宇航员在地球上的重力,则由 $m=G/g$ 可求其在地球上的质量为 70 kg。又因质量不随位置而变,故宇航员在月球上的质量仍为 70 kg。

(答案) A

拓展知识
知识❶ 悬挂法、支持法找物体重心
知识❷ 稳度和提高稳度的诀窍
知识❸ 重力与地球引力

知识 1 悬挂法、支持法找物体重心

1.悬挂法:如图所示,先在 A 点把薄板悬挂起来,薄板静止时,所受的重力与悬绳的拉力在同一竖直线上,所以薄板的重心一定在通过 A 点的竖直线 AB 上。然后在 C 点把薄板悬挂起来,同理知,薄板的重心一定在通过 C 点的竖直线 CD 上,AB 和 CD 的交点 O 就是薄板重心的位置。

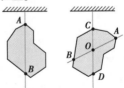

2.支持法:如图所示,把汤匙放在手指上,仔细调节支撑汤匙的支点的位置,使汤匙在手指上平衡,这时就可知道汤匙的重心就在支点上方。

知识 2 稳度和提高稳度的诀窍

1.稳度就是物体的稳定程度。稳度越大,物体就越不容易翻倒。

2.提高稳度的方法主要有两种:增大支撑面和降低重心。

（1）增大支撑面

几个提高稳度的例子如图。

(a)起重汽车放下支腿 增大支撑面　　(b)台灯有个大底座　(c)下大上小的茶壶

（2）降低重心

①通过降低重心来提高稳度的例子也是很多的。各种车辆都把底盘做得很重，重心降得很低；赛车选手几乎是平躺在轮子之间；在用卡车装货时，要注意把重的货物装在下面，轻的装在上面，而且货物不能装得过高。

②如果能把重心降到支点以下，还可以制作出一些有趣的小玩意。如图。

螺帽

螺帽

在小丑娃娃的手上和怪鸟的尾巴上固定一个螺帽，就可以把它们的重心降到支点以下

方法清单

方法**1** 重力示意图的画法
方法**2** 公式法求解与重力有关的问题
方法**3** 实验探究重力与质量的关系

方法 **1** 重力示意图的画法

作重力的示意图步骤如下：

（1）要找准重力的作用点——重心；

（2）重力的方向竖直向下，竖直向下画出一条线段表示重力的大小；

（3）在线段末端画上箭头表示重力的方向，在箭头旁标出所画重力的符号；

（4）重力的大小是具体数值时，要在箭头附近标注重力的大小。

例 如图所示，一个小球在挡板的作用下静止在斜面上，请画出小球所受重力的示意图。

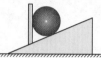

（解析）小球所受重力的方向总是竖直向下，作用在小球的重心上。

例 如图所示，用同样的卡车甲、乙分别装载同质量的钢材和棉花，_____车容易翻车。这是因为____

_____。

甲　　　　　　　乙

（解析）当卡车所拉货物的质量分布均匀时，重心在几何中心，所以装棉花的乙车重心高，稳度小。

（答案）乙　相同条件下重心越高，稳度越小，乙车重心高

知识 **3** 重力与地球引力

1.地球上物体的重力是由于地球吸引而产生的。

2.物体随地球做匀速圆周运动所需的向心力也来源于地球对物体的引力，向心力和重力都是引力的分力，所以重力不是地球引力。

3.同一物体在地球上不同地点所受重力也稍有不同，从赤道到两极重力逐渐增大。

（答案）如图所示

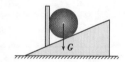

方法 **2** 公式法求解与重力有关的问题

1.与重力有关的计算有两类

（1）已知物体的质量 m，用公式 $G=mg$ 求物重；

（2）已知物重 G，用公式 $m=\dfrac{G}{g}$ 求物体的质量。

2. 一般 g 取 9.8 N/kg，若题中标明了 g 取 10 N/kg，则用该数据进行计算。

例 1 刘星同学的质量为 40_____（选填"kg""g"或"mg"），则他的体重为_____N（g 取 10 N/kg）。

（解析）根据常识，刘星同学的质量只能为 40 kg，则他的体重 $G=mg=40\ \text{kg}\times10\ \text{N/kg}=400\ \text{N}$。

（答案）kg　400

例 2 一座桥的桥头立有这样的一块牌子，如图所示。现有一自重为 49 000 N 的大卡车，装了 7 m³ 的石子，石子的密度为 2.5×10^3 kg/m³，这辆卡车能否从该桥上通过？

(解析) 根据题意,本题需求大卡车的质量 m_1,石子的质量 m_2,再求出总质量 $m = m_1 + m_2$。若 $m > 20$ t,则卡车不能从该桥上通过;若 $m \leq 20$ t,则卡车能从该桥上通过。

$$m_1 = \frac{G_1}{g} = \frac{49\ 000\ \text{N}}{9.8\ \text{N/kg}} = 5\ 000\ \text{kg} = 5\ \text{t}$$

$$m_2 = \rho_2 V_2 = 2.5 \times 10^3\ \text{kg/m}^3 \times 7\ \text{m}^3 = 17.5 \times 10^3\ \text{kg} = 17.5\ \text{t}$$

$$m = m_1 + m_2 = 5\ \text{t} + 17.5\ \text{t} = 22.5\ \text{t} > 20\ \text{t}$$

所以这辆卡车不能从该桥上通过。

(答案) 见解析

方法 3 实验探究重力与质量的关系

在探究"物体所受重力大小与物体质量的关系"时,需用弹簧测力计测出物体的重力,用天平测出物体的质量,然后通过分析物体的重力与质量之间的关系得出结论。

(例) 某同学探究"物体所受重力大小与物体质量的关系"的实验记录如下表:

实测物体	物体质量 m(kg)	重力 G(N)	比值 G/m(N/kg)
物体 1	0.1	0.98	9.8
物体 2	0.2	1.96	9.8
物体 3	0.3	2.94	9.8

(1)在实验过程中,需要的两个测量工具是 _____。

(2)分析表中数据,能得出的结论是 _____。

(解析) (1)两个测量工具分别是测重力和质量的工具,即弹簧测力计和天平;(2)从表中数据可看出重力与质量的比值为9.8 N/kg,说明物体所受重力与物体质量成正比。

(答案) (1)弹簧测力计、天平

(2)物体所受的重力与物体质量成正比(物体重力和质量的比值是定值,或物体重力和质量的比值是9.8 N/kg)

运动和力

知识梳理

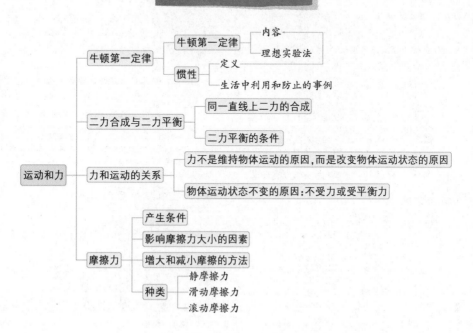

牛顿第一定律
 — 牛顿第一定律 — 内容
                — 理想实验法
 — 惯性 — 定义
        — 生活中利用和防止的事例

二力合成与二力平衡
 — 同一直线上二力的合成
 — 二力平衡的条件

力和运动的关系
 — 力不是维持物体运动的原因,而是改变物体运动状态的原因
 — 物体运动状态不变的原因:不受力或受平衡力

摩擦力
 — 产生条件
 — 影响摩擦力大小的因素
 — 增大和减小摩擦的方法
 — 种类 — 静摩擦力
        — 滑动摩擦力
        — 滚动摩擦力

运动和力

第 1 节　牛顿第一定律

知识清单

基础知识
知识 **1** 牛顿第一定律
知识 **2** 惯性
知识 **3** 惯性的利用
知识 **4** 惯性的危害

知识 **1** 牛顿第一定律

1.伽利略的斜面实验:伽利略通过斜面实验认识到运动物体受到的阻力越小,它的速度减小得就越慢,它运动的时间就越长。他还进一步推理得出,在理想情况下,如果表面绝对光滑,物体受到的阻力为零,它的速度将不会减小,这时物体将以恒定的速度永远运动下去。

2.笛卡儿的推论:法国科学家笛卡儿进一步补充了伽利略的结论,指出如果运动物体不受任何力的作用,不仅速度大小不变,而且运动方向也不变,将沿原来的方向匀速运动下去。

3.牛顿第一定律:一切物体在没有受到力的作用时,总保持静止状态或匀速直线运动状态。这就是著名的牛顿第一定律(又称惯性定律)。

力维持物体运动还是改变物体的运动状态

（1）亚里士多德的错误观点：力是维持物体运动的原因，即物体受力才运动。

（2）牛顿第一定律表明，力是改变物体运动状态的原因，即物体不受力也能保持原来的静止或匀速直线运动状态不变，物体运动状态改变必定受力。

（3）实际上，不受任何外力的物体是没有的。在某一方向上不受外力或在某一方向上受合力为零的情况，也可应用牛顿第一定律。定律中"静止状态或匀速直线运动状态"实质是物体保持原状态不变，即物体不受外力作用时，原来静止的物体仍然静止，原来处于运动状态的物体会保持原来的速度做匀速直线运动——直到有外力改变这种状态（如图）。

例 如图是伽利略著名的理想斜面实验，实验设想的步骤有：

①减小第二个斜面的倾角，小球在该斜面上仍然要达到原来的高度。

②两个对接的斜面，让静止的小球沿一个斜面滚下，小球将滚上另一个斜面。

③继续减小第二个斜面的倾角，最后使它达到水平，小球将沿水平面做持续的匀速运动。

④如果没有摩擦，小球将上升到原来释放时的高度。

（1）请将上述步骤按照正确的顺序排列 _____
_____（只填写序号）。

（2）在上述设想的步骤中，有的属于可靠事实，有的则是理想化的推论。下面关于这些事实和推论的分类正确的是 （ ）

A.①是事实，②③④是推论

B.②是事实，①③④是推论

C.③是事实，①②④是推论

D.④是事实，①②③是推论

（解析） 实验中，第一步②与第四步③容易确定；事实上由于受摩擦力影响，小球达不到原来的高度；第二步应假设没有摩擦，才有第三步中小球仍然达到原来的高度，所以④是第二步，①是第三步。第一步②是事实，二、三、四步即④、①、③都是推论。

（答案） （1）②④①③ （2）B

知识 2 惯性

惯性	物体保持静止状态或匀速直线运动状态不变的性质叫做惯性
对惯性的正确认识	**惯性是物体本身的固有属性，一切物体都具有惯性**
	惯性与物体所处的运动状态无关。对任何物体，无论是运动还是静止，无论是运动状态改变还是不变，物体都具有惯性。不能认为：运动的物体具有惯性，静止的物体不具有惯性，或物体运动的速度大，惯性就大
	惯性大小只与物体的质量有关。物体的质量越大，其运动状态越难改变，我们就说它的惯性越大；物体的质量越小，其运动状态越容易改变，我们就说它的惯性越小。物理学中就用质量来量度物体惯性的大小

例 如图为小车载着木块向右运动过程中发生的现象，下列判断正确的是 （ ）

甲 乙

A.都是在小车突然停止时发生

B.都是在小车突然启动时发生

C.图甲所示的现象是小车在运动中突然停止或突然加速时发生

D.图乙所示的现象是小车在运动中突然停止或突然减速时发生

（解析） 当小车突然启动或突然加速时，木块下端受摩擦力作用而随车加速，由于惯性木块上端仍保持原来的静止或低速状态，使得木块向后倾倒；当小车突然减速或突然停止时，木块下端受摩擦力作用而随车减速，由于惯性木块上端仍保持原来的运动状态，使得木块向前倾倒。故 A、B、C 错误，D 正确。故选 D。

（答案） D

知识 3 惯性的利用

1.生活中利用惯性的例子

（1）在跳远比赛时，运动员跳起后，由于惯性，在空中仍保持一定的速度继续向前运动，最后落在前方。

（2）人骑车时，当自行车运动起来后，人停止蹬车，自行车仍会向前运动一段距离，并不会立即停下。

（3）拍打衣服上的灰尘时，由于受力的作用，衣服离开原地，但灰尘由于惯性要保持原来的静止状态，仍留在原地,这样可使衣服与灰尘分离。

(4)斧头的斧柄松了以后,使斧柄的下端用力撞击树墩,这一过程中,斧头和斧柄一起快速向下运动,当斧柄撞到树墩后,由于受到树墩的阻力而突然停止运动,但斧头由于惯性仍会保持原来的运动状态,继续向下运动,所以会牢牢地套在斧柄上(如图)。

(5)一摞棋子,用力击打下面某个棋子,被击打的棋子受力运动离开原地,它上面的棋子由于惯性要保持原来的静止状态,但由于被击打的棋子离开了,上面的棋子会竖直下落(如图)。

2.对于有益的惯性,我们往往想办法来增大它。惯性只与质量有关,因此通过增加质量来增大惯性。

知识 4 惯性的危害

1.惯性对我们生活中的很多方面造成了不利的影响。

(1)汽车突然启动时,站在车厢里的乘客的脚虽然与汽车一起改变运动状态,但是人的上身由于惯性还会保持原来的运动状态,因此往往会向后摔倒;坐着的乘客由于惯性,头部容易磕到座椅的靠背上(如图)。

(2)汽车突然刹车时,站在车厢里的乘客的脚随车一起减速,上身由于惯性还会保持原来的运动状态,往往会向前摔倒;坐着的乘客由于惯性,头部容易磕到前排座椅的靠背上(如图)。

(3)汽车本身也有惯性,刹车后很难立即停下,还要向前运动一段距离,容易导致车祸的发生。

2.防止惯性的危害

(1)为了防止汽车在突然刹车或突然减速时对人造成伤害,强制司乘人员使用安全带,并在汽车上安装安全气囊;另外还对汽车的行驶速度进行限制。

(2)要真正地减小惯性就要减小物体的质量。对载重汽车进行限载,既可以减小它对地面的压强,又能减小它的惯性,从而降低车祸的发生率。

例 下列关于惯性的说法正确的是 ( )

A.太空中的宇航员不具有惯性

B.物体运动时具有惯性,静止时不具有惯性

C.汽车在转弯时减速,是为了防止惯性带来的危害

D.运动员起跑时用力蹬地,是为了增大惯性提高成绩

(解析) 一切物体不管它是否受力,也不管它是否运动和怎样运动,都具有惯性,故 A、B 错误;汽车转弯时减速,是为了防止惯性带来的危害,故 C 正确;惯性的大小只与质量有关,运动员起跑时用力蹬地,并不能增大惯性,故 D 错误。

(答案) C

拓展知识 **知识** 力与惯性

知识 力与惯性

1.惯性不是力。力是物体对物体的作用,发生力的作用时,必然要涉及两个相互作用的物体,单独一个物体不会产生力的作用。

2.每个物体都具有惯性,惯性只有大小没有方向,不能把惯性说成是"惯性力""受到惯性作用"或"克服物体的惯性",一般只能说"具有惯性"。

方法 **理想实验法探究牛顿第一定律**

牛顿第一定律是在观察和实验的基础上通过科学推理得出的,所运用的方法叫理想实验法。

例 如图为某同学"探究牛顿第一定律"的实验装置。实验中该同学先后三次将同一木块放在同一斜面上的同一高度,然后分别用不同的力推了一下木块,使其沿斜面向下运动,改变水平面的粗糙程度,观察木块运动的距离,从而得出力和运动的关系。

水平毛巾表面　　水平棉布表面　　水平木板表面

(1)该同学在实验操作中有一处明显的错误是(不要求解释错误的原因):_____。

(2)更正错误后进行实验,从实验中可观察到,随着摩擦力的减小,木块在水平面上运动的距离____,运动的时间越来越_____。但由于实验中摩擦力_____,所以不可能观察到木块在水平面上做匀速运动的情形。

(3)在上述实验的基础上,可以推测:如果摩擦力减小为零,水平面足够长,那么木块在水平面上的运动速度既不减小,也不增大,运动方向也不发生改变,木块将做_____。

解析 (1)本实验应使木块滑到底端时速度相同,让木块从同一高度静止滑下(或用相同的力推一下木块)。

(2)随着摩擦力的减小,对木块的阻碍作用减小,木块滑行距离变长,运动时间变长。如果摩擦力减小为零,木块将做匀速直线运动。

(3)摩擦力为零时,木块将做匀速直线运动。

答案 (1)分别用不同的力推了一下木块
(2)变长　长　不可能为零
(3)匀速直线运动

点拨 ①本实验和探究"真空不能传声"所用的方法都是理想实验法。

②实验中让木块从同一高度静止滑下(或用相同的力推一下木块)是为了控制木块滑到斜面底端时获得相同的速度,这里用到了控制度量法。

第2节　二力合成与二力平衡

知识清单

基础知识
知识**1** 力的合成
知识**2** 平衡状态与平衡力
知识**3** 二力平衡
知识**4** 平衡力与相互作用力
知识**5** 力和运动的关系

知识 **1** **力的合成**

1.一个力如果它的作用效果跟几个力共同作用时的效果相同,这个力就叫做那几个力的合力。求几个力的合力,叫力的合成。

温馨提示

①合力是为了表示几个力的作用效果而引入的,它并不是存在于物体受到的这几个力之外的力。

②研究合力时用到了等效替代法。

2.同一直线上二力的合成

(1)同一直线上同方向的二力的合力,大小等于这两个力大小之和,方向与这两个力方向相同。记作:$F = F_1 + F_2$。

如图所示,既有人在车前拉,又有人在车后推,车同时受到拉力 F_1 和推力 F_2 的作用,并且这两个力方向相同,则拉力和推力的合力大小 $F = F_1 + F_2$。

(2)同一直线上相反方向的二力的合力,大小等于这两个力大小之差的绝对值,方向和较大的力的方向相同。记作:$F = |F_1 - F_2|$。

例 把一个质量是 0.5 kg 的篮球竖直向上抛出,假定运动过程中空气对它的阻力恒为 0.5 N,则篮球在竖直上升和下落过程中所受力的合力分别是(g 取 10 N/kg)　　　　　　　　( )

A.5.5 N　5 N　　　　　　B.5.5 N　4.5 N
C.4.5 N　5.5 N　　　　　　D.5 N　4.5 N

（解析）篮球的重力 $G = mg = 0.5$ kg×10 N/kg = 5 N,篮球在竖直上升过程中,重力和空气阻力的方向都竖直向下,所以合力为 5 N+0.5 N = 5.5 N。篮球在下落过程中,重力的方向竖直向下,空气阻力的方向竖直向上,所以合力为 5 N−0.5 N=4.5 N。

（答案）B

知识 **2** 平衡状态与平衡力

1.平衡状态

物体处于静止或匀速直线运动的状态叫平衡状态。

2.平衡力

(1)若物体在几个力的作用下保持平衡状态,我们就把这几个力称为平衡力,这几个力的合力为零。牛顿第一定律中"没有受到力的作用",可以理解为"物体受到了平衡力的作用"。

(2)悬挂着的电灯能保持静止,是因为电灯受到的重力和灯绳对它的拉力是一对平衡力(图甲);在平直公路上做匀速直线运动的汽车,受到向前的牵引力和地面、空气对它向后的阻力,这时牵引力和阻力是一对平衡力(图乙)。桌面上的书保持静止,书受到的重力和桌面对书的支持力是一对平衡力(图丙)。

甲　　　　乙　　　　丙

（例）直升机沿竖直方向匀速升空时,在竖直方向上受到升力 F、重力 G 和阻力 f,下面关于这三个力的关系式正确的是 （　　）

A.$F>G+f$ 　　　　B.$F<G−f$
C.$F=G+f$ 　　　　D.$F=G−f$

（解析）直升机竖直匀速升空时,受平衡力作用,受到的竖直向上的升力与竖直向下的重力和空气阻力之和相等,即 $F=G+f$,故应选 C。

（答案）C

知识 **3** 二力平衡

二力平衡	二力平衡条件	
物体在两个力作用下保持静止或匀速直线运动状态,我们就说这两个力平衡	同体	两个力作用在同一物体上
	等值	两个力大小相等
注意	反向	两个力方向相反
二力平衡时要求四个条件同时具备,缺一不可	共线	两个力在同一直线上

（例）如图所示,把小车放在水平桌面上,向挂在小车两端的托盘里加相同砝码,下列说法正确的是 （　　）

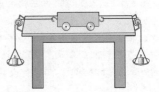

A.小车对桌面的压力与桌面对小车的支持力是一对平衡力

B.小车受到的重力与桌面对小车的支持力是一对平衡力

C.小车受到的重力与小车对桌面的压力是一对平衡力

D.细绳拉小车的力与细绳拉托盘的力是一对平衡力

（解析）小车对桌面的压力与桌面对小车的支持力的受力物体不同,不是一对平衡力,而是一对相互作用力,A 错误;小车受到的重力和桌面对小车的支持力的受力物体都是小车,且大小相等、方向相反、作用在同一直线上,所以是一对平衡力,B 正确;小车受到的重力与小车对桌面的压力的受力物体不同,所以不是平衡力,C 错误;细绳拉小车的力和细绳拉托盘的力的受力物体不同,所以不是平衡力,D 错误。故选 B。

（答案）B

知识 **4** 平衡力与相互作用力

		作用力和反作用力	相互平衡的两个力
相同点	大小	相等	相等
	方向	相反,且在同一直线上	相反,且在同一直线上
区别	作用对象	分别作用在两个物体上	共同作用在同一个物体上
	作用时间	同时产生,同时消失	一个力消失,另一个力可以存在
	力的作用效果	作用力和反作用力分别作用在不同的物体上,一般产生不同的效果	两个力共同作用在同一个物体上,使物体保持平衡

第4部分

压力与支持力二力平衡吗?

二力平衡的条件是:"同体、等值、反向、共线";对于水平桌面上静止的木块(如图所示),压力 F 的受力物体是桌面,支持力 N 的受力物体是木块,二者虽然"等值、反向、共线",但受力物体不是同一物体(即不"同体"),二力不平衡,二力互为作用力和反作用力;木块所受的重力 G 和木块所受的支持力 N 是一对平衡力。

例 足球进校园,深受同学们喜爱。踢出去的足球在水平草地上滚动过程中,以下两个力是一对平衡力的是　　　　　　　　　　　　(　　)

A.脚对球的作用力与草地对球的阻力

B.脚对球的作用力与球对脚的作用力

C.球向前的惯性力与草地对球的阻力

D.球所受的重力与草地对球的支持力

解析 一对平衡力的条件是:同体、等值、反向、共线。踢出去的足球已不再受到脚的作用力,A、B 错误;C 选项中,惯性力是不存在的,D 选项中的两个力是一对平衡力。

答案 D

知识 5 力和运动的关系

条件	力的方向与物体的运动方向	物体所处状态	运动状态
不受力 合力为零 受平衡力	—	静止状态或匀速直线运动状态	不变
合力不为零	相同	速度增大,并且做直线运动	改变
	相反	速度减小,仍做直线运动	
	不在同一条直线上	运动方向改变,做曲线运动	

例 下列说法中正确的是　　　　　　　(　　)

A.如果苹果在下落的过程中,速度越来越大,则苹果受力是不平衡的

B.将水桶从地面上提起来,手对水桶的作用力大于水桶对手的作用力

C.木箱静止在地面上,木箱对地面的压力与木箱所受的重力大小相等

D.沙狐球离开手后,在水平台面上滑行得越来越慢,是由于沙狐球受到阻力作用

解析 苹果下落的速度越来越大,说明运动状态一直在变,则苹果受力一定是不平衡的,所以 A 正确;将水桶从地面上提起来,手对水桶的作用力和水桶对手的作用力是一对相互作用力,大小一定相等,所以 B 错;木箱静止在地面上,地面并不一定水平,另外木箱在竖直方向上不只受重力和地面的支持力,还可能受别的外力,则木箱对地面的压力不一定等于木箱所受的重力,所以 C 错;沙狐球离开手后,在水平台面上滑行得越来越慢,是由于沙狐球受到与运动方向相反的阻力作用,所以 D 正确。故本题应选 A、D。

答案 AD

 拓展知识　　知识 二力平衡的理解

知识 二力平衡的理解

1.二力平衡是力的分析中最简单、最基本的情况。若一物体处于二力平衡状态,我们了解了其中一个力,对另一个力也就了如指掌。如图所示,一物体放在水平桌面上,它受到重力和桌面对它的支持力,物体处于平衡状态。我们知道了物体的重力,根据等大、反向、共线的关系,也就知道了支持力的大小、方向。

2.二力平衡中力不仅使物体保持平衡状态,还可能使物体发生形变(只不过有时效果不明显,但形变还是有的,如静止在地面上的物体受重力和地面支持力的作用,发生了微小形变)。因此,两个力并不是完全抵消而没有产生任何作用效果。

3.物体在平衡力作用下处于平衡状态,若再增加(或减少)一对(或多对)平衡力,物体仍然处于平衡状态。

4.平衡力可以通过受力示意图形象地描绘出来。

例 如图所示,一均匀小球静止在竖直墙边的光滑水平面上,画出该球受力示意图。

解析 这个球在竖直方向上显然受到重力和支持力。两个力作用在同一条直线上,大小相等,方向相反,是一对平衡力。

问题是竖直墙壁对球有没有作用力。假设竖直墙壁对球有一个向左的力(施力物体只能是竖直墙壁),根据题设条件,球是静止的,还应当受到一个水平向右的力与之平衡;因为水平向右的力不存在,所以向左的力也不存在。

(答案) 如图所示

方法清单 方法❶ 概念法判断二力平衡
方法❷ 控制变量法探究二力平衡的条件
方法❸ 隐含"二力平衡"的变形题

方法 **1** 概念法判断二力平衡

判断一对力是否是平衡力,有两种方法。

(1)根据二力平衡条件判断,只要两个力"同体、等值、反向、共线",那么,这两个力就是一对平衡力。

(2)根据物体的运动状态是否改变判断,如果物体在某一方向上受到一对力的作用而运动状态保持不变,那么这一对力就是平衡力,反之,就不是平衡力。

例 如图所示,升降机以 1 m/s 的速度匀速上升时,升降机对人的支持力为 500 N。下列说法正确的是 ( )

A.升降机静止在十楼时对人的支持力小于 500 N

B.升降机以 1.5 m/s 的速度匀速上升时对人的支持力大于 500 N

C.升降机以 2 m/s 的速度匀速下降时对人的支持力等于 500 N

D.升降机以 1 m/s 的速度匀速下降时对人的支持力小于 500 N

(解析) 匀速直线运动是一个平衡状态,在这种情况下无论其速度及运动方向如何,人所受的重力与受到升降机的支持力均是一对平衡力,因此 A、B、D 均错,C 正确。

(答案) C

方法 **2** 控制变量法探究二力平衡的条件

1.用控制变量法探究二力平衡的条件,分析问题时要注意控制不变的物理量和改变的物理量。

(1)探究"同体"的两个力才能平衡,需控制两个力"等值、反向、共线"。

(2)探究"共线"的两个力才能平衡,需控制两个力"同体、等值、反向"。

2.注意控制其他方面的因素相同。如给小车所施加的拉力必须是水平的,故绳所跨的两滑轮必须调整

到等高处,这样容易判断力的方向是相同还是相反,以及是否共线。

例 如图是小华同学探究二力平衡条件时的实验情景。

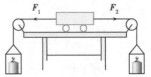

(1)实验的目的是:探究当小车只受两个力作用而处于静止或_____状态时,这两个力有怎样的关系。实验中桌面_____(选填"一定"或"不一定")要水平。

(2)要验证作用在小车上的两个"大小相等、方向相反,但不作用在同一条直线"的力是否平衡,实验的操作是将小车_____,松手后观察小车是否平衡。若实验时作用在小车上的两个力方向相同,则小车_____(选填"可能"或"不可能")处于平衡状态。

(3)在探究同一问题时,小明用木块代替小车,你认为小华和小明的方案中,_____的方案更好,另一方案存在的缺陷是_____。

(解析) (1)平衡状态指静止或匀速直线运动状态,桌面一定要水平。

(2)将小车旋转一个角度后,两边的拉力不在同一条直线上,用来研究不在同一条直线上的两个力能否平衡。若实验时作用在小车上的两个力方向相同,则小车不可能处于平衡状态。

(3)将小车换成木块,木块与桌面之间的摩擦力会影响实验结果。

(答案) (1)匀速(直线)运动 一定
(2)转动(或扭转) 不可能
(3)小华 有摩擦力(影响)

方法 **3** 隐含"二力平衡"的变形题

考查二力平衡与平衡状态的试题很多,形式变化多样,有时条件直接给出,而有时条件具有隐蔽性。要准确把握平衡力和平衡状态的对应关系,适应多变题型。

例 1 如图所示,各用 4 N 的水平力沿相反的方向拉弹簧测力计的两端(弹簧测力计自重不计),则下列说法中正确的是 ( )

A.弹簧测力计的示数为 4 N,弹簧测力计受的合力为 4 N

B.弹簧测力计的示数为 0 N,弹簧测力计受的合力为 0 N

C.弹簧测力计的示数为 8 N,弹簧测力计受的合力为 0 N

D.弹簧测力计的示数为 4 N,弹簧测力计受的合力为 0 N

(解析) 如图所示,弹簧测力计的读数为 4 N,弹簧测力计受水平向右 4 N 的拉力和绳对它水平向左 4 N 的拉力而处于静止状态,隐含"二力平衡"这一特点,同理题图中弹簧测力计示数也是 4 N,也就是说弹簧测力计测的是一端的力的大小。

(答案) D

例 2 如图所示,物体受到水平向右的拉力作用,在水平地面上做匀速直线运动,请你画出物体在竖直方向上所受到力的示意图。

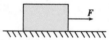

(解析) 因物体做匀速直线运动,隐含"二力平衡",水平方向上是拉力与摩擦力二力平衡,竖直方向上是重力与支持力二力平衡。在竖直方向上画力的示意图,只画出重力和支持力的示意图即可,注意二力共用一个作用点。

(答案) 如图所示

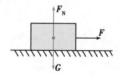

第 3 节　摩擦力

知识清单

基础知识

知识**1** 摩擦力
知识**2** 摩擦力的方向
知识**3** 影响滑动摩擦力大小的因素
知识**4** 增大、减小摩擦的方法
知识**5** 摩擦力的分类

知识 1　摩擦力

1.滑动摩擦力的定义:一个物体在另一个物体表面上滑动时,在接触面上会产生一种阻碍相对运动的力,这种力就叫做滑动摩擦力。

2.摩擦力产生的条件:(1)两物体接触面粗糙不平;(2)两物体之间发生相对运动或具有相对运动趋势;(3)两物体之间相互挤压发生弹性形变,接触面上有压力产生。

3.摩擦力的作用效果:总是阻碍物体之间的相对运动或相对运动趋势。

例 关于摩擦力,下列说法正确的是　　　(　　)

A.相互挤压的粗糙物体间一定存在摩擦力

B.运动的物体一定受到滑动摩擦力

C.静止的物体一定受到静摩擦力

D.相互挤压的粗糙物体之间相对滑动时,才受到滑动摩擦力

(解析) 当物体放在水平的地面上,虽然物体和地面相互接触并挤压,接触面粗糙,但它们之间由于没有相对运动或相对运动的趋势,所以物体不受摩擦力,故 A、C 错误。当物体随传送带一起做匀速直线运动时,因为物体与传送带保持相对静止,所以物体不受滑动摩擦力,如图所示,故 B 错误。

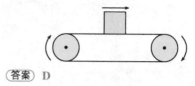

(答案) D

知识 2　摩擦力的方向

摩擦力的方向总是沿接触面的切线方向,和物体的相对运动方向或相对运动趋势方向相反。如牙刷相对水平面向右运动时,由刷毛弯曲的形状可看出:牙刷受到水平向左的摩擦力(如图)。

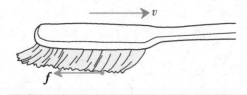

<table>
<tr><td rowspan="1">易混对比</td><td colspan="1" align="center">对相对运动方向的理解</td></tr>
</table>

对相对运动方向的理解

"相对运动方向"不是"运动方向";水平地面上拉物体前进时:物体相对地面向前运动(相对运动方向向前),物体受到地面对它向后的摩擦力(摩擦力方向向后);人走路时,脚向后蹬地,脚相对地面有向后运动的趋势,地面给鞋底的摩擦力方向向前,有利于人向前运动。

摩擦力有时阻碍运动,有时有利于运动,无论哪种情况,摩擦力的方向与相对运动方向或相对运动趋势方向相反。

例 如图所示,在 15 N 的水平拉力 F 作用下,木板 A 在水平地面上匀速向右运动的过程中,物体 B 相对于地面静止,此时弹簧测力计的示数为 3 N,则 B 所受滑动摩擦力方向水平向_____(选填"左"或"右"),A 受到地面的摩擦力大小为_____N。

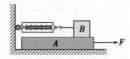

解析 滑动摩擦力的方向总是与物体相对运动的方向相反,题中 B 相对 A 向左运动(选 A 为参照物,B 向左运动,所以相对运动方向向左),故 B 所受摩擦力方向向右。

对 A 受力分析,拉力 F 向右为 15 N,B 对 A 的摩擦力向左为 3 N,则地面对 A 的摩擦力向左,大小为 15 N−3 N=12 N。

答案 右 12

知识 3 影响滑动摩擦力大小的因素

1.滑动摩擦力的大小与接触面的粗糙程度有关,其他条件相同时,接触面越粗糙,滑动摩擦力越大;滑动摩擦力的大小与压力有关,其他条件相同时,压力越大,滑动摩擦力越大。

2.滑动摩擦力与接触面的大小、物体运动的快慢、物体运动的方向等因素无关。

例 为了探究影响物体受到滑动摩擦力大小的因素,某小组同学利用木块 A、砝码 B、弹簧测力计等进行实验。实验中,他们先在同一水平桌面上分别以不同的速度匀速拉动木块,然后通过在木块 A 上增加砝码 B 以改变 A 对桌面的压力大小,并用测力计测量木块 A 受到的滑动摩擦力大小,研究过程如图(a)、(b)和(c)所示,三次实验中木块 A 的速度大小关系为 $v_1 = v_3 > v_2$。请仔细观察图中的操作和测量结果,然后归纳

得出初步结论。

①比较(a)和(b)两图可知：_____。

②比较(a)和(c)两图可知：_____。

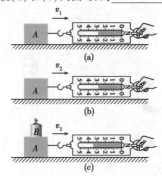

解析 实验采用的是控制变量法,根据图中数据可归纳得出结论。

答案 ①当压力一定时,物体在同一接触面上受到的滑动摩擦力大小与其运动的速度大小无关

②当接触面的粗糙程度相同时,压力越大,物体受到的滑动摩擦力越大

知识 4 增大、减小摩擦的方法

增大有益摩擦的方法	(1)增大接触面的粗糙程度;(2)增大压力;(3)变滚动为滑动
减小有害摩擦的方法	(1)使接触面变光滑;(2)减小压力;(3)用滚动代替滑动;(4)使接触面分离

例 如图所示的措施中,为了减小摩擦的是
( )

机械表保养时上油
A

防滑垫表面做得凹凸不平
B

旋钮侧面制有条纹
C

轮胎上制有花纹
D

解析 防滑垫表面做得凹凸不平,旋钮侧面制有条纹,轮胎上制有花纹,都是通过增大接触面的粗糙程度来增大摩擦,B、C、D 项错误;机械表保养时上油,可使零件表面形成油膜,减小摩擦。故选 A。

答案 A

知识 5 摩擦力的分类

	滑动摩擦力	滚动摩擦力	静摩擦力
解释	一个物体在另一个物体表面上滑动时产生的摩擦力	一个物体在另一个物体上滚动时产生的摩擦力	相对静止的两个物体之间的摩擦力
产生条件	(1)两物体相互接触、挤压 (2)接触面粗糙 (3)有相对运动	—	(1)两物体相互接触、挤压 (2)接触面粗糙 (3)有相对运动趋势
方向	与物体相对运动的方向相反	—	与物体相对运动趋势方向相反

例 如图所示,一物体A放在粗糙水平面上,A的重力为20 N,此时物体A受到的摩擦力为____N。现用一弹簧测力计沿水平方向拉A,A未动,此时弹簧测力计的示数为2 N,则物体A受到的摩擦力为_____N。增大拉力,当弹簧测力计的示数为5 N时,物体A仍然未动,则此时A受到的摩擦力为_____N。后来,A在弹簧测力计拉力作用下做匀速直线运动,此时弹簧测力计的示数为4.5 N,则此时A受到的摩擦力为_____N。若再将一砝码放于A上,仍然使A做匀速直线运动,则弹簧测力计的示数会_____(选填"增大"或"减小")。若拿来几个圆柱形的钢棒垫在物体A的下面,则弹簧测力计匀速拉动A时的示数比刚才会_____(选填"增大"或"减小")。

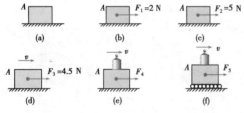

(a) (b) (c) (d) (e) (f)

（解析）(a)图所示状态,A放在水平面上,A相对粗糙水平面既无相对运动也无相对运动趋势,所以此时A不受摩擦力。反过来考虑,如果A受摩擦力作用,那么A将不能保持静止而运动起来。(b)、(c)两图所示的状态,A均处于静止,所以A在水平方向上受平衡力的作用,由此可分析出对应于F_1和F_2的静摩擦力f_1和f_2的大小。(d)、(e)两图所示情况属滑动摩擦。(f)图所示情况属于滚动摩擦。

（答案） 0　2　5　4.5　增大　减小

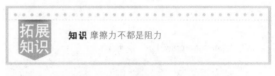

知识 摩擦力不都是阻力

知识 摩擦力不都是阻力

1.不能把摩擦力只看做是一种阻力,有时可以是动力。

2.应用举例:(1)放在卡车上的货物,随卡车一起加速运动时,货物受到的静摩擦力是阻碍它与卡车之间相对运动趋势,但却是使它能够随卡车一起运动的动力。(2)传送带运送物体时,如图所示,物体就是依靠传送带对它的摩擦力才能运动的。在刚开始物体加速运动的时间内,物体受到的摩擦力方向与物体的运动方向一致。一旦物体在水平传送带上做匀速直线运动后,物体与传送带之间就没有了相对运动或相对运动的趋势,物体与传送带之间也就没有了摩擦力。这里,传送带也是靠与皮带轮的摩擦转动的。(3)人走路、汽车启动都靠摩擦,这时摩擦是有益的。

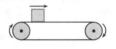

方法清单

方法1 控制变量法探究滑动摩擦力大小与什么因素有关
方法2 平衡状态中摩擦力大小的判断方法
方法3 逆向思维法解决摩擦力实验中弹簧测力计示数不稳定的问题

方法 1 控制变量法探究滑动摩擦力大小与什么因素有关

在探究"滑动摩擦力的大小与什么因素有关"这个问题时用到控制变量法。

(1)使木块在同一木板上面匀速滑动,即保持接触面的粗糙程度相同,改变压力的大小,测出滑动摩擦力的大小,探究滑动摩擦力与压力大小的关系。

(2)保持压力相同,改变接触面的粗糙程度,让木块分别在较光滑的木板上和较粗糙的毛巾上匀速滑动,测出滑动摩擦力的大小。根据测出的数据进行分析,得出滑动摩擦力的大小与接触面的粗糙程度的关系。

例 在"探究影响滑动摩擦力大小的因素"实验中,实验小组的同学利用长木板、玻璃板及一些完全相同的木块,进行了如图所示的实验:

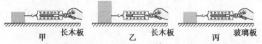

甲　长木板　乙　长木板　丙　玻璃板

(1)实验中用弹簧测力计拉动木块沿水平方向做_____直线运动来测量滑动摩擦力的大小;

(2)由甲、丙两图可知滑动摩擦力的大小与接触面的_____有关;

(3)由_____两图可知,滑动摩擦力的大小与压力大小有关。

(解析)(1)当物体做匀速直线运动时,所受拉力和滑动摩擦力是一对平衡力,此时两力大小相等,弹簧测力计的示数等于滑动摩擦力的大小;(2)甲、丙两图中,压力大小相同,接触面的粗糙程度不同,所以这两个实验探究的是滑动摩擦力大小与接触面的粗糙程度的关系;(3)在探究滑动摩擦力大小与压力大小的关系时,要控制接触面的粗糙程度相同,所以选甲、乙两图对比。

(答案)(1)匀速　(2)粗糙程度　(3)甲、乙

方法2 平衡状态中摩擦力大小的判断方法

根据二力平衡的知识,一对平衡力一定大小相等,方向相反,作用在同一物体上。故可通过对物体进行受力分析,从而判断摩擦力大小。这也是判断各种摩擦力大小最行之有效的方法。

(例)用手握住重5 N的酱油瓶子,瓶子静止悬在空中,瓶口竖直向上,此时手的握力为30 N,瓶子受到的竖直向上的摩擦力大小为_____N;若使手的握力增加为35 N,瓶子受到手的摩擦力大小为_____N。

(解析)本题可从运动状态着手分析。以酱油瓶子为研究对象,因为瓶子静止悬在空中,处于平衡状态,所受合力为零,瓶子受到的竖直向上的摩擦力和竖直向下的重力是一对平衡力,所以摩擦力的大小等于重力,为5 N。当手的握力增加为35 N后,瓶子仍处于静止状态,受到手的摩擦力大小等于重力,仍然为5 N。

(答案)5　5

方法3 逆向思维法解决摩擦力实验中弹簧测力计示数不稳定的问题

1.要测量木块与长木板之间的摩擦力,只有当木块做匀速直线运动时,弹簧测力计的示数才等于摩擦力的大小,实际操作过程中,木块的运动状态不稳定,弹簧测力计的示数就不稳定,很难读数。

2.运用逆向思维,改拉长木板,当拉动长木板时,木块相对于地面处于静止状态,较好地解决了这个问题。

(例)如图a所示,小明在"研究影响滑动摩擦力大小的因素"的实验中,用弹簧测力计拉着木块分别在粗糙程度不同的甲、乙水平木板上做匀速直线运动,通过改变放在木块上的砝码改变压力,分别测出木块在甲、乙木板上滑动时的摩擦力,并根据实验数据描点画出了滑动摩擦力 $f_摩$ 与对应压力 $F_压$ 关系的图像。

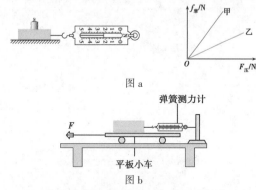

图a

图b

(1)分析图像甲或乙可知,木块对木板的_____越大,木块所受的滑动摩擦力也就越大;比较图像可知,_____(选填"甲"或"乙")木板更粗糙。

(2)小明在实验中发现,拉着木块运动时很难控制"匀速",于是他设计了如图b所示的装置,将弹簧测力计固定,改为拉动平板小车,当他水平向左拉平板小车时,木块所受到的摩擦力的方向为_____。这样改进后的装置的优点是_____。

(解析)(1)分析图像可看出 $f_摩$ 随 $F_压$ 变大而变大。压力 $F_压$ 相同时,甲对应的摩擦力大于乙对应的摩擦力,所以甲木板更粗糙。(2)向左拉动平板小车时,木块相对小车向右运动,所以受到的摩擦力方向向左。改进后的方法中虽然木块相对小车运动,仍受滑动摩擦力,但弹簧测力计相对于木块和桌面静止,便于读数,误差更小。

(答案)(1)压力　甲

(2)水平向左(填向左也可以)

即使小车不做匀速直线运动,对读数也不会产生影响

压强

知识梳理

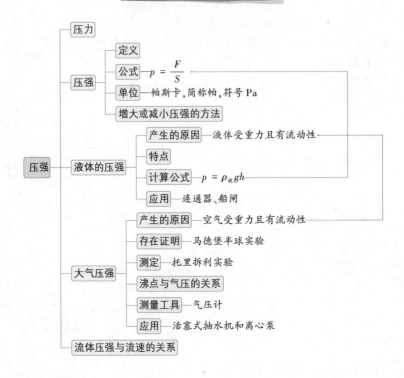

压强
- 压力
- 压强
  - 定义
  - 公式　$p = \dfrac{F}{S}$
  - 单位——帕斯卡,简称帕,符号 Pa
  - 增大或减小压强的方法
- 液体的压强
  - 产生的原因——液体受重力且有流动性
  - 特点
  - 计算公式　$p = \rho_液 gh$
  - 应用——连通器、船闸
- 大气压强
  - 产生的原因——空气受重力且有流动性
  - 存在证明——马德堡半球实验
  - 测定——托里拆利实验
  - 沸点与气压的关系
  - 测量工具——气压计
  - 应用——活塞式抽水机和离心泵
- 流体压强与流速的关系

第 1 节　压强

知识清单

基础知识

知识 1 压力
知识 2 压力和重力的区别与联系
知识 3 影响压力作用效果的因素
知识 4 压强
知识 5 增大和减小压强在实际生活中的应用

知识 1 压力

1.定义及单位:垂直作用在物体表面上的力叫压力,用 F 来表示,单位是牛(N)。

2.产生的条件:只有相互接触且发生挤压的物体之间才有压力。

(1)静止在水平地面上、紧靠墙角的小球,由于墙与小球之间无挤压作用,所以它们之间不存在压力(如图)。

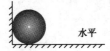

（2）人靠墙站立时，由于墙与人之间有挤压作用，所以它们之间存在压力（如图）。

3.方向：压力的方向与接触面垂直且指向受压物体。按图钉时，压力的方向总是与接触面垂直（如图）。

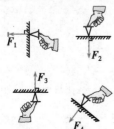

4.作用点：在受压物体的接触面上。

例1 在图中画出沿斜面向下滚动的小球对斜面压力的示意图。

（解析）压力的作用点应画在斜面上，并且力的方向应垂直于斜面。注意要标上方向。

（答案）如图所示

例2 如图所示，在游泳池的底部和侧壁，铺满了面积相等的小瓷砖，请画出水对 A、B 两瓷砖压力的示意图。

（解析）压力方向与接触面垂直，且指向受压物体。

（答案）如图所示

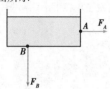

知识 2 压力和重力的区别与联系

	重力	压力
定义	由于地球的吸引而使物体受到的力	垂直作用在物体表面上的力
产生原因	由于地球的吸引而产生	由于物体对物体的挤压而产生
方向	总是竖直向下	垂直于接触面且指向受压物体
作用点	物体的重心	在受压物体的接触面上
施力物体	地球	对受压物体产生挤压作用的物体
联系	在通常情况下，静止在水平地面上的物体，其对地面压力的大小等于重力	

易混对比

压力是由物体的重力产生的吗？

物体受重力作用，可能对接触面产生压力，但压力大小不一定等于物体的重力。静止在水平地面上的物体，其对地面的压力大小：$F_压=G$（如图1）；若在物体上方加一个竖直向下的外力，则地面受到的压力：$F_压=G+F_外$（如图2）；若有一个外力（$F_外<G$）竖直向上提升物体时，地面所受压力：$F_压=G-F_外$（如图3）；若物体静止在斜面上，斜面所受压力为物体重力的分力，此时：$F_压<G$（如图4）。

有的情况下，接触面所受压力与所接触物体的重力无关；当一个水平外力把物体紧压在竖直墙面上静止时，墙面所受压力：$F_压=F_外$（如图5），与物重无关。

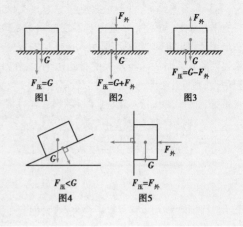

知识 3 影响压力作用效果的因素

1.啄木鸟的嘴能啄破树皮,骆驼的脚会往沙地中陷入一些,都是压力作用效果的表现。

2.压力的作用效果不仅跟压力的大小有关,还跟受力面积的大小有关。

(1)切割物品,用力较大时,便于切割,这表明受力面积一定时压力大小不同,压力作用效果不同。

(2)两个体重差不多的人在雪地里,没穿滑雪板行走的人陷到雪中,而穿滑雪板行走的人没有陷入雪中(如图所示),这表明压力一定时受力面积不同,压力的作用效果不同。

知识 4 压强

物理含义	表示压力作用效果的物理量
定义	物体所受压力的大小与受力面积之比
公式	$p = \dfrac{F}{S}$
单位	帕斯卡,简称帕,符号是 Pa,1 Pa = 1 N/m²
增大压强的方法	①受力面积一定时增大压力;②压力一定时减小受力面积;③在增大压力的同时减小受力面积
减小压强的方法	①受力面积一定时减小压力;②压力一定时增大受力面积;③在减小压力的同时增大受力面积

例 如图甲所示,将一块质地均匀的长木板平放在水平桌面上,用水平力 F 向右缓慢推动木板,使其右端渐渐露出桌面,如图乙所示。在推动木板使其右端逐渐离开桌面边缘至木板中心到达桌面边缘的过程中,长木板对桌面的压力_____,压强_____,如果水平推力 F 一直保持不变,则木板受到的合力将会_____。(选填"变大""变小"或"不变")

解析 在推动木板过程中,木板对桌面的压力始终等于其重力,即压力不变;推动过程中受力面积减小,根据 $p = \dfrac{F}{S}$ 可知,压强变大;木板对桌面的压力不

变,接触面粗糙程度不变,因此木板受到的摩擦力大小不变,又因为水平推力 F 不变,重力和支持力也不变,故其所受合力大小不变。

答案 不变 变大 不变

知识 5 增大和减小压强在实际生活中的应用

1.增大压强

(1)刀斧、切削工具的刀片都会磨得很薄,图钉(如图甲)、针、锯齿的尖端加工得很尖,这些都是采用减小受力面积的方法增大压强。

(2)刹车时必须用力握住车闸,农民犁地时为了犁得深些往往找个人站在犁耙上,这些都是采用增大压力的方法来增大压强。

2.减小压强

(1)高楼大厦的墙基很宽,载重汽车装有很大的轮子,铁轨下铺设枕木(如图乙),滑雪时穿上滑雪板,书包背带较宽(如图丙),这些都是采用增大受力面积的方法来减小压强。

(2)现代建筑中广泛使用空心砖,是采用减小压力的方法来减小压强。

图钉尖很尖锐	铁轨下铺设枕木	书包背带较宽
甲	乙	丙

例 如图所示的压路机,关于它涉及的物理知识,下列说法中错误的是 ( )

A.碾子由钢铁制成,利用了钢铁硬度大的特性

B.碾子质量很大,是为了增大对路面的压力

C.碾子很粗很宽,是为了减小对路面的压强

D.橡胶轮胎外表制有花纹,是为了增大与路面的摩擦

解析 压路机是用来压实路面的,碾子很粗很宽是为了增大碾压路面的面积,而不是为了减小压强,故选 C。

答案 C

拓展知识

知识 对压强公式 $p = \dfrac{F}{S}$ 的理解

知识 对压强公式 $p = \dfrac{F}{S}$ 的理解

1.此公式适用于任何情况,即固体、液体、气体的压强计算都可用此公式。

2.此公式中各物理量单位分别是 $p \to Pa$、$F \to N$、$S \to m^2$。在计算压强时,只有当 F 的单位为 N,S 的单位为 m^2 时,压强的单位才能是 Pa,因此在计算中必须统一单位。

3.一张报纸平放时对桌子的压强约 0.5 Pa。成人站立时对地面的压强约为 1.5×10^4 Pa,它表示:人站立时,其脚下的地面每平方米面积上,受到脚的压力为 1.5×10^4 N。

4.公式中的 F 是压力而不是重力。即使在某些情况下,压力在数值上等于物体所受的重力,也不应把公式直接写成 $p = \dfrac{G}{S}$,而应先注明 $F = G$ 得:$p = \dfrac{F}{S} = \dfrac{G}{S}$。

5.公式中的受力面积 S,是指受力物体发生形变的那部分面积,也就是两物体的实际接触面积,而不一定是受力物体的表面积。如图所示,一个圆台形物体置于水平地面上,分别采用 A、B 两种方式放置,对地面的压力不变,但 A 中受力面积为 S_2,B 中受力面积为 S_1,而它们都与水平地面的面积大小无关。

（图：圆台放置方式 A、B）

6.由公式推导出 $F = pS$ 和 $S = \dfrac{F}{p}$,可用于计算压力和受力面积的大小。

方法清单

方法① 控制变量法探究压力作用效果与哪些因素有关

方法② 巧用 $p = \rho gh$ 求柱体压强

方法 1 控制变量法探究压力作用效果与哪些因素有关

在探究压力作用效果与哪些因素有关时,需用控制变量的方法。

（1）研究压力作用效果与压力大小的关系时,需控制受力面积不变;

（2）研究压力作用效果与受力面积的关系时,需控制压力大小不变。

例 1 电动汽车是正在大力推广的新型交通工具,它具有节能、环保的特点。如图,是一辆停放在水平地面上的电动汽车,质量为 1.6×10^3 kg,每个轮胎和地面的接触面积为 2×10^{-2} m^2,g 取 10 N/kg。求:

（1）车对地面的压力;

（2）车对地面的压强。

（解析）（1）车重 $G = mg = 1.6 \times 10^4$ N

地面对车的支持力 $F_N = G$

车对地面的压力 $F_N' = F_N = G = 1.6 \times 10^4$ N

（2）$S = 4 \times 2 \times 10^{-2}$ $m^2 = 8 \times 10^{-2}$ m^2

$p = \dfrac{F_N'}{S} = 2 \times 10^5$ Pa

（答案）（1）1.6×10^4 N （2）2×10^5 Pa

例 2 底面积为 2 m^2 的长方体木箱放在水平桌面上,如图所示,木箱重 100 N,水平桌面面积为 1.5 m^2,则木箱对桌面产生的压强多大?

（解析） 要计算木箱对桌面的压强,关键是找受力面积即实际接触的面积。

$F = G = 100$ N,$S = 1.5$ m^2

$p = \dfrac{F}{S} = \dfrac{100\ N}{1.5\ m^2} \approx 66.7$ Pa。

（答案） 66.7 Pa

点拨 这两道题中要充分理解受力面积为接触面积:汽车四轮着地,接触面积为一个轮胎触地面积的 4 倍;木箱与桌面的接触面积为桌面面积。

例 1 如图是"探究影响压力作用效果的因素"实验。如甲图所示,将小桌放在海绵上;如乙图所示,在小桌上放一个砝码;如丙图所示,把小桌翻过来,桌面朝下,并在它上面放一个砝码。①比较_____两图可知,当受力面积一定时,压力越大,压力的作用效果越明显;②比较乙、丙两图可知,当压力一定时,_____,压力的作用效果越明显;③此实验中运用到的主要探究方法是_____。

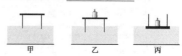

解析 本题主要运用控制变量法,甲、乙两图中受力面积相同,乙图中海绵受到的压力大,效果明显;乙、丙两图中压力相同,乙图中海绵受力面积小,效果明显。

答案 ①甲、乙 ②受力面积越小 ③控制变量法

例2 小明同学利用 A、B 两物体、泡沫塑料等器材探究"压力的作用效果与什么因素有关"的实验。如图所示。

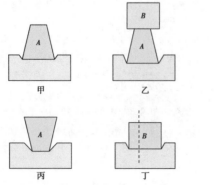

(1)实验中小明是通过观察＿＿＿＿＿＿＿＿＿来比较压力作用效果的。

(2)比较甲、乙两图所示实验,能够得到的结论是＿＿＿＿＿＿＿＿＿＿＿＿＿＿＿＿。

(3)若要探究"压力的作用效果与受力面积的关系",应比较图＿＿＿＿＿＿所示实验。

(4)小明同学实验时将物体 B 沿竖直方向切成大小不同的两块,如图丁所示。他发现它们对泡沫塑料的压力作用效果相同,由此他得出的结论是:压力的作用效果与受力面积无关。你认为他在探究过程中存在的问题是＿＿＿＿＿＿＿＿＿＿＿＿。

解析 (1)压力的作用效果由泡沫塑料的形变程度反映出来。(2)甲、乙两图中控制受力面积相同,探究压力作用效果与压力大小的关系。(3)甲、丙两图中控制压力相同,探究压力作用效果与受力面积的关系。(4)探究压力作用效果与受力面积的关系时,需控制压力相同,将物体 B 竖直切成大小不同的两块,不能控制两块物体对泡沫塑料的压力相同。

答案 (1)泡沫塑料形变程度(或压痕的深浅)

(2)受力面积一定时,压力越大,压力的作用效果越明显

(3)甲、丙

(4)没有控制压力相同

方法 2 巧用 $p=\rho gh$ 求柱体压强

将一密度均匀、高为 h 的柱体放在水平桌面上,桌面受到的压强 $p=\dfrac{F}{S}=\dfrac{G}{S}=\dfrac{\rho gV}{S}=\dfrac{\rho gSh}{S}=\rho gh$,所以柱体(包括圆柱体、长方体、正方体等)产生的压强,只与柱体的密度和高度有关,而与柱体的重力、体积和底面积等因素无关,应用公式 $p=\rho gh$ 就给解这类题带来很大的方便。

例 如图所示,三个材料相同,但粗细、长短都不相同的均匀实心铁制圆柱体竖直放在水平地面上,对地面的压强最小的是 ( )

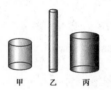

A.甲铁柱 B.乙铁柱
C.丙铁柱 D.无法确定

解析 由于三个圆柱体的密度相同,而甲的高度最低,根据公式 $p=\rho gh$ 可知,甲对地面的压强最小。正确选项为 A。

答案 A

点拨 求密度均匀的柱体对地面产生的压强时,除了用压强的定义式 $p=\dfrac{F}{S}$ 外,还可应用公式 $p=\rho_物 gh$ 来计算,此公式与求液体压强的公式 $(p=\rho_液 gh)$ 相同。

第2节 液体的压强

知识清单

 基础知识

知识① 液体压强的特点
知识② 压强计
知识③ 连通器
知识④ 船闸
知识⑤ 帕斯卡原理

知识 1 液体压强的特点

产生原因	①液体受到竖直向下的重力作用,对支撑它的容器底部产生压力和压强 ②液体没有固定的形状,能够流动,对限制它流动的容器的侧壁产生压力和压强 ③液体内部各相邻部分之间互相挤压,液体内部向各个方向都有压强
特点	①液体内部向各个方向都有压强;②在同一深度,向各个方向压强相等;③深度增大,液体的压强增大;④液体的压强还与液体的密度有关,在深度相同时,液体密度越大,压强越大
计算公式	$p=\rho g h$
生活实例	潜水员使用不同的潜水服,潜水越深,潜水服抗压能力越强(如图甲);水坝上窄下宽(如图乙),是因为液体压强随深度增加而增大  甲  乙

例 如图所示玻璃管两端开口处蒙上的橡皮膜绷紧程度相同。将此装置置于水中,选项图中的哪幅图能反映橡皮膜受到水的压强后的凹凸情况 (　　)

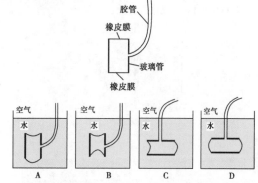

(**解析**) 橡皮膜受到水的压强后会向内凹,排除A、C、D三项。根据液体内部压强特点可知:同种液体内部,越深处压强越大,所以 B 中下部橡皮膜比上部凹入得多,故 B 项正确。

(**答案**) B

知识 2 压强计

1.压强计是测量液体内部压强的仪器(如图甲),它由探头、U 形管、软管等组成。

2.如果液体内部存在压强,放在液体里的探头的薄膜(橡皮膜)就会发生形变,U 形管左右两侧液面就会产生高度差,如图乙所示。

3.高度差越大,薄膜(橡皮膜)受到的压强越大。

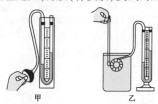

例 在"研究液体的压强"实验中:
(1)图甲所示的仪器叫_____;

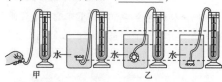

(2)比较图乙中的三个图,可以得到的结论是:__

_____。

(**解析**) 由图乙可看出橡皮膜在液体的同一深度朝向了不同方向,并且能够看出压强计左右两侧液面高度差相等。

第④部分

第④部分 第10章 压强 **135**

（答案）（1）压强计 （2）同一深度,液体向各个方向的压强相等

知识 3 连通器

1.定义:上端开口、下端连通的容器叫连通器。

2.特点:连通器里的同种液体不流动时,各部分中的液面总保持相平(如图)。

连通器

温馨提示 理解连通器的特点(原理)时要注意两个条件:①连通器里只有一种液体;②在液体不流动的情况下。

如果连通器内不止一种液体或液体还在流动,容器中的液面不一定相平。

3.应用:乳牛自动喂水器、茶壶、锅炉水位计、水塔、船闸等。如图所示。

船闸　　　茶壶　　　锅炉水位计

（例）如图所示,容器 A、B 内盛有液面在同一水平面的清水,用带有阀门 K 的斜管将两容器相连,当阀门 K 打开时水_____流动(选填"会"或"不会")。

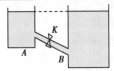

（解析）当阀门打开时,A、B 两容器构成一个连通器,根据连通器的原理,A、B 两容器的液面相平,因此水不会流动。

（答案）不会

知识 4 船闸

1.船闸是利用连通器的原理工作的。通过闸门和阀门的打开、关闭,调节闸室内的水位分别与上、下游水位相平,使船经过船闸从上游驶往下游或从下游驶往上游。

2.下面描述的是一艘轮船由上游通过船闸驶往下游的情况。

（1）如图1,船在上游(打开上游阀门 A,阀门 B 是关闭的,这样闸室和上游水道构成了一个连通器)。

（2）如图2,船进入闸室中(闸室水面上升到和上游水面相平后,打开上游闸门 C,船驶入闸室)。

（3）如图3,船准备出闸室(关闭阀门 A 和闸门 C,打开下游阀门 B,闸室和下游水道构成了一个连通器)。

（4）如图4,船到了下游(闸室水面下降到跟下游水面相平后,打开下游闸门 D,船驶向下游)。

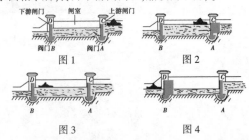
图1　　　　　　　图2

图3　　　　　　　图4

知识 5 帕斯卡原理

1.加在密闭液体上的压强,能够大小不变地由液体向各个方向传递,这个规律被称为帕斯卡原理。

2.帕斯卡原理揭示了液体压强的传递规律,是许多液压系统和液压机工作的基础。如用于维修汽车的液压千斤顶(如图)、汽车的液压刹车系统、铲车等都用了液压技术。

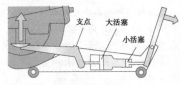
支点　大活塞　小活塞
液压千斤顶原理图

3.液压机的工作原理如图所示,两个活塞与同一容器中的液体相接触。施加于小活塞的压强被液体传递给大活塞,大活塞便可以产生一个与其表面面积成正比的力。

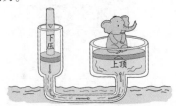
下压　上顶

（例）如图所示,小活塞的面积为 0.01 m²,大活塞的面积为 0.2 m²,求作用在小活塞上的力至少为多大时,在大活塞上能举起质量为 $2\,000$ kg 的物体?（$g=10$ N/kg）

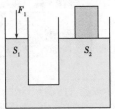
F_1
S_1　　　S_2

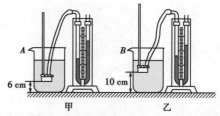

（解析）$F_2=G=mg=2\ 000\ \text{kg}\times10\ \text{N/kg}=20\ 000\ \text{N}$，

$p_1=\dfrac{F_1}{S_1}$，$p_2=\dfrac{F_2}{S_2}$，因为 $p_1=p_2$，所以 $\dfrac{F_1}{S_1}=\dfrac{F_2}{S_2}$，$F_1=\dfrac{F_2}{S_2}\times S_1=$

$\dfrac{20\ 000\ \text{N}}{0.2\ \text{m}^2}\times0.01\ \text{m}^2=1\ 000\ \text{N}$。

（答案）$1\ 000\ \text{N}$

拓展知识

知识1 对液体压强公式 $p=\rho gh$ 的理解
知识2 液体对容器底的压力与液体的重力

知识 1 对液体压强公式 $p=\rho gh$ 的理解

1.由公式 $p=\rho gh$ 可知，液体内部的压强只跟液体的密度和深度有关，而跟液体的质量、重力、体积以及容器的形状、底面积等无关。

2.公式只适用于计算静止的液体产生的压强，对流动的液体不适用。

3.在液体压强公式中 h 表示深度，指从液面到液体中某点的距离。判断出 h 的大小是计算液体压强的关键。如图所示，甲图中 A 点的深度为 30 cm，乙图中 B 点的深度为 40 cm，丙图中 C 点的深度为 50 cm，丁图中 a、b、c 三处水的深度 $h_a>h_b>h_c$。

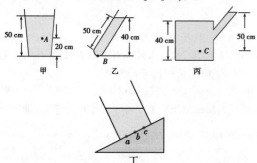

甲 乙 丙

丁

4.运用公式时应统一单位：ρ 的单位用 kg/m^3，h 的单位用 m，计算出的压强单位才是 Pa。

5.用公式求出的压强是液体由于自身重力产生的压强，它不包括液体受到的外加压强。

易混对比

公式 $p=\dfrac{F}{S}$ 与 $p=\rho gh$ 的区别和联系

$p=\dfrac{F}{S}$ 是压强的定义式，无论固体、液体还是气体，它都是普遍适用的；而 $p=\rho gh$ 是结合液体的具体情况通过 $p=\dfrac{F}{S}$ 推导出来的，所以适用于液体。

（例）水平实验桌面上有微小压强计、刻度尺和装有适量水的 A、B 两个烧杯。小亮学习了液体内部压强跟哪些因素有关的知识后，又提出了新的猜想，为此他利用提供的实验器材进行了如下实验探究。

①将微小压强计的探头放入 A 烧杯的水中，探头到烧杯底的距离为 6 cm，如图甲所示，记录微小压强计 U 形管两侧的液面高度差 h_1；

②将微小压强计的探头放入 B 烧杯的水中，探头到烧杯底的距离为 10 cm，如图乙所示，记录微小压强计 U 形管两侧的液面高度差 h_2；

小亮发现 h_1 大于 h_2，于是小亮得出结论"液体内部任意一点的压强跟该点到容器底的距离有关"。请你利用这些器材，设计一个实验证明小亮的结论是错误的。写出实验步骤和实验现象。

（解析）实验步骤：

①将微小压强计的探头放入烧杯的水中，用刻度尺分别测量探头到烧杯底的距离 L_1，探头到水面的距离 H，读出压强计 U 形管两侧的液面高度差 h_1，将以上数据记录在表格中。

②向烧杯中倒入适量的水，调整探头所在的位置，使探头到水面的距离仍为 H，用刻度尺测量探头到烧杯底部的距离 L_2，读出压强计 U 形管两侧的液面高度差 h_2，将以上数据记录在表格中。

实验现象：通过数据可发现 $L_1\neq L_2$，$h_1=h_2$。

由此证明液体内部任意一点的压强跟该点到容器底的距离 L 无关，所以小亮的结论是错误的。

（答案）见解析

知识 2 液体对容器底的压力与液体的重力

1.由于液体具有流动性，静止在水平放置的容器中的液体，对容器底的压力不一定等于液体的重力。

2.液体对容器底的压力 $F=pS=\rho ghS$，而 Sh 的含义是以容器底为底、以液体深度为高的柱体的体积，即 $V_柱=Sh$，所以 $F=pS=\rho ghS=\rho gV_柱=m_柱 g=G_柱$，$G_柱$ 的含义是以 $V_柱$ 为体积的那部分液体的重力。

3.液体对容器底的压力 F 与液体重力 $G_液$ 的关系：

（1）只有当容器是柱体时，液体对容器底的压力才等于液体的重力（如图甲）。

（2）底小口大的容器底受到的压力小于液体的重力（如图乙）。

（3）底大口小的容器底受到的压力大于液体的重力（如图丙）。

第 4 部分

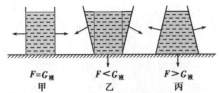

$F=G_液$
甲

$F<G_液$
乙

$F>G_液$
丙

例 如图所示,一个密封的圆台状容器,内装一定质量的水,放在水平桌面上,现把它倒置过来,则 (　)

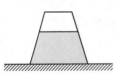

A.水对容器底的压强增大

B.水对容器底的压力增大
C.容器对桌面的压强减小
D.容器对桌面的压强减小

(解析) 倒置后,小底面在下,液面升高,据 $p=\rho gh$,水对容器底的压强增大,故 A 正确;由于倒置后,侧面对水的反作用力斜向上,故底面所受的压力小于水重,而倒置前,侧面对水的反作用力斜向下,故底面所受的压力大于水重,故倒置后,水对底面的压力变小,故 B 错误;容器放置在水平桌面上,压力等于重力,倒置后压力大小不变,受力面积 S 变小;由 $p=\dfrac{F}{S}$ 可知,压强变大,故 C、D 错误。

(答案) A

方法清单

方法① 比较法区别液体对容器底的压强、压力与容器对支持面的压强、压力

方法② 控制变量法探究液体压强规律

方法③ 液体压强中隐含"密度不同"的有关计算

方法 1 比较法区别液体对容器底的压强、压力与容器对支持面的压强、压力

在盛有液体的容器中,液体对容器底的压强和压力与容器对支持面的压强和压力不是一回事。

1.处理液体问题时,先求压强再算压力。

2.容器对支持面的压力和压强,可视为固体问题处理,先分析压力大小,再根据 $p=\dfrac{F}{S}$ 计算压强大小。

例 1 如图所示,底面积相同的甲、乙两容器中装有质量和深度均相同的不同种液体,则甲、乙两容器中液体的密度 $\rho_甲$ 和 $\rho_乙$ 的关系以及液体对容器底的压力 $F_甲$ 和 $F_乙$ 的关系,正确的是 (　)

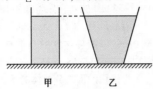

甲　　乙

A.$\rho_甲=\rho_乙$,$F_甲<F_乙$　　B.$\rho_甲>\rho_乙$,$F_甲=F_乙$
C.$\rho_甲<\rho_乙$,$F_甲>F_乙$　　D.$\rho_甲>\rho_乙$,$F_甲>F_乙$

(解析) 已知甲、乙的底面积相同,由图可知,$V_甲<V_乙$,液体质量 $m_甲=m_乙$,由 $\rho=\dfrac{m}{V}$ 可知 $\rho_甲>\rho_乙$;甲容器中液体对容器底部的压力 $F_甲=m_甲g$,乙容器中液体重力有一部分被容器侧壁承担,$F_乙<m_乙g$,因此,$F_甲>F_乙$,故选 D。

(答案) D

例 2 如图所示,一开口的杯子,装上 8 cm 高的水后,放在水平桌面上。已知杯子内部底面积为 50 cm²,外部底面积为 60 cm²;杯子装上水后的总质量为 0.6 kg,则水对杯底的压力为_____N,杯子对桌面的压强为_____Pa。(g 取 10 N/kg)

(解析) 从杯子的形状可知,杯中水对杯底的压力并不等于水的重力。求液体对容器底的压力时,一般是先求出压强,再根据 $F=pS$ 求压力。$F=pS=\rho ghS=1.0\times10^3$ kg/m³$\times10$ N/kg$\times8\times10^{-2}$ m$\times5\times10^{-3}$ m² $=4$ N,而杯子对桌面的压力等于杯子与水的总重力,即 $F'=0.6$ kg$\times10$ N/kg$=6$ N,压强为 $p'=\dfrac{F'}{S'}=\dfrac{6\ N}{6.0\times10^{-3}\ m²}=1\times10^3$ Pa。

(答案) 4　1×10^3

方法 2 控制变量法探究液体压强规律

由于液体压强跟液体的深度和液体密度有关,所以在探究液体压强的规律时要采用控制变量法。(1)在探究液体压强与深度的关系时,要保持液体密度不变。(2)在探究液体压强与液体密度的关系时,要保持深度不变。

例 下表是小明同学利用图示的实验装置探究液体压强规律时所测得的部分数据。

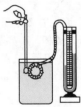

实验次数	深度 h/cm	橡皮膜在水中的方向	U形管左右液面高度差 Δh/cm
1	3	朝上	2.6
2	6	朝上	5.4
3	9	朝上	8.2
4	9	朝下	8.0
5	9	朝左	8.2
6	9	朝右	8.2

（1）实验所得的数据中有一组是错误的，其实验序号为_____。

（2）综合分析实验数据，可以归纳得出液体压强的规律：①_____，该结论是通过分析比较实验序号为_____的数据得出来的。②_____，该结论是通过分析比较实验序号为_____的数据得出来的。

（解析）（1）在液体内部同一深度处，向各个方向的压强是相等的，而第4次实验中记录的数据与第3、5、6次实验中记录的数据不相等，故第4次实验中记录的数据是错误的。（2）从第1、2、3次实验可看出，随着液体深度的增加，液体的压强增大；从第3、5、6次实验可看出，在同一深度，液体内部向各个方向的压强相等。

（答案）（1）4　（2）①液体内部的压强随深度的增加而增大　1、2、3　②在同一深度，液体内部向各个方向的压强相等　3、5、6

（点拨）①控制同种液体，比较1、2、3时，橡皮膜的方向不变，探究液体内部压强与深度的关系；比较3、5、6时，深度相同，探究液体内部压强与橡皮膜朝向的关系。

②通过压强计U形玻璃管内液面高度差反映液体压强的大小，这种方法为转换法。

方法 3　液体压强中隐含"密度不同"的有关计算

由液体的压强公式 $p=\rho gh$ 可知，液体的压强大小取决于液体的密度和深度，深度的不同比较直观，一眼可以看到，而密度不同需引起注意。有时题中直接给出物质不同，密度不同，有时则隐含着密度不同，需要自己发现。

例1　如图所示，两支相同的试管，盛等质量的液体，甲管竖直放置，乙管倾斜放置，液体对管底压强的大小关系是　　　　　　　　　（　）

A. $p_甲 < p_乙$

B. $p_甲 > p_乙$

C. $p_甲 = p_乙$

D. 上述三种情况都有可能

（解析）比较压强就从甲、乙两支试管中液体的密度和深度分析。已知 h 相等，因此本题只要比较出甲、乙两支试管中液体的密度，即可判断出正确答案。

要比较密度很容易想到密度公式 $\rho = \dfrac{m}{V}$，质量关系已知，从而转向寻找甲、乙两支试管中液体的体积关系，这样问题就得到了解决。由题意可知，两试管液面相平，高度相等，两试管中所装的液体质量相等，但乙管倾斜放置，$V_甲 < V_乙$，所以 $\rho_乙 < \rho_甲$，据 $p = \rho gh$ 可知 $p_甲 > p_乙$。

（答案）B

例2　如图所示，甲、乙、丙三个完全相同的容器中分别盛有酒精、硫酸和水，已知容器底受到的压强相等，则可推断（$\rho_{硫酸} > \rho_水 > \rho_{酒精}$）　　　（　）

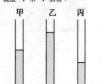

A. 甲中盛的是硫酸

B. 乙中盛的是硫酸

C. 丙中盛的是硫酸

D. 无法判断

（解析）三个容器完全相同，三种液体对容器底的压强相等。由液体压强公式 $p = \rho gh$ 可知：h 越大，ρ 越小，所以乙中盛的是酒精，甲中盛的是水，丙中盛的是硫酸。

（答案）C

第3节　大气压强

 基础知识

- 知识1 大气压强
- 知识2 大气压强变化的规律
- 知识3 托里拆利实验
- 知识4 活塞式抽水机
- 知识5 离心式水泵

知识 1 大气压强

定义	大气对浸在它里面的物体的压强叫做大气压强,简称大气压或气压
产生原因	包围地球的大气由于受到重力的作用,而且能够流动,因而大气对浸在它里面的物体产生压强
存在证明	①马德堡半球实验　②覆杯实验(如图) ③瓶吞鸡蛋实验 
应用	生活中:①钢笔吸墨水　②吸管吸饮料 ③针管吸药液　④塑料吸盘
	生产中:①活塞式抽水机　②离心式水泵
测量	气压计:①水银气压计 ②金属盒气压计

例 在铁桶内放少量的水,用火加热,水沸腾之后把桶口堵住,然后浇上冷水,铁桶变扁,如图所示。关于铁桶变扁的原因,下列说法正确的是　　（　　）

A.冷水的压力使铁桶变扁
B.大气压使铁桶变扁
C.铁桶内空气膨胀使铁桶变扁
D.铁桶变扁与力无关

(解析) 铁桶内放少量的水,用火加热,水沸腾产生水蒸气,把桶口堵住,浇上冷水,大量水蒸气液化,使桶内气压变小,铁桶外部大气压大于内部气压,在大气压作用下,铁桶被压扁。故选 B。

(答案) B

知识 2 大气压强变化的规律

	具体描述	应用说明
与海拔的关系	海拔越高,气压越低	海拔越高,空气越稀薄
与天气、季节的关系	一般晴天比阴天气压高,冬天比夏天气压高	空气中水蒸气含量越大,气压越低
与体积的关系	温度不变的气体,体积越小,压强越大;体积越大,压强越小	打气筒打气
沸点与气压的关系	液体的沸点随气压减小而降低,随气压增大而升高	在青藏高原上,水的沸点仅在80℃左右,家用压力锅内水的沸点可达120℃左右

例 如图所示,把一根两端开口的细玻璃管,通过橡皮塞插入装有红色水的玻璃瓶中,从管口向瓶内吹入少量气体后,瓶内的水沿玻璃管上升的高度为 h。不考虑温度的影响,把这个自制气压计从山下移到山上后　　（　　）

A. h 增大,瓶内气压大于外界气压
B. h 减小,瓶内气压大于外界气压
C. h 增大,瓶内气压小于外界气压
D. h 减小,瓶内气压小于外界气压

(解析) 当细玻璃管内液体不流动时,瓶内液体处于平衡状态,对瓶内液面分析,可得 $p_内 = p_{大气} + p_h$,即 $p_内 > p_{大气}$,大气压随高度的增加而减小,将自制气压计移到山上后外界气压减小,瓶内气体的气压会将红色水向外压,h 会增大,只有 A 项正确。

(答案) A

知识 3 托里拆利实验

1.准确测量大气压数值的实验:托里拆利实验。

2.托里拆利实验的步骤

(1)如图甲,取一根一端开口、一端封闭的长约1米的玻璃管,往里面注满水银。

(2)如图乙,将开口一端朝下,浸没在水银中,且将玻璃管竖直放置(管顶要为真空)。

(3)如图丙,用刻度尺测出水银柱的高度差为760 mm,即得所测的大气压的值。通常把这样大小的大气压叫做标准大气压。

(4)标准大气压数值的计算:$p_{大气} = p_{水银柱} = \rho_{水银}gh = 13.6 \times 10^3$ kg/m^3×9.8 N/kg×0.76 m ≈ 1.013× 10^5 Pa。

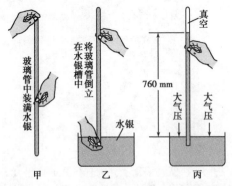

甲　　乙　　丙

温馨提示 (1)若用水做托里拆利实验,根据 $\rho_水 gh_水 = \rho_水 gh_水$ 可求1标准大气压支持的水柱高度 $h_水 = 10.34$ m,所以不用水做此实验。

(2)此实验中通过水银柱的高度来求大气压的值,运用了转换法。

3.托里拆利实验注意事项

(1)玻璃管中要充满水银,不能留有气泡。

(2)在做实验时要将玻璃管竖直放置。

(3)测量高度差时要测水银面到玻璃管中液面的距离。

(4)管内水银柱的高度差只随外界大气压强的变化而变化,与管的粗细、倾斜角度、管的长度及将玻璃管提起还是压下无关。

例 1 小梁同学用实验测量某地大气压的值。她在长约1米,一端封闭的玻璃管里灌满水银,用手指将管口堵住,然后倒插入水银槽中,放开手指,管内水银面下降到一定高度时就不再下降,如图所示。(g 取10 N/kg)

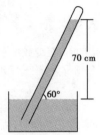

(1)已知水银的密度为 13.6×10^3 kg/m^3,她通过数据计算得出大气压的值为_____Pa。

(2)如果我们将此装置拿到海平面去测量,则测量结果将_____她测量的值。(选填"大于"或"小于")

(3)小杨同学也利用此装置测量小梁同学所在地大气压的值,他把水银换成水,将玻璃管灌满水后倒插在水槽内时,发现管中的水柱不会下降。如果你来测量,且能够测出,则玻璃管长度_____。(选填"必须大于10 m"或"可以小于 10 m")

解析 (1)由题图可知,实验中水银柱高度是70 cm,大气压强等于水银柱的压强,$p_{水银} = \rho_{水银}gh = 13.6×10^3×10×0.7$ Pa = $9.52×10^4$ Pa;

(2)海拔越低气压越高,故在海平面的测量结果将大于她测量的值;

(3)把水银换成水后,液体压强大小不变,仍为 $9.52×10^4$ Pa。根据 $p = \rho gh$ 可知,$h = \dfrac{p}{\rho_水 g} = \dfrac{9.52×10^4 \text{ Pa}}{1.0×10^3 \text{ kg/m}^3×10 \text{ N/kg}} = 9.52$ m,所以可以选用长度小于 10 m 的玻璃管。

答案 (1)$9.52×10^4$　(2)大于　(3)可以小于 10 m

例 2 有一根 300 mm 长的玻璃管,灌满水银后竖直倒插入水银槽中(外界气压约 1 标准大气压),当玻璃管顶不小心弄出一个小孔时,此时将看到　　(　　)

A.水银喷到高于管顶 460 mm 以上处

B.水银喷到高于管顶 460 mm 以下处

C.水银不喷出,仍充满玻璃管

D.水银在管内立即下降

解析 外界气压约为 1 标准大气压时,由托里拆利实验可知,它约能支持 760 mm 高的水银柱,现玻璃管只有 300 mm 长,由于大气压强的作用,不但能使水银充满整个玻璃管,还会对管顶产生向上的压强。但当管顶开一个小孔时,管顶部的水银面和水银槽中的水银面都受到大气压强的作用,因而管内水银柱在自身重力的作用下立即下落,最终跟水银槽内的液面相平。

答案 D

第④部分

知识 4 活塞式抽水机

1.活塞式抽水机也叫吸取式抽水机,是利用活塞的移动来排出空气,造成内、外气压差,使水在大气压作用下上升。

2.工作过程

(1)如图甲所示,提起活塞时,活塞上方的阀门 A 关闭,圆筒内气压减小,大气压迫使水冲开底阀 B,进入圆筒中。

(2)如图乙所示,压下活塞时,抽水机的底阀 B 关闭,活塞上方的阀门 A 打开,圆筒内的水进入到活塞上方。

(3)如图丙所示,再提起活塞时,活塞上方的阀门 A 关闭,它上面的水从出水管流出,同时大气压迫使水冲开底阀 B 进入圆筒中。这样,活塞不停地上下移动,水就从管口连续不断地流出。

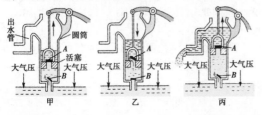

甲   乙   丙

知识 5 离心式水泵

1.工作过程

(1)离心式水泵简称离心泵,水泵在启动前,先往泵壳内灌满水,排出泵壳内的空气。

(2)启动后,叶轮在电动机的带动下高速旋转,泵壳里的水也随叶轮高速旋转,同时被甩入出水管中,这时叶轮附近的压强减小,大气压使水推开底阀,向上进入泵壳,进来的水又被叶轮甩入出水管,这样一直循环下去,就不断地把水抽到了高处,如图。

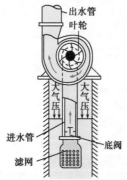

2.活塞式抽水机和离心式水泵都是利用大气压把水抽上来,因为大气压有一定的限度,因而抽水机抽水的高度也有一定的限度,不超过 10.3 米。

知识 利用大气压的知识解释有关现象

1.利用大气压的知识可以解释许多生活中的相关现象:

①钢笔吸墨水时,按下弹簧片排出管内空气,松开后,管内气压小于大气压,墨水在大气压的作用下被压进橡皮管内(如图甲)。

②用吸管喝饮料时,用力吸吸管,吸管内的压强减小,饮料在外界大气压的作用下被压进吸管,从而喝到饮料(如图乙)。

甲   乙

2.生活中,人体表面受到大气压强的作用,1 标准大气压比躺倒的大象对地面的压强还大;人们之所以没有感觉到这么大的大气压力,是因为身体内部也有压强,内外压强近似相等,再加上人生活在大气中,对大气压的作用早已适应。

例 我们每时每刻都要呼吸,利用胸部扩张和收缩的方式呼吸叫胸式呼吸,下列能正确表述胸式呼吸动作的是 (　　)

①吸气时胸部扩张,肺内气压低于大气压

②吸气时胸部收缩,肺内气压低于大气压

③呼气时胸部扩张,肺内气压高于大气压

④呼气时胸部收缩,肺内气压高于大气压

A.①和②　　　　　　B.①和④

C.②和③　　　　　　D.③和④

解析 呼吸时,通过改变肺内气压,从而使其与外界大气压产生压强差,使气体吸入或呼出。由气体压强和体积的关系可知:当体积增大时,气压减小;当体积减小时,气压增大。要吸气就必须使肺内气压小于外界大气压,即必须通过胸部扩张,使肺内压强减小,大气压将气体压入肺内;呼气则相反。

答案 B

方法 **利用二力平衡粗测大气压的值**

测量大气压时,除了可以用托里拆利实验和气压计测量外,还可以根据二力平衡粗略测量大气压的值。例如,可用弹簧测力计拉注射器针筒的办法,根据二力平衡粗测大气压的值。

例 1 1654 年,马德堡市长和他的助手做了著名的"马德堡半球实验",证明了大气压的存在。

(1)实验中,他们把两个铜半球壳灌满水后合在一起,再把水全部抽出,此时球内接近_____,周围的_____把两个铜半球紧紧地压在一起。

(2)如图,某校同学用底面积为 500 cm² 的平底压力锅代替铜半球模拟上述实验,在山底比在山顶拉开锅的最小拉力要_____(山底与山顶气温相同)。在山底,当锅两边受到的拉力均为 4 000 N 时,锅恰好被拉开,此时锅内空气的压强约为_____Pa(大气压取 10^5 Pa)。

(解析) (1)实验中,他们把两个铜半球壳灌满水后合在一起,再把水全部抽出,此时球内接近真空,外面的大气压力就将两个半球紧紧地压在一起。通过上述实验不仅证明了大气压的存在,而且证明了大气压是很大的。

(2)因为气压随高度的增加而减小,在山底比在山顶的气压大,所以在山底比在山顶拉开锅的最小拉力要大;已知 $F = 4\ 000$ N,$S = 500$ cm² $= 0.05$ m²,

$p = \dfrac{F}{S} = \dfrac{4\ 000\ \text{N}}{0.05\ \text{m}^2} = 8 \times 10^4$ Pa。

此时锅内空气的压强 $p_{内} = p_{气} - p = 10^5$ Pa $- 8 \times 10^4$ Pa $= 2 \times 10^4$ Pa

(答案) (1)真空 大气压力(大气、空气、大气压强)

(2)大 2×10^4

例 2 小明同学利用注射器、弹簧测力计、刻度尺等器材测量大气压强的值,实验步骤如下:

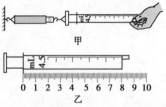

(1)把注射器的活塞推至注射器筒的底端,这样做的目的是_____。然后用橡皮帽堵住注射器的小孔。

(2)如图甲所示,用细尼龙绳拴住注射器活塞的颈部,使绳的另一端与弹簧测力计的挂钩相连,然后水平向右慢慢拉动注射器筒,当注射器中的活塞_____时,记下弹簧测力计的示数为 8.2 N。

(3)如图乙,用刻度尺测出注射器的全部刻度的长度为_____,计算得到活塞的横截面积为_____cm²。

(4)计算得到大气压强的数值为_____Pa。

(5)小明了解到班内同学的实验误差普遍很大,有的偏大,有的偏小。请分析,该实验过程中导致误差的因素有(请写出两条):

① _____。

② _____。

(解析) (1)把注射器的活塞推至注射器筒的底端是为了排出筒内空气。

(2)当活塞刚开始滑动时,拉力大小等于大气对活塞的压力。

(3)注射器全部刻度长 $L = 8.00$ cm $- 2.00$ cm $= 6.00$ cm,容积 $V = 4.5$ mL $= 4.5$ cm³

活塞的横截面积 $S = \dfrac{V}{L} = \dfrac{4.5\ \text{cm}^3}{6.00\ \text{cm}} = 0.75$ cm²。

(4)$p = \dfrac{F}{S} = \dfrac{8.2\ \text{N}}{0.75 \times 10^{-4}\ \text{m}^2} \approx 1.1 \times 10^5$ Pa。

(5)实验误差大的原因主要有:注射器筒内空气排不净,弹簧测力计示数不稳等。

(答案) (1)排出筒内空气 (2)刚开始滑动

(3)6.00 cm 0.75 (4)1.1×10^5 (5)见解析

第4节 流体压强与流速的关系

基础知识

知识 1 流体压强与流速的关系
知识 2 飞机的升力

知识 1 流体压强与流速的关系

1.流体:液体和气体除了有一定的质量外,还都能够流动。它们统称为流体。

2.流体压强与流速的关系:在气体和液体中,流速大的位置压强小,流速小的位置压强大。

小实验:(1)如图甲,在两支筷子中间放上两个乒乓球,用吸管向中间吹气,两个乒乓球会向中间靠拢;(2)如图乙,在水面上放上两只小纸船,用水管向中间的水域冲水,两只小纸船也会向中间靠拢;(3)如图丙,向两张自然下垂的白纸中间向下吹气,两张纸相互靠拢。

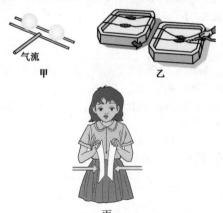

丙

3.生活中跟流体的压强相关的现象
(1)窗外有风吹过,窗帘向窗外飘;
(2)火车站台上设有安全线;
(3)家用煤气灶灶头;
(4)两艘船不能并排行驶;
(5)踢足球时的"香蕉球";
(6)打乒乓球时发出的"旋转球"等。

例 如图所示的实验中不能揭示流体压强与流速关系的实验是 ( )

解析 用吸管吸饮料时,利用了大气压,不能揭示流体压强与流速的关系,B 符合题意。

答案 B

知识 2 飞机的升力

(1)机翼的形状是上凸下平的(如图所示)。

(2)当飞机高速行驶时,机翼与周围的空气发生相对运动,迎面而来的气流被机翼分成上、下两部分。

(3)由于机翼横截面的形状上、下不对称,在相同时间内,机翼上方气流通过的曲线路程较长,机翼下方气流通过的直线路程较短,这就造成机翼上部气流的速度比机翼下部气流的速度大。由于流速大的地方压强小,流速小的地方压强大,因此,机翼上部的压强要小于机翼下部的压强。

(4)巨大的机翼就是靠上、下气流的压强差产生了向上的升力,从而使飞机升空飞翔。

例 地效翼船(如图)是一种经济、安全的飞行器,其工作原理是:在贴近水面或地面飞行时,离地表很近的带有翼刀或隔断端板的机翼下方,就会形成气流的堵塞,空气流速减小,压强_____,使机翼上下表面间的压力差增大,从而产生一个_____(填"向上"或"向下")的力。与轮船、飞机相比,没有了水和高空气流的阻力,相同条件下,所需的推进功率_____(填"较小"或"较大"),油耗较低。

解析 机翼下方空气流速减小,压强增大,使上下表面有较大的压力差,从而产生一个向上的力。和轮船、飞机相比,地效翼船不受水的阻力,也没有高空气流的阻力,因此所需的推进功率较小。

答案 增大 向上 较小

拓展知识 知识 科学解释足球中的"香蕉球"是怎么回事

知识 科学解释足球中的"香蕉球"是怎么回事

1.如果你经常观看足球比赛的话,一定见过罚前场任意球。进攻方的主罚队员起脚一记劲射,球绕过了"人墙",眼看要偏离球门飞出,却又沿弧线拐过弯来直射球门,让守门员措手不及,眼睁睁地看着球进了大门。这就是颇为神奇的"香蕉球"。

2.足球在气流中运动时,如果其一侧旋转的方向与气流同向,则会在球体的这一侧产生低压,而在球体的另一侧则会产生高压。当足球旋转时,除了可以改变球体周围的气流,球的运动轨迹也会相应发生改变。足球不仅可以侧旋,触球部位的不同,还可以产生不同的旋转,从而使足球上飘和下沉。这样就达到了迷惑防守方的目的。

方法 **流体压强相关问题的解法**

在实际生活和生产中有许多利用流体压强跟流速的关系来工作的装置和常见现象,分析时要注意:(1)首先要弄清哪部分流速大,哪部分流速小;(2)流速大处压强小,压力也小,流速小处压强大,压力也大;(3)物体受压力差作用而产生各种表现形式和现象。

例1 如图所示,某同学在探究流速大小对流体压强的影响时,在倒置的漏斗里放一个乒乓球,用手指托住乒乓球,然后从漏斗口向下用力吹气,当他将手指移开时,乒乓球没有下落。该现象可说明乒乓球上方气体流速_____(选填"增大"、"减小"或"不变")、压强_____(选填"变大"、"变小"或"不变")。

（解析） 从漏斗口向下吹气时,乒乓球上方气体流速大,根据"流速大的地方压强小"可知,乒乓球上方压强小,受到一个向上的力,因此掉不下来。

（答案） 增大　变小

例2 如图所示,是一个蓄水箱示意图,箱内装满水,M、N是管内同一水平线上的两点,K是阀门,K关闭时M、N两点的压强分别为p_M、p_N,K打开流出水时,M、N两点的压强分别为p_M'、p_N',则　　　　（　　）

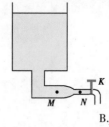

A.$p_M = p_N$　　　　　　　　B.$p_M > p_N$
C.$p_M' = p_N'$　　　　　　　D.$p_M' > p_N'$

（解析） 当阀门K关闭时,M、N所处的深度相同,水的密度一定,根据$p = \rho gh$可知,$p_M = p_N$,故A正确,B错误;K打开流出水时,M处的横截面积大,N处的横截面积小,同质量的水流过时,M处的流速小,压强大,N处的流速大,压强小,即$p_M' > p_N'$,故C错误,D正确。选A、D。

（答案） AD

浮力

知识梳理

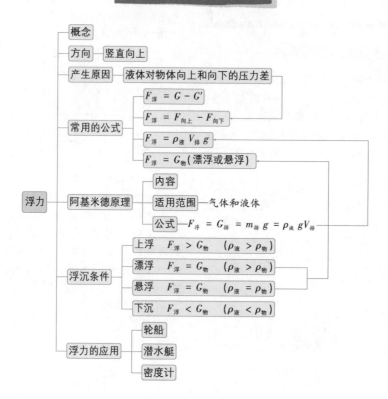

浮力 —
- 概念
- 方向 — 竖直向上
- 产生原因 — 液体对物体向上和向下的压力差
- 常用的公式
  - $F_浮 = G - G'$
  - $F_浮 = F_{向上} - F_{向下}$
  - $F_浮 = \rho_液 V_排 g$
  - $F_浮 = G_物$(漂浮或悬浮)
- 阿基米德原理
  - 内容
  - 适用范围 — 气体和液体
  - 公式 — $F_浮 = G_排 = m_排 g = \rho_液 g V_排$
- 浮沉条件
  - 上浮 $F_浮 > G_物$ $(\rho_液 > \rho_物)$
  - 漂浮 $F_浮 = G_物$ $(\rho_液 > \rho_物)$
  - 悬浮 $F_浮 = G_物$ $(\rho_液 = \rho_物)$
  - 下沉 $F_浮 < G_物$ $(\rho_液 < \rho_物)$
- 浮力的应用
  - 轮船
  - 潜水艇
  - 密度计

第1节 浮力

知识清单

 基础知识
知识 **1** 浮力
知识 **2** 浮力产生的原因

知识 1 浮力

1.定义:浸在液体或气体中的物体受到竖直向上的托力,这个托力叫做浮力。

2.施力物体与受力物体:浮力的施力物体是液体或气体,受力物体是浸入液体或气体中的物体。

3.方向:浮力的方向总是竖直向上的。

例 在图中画出浮在水面上的木块 A 所受力的示意图。

（解析）要画木块 A 所受力的示意图,首先要分析木块 A 的受力,因木块漂浮在水面上,所以它受到的重力和浮力大小相等,方向相反,二力平衡。

（答案）如图所示

知识 2 浮力产生的原因

1.以液体为例,浮力是由于浸在液体中的物体上、下表面存在压力差而产生的。

2.如图所示,浸没在液体中的立方体,左右两侧面、前后两侧面所受液体的压力大小相等,方向相反,彼此平衡;上、下两表面处在液体中不同深度,所受到的液体的压强不同,因受力面积相等,所以受到的压力不相等。下表面所受到的竖直向上的压力大于上表面所受到的竖直向下的压力,因而产生了浮力,$F_{浮}=F_{向上}-F_{向下}$,浮力的方向总是竖直向上的。

（例）一个边长为 10 cm 的正方体浸没在水中,下表面距水面 30 cm,物体下表面受到水的压强是____Pa,物体受到的浮力是____N。(g 取 10 N/kg)

（解析）边长为 10 cm 的正方体的一个面的面积为 $S=0.01 \text{ m}^2$,上表面距水面的距离:$h=0.3 \text{ m}-0.1 \text{ m}=0.2 \text{ m}$。上表面受到的压强为:$p_{上}=\rho_{水}gh=1.0\times10^3\times10\times0.2 \text{ Pa}=2\times10^3 \text{ Pa}$。物体上表面受到的压力:$F_{向下}=p_{上}S=2\times10^3 \text{ Pa}\times0.01 \text{ m}^2=20 \text{ N}$。物体下表面受到的压强为:$p_{下}=\rho_{水}gh'=1.0\times10^3\times10\times0.3 \text{ Pa}=3\times10^3 \text{ Pa}$。物体下表面受到的压力:$F_{向上}=p_{下}S=3\times10^3 \text{ Pa}\times0.01 \text{ m}^2=30 \text{ N}$。

物体受到的浮力:$F_{浮}=F_{向上}-F_{向下}=30 \text{ N}-20 \text{ N}=10 \text{ N}$。

（答案）3×10^3　10

拓展知识 **知识** 对"压力差法"的理解

知识 对"压力差法"的理解

根据浮力产生的原因,物体浸在液体中受到的浮力等于物体受到液体向上和向下的压力差,即 $F_{浮}=F_{向上}-F_{向下}$。此方法多用于求解形状规则的物体受到的浮力。

（1）当物体上表面露出液面时,$F_{向下}=0$,则 $F_{浮}=F_{向上}$。如:物体漂浮时,受到的浮力等于液体对它向上的压力。

（2）浸在液体中的物体不一定都受到浮力。如:桥墩、拦河坝等因其下底面同河床紧密黏合,水对它向上的压力 $F_{向上}=0$,故物体不受浮力作用。

（3）同一物体浸没在液体的不同深度,所受的压力差不变,浮力不变。

（4）浮力的实质是液体对物体各个表面压力的合力。因此,在分析物体的受力情况时,浮力和液体的压力不能同时考虑。

（例）如图所示,A 和 B 是能自由移动的正方体,C 和 D 是容器自身凸起的一部分,现往容器里注入一些水,则下列说法中错误的是（　　）

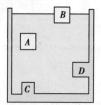

A.A 物体一定受浮力作用

B.B 物体一定受浮力作用

C.C 部分一定受浮力作用

D.D 部分一定受浮力作用

（解析）由 $p=\rho gh$ 可知:A 物体下表面受到的压强大于上表面受到的压强,又因为上、下表面面积相等,所以下表面受到的压力大于上表面的压力,A 一定受到浮力的作用。再看 B 物体,其上表面不受水的压力作用,下表面受到水向上的压力,所以也受到浮力的作用。C 部分底部与容器紧密结合,所以不受水对其向上的压力,而 $F_{浮}=F_{向上}-F_{向下}$,所以 C 部分一定不受浮力作用,但受到水向下的压力。D 部分是侧面与容器紧密结合,但其上、下表面都要受到水的压力,且向上的压力大于向下的压力,所以 D 部分一定受浮力作用。

（答案）C

第 4 部分

方法 1 称重法求物体所受的浮力

1.由于浮力的方向竖直向上,与重力的方向刚好相反,可以先把物体挂在弹簧测力计下,测得物体在空气中的重力 G,再把物体浸没在液体中,记下弹簧测力计的示数 G',则物体在液体中所受的浮力 $F_浮 = G - G'$,这种求浮力的方法为称重法,如图所示。

2.此法适用于求解在液体中下沉的物体所受到的浮力。

例 一物体在空气中用弹簧测力计测其重力,读数为 15 N,浸没在水中时,读数为 10 N;浸没在酒精中时,读数为 11 N,则物体在水中所受的浮力大小是____N,在酒精中所受的浮力大小是____N,浮力的方向均是_____。

(解析) 根据 $F_浮 = G - G'$,可求物体在水中所受浮力 $F_1 = 15 \text{ N} - 10 \text{ N} = 5 \text{ N}$,在酒精中所受浮力 $F_2 = 15 \text{ N} - 11 \text{ N} = 4 \text{ N}$,方向均为竖直向上。

(答案) 5 4 竖直向上

方法 2 平衡法求物体所受的浮力

对于漂浮在液面或浮在空中且静止的物体,因物体处于平衡状态,根据二力平衡条件有:$F_浮 = G_物$。由物体所受重力大小可知浮力大小。

例 甲、乙两个完全相同的杯子盛有不同浓度的盐水,将同一个鸡蛋先后放入其中,当鸡蛋静止时,两个杯子中液面恰好相平,鸡蛋所处的位置如图所示。则 ( )

甲   乙

A.鸡蛋在甲、乙两杯中排开的盐水体积一样大
B.鸡蛋在两个杯里受到的浮力一样大
C.甲、乙两杯底部所受的液体压强一样大
D.鸡蛋在乙杯中受到液体的浮力较大

(解析) 由题图可知,排开盐水的体积 $V_甲 > V_乙$,A 错误;鸡蛋在甲杯中悬浮,在乙杯中漂浮,所受浮力都等于鸡蛋的重力,所以在两杯中所受浮力一样大,B 正确,D 错误;两杯中液面相平,说明液体深度相同,鸡蛋在甲杯中悬浮,在乙杯中漂浮说明液体密度 $\rho_乙 > \rho_甲$,根据 $p = \rho g h$ 可知,乙杯杯底受到液体的压强大,C 错误。

(答案) B

第 2 节　阿基米德原理

知识清单

知识 1 浮力大小跟哪些因素有关

浸在液体中的物体受到浮力的大小:①跟物体浸入液体中的体积 $V_排$ 有关,$\rho_液$ 一定时 $V_排$ 越大,物体所受浮力越大;②跟液体的密度 $\rho_液$ 有关,$V_排$ 一定时 $\rho_液$ 越大,物体所受浮力越大;③跟物体浸入液体中的深度无关;④跟物体本身密度大小无关。

例 在探究"浮力的大小与什么因素有关"的实验中,小明同学和他的同伴们进行了如图所示的一系列实验,实验中的铜块与铝块体积相同,实验数据在图中已列出。

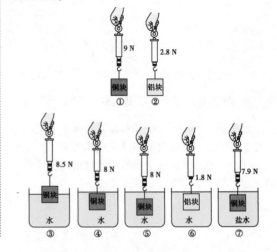

(1)图①③④三次实验是为了探究浮力的大小与哪个因素的关系？

(2)分析①②④⑥四次实验得到的结论是什么？

(3)为探究浮力大小跟物体浸没在液体中深度的关系，应选哪几次实验分析比较？

（解析）(1)由①③④：液体密度一定时，物体排开液体的体积越大，受到的浮力越大，所以这三次实验是为了探究浮力大小与物体排开液体体积的关系，结论是：在液体密度相同时，物体排开液体的体积越大，物体受到的浮力越大。

(2)铜块受到的重力为 $G_{铜}=9$ N，铝块受到的重力为 $G_{铝}=2.8$ N，重力不相等，则质量不相等，因为体积相同，则密度不相等；铜块受到的浮力为 $F_{铜浮}=9$ N-8 N$=1$ N，铝块受到的浮力为 $F_{铝浮}=2.8$ N-1.8 N$=1$ N，浮力相等。所以物体受到的浮力大小与物体的密度无关。

(3)要探究浮力大小与物体浸没在液体中深度的关系，需要控制 $\rho_{液}$ 和 $V_{排}$ 相同，即比较同一物体浸没在相同液体中的不同深度时受到的浮力，所以选择①④⑤。

（答案）(1)物体排开水的体积

(2)浮力的大小与物体的密度无关（其他说法正确的均可）

(3)①④⑤

（点拨）探究过程中用到了控制变量法。

知识 2 阿基米德原理

1.原理内容：浸在液体中的物体受到向上的浮力，浮力的大小等于它排开的液体所受的重力。

2.公式：$F_{浮}=G_{排}=m_{排}g=\rho_{液}gV_{排}$

式中 $\rho_{液}$ 表示液体的密度，$V_{排}$ 是被物体排开的液体的体积。

3.实验探究阿基米德原理

(1)实验时，用称重法求出物体所受浮力大小，用弹簧测力计测出排开液体重力的大小，最后把浮力与排开液体的重力相比较。

(2)实验过程中注意溢水杯中液体的液面达到溢水口，以保证物体排开的液体全部流入小桶。

（例）在探究"浮力大小等于什么"的实验中，小明同学的一次操作过程如图所示。

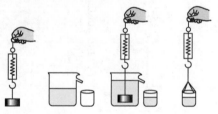

(1)测出铁块所受到的重力 $G_{铁}$；

(2)将水倒入溢水杯中；

(3)把铁块浸入溢水杯中，读出弹簧测力计示数 F；

(4)测出小桶和被排开水的总重力 G；

(5)记录、分析数据，归纳总结实验结论，整理器材。

分析评估小明的实验，指出存在的问题并改正。

（解析）在探究"浮力大小等于什么"的实验中，探究的结论是浮力的大小等于物体排开的液体所受到的重力，所以实验时，需要测出铁块受到的浮力和它排开水的重力，进行比较，得出结论。实验过程中需要测空小桶的重力，并且将溢水杯中的水加至溢水口处。

（答案）存在的问题：(1)没有测空小桶的重力；(2)溢水杯中的水量不足。

改正：(1)测空小桶的重力；(2)将溢水杯中的水加至溢水口处。

拓展知识　知识 阿基米德原理的五点透析

知识 阿基米德原理的五点透析

1.原理中所说的"浸在液体中的物体"包含两种状态：一是物体的全部体积都浸入液体里，即物体浸没在液体里；二是物体的一部分体积浸入液体里，另一部分露在液面以上。

2.$G_{排}$ 是指物体排开的液体所受的重力，$F_{浮}=G_{排}$ 表示物体受到的浮力的大小等于被物体排开的液体的重力。

3.$V_{排}$ 表示被物体排开的液体的体积，当物体全部浸入液体里时，$V_{排}=V_{物}$；当物体只有一部分浸入液体里时，$V_{排}<V_{物}$。

4.由 $F_{浮}=G_{排}=\rho_{液}gV_{排}$ 可以看出，g 一定时，浮力的大小只跟液体的密度和物体排开液体的体积这两个因素有关，而跟物体本身的体积、密度、形状、在液体中的深度、液体的多少等因素无关。

5.阿基米德原理也适用于气体，但公式中 $\rho_{液}$ 应改为 $\rho_{气}$。

方法 **1** 控制变量法探究浮力大小与哪些因素有关

探究浮力的大小跟哪些因素有关时,用"控制变量法"的思想去分析和设计实验:

①探究 $F_浮$ 与 $\rho_液$ 的关系时,应控制 $V_排$ 不变;

②探究 $F_浮$ 与 $V_排$ 的关系时,应控制 $\rho_液$ 相同。

例 在"探究浮力的大小跟哪些因素有关"的实验时,小丽提出如下猜想:

猜想一:浮力的大小跟物体排开液体的体积有关;

猜想二:浮力的大小跟液体的密度有关;

猜想三:浮力的大小跟物体的密度有关。

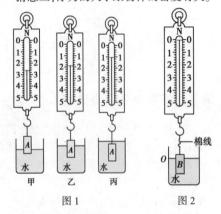

图1　　　　　图2

(1)小丽用重为 3.2 N 的物体 A 做了如图1所示的实验。该实验验证了猜想_____是正确的,可得出:在同种液体中,物体排开液体的体积越大,受到的浮力_____。实验中,物体 A 浸没时受到的浮力为_____N,方向_____。

(2)下表是小丽验证猜想二时收集的实验数据:

液体种类	物体A在液体中的状态	弹簧测力计的示数/N	物体A受到的浮力/N
酒精	浸没	1.4	1.8
盐水	浸没	0.8	2.4

分析比较表中数据和图1实验中_____(选填"甲"、"乙"或"丙")的数据可知:浮力的大小与液体的密度_____。

(3)为验证猜想三,小丽选用了与物体 A 密度不同的物体 B 进行实验。她将物体 B 逐渐浸入水中,容器中的水面上升至图示 O 位置时,发现棉线松弛,弹簧测力计示数变为0,如图2所示。取出物体 B 后,小

丽又将物体 A 缓慢浸入水中,她在水面上升到_____(选填"O 点之上"、"O 点"或"O 点之下")位置时,读取弹簧测力计的示数,这样做是为了控制_____相同,以便判断浮力的大小与物体的密度是否有关。

解析 (1)观察题图1可知,甲、乙、丙三个步骤中改变了 $V_排$,测力计示数依次减小,所以验证了猜想一是正确的,可得出:在同种液体中,$V_排$ 越大,浮力越大;物体 A 在水中浸没时所受拉力 $F=1$ N,$F_浮=3.2$ N -1 N $=2.2$ N,方向竖直向上。

(2)研究浮力大小与 $\rho_液$ 的关系时,应控制 $V_排$ 不变,故应选择丙的数据与表中数据一起比较,物体 A 在水中浸没时,受到的浮力为 2.2 N,物体 A 在酒精中浸没时,受到的浮力为1.8 N,物体 A 在盐水中浸没时,受到的浮力为 2.4 N,可知 $F_浮$ 与 $\rho_液$ 有关。

(3)研究浮力大小与物体密度是否有关时,要控制 $\rho_液$ 与 $V_排$ 不变,改变 $\rho_物$,因此应让物体 A 浸入水中时,液面也升高到 O 点位置,这样既控制了 $\rho_液$,又控制了 $V_排$。

答案 (1)一　越大　2.2　竖直向上

(2)丙　有关

(3)O 点　排开液体的体积

方法 **2** 公式法计算浮力

1.利用阿基米德原理公式 $F_浮=\rho_液 gV_排$,可以计算物体所受浮力大小。

2.该公式适用于任何形状的物体受到的浮力。

3.可用变形式 $V_排=\dfrac{F_浮}{\rho_液 g}$ 来计算 $V_排$ 或物体的体积。

> **温馨提示** 计算浮力共有四种方法,分别是:①称重法、②平衡法、③压力差法、④公式法。

例 弹簧测力计下挂着一重为 2 N 的物体,物体一半体积浸入水中静止时,弹簧测力计示数如图所示,其示数为_____N,物体体积为_____m^3(已知水的密度为 $\rho_水=1.0\times10^3$ kg/m³,g 取 10 N/kg)。

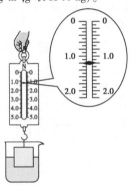

（解析）由题图知，此弹簧测力计的分度值为 0.1 N，示数为 1.2 N。物体受到的浮力：$F_浮 = G - F_示 = 2\text{ N} - 1.2\text{ N} = 0.8\text{ N}$，由 $F_浮 = \rho_水 g V_排$ 可得，$V_排 = \dfrac{F_浮}{\rho_水 g}$

$\dfrac{0.8\text{ N}}{1.0 \times 10^3\text{ kg/m}^3 \times 10\text{ N/kg}} = 8 \times 10^{-5}\text{ m}^3$。物体的体积：$V = 2 \times 8 \times 10^{-5}\text{ m}^3 = 1.6 \times 10^{-4}\text{ m}^3$。

（答案）1.2 1.6×10^{-4}

方法 3 图像法研究物体所受浮力大小与深度的关系

1.物体逐渐浸入液体中时，研究浮力与深度关系的图像有两种：一种是物体所受浮力的大小 $F_浮$ 与物体下表面浸入液体中深度 h 的关系图像；另一种是弹簧测力计示数 F 与物体下表面浸入液体中深度 h 的关系图像。

2.判断物体浸入液体中所受浮力大小变化可以分为两个过程：一是从接触液面到刚好浸没，这个阶段随着深度的增加，物体排开液体的体积不断增大，浮力也随着增大；二是浸没后，物体排开液体的体积不再变化，故物体所受浮力也不再改变。

（例）小明游泳时发现，人在水中越往深处走就觉得所受的浮力越大。由此他猜想："浮力的大小可能与物体浸入水中的深度有关或者与物体排开水的体积有关"，于是他找来一个金属圆柱体、弹簧测力计、烧杯和水等器材进行了如图 1 所示的探究。

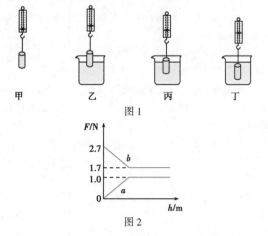

图 1

图 2

（1）分析图中弹簧测力计示数的变化可知：物体排开水的体积越大，物体所受的浮力就_____（选填"越大"或"越小"）。

（2）小明绘制了弹簧测力计对金属圆柱体的拉力和金属圆柱体所受浮力随浸入水中深度变化的图像，如图 2 所示。

分析图像可知：描述金属圆柱体所受浮力的变化情况的图像是_____（选填"a"或"b"）；该金属圆柱体在空气中所受的重力为_____N，当金属圆柱体完全浸入水中后所受的浮力是_____N，金属圆柱体浸没水中后所受浮力大小与金属圆柱体所处的深度_____（选填"有"或"无"）关。

（3）在上述实验的基础上，请你再增加一个实验步骤，用来研究浮力大小与液体密度的关系。

（解析）（1）浸入水中的金属圆柱体受竖直向下的重力、竖直向上的浮力和竖直向上的拉力，其排开水的体积变大，测力计示数变小，则表示受到的浮力变大。

（2）由（1）的结论可知金属圆柱体浸没前，浸入水中的深度越大，排开水的体积越大，所以浮力也越大。浸没后，排开水的体积不变，所以浮力大小不变。图中 a 图线表示浮力先变大后不变，b 图线表示拉力先变小后不变，所以应选 a。图线 b 中深度为 0 时的拉力即等于金属圆柱体的重力 $G = 2.7$ N。由图线 a 可知浸入水中的金属圆柱体浸没后受到的浮力 $F_浮 = 1$ N。由图可知浸没后浮力大小与浸入水中的金属圆柱体所处深度无关。

（3）见答案。

（答案）（1）越大（2）a 2.7 1 无（3）换用一杯密度与水不同的液体，将金属圆柱体浸没在液体中，观察弹簧测力计的示数，与丁图比较得出结论（或往丁图实验的烧杯中加入适量的盐或加入其他能改变液体密度的可溶性物质，观察弹簧测力计示数变化情况）。

第3节 物体的浮沉条件及应用

基础知识
知识 ① 物体的浮沉条件
知识 ② 密度计
知识 ③ 浮力的应用

知识 1 物体的浮沉条件

上浮	下沉	悬浮	漂浮	沉底
$F_浮 > G$	$F_浮 < G$	$F_浮 = G$	$F_浮 = G$	$F_浮 + N = G$
$\rho_液 > \rho_物$	$\rho_液 < \rho_物$	$\rho_液 = \rho_物$ $V_排 = V_物$	$\rho_液 > \rho_物$ $V_排 < V_物$	$\rho_液 < \rho_物$ $V_排 = V_物$
处于动态(运动状态不断改变),受非平衡力作用		可以停留在液体中的任何深度处	是"上浮"过程的最终状态	是"下沉"过程的最终状态
		处于静态,受平衡力作用		

易混对比

判断物体的浮沉

　　判断物体的浮沉通常有两种方法:(1)比较物体所受浮力和重力的大小关系;如果浮力大于重力,则物体上浮,反之则下沉,刚好相等则悬浮(或漂浮);(2)比较物体密度和液体密度的大小关系,如果物体密度小于液体的密度,则物体上浮(最终漂浮在液面上),反之则下沉(最终会沉底),刚好相等则悬浮。

　　在液体中悬浮的实心物体分成两小块后,每一小块物体在该液体中也处于悬浮状态,就是因为物体密度等于液体密度。

　　例 小明用手将小球浸没在水中,小球排开水的质量是 0.1 kg,此时小球受到的浮力是_____N($g=$ 9.8 N/kg)。若小球的质量为 0.3 kg,松手后小球会_____(选填"上浮"、"悬浮"或"下沉")。

　　解析 $F_浮 = G_排 = m_排 g = 0.1$ kg × 9.8 N/kg =

0.98 N;

$G_物 = m_物 g = 0.3$ kg × 9.8 N/kg = 2.94 N,

$F_浮 < G_物$,所以小球会下沉。

答案 0.98　下沉

知识 2 密度计

1. **定义**:密度计是一种测量液体密度的仪器(如图)。

2. **原理**:漂浮在液体中的物体所受的浮力等于重力,即 $F_浮 = G$。

3. **构造**:密度计是一根粗细不均匀的密封玻璃管,管的下部装有少量密度较大的铅丸或水银。

4. **读数**:使用时将密度计竖直地放入待测的液体中,待密度计平稳后,从它的刻度处读出待测液体的密度。

5. **分类**:常用密度计有两种,一种测密度比纯水大的液体,叫重表;另一种测密度比纯水小的液体,叫轻表。

6. **刻度**:密度计在不同的液体中所受浮力相同,由 $F_浮 = \rho_液 g V_排$ 可知,$\rho_液$ 增大时,$V_排$ 减小,密度计在液面以上的部分增大,刻度越靠下密度值越大;另外注意密度计的刻度是不均匀的。

　　例 如图所示为一种自制简易密度计,它是在木棒的一端缠绕一些铜丝做成的,用它来测量液体密度时,该密度计_____在被测液体中(选填"悬浮"、"漂浮"或"下沉")。将其分别放入装有液体(密度为 ρ_1 和 ρ_2)的两个烧杯中,可以判断:ρ_1_____ρ_2。若该密度计两次测量中排开液体的质量分别为 m_1、m_2,则 m_1_____m_2。(后两空选填"<"、"="或">")

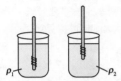

(解析) 用密度计测量液体密度时,它漂浮在被测液体中,由于自身重力不变,所以浮力不变。根据 $F_浮 = \rho_液 g V_排$ 可知:$F_浮$ 一定时,$\rho_液$ 与 $V_排$ 成反比,$V_排$ 大的液体密度小,故 $\rho_1 < \rho_2$;由于 $F_浮 = G_排液$,$G_排液$ 相等,所以排开液体的质量 $m_1 = m_2$。

(答案) 漂浮 < =

知识 **3** 浮力的应用

1.盐水选种

我国农民常采用盐水浸泡法来选种,这种方法是把种子放入浓度适宜的盐水中,干瘪、虫蛀的种子密度小于盐水的密度,会上浮至液面,而饱满的种子密度大于盐水的密度,会沉在底部。

2.轮船

(1)轮船是用密度大于水的钢铁制成的,把它做成空心,使它的平均密度小于水的密度,它就会漂浮在水面上,这时轮船受到的浮力等于自身的重力。

(2)只要轮船的重力不变,无论轮船在海里还是河里,它受到的浮力不变。根据阿基米德原理 $F_浮 = G_排 = \rho_液 g V_排$,它在海里和河里浸入水中的体积不同,船从河里驶入海里,船身会上浮一些。

(3)轮船的大小通常用排水量来表示,排水量就是轮船按设计的要求装满货物即满载时排开水的质量。

> **温馨提示** 在理解轮船从河里驶入海里是上浮还是下沉等类似问题时,可以把轮船看做密度计,由于海水密度较大,所以船会上浮一些。

例 2010 年 1 月 29 日全球最大的太阳能动力船"星球太阳号"在德国基尔下水,如图,开始了行程 4 万公里,需 140 天的环球之旅。船的排水量为 60 吨,则受到的最大浮力是_____N。($g = 10$ N/kg)

(解析) 排水量是指轮船满载时排开水的质量,即 $m_排 = 60$ t $= 6 \times 10^4$ kg,则 $F_浮 = G_排 = m_排 g = 6 \times 10^4$ kg$\times$ 10 N/kg $= 6.0 \times 10^5$ N。

(答案) 6.0×10^5

3.潜水艇

(1)潜水艇的上浮和下沉是靠调节水舱里水的多少来控制自身的重力而实现的,如图所示。

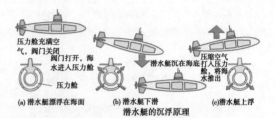

压力舱充满空气,阀门关闭   阀门打开,海水进入压力舱   压缩空气,压力舱,将海水推出   压力舱

(a) 潜水艇漂浮在海面 (b) 潜水艇下潜 (c)潜水艇上浮
潜水艇的沉浮原理

(2)无论下潜多深,浸没在水中的潜水艇排开水的体积始终不变,所以潜水艇所受的浮力始终不变。若要下沉,可充水,使 $F_浮 < G$;若要上浮,可排水,使 $F_浮 > G$。在潜水艇浮出水面的过程中,因为排开水的体积减小,所以浮力减小;当潜水艇在海面上行驶时,受到的浮力大小等于潜水艇的重力。

> **拓展知识**
> 知识**1** 气球的浮沉
> 知识**2** 曹冲称象过程中的浮力知识

知识 **1** 气球的浮沉

1.物体在空气中时,上、下表面受到空气的压力差就是空气的浮力。故物体在空气中称得的重量,并不是物体真正的重量。由于物体在空气中所受的浮力很小,故可以忽略不计。

2.氢气球和热气球浮沉条件比较:

	上升	下降
氢气球	充入密度小于空气的氢气	放掉球内部分气体,使球的体积减小
热气球	充入加热后的热空气	停止加热,热空气冷却,热气球内空气密度增大

3.飞艇:飞艇是将氢气和氦气贮存于椭圆形的气囊中,因这些气体密度比空气小,所以能借助空气的浮力上升。

例 0 ℃、1 个标准大气压下,体积为 4×10^{-3} m^3 的氢气球,在地面附近受到空气的浮力约为_____N。图中,氢气气球会上浮,而空气气球却浮不起来,这是因为_____。

(解析) $F_浮 = \rho_{空气} g V_排 = 1.29$ kg/m$^3 \times 9.8$ N/kg$\times 4 \times 10^{-3}$ m$^3 \approx 0.051$ N。

（答案）0.051　氢气球受到的浮力大于自身重力,而空气球受到的浮力小于自身重力(其他合理答案均可)

知识 2　曹冲称象过程中的浮力知识

曹冲称象时,用石块代替大象,使两次船排开水的体积相同,由阿基米德原理公式 $F_浮=\rho_液 gV_排$ 可知:船两次所受浮力相同,根据浮沉条件:漂浮时重力等于浮力,有 $G_船+G_象=G_船+G_石$,即 $G_象=G_石$。

实验中用到了浮沉条件及阿基米德原理等知识,且用到了等效替代的物理方法。

方法清单

方法 1 利用浮力知识求物体或液体的密度
方法 2 液面升降问题的解法

方法 1　利用浮力知识求物体或液体的密度

1.若 $\rho_物>\rho_液$,物体浸没在液体中,由阿基米德原理有 $F_浮=\rho_液 gV_排$,由称重法有 $F_浮=G-G'$,可求出 $V_排=\dfrac{G-G'}{\rho_液 g}$,又因为 $G=mg=\rho_物 gV_物$,此时 $V_物=V_排$,可得 $\rho_物=\dfrac{G}{G-G'}\rho_液$。根据此式,已知 $\rho_液$,可求出 $\rho_物$;已知 $\rho_物$,可求出 $\rho_液$。

2.对于漂浮的物体,浮力等于重力,而浮力 $F_浮=\rho_液 gV_排$,重力 $G_物=\rho_物 gV_物$,因 $F_浮=G_物$,只要知道 $V_排$ 与 $V_物$ 的关系和 $\rho_液$(或 $\rho_物$)就可求出 $\rho_物$(或 $\rho_液$)。

例 如图所示,是小鹰同学测量某种液体密度的过程,请你根据实验数据,求:(g 取 10 N/kg)

(1)小石块的质量;
(2)小石块的体积;
(3)液体的密度。

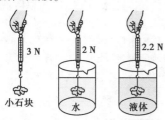

小石块　水　液体

（解析）(1)小石块的质量:$m=\dfrac{G}{g}=\dfrac{3\ N}{10\ N/kg}=0.3\ kg$

(2)小石块浸没在水中时:$F_浮=G-F_拉=3\ N-2\ N=1\ N$

$V_石=V_排=\dfrac{F_浮}{\rho_水 g}=\dfrac{1\ N}{1\times10^3\ kg/m^3\times10\ N/kg}=1\times10^{-4}\ m^3$

(3)小石块浸没在液体中时:

$F_浮'=G-F_拉'=3\ N-2.2\ N=0.8\ N$

由 $F_浮'=\rho_液 V_排 g$

得 $\rho_液=\dfrac{F_浮'}{V_排 g}=\dfrac{0.8\ N}{1\times10^{-4}\ m^3\times10\ N/kg}=0.8\times10^3\ kg/m^3$

（答案）(1)0.3 kg　(2)1×10⁻⁴ m³　(3)0.8×10³ kg/m³

例 有一木块,放入水中时有 $\dfrac{2}{5}$ 的体积露出水面,放入某种液体中时有 $\dfrac{3}{4}$ 的体积没入液体中,求木块和液体的密度。

（解析）当木块漂浮在水中时:

$F_{浮水}=G_木$,即 $\rho_水 g\cdot\left(1-\dfrac{2}{5}\right)V_木=\rho_木 gV_木$,

所以 $\rho_木=\dfrac{3}{5}\rho_水=0.6\times10^3\ kg/m^3$,

木块在某种液体中漂浮时,$F_{浮液}=G_木$,

即 $\rho_液 g\cdot\dfrac{3}{4}V_木=\rho_木 gV_木$,

所以 $\rho_液=\dfrac{4}{3}\rho_木=\dfrac{4}{3}\times0.6\times10^3\ kg/m^3=0.8\times10^3\ kg/m^3$

（答案）0.6×10³ kg/m³　0.8×10³ kg/m³

方法 2　液面升降问题的解法

1.组合物体漂浮类型

(1)要看液面是上升还是下降,关键是比较前后两次物体排开液体的体积的变化。设物体原来排开液体的体积为 $V_排$,后来排开液体的体积为 $V_排'$,若 $V_排'>V_排$,则液面上升;若 $V_排'<V_排$,则液面下降;若 $V_排'=V_排$,则液面高度不变。

(2)根据阿基米德原理知,物体在液体中所受的浮力 $F_浮=\rho_液 gV_排$,故 $V_排=\dfrac{F_浮}{\rho_液 g}$,因液体的密度 $\rho_液$ 不

154　初中物理知识清单

变,故物体排开液体的体积取决于物体所受的浮力,所以只要判断出物体前后所受浮力的变化情况,即可判断出液面的升降情况。

例1 一个水槽内漂浮着一个放有小铁球的烧杯,若将小铁球取出放入水槽里,烧杯仍漂浮在水槽中,则水面将 ( )

　　A.上升　　B.不变　　C.下降　　D.无法判断

（解析）装有铁球的烧杯漂浮在水中,烧杯所受的浮力 $F_浮$ 与烧杯和铁球的总重力平衡,则有: $F_浮 = G_铁 + G_杯$。

把铁球放入水槽中,铁球下沉,铁球单独受到的浮力 $F_{浮1} < G_铁$;烧杯单独受到的浮力 $F_{浮2} = G_杯$。铁球放入水槽中后,铁球和烧杯所受浮力之和 $F_浮' = F_{浮1} + F_{浮2}$,因此 $F_浮' < F_浮$,烧杯和铁球后来排开水的体积之和小于原来排开水的体积,所以水面下降,故正确选项为C。

（答案）C

2.纯冰熔化类型

（1）若冰块漂浮于水中,则冰熔化后液面高度不变;若冰块漂浮于密度大于水的液体中,则冰熔化后液面上升;若冰块漂浮(或浸没)于密度小于水的液体中,则冰熔化后液面下降。

（2）要判断液面的升降,必须比较冰排开液体的体积与冰熔化成水的体积之间的关系。若冰漂浮在液面上,则所受的浮力与重力相等,即 $F_浮 = G_冰$。冰块所受的浮力 $F_浮 = \rho_液 g V_排$,冰块的重力 $G_冰 = m_冰 g$,由此可得: $V_排 = \dfrac{m_冰}{\rho_液}$;冰熔化成水的体积 $V_化 = \dfrac{m_冰}{\rho_水} = \dfrac{m_水}{\rho_水}$。当 $\rho_液 = \rho_水$ 时, $V_化 = V_排$,液面高度不变;当 $\rho_液 > \rho_水$ 时, $V_化 > V_排$,液面高度上升;当 $\rho_冰 < \rho_液 < \rho_水$ 时, $V_化 < V_排$,液面高度下降;当 $\rho_液 \leqslant \rho_冰$ 时, $V_化 < V_排$,液面高度下降。

例2 如图所示,烧杯中的冰块漂浮在水中,冰块上部高出杯口,杯中水面恰好与杯口相平,待这些冰全部熔化后 ( )

　　A.将有水从杯中溢出

　　B.不会有水从杯中溢出,杯中水面也不会下降

　　C.烧杯中水面下降

　　D.熔化过程中水面下降,完全熔化后有水溢出

（解析）冰熔化后烧杯中的水面高度将保持不变,故不会有水溢出。

（答案）B

第12章 功和机械能

知识梳理

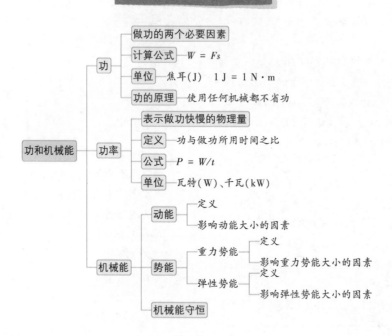

功和机械能
- 功
  - 做功的两个必要因素
  - 计算公式 $W = Fs$
  - 单位 焦耳(J) $1\,J = 1\,N \cdot m$
  - 功的原理 使用任何机械都不省功
- 功率
  - 表示做功快慢的物理量
  - 定义 功与做功所用时间之比
  - 公式 $P = W/t$
  - 单位 瓦特(W)、千瓦(kW)
- 机械能
  - 动能
    - 定义
    - 影响动能大小的因素
  - 势能
    - 重力势能
      - 定义
      - 影响重力势能大小的因素
    - 弹性势能
      - 定义
      - 影响弹性势能大小的因素
  - 机械能守恒

第1节 功

知识清单

基础知识
知识 1 做功的两个必要因素
知识 2 力对物体不做功的三种情况
知识 3 功的计算

知识 1 做功的两个必要因素

1.功:物体在力的作用下且在这个力的方向上移动了一段距离,我们就说力对物体做了功。吊车的作用力使货物上升一段距离,吊车的作用力对货物做了功;汽车的牵引力使汽车移动一段距离,牵引力对汽车做了功,如图(a)、(b)所示。

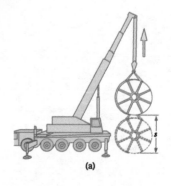

(a)

(b)

做功的过程是能量转化的过程。功是能量转化的量度。

2.做功的两个必要因素:一个是作用在物体上的力,另一个是物体在这个力的方向上移动的距离。

例 如图所示的四种情景中,人对物体做功的是 （ ）

举重运动员
举着杠铃不动
A

工人将货箱
从地面搬到桌上
B

修理工用力推
汽车,汽车没动
C

大力士支撑着
大轮胎静止不动
D

解析 做功有两个必要因素,缺一不可,A、C、D均是有了力,而物体没有在力的方向上移动距离,因此没有做功;只有 B,人对物体做了功。

答案 B

知识 **2** 力对物体不做功的三种情况

情况	原因	实例
有距离无力	物体没有受到力的作用,但由于惯性通过了一段距离,这时没有力做功	足球离开脚后在水平面上滚动了 10 m,这 10 m 过程中,人对足球没有做功
有力无距离	有力作用在物体上,但物体没动,即物体没有通过距离	一辆汽车停在路边,一个人用很大的力却没有推动它,推力对汽车不做功
力与距离垂直	物体受到了力的作用,也通过了一段距离,但通过的距离与力的方向垂直	提着水桶水平移动一段距离,竖直提水桶的力不做功

知识 **3** 功的计算

1.公式:力学中,功等于力与物体在力的方向上移动的距离的乘积,即功=力×距离。

功的计算公式为 $W=Fs$。W:功,F:力,s:距离。

温馨提示 在利用该公式进行计算时,须注意三点:

（1）物体移动的距离必须是在力的方向上(同向性);

（2）力与物体移动的距离必须对应于同一物体(同体性);

（3）力与物体移动的距离必须对应于同一段时间(同时性)。

2.单位:国际单位制中,力的单位是 N,距离的单位是 m,功的单位是焦耳,简称焦,用符号 J 表示,$1\ J=1\ N\cdot m$。

3.变形式:$F=\dfrac{W}{s}$、$s=\dfrac{W}{F}$可求力和物体在力的作用下移动的距离

例 用水平拉力先后两次拉着重为 20 N 的同一物体,沿同一水平面做直线运动。第一次拉力为 10 N,物体恰好做匀速直线运动,拉力对物体做了 20 J 的功;第二次将拉力增大为 20 N,拉力对物体做了 48 J 的功。分析两次做功过程,以下判断正确的是 （ ）

A.第一次物体受到的摩擦力是 10 N,物体运动了 1 m

B.第一次物体受到的摩擦力是 20 N,物体运动了 2 m

C.第二次物体受到的摩擦力是 10 N,物体运动了 2.4 m

D.第二次物体受到的摩擦力是 20 N,物体运动了 4.8 m

解析 第一次拉动物体时,物体做匀速直线运动,所以 $f_1=F_1=10$ N,第二次拉动物体时,滑动摩擦力大小不变,$f_2=10$ N,而拉力 $F_2=20$ N,所以物体将会加速运动。由题意知 $W_1=20$ J,所以 $s_1=\dfrac{W_1}{F_1}=2$ m;$W_2=48$ J,$F_2=20$ N,所以 $s_2=\dfrac{W_2}{F_2}=2.4$ m。故正确选项为 C。

答案 C

拓展知识 **知识** 功的原理

知识 功的原理

1.功的原理:忽略机械自重和摩擦时,使用简单机械所做的功等于人们不使用机械而直接做的功,或者说使用机械不省功。

如图甲,如果直接用手把重为 G 的物体提升一定的高度 h,手提物体的力大小等于 G,手移动的距离等于 h,手做的功是 $W_1=G\cdot h$。如图乙,使用动滑轮,提

力变为 $\frac{G}{2}$（不考虑动滑轮的自重及摩擦），手移动的距离变为 $2h$，使用动滑轮时手做的功 $W_2 = \frac{G}{2} \cdot 2h = Gh$。可见，$W_2 = W_1$，所以使用机械时对物体做的功等于不使用机械时直接对物体做的功。

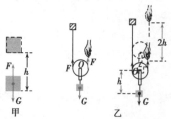

甲　　　乙

2.功的原理对于任何机械都适用，它是成立在一种"理想化"的状态。例如，杠杆、滑轮中机械自身的重力及工作时的摩擦都是客观存在的，所以在应用功的原理进行计算时，是一种"理想化"状态下的计算。

3.使用简单机械可以省力，或者可以省距离，但省力必然费距离，省距离必然费力，即力跟物体在力的方向上通过的距离的乘积是一个不变量。例如动滑

轮，由于有两根绳子承重，所以可以省一半的力，但绳端却要移动两倍的距离。使用定滑轮，既不省力，又不费力，但可以改变力的方向，做功方便。

例 如图所示，$AC > AB$，沿光滑斜面 AC 和 AB 分别将同一重物从底部匀速推到顶端，所用推力分别为 F_1 和 F_2，所做的功分别为 W_1 和 W_2，则 　　（　　）

A.$F_1 > F_2$　　$W_1 = W_2$

B.$F_1 = F_2$　　$W_1 = W_2$

C.$F_1 < F_2$　　$W_1 = W_2$

D.$F_1 < F_2$　　$W_1 < W_2$

(解析) 根据功的原理，在理想情况下，用机械做的功与不用机械直接做的功相等。同一个重物沿不同斜面上升到同一高度，都是克服重力做功的过程，重力不变，提升高度不变，推力所做的功就相等，故 $W_1 = W_2 = W$；而推力做功 $FL = W$，当 W 一定时，斜面 L 越长，所需要的推力就越小，故有 $F_1 < F_2$。

(答案) C

方法清单　方法 概念法判断力对物体是否做功

方法 **概念法判断力对物体是否做功**

1.判断方法

判断力对物体是否做功，根据功的概念，可以从物体是否受力及在该力的方向上是否移动了距离来进行判断。

2.生活中常见的例子

（1）如冰块在光滑冰面上匀速滑动，水平方向上没有受到力的作用，只是在竖直方向上受重力和支持力。因此，水平方向上没有力对冰块做功，而竖直方向上，重力、支持力的方向都与冰块运动的方向垂直，所以重力、支持力也没有对冰块做功。

（2）人用力推车行驶一段距离，人对车有水平推力，且车沿水平方向通过了距离，符合做功的两个必要因素，推力做了功。

（3）如图所示，一个小球在水平桌面上滚动并落到地面上，下落过程中，小球做曲线运动，由于重力方向竖直向下，重力做功为 $W = Gh$。

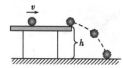

例 下列有关功的说法正确的是 　　（　　）

A.足球在水平地面上滚动时重力对足球没有做功

B.吊车吊着重物使其沿水平方向匀速移动过程中，吊车对重物做了功

C.运动员举着杠铃在空中停留的时间内对杠铃要做很大的功

D.用相同的力将质量不同的两个物体沿力的方向移动相同的距离所做的功不同

(解析) 足球在水平地面上滚动时，在重力的方向（竖直方向）上没有通过距离，重力没有做功，故 A 正确；吊车吊着重物在水平方向匀速移动过程中，在竖直方向（拉力的方向）上没有移动距离，故吊车没有对重物做功，故 B 错误；杠铃停留在空中没有移动距离，故运动员对杠铃没有做功，C 错误；根据 $W = Fs$，又知力 F 和在力的方向上移动的距离均相同，则所做的功 W 就相同，故 D 错误。

(答案) A

第2节　功率

基础知识　知识1 比较做功的快慢
知识2 功率
知识3 对推导公式 $P=Fv$ 的理解

知识 1 比较做功的快慢

1.在相同的时间内,比较做功的多少,做功越多,功率越大,这是物理学中经常采用的方法。

2.在完成相同功的条件下,比较所用时间的长短,所用时间越短,功率越大。

3.在做功的多少和所用时间都不相同的情况下,通过 $P=W/t$ 计算后进行比较。

例 我们可以用两种方法来判断物体做功的快慢,如图所示,表示用挖掘机挖土与人力挖土做功的快慢不同,它所用的判断方法是:做功的时间相同,比较做功多少。另一种判断方法是:_____相同,比较_____。

做功时间相同

解析 判断物体做功的快慢,经常用做功的时间相同,比较做功的多少或做功的多少相同,比较所用时间的长短两种方法。

答案 做功的多少　做功的时间

知识 2 功率

1.意义:表示物体做功快慢的物理量。

2.定义:功与做功所用时间之比叫做功率。

3.公式: $P=\dfrac{W}{t}$,其中 P 代表功率,单位为 W; W 代表功,单位为 J; t 代表时间,单位为 s。

4.单位之间的换算关系: $1\ kW=10^3\ W$ 。

5.决定因素:(1)功的大小,(2)做功时间的长短。

例 如图所示,重为 150 N 的物体在大小为40 N 的水平拉力 F 作用下,向右匀速运动了 10 m,所用时间为 20 s,则拉力做的功是_____J,拉力做功的功率为_____W。

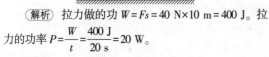

解析 拉力做的功 $W=Fs=40\ N\times10\ m=400\ J$ 。拉力的功率 $P=\dfrac{W}{t}=\dfrac{400\ J}{20\ s}=20\ W$ 。

答案 400　20

知识 3 对推导公式 $P=Fv$ 的理解

1. $P=\dfrac{W}{t}=\dfrac{Fs}{t}=Fv$,此公式对功率的实际应用有较大的意义。

2.汽车发动机的功率一定,由 $F=\dfrac{P}{v}$ 可知,牵引力与速度成反比,在汽车爬坡时,司机采用的措施是换挡减速,以获得更大的牵引力(如图)。

例 "歼-10"是我国自行研发的新型战机,当发动机以 1.2×10^5 N 的推力使其以二倍声速(声速为 340 m/s)飞行时,10 s 内飞行的距离是_____m,发动机推力的功率是_____W。

解析 $s=vt=2\times340\ m/s\times10\ s=6\ 800\ m$

$P=\dfrac{W}{t}=\dfrac{Fs}{t}=\dfrac{1.2\times10^5\ N\times6\ 800\ m}{10\ s}=8.16\times10^7\ W$

或 $P=Fv=1.2\times10^5\ N\times(2\times340\ m/s)=8.16\times10^7\ W$

答案 6 800　 8.16×10^7

拓展知识　知识 类比法建立功率的概念

知识 类比法建立功率的概念

	比较物体运动的快慢		比较做功的快慢	
方法	相同时间,比较路程的长短	相同路程,比较时间的长短	相同时间,比较做功的多少	做功相同,比较时间的长短
定义	通过的路程与通过这段路程所用时间之比,定义为速度,公式 $v=\dfrac{s}{t}$		做的功与做功所用时间之比,定义为功率,公式 $P=\dfrac{W}{t}$	

方法 公式法计算功率

1.运用 $P=\dfrac{W}{t}$ 时一定要注意三个量的对应关系，不能张冠李戴。单位要统一，P、W、t 的单位分别是瓦、焦、秒。

2.由于 $W=Fs$，所以 $P=\dfrac{W}{t}=\dfrac{Fs}{t}=Fv$，也是计算功率的一个公式。$F$ 的单位：N；v 的单位：m/s；P 的单位：W。

例 为了增强体能，全班同学进行爬楼梯训练，体重 500 N 的小刚在 10 s 内连续爬楼梯的总高度为 7 m，求：

(1)小刚爬楼梯所做的功。

(2)小刚爬楼梯的功率。

(解析) (1)小刚爬楼梯所做的功等于克服重力做功：$W=Gh=500\ \text{N}\times7\ \text{m}=3\ 500\ \text{J}$。

(2)$P=\dfrac{W}{t}=\dfrac{3\ 500\ \text{J}}{10\ \text{s}}=350\ \text{W}$。

(答案) (1)3 500 J　(2)350 W

第3节　动能和势能

知识清单

基础知识
知识 1 能量
知识 2 动能
知识 3 势能

知识 1 能量

1.定义：如果一个物体能够对别的物体做功，我们就说这个物体具有能量，简称能。做的功越多，就表明这个物体的能量越大。

流动着的风、张开的弓、举高的重锤都可以对别的物体做功，说明它们都具有能。如图(a)、(b)、(c)。

(a)风可以使帆船前进而做功　(b)张开的弓可以使箭射出来做功　(c)举高的重锤将铁桩打入土中而做功

温馨提示 判断一个物体是否具有能就看它能否做功，"能够做功"并不等于正在做功，只要该物体具有做功的本领，不论它是否正在做功，只要做功的本领始终存在，则该物体就具有能。

2.能量的单位：在国际单位制中能量的单位是焦耳(J)。

知识 2 动能

定义	物体由于运动而具有的能
判断物体是否具有动能的方法	看此物体是否运动，若物体是运动的，则它必定具有动能
实例	航行的帆船、急流的河水等
决定因素	物体的质量和物体的运动速度
比较大小的方法	相同质量时比速度，相同速度时比质量

例 用力拉着物块在水平台面上运动，达到一定速度后，撤去拉力，物块做减速运动直至停止，物块从撤去拉力到停止前的过程中，以下说法正确的是

(　　)

A.物块的惯性越来越小

B.物块所受滑动摩擦越来越小

C.物块的重力势能越来越小

D.物块的动能越来越小

(解析) 从撤去拉力到停止前的过程中，惯性大小不变，因为惯性大小只和质量有关，A 项错误；物块所受滑动摩擦大小不变，因为压力大小和接触面粗糙程度均不变，B 项错误；重力势能大小不变，因为物块的质量和相对于水平台面的高度均不变，C 项错误；撤去拉力后，物块速度越来越小且质量不变，则动能越来越小，D 项正确。所以选 D。

(答案) D

知识 3 势能

1. 势能包括重力势能和弹性势能。单位是焦耳(J)。
2. 重力势能

定义	物体由于被举高而具有的能
判断物体是否具有重力势能的方法	看此物体相对某一个平面是否被举高,即相对此平面有没有一定的高度。若有一定的高度,则物体具有重力势能
实例	被举高的重锤、吊在天花板上的吊灯、山上的石块
决定因素	物体的质量和被举高的高度
比较大小的方法	相同质量时比高度,相同高度时比质量

例 1 2016 年 4 月 24 日定为首个中国航天日,是为了纪念我国首枚人造卫星东方红一号发射成功,卫星加速升空的过程中重力势能_____,动能_____(选填"变大"、"变小"或"不变")。

(解析) "升空"说明高度在增加,故重力势能变大;"加速"说明速度在变大,动能也就变大。

(答案) 变大　变大

3. 弹性势能

定义	物体由于发生弹性形变而具有的能
判断物体是否具有弹性势能的方法	看此物体是否发生了弹性形变,物体有弹性无形变或有形变无弹性都没有弹性势能,必须既有弹性又有形变
实例	拉伸的弹簧、拉弯的弓、压弯的树枝
决定因素	弹性形变的大小和材料
比较大小的方法	同一物体形变量变大,弹性势能变大,不同物体还要看材料

例 2 为了探究"弹簧的弹性势能跟哪些因素有关"。小明同学设计了如图所示的装置,并进行了如下实验。

方法清单
方法① 控制变量法探究动能大小与哪些因素有关
方法② 控制变量法探究重力势能大小与哪些因素有关

方法 1 控制变量法探究动能大小与哪些因素有关

1. 探究动能大小与哪些因素有关时,用控制变量

①将弹簧放在水平面上,一端固定。
②在弹性限度内,用物块(物块与弹簧不连接)将弹簧压缩。测量并记录弹簧的形变量 ΔL。
③由静止释放物块,测量并记录物块在水平面上滑行的距离 s。
④多次改变弹簧的形变量,重复步骤②③。
⑤分析实验数据得出结论。
请回答以下问题:
(1)本实验中,探究了弹簧弹性势能大小跟_____的关系。
(2)本实验中,弹簧弹性势能大小是通过_____来间接反映的。
(3)本实验中,从物块离开弹簧到静止,物块将_____能转化为_____能。

(解析) (1)由步骤②③④可知,本实验中,探究了弹簧弹性势能大小跟弹簧形变量的关系。

(2)由于弹性势能的大小不便于用仪器直接测量,本实验是通过比较物块滑行的距离来判断弹簧弹性势能大小的。

(3)本实验中,物块离开弹簧后,因为受到摩擦力的作用,速度减小,动能不断减小,在此过程中,木块克服摩擦力做功,将动能转化为内能。

(答案) (1)弹簧形变量
(2)物块滑行的距离
(3)动　内

拓展知识 知识 重力势能的相对性

知识 重力势能的相对性

1. 物体所处的高度具有相对性,所以物体重力势能的大小也具有相对性。

2. 放在桌面上的铁块,相对于地面来说有一定的高度,所以铁块具有一定的重力势能;若相对于桌面来说其高度为零,则铁块的重力势能就为零。

3. 在不特别指出参考平面的情况下,一般以地面为参考平面。

法。影响动能大小的因素不是只有一个,要研究与其中一个因素的关系时,应该保证其他因素不变。

2. 在研究动能的大小与质量的关系时,应保证物体具有相同的速度(把质量不同的小球放在斜面的同一高度处,可以使小球在到达平面时具有相同的速度)。

例 某同学在探究"物体的动能跟哪些因素有关"时,提出了如下猜想:

猜想一:物体动能大小与物体的质量有关

猜想二:物体动能大小与物体的运动速度有关

为了验证上述猜想,老师提供了如下器材:斜槽、刻度尺、三个钢球(质量分别为 0.1 kg、0.2 kg 和 0.3 kg)、木块和长木板。

实验装置如图所示,让钢球从高为 h 的斜槽上由静止滚下,碰到水平面上的木块后,将木块撞出一段距离。在同样的平面上,木块被撞得越远,说明钢球的动能越大。

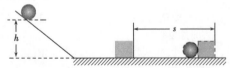

该同学利用上述器材和装置进行了实验,并在下表中记录了实验获得的数据。

次数	钢球的质量 m/kg	钢球下落的高度 h/cm	木块移动的距离 s/cm
1	0.1	10	8
2	0.1	25	19
3	0.2	20	26
4	0.2	10	15
5	0.3	10	22
6	0.3	15	30

请你完成下列任务:

(1)为了便于验证猜想一,请重新设计一个实验表格,并将上表中的相关数据全部筛选整理后填入你所设计的表中。

(2)分析重新设计的表中数据,可以得到的实验结论是 _____ ____。

解析 (1)因为物体的动能大小与物体的质量和速度有关,所以在验证"物体的动能与物体质量有关"的实验中,应控制物体的速度一定,即让质量不同的钢球从斜面的同一高度滚下;(2)分析表中数据可得:当物体的运动速度一定时,物体的质量越大,动能越大。

答案 (1)如下表所示

次数	钢球下落的高度 h/cm	钢球的质量 m/kg	木块移动的距离 s/cm
1	10	0.1	8
2	10	0.2	15
3	10	0.3	22

(2)当物体的运动速度一定时,物体的质量越大,动能就越大

方法 2 控制变量法探究重力势能大小与哪些因素有关

1.重力势能的大小与质量和高度有关。要用控制变量法进行探究。

2.研究重力势能大小与质量的关系时,保持高度不变;研究重力势能大小与高度的关系时,保持物体质量不变。

例 如图所示,用装有细沙的容器、三脚小桌和质量不同的木块做"探究重力势能大小与哪些因素有关"的实验。

(1)该实验是通过观察比较_____来间接判断物体重力势能的大小。

(2)实验中采用质量不同的木块,是为了探究物体重力势能大小与物体_____的关系,操作时应该让木块从_____(选填"相同"或"不同")的高度自由下落。

(3)若要探究物体重力势能大小与物体高度的关系,请简要说明具体做法。

解析 (1)由题意知,实验是通过观察比较小桌在细沙中下陷的深度来间接判断物体重力势能的大小。(2)实验中采用质量不同的木块,是为了探究重力势能与质量的关系,在探究过程中要注意让木块从同一高度由静止落下。(3)若要探究物体重力势能大小与物体高度的关系,则需让同一木块从不同高度下落,比较小桌下陷的深度。

答案 (1)小桌下陷的深度 (2)质量 相同 (3)让同一木块从不同高度下落,比较小桌下陷的深度

第4节　机械能及其转化

知识清单

基础知识
知识❶ 机械能及其转化
知识❷ 机械能守恒
知识❸ 滚摆、单摆

知识 1　机械能及其转化

1.机械能

动能与势能统称为机械能。

2.转化方式

（1）动能和重力势能可以相互转化。①动能转化为重力势能的表现是速度减小,所处的高度增加;②重力势能转化为动能的表现是所处的高度减小,速度增大。

（2）动能和弹性势能可以相互转化。①动能转化为弹性势能的表现是速度减小,形变增大;②弹性势能转化为动能的表现是速度增大,形变减小。动能和弹性势能的相互转化可以发生在同一物体上,也可以发生在不同物体之间。

（3）机械能也可以转化为其他形式的能量。

3.动能和势能的相互转化实例

现象	现象分析	能量转化
从斜坡上滚下的小球	小球从斜坡上滚下的过程中,速度越来越大,高度越来越小,故重力势能减少,动能增加	重力势能转化为动能
自行车上坡前加紧蹬几下	自行车上坡前加紧蹬几下,其目的是增大自行车的动能,这样转化成的重力势能就大,上坡就越容易	动能转化为重力势能
钟表的发条拧得越紧维持时间越长	发条拧得越紧,弹性势能越大,那么钟表走动过程中转化成的动能就越大,维持时间越长	弹性势能转化为动能

续表

现象	现象分析	能量转化
皮球自由落地到弹起	皮球在下落过程中,高度减小,速度增大,故重力势能减少,动能增加;在接触地面发生弹性形变的过程中,动能减少,弹性势能增加;在恢复形变的过程中,弹性势能减少,动能增加;在离开地面上升的过程中,动能减少,重力势能增加	下落时,重力势能转化为动能,发生弹性形变时,动能转化为弹性势能;恢复形变时,弹性势能转化为动能;上升时,动能转化为重力势能

例 2015 年 4 月 25 日,尼泊尔发生里氏 8.1 级强震。地震发生后,我国快速行动参与救援。救灾过程中,飞机在一定高度匀速飞行,向灾区投放物资,则飞机的机械能会_____。

解析 飞机飞行时,始终沿水平方向,高度及速度不变,但质量变小,故动能和重力势能都变小,飞机的机械能为动能与重力势能之和,故机械能变小。

答案 变小

知识 2　机械能守恒

1.动能与势能之间是可以相互转化的,即动能可以转化成势能,势能也可以转化成动能。

2.在只有动能与势能相互转化的过程中,机械能的总和保持不变,机械能守恒。

3.玩具小车在图示的弧形轨道上运动过程中,重力势能和动能相互转化,不考虑摩擦力和空气阻力的影响,机械能守恒。

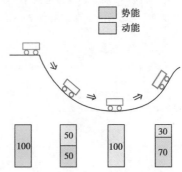

第④部分

4.卫星绕地球转动时,动能和势能相互转化,机械能不变。卫星运行到近地点时,重力势能最小,动能最大;运行到远地点时,重力势能最大,动能最小(如图)。

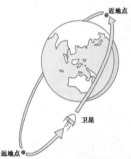

例 掷实心球是某市的中考体育加试项目之一。掷出去的实心球从 a 处出手后,在空中运动的轨迹如图所示,球最终停在水平地面 e 点处(不计空气阻力)。则实心球 (   )

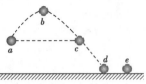

A.在 a 处重力势能最小

B.在 b 处动能为零

C.在 a、b、c 三处机械能相等

D.在 d 处动能为零

(解析) 物体重力势能的大小与物体的质量和被举的高度有关。实心球的质量不变,a 处位置不是最低处,所以 A 项错。实心球在 b 处具有水平向右的速度,所以动能不为零,B 项错。不计空气阻力,实心球在空中运动过程中只有重力做功,所以机械能守恒,C 项正确。由 b 到 d 的过程是重力势能转化为动能的过程,实心球落到 d 点后继续运动,到 e 处停止,所以实心球在 d 处的动能不为零,D 项错。

(答案) C

知识 3 滚摆、单摆

1.滚摆

(1)定义:滚摆(如图)又称麦克斯韦滚摆,它是在学习机械能时,常用来演示重力势能和动能之间相互转化的仪器。

(2)理解

①做滚摆实验时,先调整悬绳,使摆轮处于水平最低位置,然后转动摆轮,使悬绳均匀地绕在摆轮的轴上,直至摆轮上升到悬绳的最上部,并且保持摆轮的轴与水平地面平行。此时,摆轮具有一定的重力势能,而动能为零。

②当由静止释放摆轮,在重力和悬绳拉力的共同作用下,摆轮边旋转,边下降,摆轮的重力势能不断减少,转化成摆轮的动能。

③当悬绳全部伸开时,摆轮的重力势能不再减少,摆轮的动能达到最大值。

④由于惯性,摆轮继续旋转,又开始把绳绕在轴上,使摆轮开始上升,随着重力势能的增加,动能不断减少,动能转化为重力势能。

⑤直到上升到开始位置,摆轮停止转动,停止上升。接着又开始新的一轮下降、上升……

⑥实际上,摆轮每次下降后再上升都不会上升到前一次的高度,这是摩擦力、空气阻力等作用的结果,使一部分机械能转化为内能。

2.单摆

(1)定义:将不可伸长且质量忽略不计的细绳一端固定,另一端悬挂一个重小球,就构成一个单摆。

(2)理解

如图,单摆中的小球在左、右运动的过程中,小球的动能与重力势能不断地相互转化。

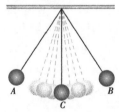

①将小球拉到一定的高度,小球具有一定的重力势能,动能为零。

②放手后,小球由最高点 A 向最低点 C 摆动过程中,重力势能减少,动能增加,重力势能转化为动能。

③由 C 向 B 摆动过程中,动能减少,重力势能增加,动能转化为重力势能。

拓展知识   知识1 水能及其利用
              知识2 风能及其利用

知识 1 水能及其利用

1.流动的水具有动能,高处的水具有势能,水所具有的机械能统称水能。

2.数千年前,人们已知道利用流水的能量来转动水车,汲水灌溉。自从 19 世纪末德国建成世界上第

一座水电站以来,水力发电就成了水能利用的主要形式。

3.当上游的水冲击水轮机的叶片时,就会使水轮机转动起来,由此带动发电机发电(如图)。

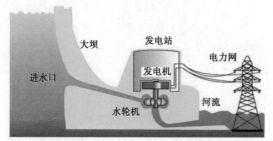

4.为了增加水的机械能,必须修筑拦河大坝来提高河流上游的水位。

方法清单   **方法** 概念法判断机械能的形式

方法 **概念法判断机械能的形式**

机械能有动能、势能两种形式,势能又分重力势能和弹性势能。判断一个物体具有哪种形式的机械能,应根据动能、重力势能、弹性势能的定义进行分析。

例 现有四种不同情景中的物体:①在水平冰面上滑行的冰块;②悬挂在教室屋顶上的日光灯;③钟表内被上紧的发条;④发射升空的火箭。其中,_____具有动能;_____具有重力势能;_____具有弹性势能。(选填物体序号)

5.潮汐也具有巨大的能量,利用海水涨潮和退潮时海水的动能带动水轮机工作。

知识 2 风能及其利用

人类很早就利用风来驱动帆船航行;利用风来推动风车做功。

风车安装在高铁架上端的水平轴上,轴可以随风转动,它的尾翼能使风车迎着风吹来的方向(如图所示)。风车转动,可带动发电机或其他机器工作

解析 动能是物体由于运动而具有的能,故在水平冰面上滑行的冰块具有动能;重力势能是物体由于被举高而具有的能,故悬挂的日光灯具有重力势能;弹性势能是物体由于发生弹性形变而具有的能,故被上紧的发条具有弹性势能;发射升空的火箭既在运动,又在上升,故它既具有动能,又具有重力势能。

答案 ①④ ②④ ③

点拨 重力势能具有相对性,通常是以水平地面为参考平面,认为位于水平地面上的物体不具有重力势能(或重力势能为零),而位于高处或空中的物体都具有重力势能。

简单机械

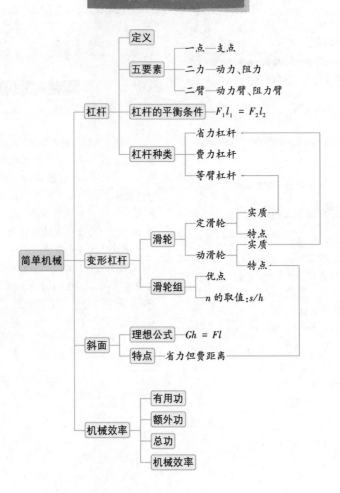

简单机械
├─ 杠杆
│   ├─ 定义
│   ├─ 五要素
│   │   ├─ 一点——支点
│   │   ├─ 二力——动力、阻力
│   │   └─ 二臂——动力臂、阻力臂
│   ├─ 杠杆的平衡条件　$F_1 l_1 = F_2 l_2$
│   └─ 杠杆种类
│   ├─ 省力杠杆
│   ├─ 费力杠杆
│   └─ 等臂杠杆
├─ 变形杠杆
│   ├─ 滑轮
│   │   ├─ 定滑轮
│   │   │   ├─ 实质
│   │   │   └─ 特点
│   │   └─ 动滑轮
│   │   ├─ 实质
│   │   └─ 特点
│   └─ 滑轮组
│   ├─ 优点
│   └─ n 的取值：s/h
├─ 斜面
│   ├─ 理想公式　$Gh = Fl$
│   └─ 特点　省力但费距离
└─ 机械效率
    ├─ 有用功
    ├─ 额外功
    ├─ 总功
    └─ 机械效率

第1节　杠杆

基础知识	知识1 杠杆	知识2 杠杆力臂的画法
	知识3 杠杆的平衡条件(杠杆原理)	知识4 杠杆的分类

知识 1 杠杆

定义	杠杆的五要素					一根硬棒成为杠杆的条件
	支点(O)	动力(F₁)	阻力(F₂)	动力臂(l₁)	阻力臂(l₂)	
在力的作用下能绕着固定点转动的硬棒(如图所示)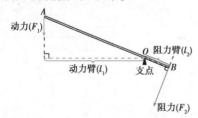	杠杆可以绕其转动的点	使杠杆转动的力	阻碍杠杆转动的力	从支点到动力作用线的距离	从支点到阻力作用线的距离	①要有力的作用 ②能绕某固定点转动

如图所示为撬棒的五要素。

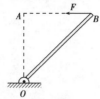

例 如图所示,OB 是以 O 点为支点的杠杆,F 是作用在杠杆 B 端的力。图中线段 AB 与力 F 的作用线在一条直线上,且 $OA \perp AB$。线段_____表示力 F 的力臂。(选填"OA"、"AB"或"OB")

解析 从支点向力的作用线作垂线段,支点到力的作用线的距离即力臂。

答案 OA

知识 2 杠杆力臂的画法

杠杆力臂的画法分三步:找点、画线、作垂线段。

1.在杠杆的示意图上,确定支点 O。

2.画好动力作用线及阻力作用线,画的时候有时要用虚线将力的作用线延长。

3.从支点 O 向力的作用线引垂线,则从支点到垂足的距离就是力臂,力臂用虚线表示,并用大括号标明,或用实线加箭头标明,在旁边标上字母 l_1 或 l_2,分别表示动力臂或阻力臂。

例 如图所示,分析人拉着拉杆旅行箱静止在水平地面上的情景,O 是轮子的转轴。以 O 为支点,请你画出拉力 F 的力臂。

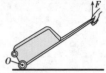

解析 杠杆力臂的画法——一找点、二画线、三作垂线段。(1)确定支点 O;(2)画出力的作用线;(3)从支点 O 向力的作用线作垂线段,则此垂线段就是力臂,力臂用虚线或实线表示并用大括号标明,在旁边标上字母 l(也可以用双向箭头、字母标中间的方法表示)。

答案 如图所示

知识 3 杠杆的平衡条件(杠杆原理)

1.杠杆平衡

杠杆静止不动或匀速转动都叫做杠杆平衡。我们在实验室所做的杠杆平衡条件的实验,是杠杆在水平位置平衡。

 (1)在实际生产和生活中,这样的平衡是不多的,在很多情况下,杠杆都是倾斜静止的;(2)杠杆不论处于怎样的静止,都可以理解成处于平衡状态。

2.杠杆的平衡条件

动力×动力臂＝阻力×阻力臂

即 $F_1 \cdot l_1 = F_2 \cdot l_2$ 或 $\dfrac{F_1}{F_2} = \dfrac{l_2}{l_1}$。

在杠杆平衡时,动力臂是阻力臂的几倍,动力就是阻力的几分之一。

3.利用杠杆的平衡条件进行计算

(1)确定杠杆支点的位置;

(2)分清动力和阻力;

(3)确定每个力的力臂;

(4)根据杠杆平衡条件列出关系式求解。

例 如图所示,小华正在做俯卧撑,可以将他的身体看做是一个杠杆,O 为支点,A 为他的重心,相关长度已在图中标明。已知他的质量 $m = 60$ kg,$g = 10$ N/kg。

(1)求小华受到的重力 G;

(2)求图示时刻地面对双手支持力 F 的力臂 l_1,并在图中画出此力臂;

(3)求图示时刻地面对双手的支持力 F。

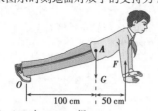

解析 (1)由 $G = mg$ 得

$G = 600$ N

(2)支持力 F 的力臂 $l_1 = 100$ cm $+ 50$ cm $= 150$ cm

力臂如图所示

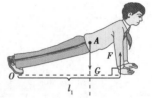

(3)由杠杆的平衡条件有:$Fl_1 = Gl_2$

得 $F = 400$ N

答案 (1)600 N (2)见解析 (3)400 N

知识 4 杠杆的分类

1.杠杆的分类

(1)杠杆平衡时,根据杠杆平衡条件:$F_1l_1 = F_2l_2$ 可知,若 $l_1 > l_2$,则 $F_2 > F_1$,省力;若 $l_1 < l_2$,则 $F_2 < F_1$,费力;若 $l_1 = l_2$,则 $F_2 = F_1$,既不省力也不费力。如图所示。

(2)列表如下

杠杆种类	力臂关系	省、费力情况	省、费距离情况	举例
省力杠杆	$l_1 > l_2$	$F_1 < F_2$ 省力	费距离	开瓶器
费力杠杆	$l_1 < l_2$	$F_1 > F_2$ 费力	省距离	镊子
等臂杠杆	$l_1 = l_2$	$F_1 = F_2$ 不省力、不费力	不省距离、不费距离	天平

2.生活中常见的杠杆

(1)省力杠杆:钉锤、手推独轮车、剪树枝的剪刀、开瓶器、扳手、核桃钳等(如图)。

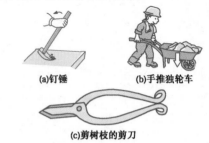

(a)钉锤　　(b)手推独轮车

(c)剪树枝的剪刀

(2)费力杠杆:人的前臂、钓鱼竿、裁缝用的剪刀、筷子、镊子等(如图)。

(a)人的前臂

(b)钓鱼竿　**(c)裁缝用的剪刀**

（3）等臂杠杆:天平、定滑轮等（如图）。

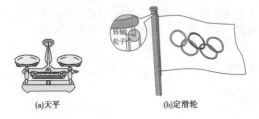

(a)天平　　　　**(b)定滑轮**

知识 **对杠杆的理解**

1.物理学中,将在力的作用下可绕固定点转动的硬棒称为杠杆。杠杆可以是直的,也可以是弯的。硬棒在外力的作用下不能变形。例如:撬棒、跷跷板、活塞式抽水机的手柄等。

2.定义中的力,是指作用在杠杆上的动力和阻力,且动力和阻力使杠杆转动的方向一定是相反的,但动力和阻力的方向不一定相反。

3.杠杆在力的作用下,绕固定点转动而不是平动。

4.不论是动力还是阻力,杠杆都是受力物体,作用于杠杆的物体都是施力物体。

5.不可把动力作用点到支点的距离作为动力臂,或把阻力作用点到支点的距离作为阻力臂。

方法清单　方法**1** 理想模型法探究杠杆的平衡条件
　　　　　方法**2** 杠杆平衡时最小动力的画法

方法 1 **理想模型法探究杠杆的平衡条件**

1.实验前要调节杠杆的平衡螺母使其在水平位置上平衡,目的是使杠杆的重心落在支点上,从而消除杠杆的重力对平衡的影响;也便于测量力臂的大小,利于探究。

2.这种消除重力对平衡影响的杠杆,实质上是一个理想模型,我们把这种研究问题的方法称为理想模型法。

3.当杠杆水平平衡时,可用杠杆上的"格数"表示力臂大小。

例 小明利用刻度均匀的轻质杠杆进行探究"杠杆的平衡条件"实验,已知每个钩码重 0.5 N。

（1）实验前,将杠杆的中点置于支架上,当杠杆静止时,发现杠杆左端下沉,这时应将平衡螺母向____（选填"左"或"右"）调节,直到杠杆在水平位置平衡。你认为实验中让杠杆在水平位置平衡的好处是____。

（2）在图甲中的 A 点悬挂 4 个钩码,要使杠杆仍保持水平位置平衡,需在 B 点悬挂____个钩码。

（3）如图乙所示,取走悬挂在 B 点的钩码,改用弹簧测力计在 C 点竖直向上拉,仍使杠杆在水平位置平衡,测力计的拉力为____N;若在 C 点改变弹簧测

力计拉力的方向,使之斜向右上方,使杠杆仍然在水平位置平衡,则测力计的读数将____（选填"变大"或"变小"或"不变"）,画出此时力 F 的力臂。

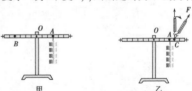

甲　　　　　　　**乙**

（解析）（1）杠杆左偏必须向右调节平衡螺母,实验中使杠杆在水平位置平衡是方便直接从杠杆的刻度上读出力臂大小——便于测量力臂。

（2）$F_A×OA=F_B×OB$,则 $F_B=1.5$ N,故需挂 3 个钩码。

（3）$F_C×OC=F_A×OA$,则 $F_C=1.5$ N,拉力方向改变,力臂减小,拉力应变大。画力臂见答案图。

（答案）（1）右　便于测量力臂

（2）3

（3）1.5　变大　力臂如图所示

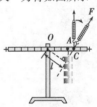

方法 2 **杠杆平衡时最小动力的画法**

由公式 $F_1l_1=F_2l_2$ 可知,当阻力、阻力臂一定时,动力臂越大,动力越小。当动力臂最大时,动力最小。

要求最小动力,必须先找出最大动力臂。

1.寻找最大动力臂的方法

(1)当动力作用点确定后,支点到动力作用点的距离即最大动力臂;(2)动力作用点没有规定时,应看杠杆上哪一点离支点最远,则这一点到支点的距离即最大动力臂。

2.作最小动力的方法

(1)找到最大动力臂后,过作用点作动力臂的垂线;(2)根据实际,动力能使杠杆沿阻力作用的反方向转动,从而确定动力的方向。

例1 如图所示,在课桌的 C 点用最小的力把桌腿 B 抬离地面,在抬起时桌腿 A 没有滑动。请在 C 点画出这个力的示意图,并标出它的力臂 l。

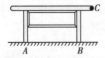

解析 把桌腿 B 抬离地面,则以 A 为支点,当力臂最长时,所用的力最小。连接 A、C,以 AC 为力臂,此力臂最长,用力最小,再过 C 点作 AC 的垂线,根据实际分析,动力 F 方向向上。

答案 如图所示

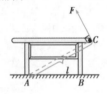

例2 拉杆式旅行箱可看成杠杆,如图所示。已知 $OA=1.0$ m,$OB=0.2$ m,箱重 $G=120$ N。请画出使箱子在图示位置静止时,施加在端点 A 的最小作用力 F 的示意图,且 $F=$ _____ N。

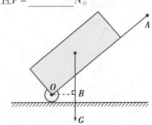

解析 把旅行箱看做一个杠杆。阻力是箱重,阻力臂 $L_2=OB$。根据杠杆平衡条件可知:阻力和阻力臂乘积一定时,动力臂越长则动力越小。作用在 A 点的力与 OA 垂直时力臂最长,$L_1=OA$。由杠杆平衡条件可得 $FL_1=GL_2$,解得:$F=GL_2/L_1=24$ N。

答案 如图所示 24

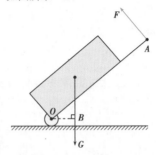

第2节 滑轮

知识清单

知识 **1 定滑轮**

1.定义:在使用过程中,轴固定不动的滑轮。

2.实质:等臂杠杆。

由图可以看出,定滑轮的支点在轴心,动力臂和阻力臂都等于定滑轮的半径。若不考虑摩擦,根据杠杆平衡条件 $F_1l_1=F_2l_2$ 分析,因为 $l_1=l_2$,所以 $F_1=F_2$。

3.特点:使用定滑轮不能省力,也不能省距离,但可以改变用力的方向。

4.重物提升高度 h 与绳子自由端通过的距离 s 的关系:$s=h$。

例 如图所示,沿三个不同方向通过定滑轮拉同一个重物 G,使重物匀速上升,则所用的拉力(摩擦不计)   (   )

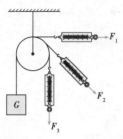

A. F_1 较大   B. F_2 较大

C. F_3 较大   D. F_1、F_2、F_3 一样大

解析 定滑轮实质是一个等臂杠杆,它的支点在轴心,通过支点画出 F_1、F_2、F_3 的力臂。会发现,三个力臂的大小相等,都等于滑轮的半径,且与阻力臂相等,故 F_1、F_2、F_3 一样大,D 选项是正确的。

答案 D

知识 2 动滑轮

1. 定义:在使用过程中,轴随物体一起运动的滑轮。("动"指轴心的位置在移动而不是转动。)

2. 实质:动力臂为阻力臂二倍的杠杆。

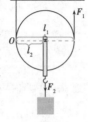

由图可以看出,动力臂等于滑轮的直径,阻力臂等于滑轮的半径。若不考虑动滑轮重和摩擦,根据杠杆平衡条件 $F_1 l_1 = F_2 l_2$ 分析,因为 $l_1 = 2l_2$,所以 $F_1 = \frac{1}{2} F_2$。

3. 特点:使用动滑轮能省力,但费距离,且不能改变用力的方向。

4. 重物提升高度 h 与绳子自由端通过的距离 s 的关系:$s = 2h$。

例 1 如图所示的动滑轮是变形杠杆,其支点是 _____ 点,若物重 $G = 50$ N,动滑轮重为 10 N,摩擦不计,当重物匀速上升时,则拉力 $F = $ _____ N。若绳子自由端通过的距离是 4 m,则重物上升的高度是 _____ m。

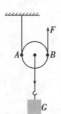

解析 A 点是动滑轮的支点;用动滑轮提升重物时,摩擦不计,但需考虑动滑轮重,$F = \frac{1}{2}(G + G_动) = \frac{1}{2}(50$ N $+ 10$ N$) = 30$ N;重物上升的高度 $h = \frac{1}{2}s = \frac{1}{2} \times 4$ m $= 2$ m。

答案 A 30   2

例 2 如图所示,在竖直向上的力 F 的作用下,重物 A 沿竖直方向匀速上升。已知 A 的重力 $G = 100$ N,重物 A 上升速度为 0.2 m/s,不计摩擦以及滑轮重和绳重,则拉力 F 的大小和滑轮上升的速度分别为 ( )

A. 50 N   0.4 m/s

B. 50 N   0.1 m/s

C. 200 N   0.4 m/s

D. 200 N   0.1 m/s

解析 由题图可知,该滑轮是动滑轮,当重物上升速度为 0.2 m/s 时,滑轮上升速度应该是重物速度的一半,即 $v_滑 = 0.1$ m/s;此时拉力应该是物重的 2 倍,即拉力大小为 200 N。

答案 D

知识 3 滑轮组

1. 定义:把定滑轮和动滑轮组合在一起的装置。

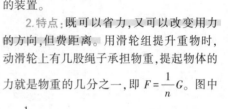

2. 特点:既可以省力,又可以改变用力的方向,但费距离。用滑轮组提升重物时,动滑轮上有几股绳子承担物重,提起物体的力就是物重的几分之一,即 $F = \frac{1}{n}G$。图中 $F = \frac{1}{3}G$。

温馨提示 在不考虑动滑轮重及摩擦的情况下有 $F = \frac{1}{n}G$,如果考虑动滑轮重则有 $F = \frac{1}{n}(G + G_轮)$。

3. 重物提升高度 h 与绳子自由端通过的距离 s 的关系:$s = nh$。

例 用如图所示的滑轮组提起重为 1 200 N 的物体时,若不考虑摩擦及绳和动滑轮的重力,则拉力是多少?

解析 在动滑轮与定滑轮之间画一虚线,将它们隔离开,只数绕在动滑轮上的绳子股数,题图中有 3 股绳子,即 $n = 3$;不计摩擦、动滑轮重力和绳子重力的情况下,$F = \frac{G}{n}$,即 $F = \frac{G}{3}$,物重 $G = 1\,200$ N,则拉力 $F = 400$ N。

答案 400 N

知识 4 斜面

1.定义:一个与水平面成一定夹角的倾斜平面。

2.特点:斜面是一种省力的简单机械。若忽略摩擦,根据功的原理可知:$FL=Gh$,即 $F=\dfrac{h}{L}G$;若斜面长 L 是斜面高 h 的 n 倍,则拉力 F 就是物体所受重力 G 的 $1/n$,即 $F=\dfrac{1}{n}G$;当斜面高度一定时,斜面越长,越省力。

$F \to$ 沿斜面拉力

$G \to$ 物体重力

$L \to$ 斜面长

$h \to$ 斜面高

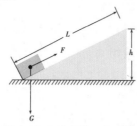

3.应用:爬山时,山的高度一定,增加斜面长度,这样更省力。

例 如图所示,用拉力 F 拉物体沿斜面匀速上升,若不计摩擦,拉力 $F=$ _____G。

解析 在不计摩擦的情况下,斜面长是斜面高的 n 倍,拉力就是重力的 $1/n$,$F=\dfrac{h}{L}G=\dfrac{1}{2}G$。

答案 $\dfrac{1}{2}$

拓展知识 知识 滑轮组由几股绳子承担物重

知识 滑轮组由几股绳子承担物重

1.有几股绳子与动滑轮相连,承担物重的绳子的股数 n 就是几;而重物上升的高度 h 与绳子自由端移动的距离 s 的关系是:$s=nh$。

2.如图,在动滑轮、定滑轮之间画一条虚线,将它们分开,只数绕在动滑轮上的绳子的股数,图中有 4 股绳子承担物重。

例 用如图所示滑轮组提升物体,物重为 G,不计绳重、摩擦和滑轮重,则拉力 $F=$ _____。

解析 在动滑轮与定滑轮之间画一条虚线把它们分开,只数绕在动滑轮上的绳子股数即可。此时绳子股数为5,则$5F=G$,所以 $F=\dfrac{1}{5}G$。

答案 $\dfrac{1}{5}G$

方法清单
- 方法1 比较法判断滑轮组的省力情况
- 方法2 判断滑轮组绕绳的方法

方法 1 比较法判断滑轮组的省力情况

1.滑轮组竖放

(1)若不考虑动滑轮自重、绳重以及摩擦,滑轮组用 n 股绳子吊着物体,提起物体所用的拉力大小就是物重的 $\dfrac{1}{n}$,即 $F_{拉}=\dfrac{1}{n}G_{物}$。

(2)若只考虑动滑轮自重,此式变为 $F_{拉}=\dfrac{1}{n}(G_{物}+G_{动})=\dfrac{1}{n}G_{总}$。

2.滑轮组横放

在不考虑绳与滑轮之间的摩擦时,滑轮组用 n 股绳子拉着物体在水平地面上做匀速直线运动,拉力大小就是物体所受地面摩擦力的 $\dfrac{1}{n}$,即 $F_{拉}=\dfrac{1}{n}f$。

例1 用四个完全相同的滑轮和两根相同的绳子组成如图所示的甲、乙两个滑轮组,在绳子的自由端用大小分别为 F_1 和 F_2 的拉力,将相同的物体匀速提升相同的高度。若不计绳重及摩擦,下列说法正确的是 ( )

 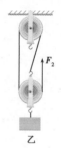

甲   乙

A.F_1 大于 F_2

B.F_1 和 F_2 做的功一定相等

C.甲、乙的机械效率不相等

D.绳子自由端移动的距离不相等,物体运动的时间可能相等

（解析）由题图可知,甲滑轮组由两股绳子承担物重,则拉力 $F_1=\dfrac{1}{2}(G+G_{动})$,绳子自由端移动的距离等于物体移动距离的 2 倍,乙滑轮组由三股绳子承担物重,则拉力 $F_2=\dfrac{1}{3}(G+G_{动})$,绳子自由端移动的距离等于物体移动距离的 3 倍,如果物体被提升的速度相同,则物体被提升相同高度所用时间将相等,物体被提升相同高度时,绳子自由端移动的距离不相等,所以选项 A、D 正确;因不计绳重及摩擦,拉力所做的功 $W=(G+G_{动})h$,因为动滑轮重、物重和提升高度均相同,所以 F_1 和 F_2 做的功相等,选项 B 正确;机械效率 $\eta=\dfrac{W_{有用}}{W_{总}}=\dfrac{Gh}{(G+G_{动})h}=\dfrac{G}{G+G_{动}}$,因为动滑轮重和物重均相同,所以甲、乙的机械效率相同,选项 C 错误。

（答案）**ABD**

例2 同一物体沿相同的水平地面被匀速拉动,如图所示,拉力分别为 $F_{甲}$、$F_{乙}$、$F_{丙}$,不计滑轮与轻绳间的摩擦,比较它们的大小,则　　　　　( )

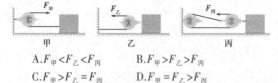

A.$F_{甲}<F_{乙}<F_{丙}$　　　B.$F_{甲}>F_{乙}>F_{丙}$

C.$F_{甲}>F_{乙}=F_{丙}$　　　D.$F_{甲}=F_{乙}>F_{丙}$

（解析）三种情况下地面对物体的摩擦力都相等,均为 f,甲图是定滑轮,$F_{甲}=f$,乙图是动滑轮,$F_{乙}=\dfrac{1}{2}f$,丙图是滑轮组,$F_{丙}=\dfrac{1}{3}f$,即 $F_{甲}>F_{乙}>F_{丙}$,选 B。

（答案）**B**

方法 2　判断滑轮组绕绳的方法

1.一般来说,在给滑轮组绕绳时,首先要确定承担物重的绳子股数 n,然后根据"奇动偶定,由内向外"的原则绕绳。"奇、偶"是指承担物重的绳子股数,"动、定"是指动滑轮和定滑轮。即如果 n 是奇数,则绳子起始端在动滑轮的小钩上,并由此开始绕起;如果 n 是偶数,则绳子起始端在定滑轮的小钩上,并由此开始绕起。

2.需要注意的是:在绕绳时,所画的线要直,并且要与两个滑轮外侧相切;在一般情况下,要在最后一股(最外层)绳子的末端用箭头标出拉力的方向。

此类问题包括以下几种类型:

(1)已知滑轮组的省力情况;

(2)未知滑轮组的省力情况;

(3)根据特定要求绕绳。

3.在给滑轮组绕绳时要注意一些特殊的要求,比如"最省力"、"人要站在地面上"、"向上拉"等,还要符合一定的物理情景。

例 一条绳子最多能承受 1 000 N 的拉力。请设计一个滑轮组,用这条绳子吊起 3 300 N 的重物,并使承担物重的绳子股数最少。(动滑轮重、绳重及摩擦不计)

（解析）先确定绳子股数 n,$\dfrac{G}{F}=\dfrac{3\ 300\ \text{N}}{1\ 000\ \text{N}}=3.3$,$n$ 的取值应为 4。根据"奇动偶定"原则,绳子固定端应在定滑轮上,若不改变力的方向,绕法如图甲所示;若改变力的方向,绕法如图乙所示。

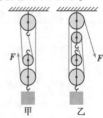

（答案）见解析

第 3 节　机械效率

知识清单

基础知识
- 知识1 有用功、额外功与总功
- 知识2 机械效率
- 知识3 功、功率和机械效率的比较

知识 1　有用功、额外功与总功

名称	概念	符号	公式	实例
有用功	对人有用的功	$W_{有}$	$W_{有}=Gh$	从井中打水时提水所做的功

名称	概念	符号	公式	实例
额外功	对人没用但又不得不做的功	$W_额$	—	从井中打水时提水桶和绳子所做的功
总功	有用功与额外功之和	$W_总$	$W_总 = W_有 + W_额$	从井中打水时手的拉力所做的功

温馨提示 区分有用功与额外功的关键是看做功需要达到什么目的。在同一做功过程中,目的不同,功的性质就不一样。例如:用桶将水从井中提出来,提水是我们需要的,而提桶是不需要的,但又不得不做的,故克服水重做的是有用功,而克服桶重做的是额外功;如果是一只桶掉入井里,我们要将桶从井中提出来,则克服桶重做的是有用功,而克服桶中可能带出来的水重做的是额外功。

例 用三种方法把沙子运上三楼,如图所示,根据图中数据算出三种方法所做有用功的大小均为____;其中一种方法做的总功最多,等于_____。

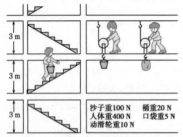

沙子重100 N　桶重20 N
人体重400 N　口袋重5 N
动滑轮重10 N

(解析) 三种方法的目的都是把沙子运上三楼,因此对沙子做的功是有用功,由于每种方法所提的沙子重 $G_沙$ 都为 100 N,提升的高度 h 都为 6 m,由公式 $W_有 = Gh$,算出这三种方法所做的有用功大小均为 600 J。由题图可知,从左至右三种方法的额外功分别是:对人与桶做的功,对动滑轮与桶做的功,对动滑轮和口袋做的功。其中对人与桶做的额外功最多,因此总功最多,由 $W_总 = W_有 + W_额 = W_有 + (G_人 + G_桶)h$,即可算出总功的大小。

$W_有 = G_沙\ h = 100\ \text{N} \times 6\ \text{m} = 600\ \text{J}$

$$W_总 = W_有 + W_额$$
$$= W_有 + (G_人 + G_桶)h$$
$$= 600\ \text{J} + (400\ \text{N} + 20\ \text{N}) \times 6\ \text{m}$$
$$= 3\ 120\ \text{J}$$

(答案) 600 J　3 120 J

知识 2 机械效率

1.**定义**:有用功跟总功的比值叫做机械效率。

2.**公式**:$\eta = \dfrac{W_有}{W_总}$。因为有用功总是小于总功,因此

机械效率总是小于 1。η 值越大,表明有用功在总功中所占比例越大,机械效率越高。

3.机械效率是反映机械性能好坏的物理量,机械效率越高,这个机械的性能越好。

4.机械效率的高低并不能决定使用机械是省力还是费力,效率高只说明有用功在总功中所占的比例大。机械效率高不一定省力。

易混对比

影响机械效率高低的因素		
	影响因素	提高机械效率的方法
杠杆	①杠杆自身的重力;②杠杆与物体之间的摩擦力;③物体的重力	杠杆自身的重力越小,杠杆与物体之间的摩擦力越小,物重越大,机械效率越高
滑轮组	①动滑轮的重力;②绳的重力;③滑轮与绳间的摩擦力;④滑轮与轴间的摩擦力;⑤物体的重力	动滑轮和绳的重力越小,滑轮与绳间的摩擦力越小,滑轮与轴间的摩擦力越小,物重越大,机械效率越高
斜面	①斜面的倾斜程度;②斜面的粗糙程度;③材料	材料一定时斜面的倾斜程度越大,斜面越光滑,机械效率越高

例 如图所示,同一滑轮采用甲、乙两种连接方式匀速提升重为 100 N 的物体,已知滑轮重 20 N(绳重及滑轮和轴处的摩擦忽略不计)。则（　　）

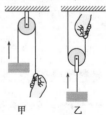

甲　　乙

A.手的拉力:$F_甲 > F_乙$;机械效率:$\eta_甲 < \eta_乙$
B.手的拉力:$F_甲 = F_乙$;机械效率:$\eta_甲 = \eta_乙$
C.手的拉力:$F_甲 > F_乙$;机械效率:$\eta_甲 > \eta_乙$
D.手的拉力:$F_甲 < F_乙$;机械效率:$\eta_甲 < \eta_乙$

(解析) 题中甲是定滑轮,乙是动滑轮。绳重及滑轮和轴处的摩擦忽略不计时,$F_甲 = G_物 = 100\ \text{N}$,$F_乙 = \dfrac{G_物 + G_轮}{2} = \dfrac{100\ \text{N} + 20\ \text{N}}{2} = 60\ \text{N}$,所以 $F_甲 > F_乙$。用两滑轮提升相同重物且提升相同高度时,有用功相同,甲种方式不做额外功,乙种方式需克服动滑轮重力做额外功,所以 $\eta_甲 > \eta_乙$。故选 C。

(答案) C

知识 **3** 功、功率和机械效率的比较

	物理意义	定义	符号	公式	单位
功	能量转化的量度	一个力作用在物体上，物体在这个力的方向上移动了一段距离，就说这个力对物体做了功	W	$W=Fs$	J
功率	表示做功快慢的物理量	功与做功所用时间之比	P	$P=\dfrac{W}{t}$	W（国际单位）kW、MW（常用单位）
机械效率	反映机械性能的物理量	有用功跟总功的比值	η	$\eta=\dfrac{W_{有}}{W_{总}}$	—

例 甲、乙、丙三位同学分别用一个动滑轮竖直向上匀速提升不同的钩码，记录数据如表，则做功最多的是____；做功最快的是____；机械效率最高的是____。（不计绳重及摩擦）

	动滑轮重/N	钩码重/N	钩码上升距离/cm	所用时间/s
甲	1	1	80	2
乙	1	2	60	1
丙	1	4	40	3

解析 做功分别为

$W_甲=G_甲h_甲=2\ \text{N}×0.8\ \text{m}=1.6\ \text{J}$

$W_乙=G_乙h_乙=3\ \text{N}×0.6\ \text{m}=1.8\ \text{J}$

$W_丙=G_丙h_丙=5\ \text{N}×0.4\ \text{m}=2.0\ \text{J}$

比较可知做功最多的为丙。

做功最快的即功率最大的。功率分别为

$P_甲=\dfrac{W_甲}{t_甲}=\dfrac{1.6\ \text{J}}{2\ \text{s}}=0.8\ \text{W}$，$P_乙=\dfrac{W_乙}{t_乙}=\dfrac{1.8\ \text{J}}{1\ \text{s}}=1.8\ \text{W}$

$P_丙=\dfrac{W_丙}{t_丙}=\dfrac{2.0\ \text{J}}{3\ \text{s}}=0.67\ \text{W}$，比较可知乙做功最快。

$\eta=\dfrac{W_有}{W_总}=\dfrac{Gh}{Gh+G_动h}=\dfrac{G}{G+G_动}$，机械效率分别为

$\eta_甲=\dfrac{1\ \text{N}}{1\ \text{N}+1\ \text{N}}×100\%=50\%$

$\eta_乙=\dfrac{2\ \text{N}}{2\ \text{N}+1\ \text{N}}×100\%≈66.7\%$

$\eta_丙=\dfrac{4\ \text{N}}{4\ \text{N}+1\ \text{N}}×100\%=80\%$

比较可知丙的机械效率最高。

答案 丙 乙 丙

拓展知识　知识**1** 滑轮组拉物体水平前进时的机械效率
知识**2** 汽车的机械效率与功率

知识 **1** 滑轮组拉物体水平前进时的机械效率

	$W_{有用}$	$W_{额外}$	$W_总$	η
拉力 F、物重 G、物体匀速移动时与地面间的摩擦力 f、物体移动距离 $s_物$、绳自由端移动距离 s、绳子股数 n	$W_{有用}=f\cdot s_物$	—	$W_总=F\cdot s$ $=F\cdot ns_物$	$\eta=\dfrac{W_{有用}}{W_总}=$ $\dfrac{f\cdot s_物}{F\cdot s}=$ $\dfrac{f\cdot s_物}{F\cdot ns_物}$ $=\dfrac{f}{n\cdot F}$

例 如图所示，用滑轮组拉动重为 70 N 的物体 A，使物体 A 在水平方向上移动5 m，所用拉力 F 为 20 N，地面对物体 A 的摩擦力为 30 N，则拉力 F 做的功为____J，滑轮组的机械效率为____。

解析 物体移动距离 $s_1=5$ m，所以自由端移动距离 $s_2=2×5$ m$=10$ m，则拉力 F 做的功 $W_总=F\cdot s_2=20$ N$×10$ m$=200$ J

克服摩擦力做的功为有用功，$W_有=f\cdot s_1=30$ N$×5$ m$=150$ J

所以机械效率 $\eta=\dfrac{W_有}{W_总}=\dfrac{150\ \text{J}}{200\ \text{J}}×100\%=75\%$

答案 200　75%

知识 **2** 汽车的机械效率与功率

1.机械效率与功率是两个完全不同的概念，这两个概念是从不同方面反映机械性能的，它们之间没有必然的联系。

2.功率大表示机械做功快；机械效率高表示机械对总功的利用率高。功率大的机械不一定机械效率高。内燃机车功率可以达到几千千瓦，但机械效率却只有30%~40%。反之，机械效率高的机械不一定功率大。安装在儿童玩具汽车里的电动机的机械效率可达80%，但功率却只有几瓦。

例 某小汽车的"经济耗油量（90 km/h）8 L/100 km"，是指这辆汽车以 90 km/h 的速度行驶100 km，消耗汽油 8 L。该汽车在经济耗油量下沿直线匀速行驶25 km，汽车的效率为 31.25%。求汽车消耗多少升汽油及汽车的功率。（汽油热值 $3.2×10^7$ J/L）

解析 汽车在经济耗油量下行驶 25 km 实际用油

$$V = \frac{8\ \text{L}}{100\ \text{km}} \times 25\ \text{km} = 2\ \text{L}$$

2 L 汽油完全燃烧放出热量 $Q_{放} = qV = 3.2 \times 10^7\ \text{J/L} \times 2\ \text{L} = 6.4 \times 10^7\ \text{J}$

汽车所做的功 $W = Q_{放} \eta = 6.4 \times 10^7\ \text{J} \times 31.25\% = 2 \times 10^7\ \text{J}$

汽车的速度 $v = 90\ \text{km/h} = 25\ \text{m/s}$

汽车行驶的时间 $t = \dfrac{s}{v} = \dfrac{2.5 \times 10^4\ \text{m}}{25\ \text{m/s}} = 1\ 000\ \text{s}$

汽车的功率 $P = \dfrac{W}{t} = \dfrac{2 \times 10^7\ \text{J}}{1\ 000\ \text{s}} = 2 \times 10^4\ \text{W}$

答案 2 L 2×10^4 W

方法清单

方法 ① 公式法计算有用功、额外功和总功
方法 ② 比较法求三种简单机械的机械效率
方法 ③ 提高滑轮组和斜面机械效率的方法

方法 1 公式法计算有用功、额外功和总功

1.总功的计算方法

(1)根据定义列式求解；

(2)总功等于有用功和额外功之和,即 $W_{总} = W_{有用} + W_{额外}$；

(3)公式法：$W_{总} = \dfrac{W_{额外}}{1-\eta}$ 或 $W_{总} = \dfrac{W_{有用}}{\eta}$。

2.有用功的计算方法

(1)根据定义列式求解；

(2)$W_{有用} = W_{总} - W_{额外}$；

(3)公式法：$W_{有用} = W_{总}\, \eta$。

3.额外功的计算方法

(1)根据定义列式求解；

(2)$W_{额外} = W_{总} - W_{有用}$；

(3)公式法：$W_{额外} = W_{总} \cdot (1-\eta)$。

例 如图所示,搬运工人用滑轮将重为 425 N 的重物匀速提升 4 m,所用拉力为 250 N,时间为 20 s,则此过程中有用功是_____J,额外功是_____J,拉力的功率是_____W,滑轮的机械效率是_____。

解析 $W_{有用} = G_{物}\, h = 425\ \text{N} \times 4\ \text{m} = 1\ 700\ \text{J}$

$n = 2$,所以 $s = 2h = 8\ \text{m}$

所以 $W_{总} = F \cdot s = 250\ \text{N} \times 8\ \text{m} = 2\ 000\ \text{J}$

所以 $W_{额外} = W_{总} - W_{有用} = 2\ 000\ \text{J} - 1\ 700\ \text{J} = 300\ \text{J}$

拉力功率：$P = \dfrac{W_{总}}{t} = \dfrac{2\ 000\ \text{J}}{20\ \text{s}} = 100\ \text{W}$

滑轮的机械效率：$\eta = \dfrac{W_{有用}}{W_{总}} = \dfrac{1\ 700\ \text{J}}{2\ 000\ \text{J}} \times 100\% = 85\%$

答案 1 700   300   100   85%

方法 2 比较法求三种简单机械的机械效率

简单机械	有用功	总功	额外功	机械效率
杠杆	$W_{有用} = Gh$	$W_{总} = Fs$	$W_{额外} = W_{总} - W_{有用}$	$\eta = \dfrac{Gh}{Fs}$
滑轮组	$W_{有用} = Gh$	$W_{总} = Fs$ $W_{总} = (G + G_{动})h$ (不计绳重、摩擦)	$W_{额外} = W_{总} - W_{有用}$ $W_{额外} = G_{动}h$ (不计绳重、摩擦)	$\eta = \dfrac{Gh}{Fs}$ $\eta = \dfrac{G}{nF}$ (n 为承担物重的绳的股数) $\eta = \dfrac{G}{G + G_{动}}$ (不计绳重、摩擦)
斜面	$W_{有用} = Gh$	$W_{总} = Fl$ $W_{总} = Gh + fl$ (f 为摩擦力)	$W_{额外} = W_{总} - W_{有用}$ $W_{额外} = fl$	$\eta = \dfrac{Gh}{Fl}$ $\eta = \dfrac{Gh}{Gh + fl}$

例1 跳板是一种娱乐活动,若支点在跳板的中央,当质量均为 60 kg 的两名运动员同时从 1.5 m 高处由静止下落到跳板的同一端时,静止在跳板另一端的质量为 50 kg 的一名女运动员向上弹起 3 m 高。若不计空气阻力,则跳板的机械效率为_____。

解析 在本题中,两名运动员从高处落下所做的功为总功,而弹起女运动员所做的功为有用功,故 $W_{有用} = G_1 h_1 = m_1 g h_1$,$W_{总} = G_2 h_2 = m_2 g h_2$,所以跳板的机

械效率为 $\eta = \dfrac{W_{有用}}{W_{总}} = \dfrac{m_1gh_1}{m_2gh_2} = \dfrac{50 \times 3}{60 \times 2 \times 1.5} \times 100\% \approx$

83.3%。

（答案）83.3%

例 2 如图所示，不计摩擦和绳重，把一个重为 20 N 的物体沿竖直方向在 4 s 内匀速提升了 2 m，所用拉力 F 为 12.5 N。下列说法中正确的是（　）

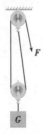

A.动滑轮重 7.5 N

B.4 s 内拉力 F 做功 25 J

C.4 s 内拉力 F 的功率为 6.25 W

D.滑轮组的机械效率为 80%

（解析）由题图可知承重的绳子股数为 2，$n = 2$，不计绳重和摩擦，由 $F = \dfrac{1}{2}(G + G_{动})$ 解得 $G_{动} = 5$ N，A 错误；绳子自由端移动的距离 $s = 2h = 2 \times 2$ m $= 4$ m，拉力做的功为 $W = Fs = 12.5$ N$\times 4$ m $= 50$ J，B 错误；拉力 F 的功率 $P = \dfrac{W}{t} = \dfrac{50\ J}{4\ s} = 12.5$ W，C 错误；该滑轮组的机械效率为 $\eta = \dfrac{W_{有用}}{W_{总}} = \dfrac{Gh}{Fs} = \dfrac{20\ N \times 2\ m}{12.5\ N \times 4\ m} \times 100\% = 80\%$，D 正确。

（答案）D

例 3 如图 1 所示，工人沿斜面把一箱货物从底端拉进车厢。货物移动的距离 s 与时间 t 的关系如图 2 所示。在此期间，工人拉这箱货物沿斜面匀速运动时的拉力为 594 N。此斜面的长为 5 m、高为 1 m，这箱货物重为 1 500 N。

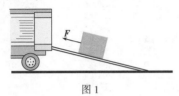

图 1

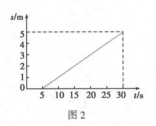

图 2

（1）0~5 s 内，这箱货物处于_____状态，工人所做的功为_____J。

（2）5~30 s 内，这箱货物运动的速度是多少？拉力做功的功率是多大？

（3）该斜面的机械效率是多少？

（解析）（1）由题图 2 可知，0~5 s，货物移动的距离为 0，处于静止状态。根据 $W = F \cdot s$ 可知，工人对货物没有做功。

（2）这箱货物运动的速度

$$v = \dfrac{s}{t} = \dfrac{5\ m}{25\ s} = 0.2\ m/s$$

拉力做的功

$W = Fs = 594$ N$\times 5$ m $= 2\ 970$ J

拉力做功的功率

$$P = \dfrac{W}{t} = \dfrac{2\ 970\ J}{25\ s} = 118.8\ W$$

（3）对这箱货物做的有用功

$W_{有用} = Gh = 1\ 500$ N$\times 1$ m $= 1\ 500$ J

拉力做的功是总功，$W_{总} = W = 2\ 970$ J

斜面的机械效率

$$\eta = \dfrac{W_{有用}}{W_{总}} \times 100\% = \dfrac{1\ 500\ J}{2\ 970\ J} \times 100\% \approx 50.5\%$$

（答案）（1）静止　0

（2）0.2 m/s　118.8 W

（3）50.5%

方法 3 提高滑轮组和斜面机械效率的方法

1.提高滑轮组机械效率的方法

（1）减小额外功在总功中占的比例，即在有用功一定的情况下，减小额外功，提高机械效率。可采取改进机械结构、减小摩擦阻力等方法。如在滑轮的转轴中加润滑油，以减小摩擦阻力，或减小滑轮组中动滑轮的自重等。

（2）增大有用功在总功中占的比例，即在额外功不变的情况下，增大有用功，提高机械效率。在滑轮组中，若不计摩擦力，提升动滑轮做的功就是额外功，这个额外功不变，增加物重可增大有用功，提高机械效率。

还可以这样理解：若动滑轮的重力为 G'，则滑轮组的机械效率还可表示为 $\eta = \dfrac{W_{有用}}{W_{有用} + W_{额外}} = \dfrac{Gh}{Gh + G'h} =$

$\dfrac{1}{1+G'/G}$。分析这个表达式可知,对于同一滑轮组(G'一定),提升重物越重,滑轮组的机械效率越高;而提升相同重物时,G'越小,滑轮组的机械效率越高。

（3）换用最简单的机械。

2.提高斜面机械效率的方法

斜面的机械效率与物体和斜面之间的摩擦有关,可减小斜面的粗糙程度,减小额外功。机械效率与斜面的倾斜程度也有关,倾斜程度越大,机械效率越高。

例 用如图所示装置测量动滑轮的机械效率。实验时,竖直向上匀速拉动弹簧测力计,使挂在动滑轮下面的钩码缓缓上升。实验数据如下表。

序号	动滑轮重力 $G_{动}$/N	钩码重力 G/N	钩码上升高度 h/m	绳的拉力 F/N	绳端移动距离 s/m	机械效率 η
①	0.1	1	0.2	0.6	0.4	83.3%
②	0.1	2	0.2	1.1	0.4	
③	0.2	2	0.2	1.2	0.4	83.3%

（1）第②次实验时,测得动滑轮的机械效率约为_____。

（2）分析表中数据可知,对于同一动滑轮,所提升钩码的重力增大,机械效率将_____;提升相同重力的钩码时,动滑轮的重力增大,其机械效率将_____。（选填"增大"、"减小"或"不变"）

（3）分析表中数据可知,$F \neq \dfrac{G_{动}+G}{2}$,可能的原因是:_____。

解析 （1）由表中实验数据可知,第②次实验时,

$$\eta = \dfrac{W_{有}}{W_{总}} \times 100\% = \dfrac{Gh}{Fs} \times 100\% = \dfrac{2\ N \times 0.2\ m}{1.1\ N \times 0.4\ m} \times 100\% \approx 90.9\%。$$

（2）由表中实验序号为①②的实验数据可知,对于同一动滑轮,所提升钩码的重力增大,机械效率将增大;由表中实验序号为②③的实验数据可知,提升相同重力的钩码时,动滑轮的重力增大,其机械效率将减小。

（3）由于滑轮与轮轴间存在摩擦以及缠绕滑轮组的绳子有重力,因此:$F \neq \dfrac{G_{动}+G}{2}$。

答案 （1）90.9%　（2）增大　减小　（3）滑轮与轮轴间有摩擦、绳子有重力(答其中一个即可)

第⑤部分

电学

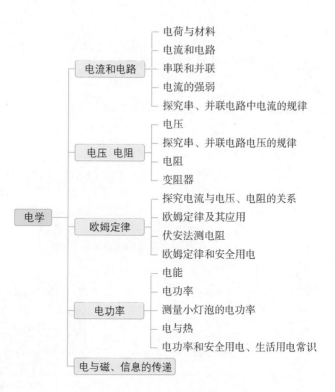

电学
- 电流和电路
  - 电荷与材料
  - 电流和电路
  - 串联和并联
  - 电流的强弱
  - 探究串、并联电路中电流的规律
- 电压 电阻
  - 电压
  - 探究串、并联电路电压的规律
  - 电阻
  - 变阻器
- 欧姆定律
  - 探究电流与电压、电阻的关系
  - 欧姆定律及其应用
  - 伏安法测电阻
  - 欧姆定律和安全用电
- 电功率
  - 电能
  - 电功率
  - 测量小灯泡的电功率
  - 电与热
  - 电功率和安全用电、生活用电常识
- 电与磁、信息的传递

电流和电路

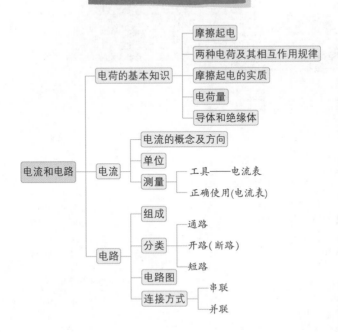

第 1 节　电荷与材料

基础知识	知识**1** 摩擦起电　知识**2** 两种电荷
	知识**3** 原子结构、电荷量与元电荷
	知识**4** 摩擦起电的原因和实质
	知识**5** 验电器　知识**6** 导体与绝缘体
	知识**7** 半导体　知识**8** 超导体

知识 **1** 摩擦起电

1.定义：用摩擦的方法使物体带电，叫摩擦起电。这时物体带的是静电，我们就说物体带了电，或者说带了电荷，带电体有吸引轻小物体的性质。如图。

与毛皮摩擦过的塑料梳子吸引小纸屑

与毛皮摩擦过的塑料棒吸引细水流

2.摩擦起电的条件：相互摩擦的物体由不同种类的物质构成。

温馨提示　油罐车底拖一条铁链，是将摩擦所产生的电荷导入大地，避免因电荷积累造成的危害。

例 干燥的冬天,化纤衣服很容易吸附灰尘,这是因为衣服摩擦带了_____,从而具有了_____轻小物体的性质。

解析 化纤衣服因摩擦带了电,而带电物体具有吸引轻小物体的性质,因此很容易吸附灰尘。

答案 电(或电荷) 吸引

知识2 两种电荷

1.两种电荷:人们通过大量的实验发现,凡是与毛皮摩擦过的橡胶棒相吸引的,必定与丝绸摩擦过的玻璃棒相排斥,由此人们得出自然界中有且只有两种电荷:正电荷和负电荷。

2.正电荷与负电荷

种类	概念	符号	相互作用规律
正电荷	丝绸与玻璃棒摩擦时玻璃棒所带的电荷规定为正电荷	+	同种电荷相互排斥,异种电荷相互吸引
负电荷	毛皮与橡胶棒摩擦时橡胶棒所带的电荷规定为负电荷	−	

温馨提示 将两个气球与同一件衣服摩擦后,带上同种电荷,相互靠近时,由于同种电荷相互排斥而张开一定角度(如图甲);用干燥的毯子将长毛的小狗包裹起来并来回摩擦,结果小狗的长毛竖了起来(如图乙),也是同种电荷相互排斥的缘故。

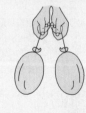

甲　　　　乙

3.两个物体(不涉及磁体)相互排斥,有两种可能:a.都带正电;b.都带负电。

4.两个物体(不涉及磁体)相互吸引,有三种可能:a.一物体带正电,另一物体带负电;b.一物体带正电,另一物体不带电;c.一物体带负电,另一物体不带电。

例 有甲、乙、丙三个轻质小球,甲球带正电,将甲与乙、丙靠近时,它们相互作用的情况如图所示,则下列判断正确的是　　　　　(　　)

甲乙　　　　　甲丙

A.乙球一定带负电,丙球可能带正电
B.乙球一定不带电,丙球可能带负电
C.乙球可能带正电,丙球一定带正电
D.乙球可能不带电,丙球一定带负电

解析 甲、乙相互吸引,乙球可能带负电,也可能不带电;甲、丙相互排斥,丙球一定带正电。故选C。

答案 C

知识3 原子结构、电荷量与元电荷

1.原子结构

(1)原子是由原子核和核外电子组成的。

(2)原子核带正电,几乎集中了原子的全部质量,所带的电荷量是元电荷的整数倍。

(3)核外电子带负电,每个电子的电荷量都为$e=1.6\times10^{-19}$ C。

(4)整个原子通常呈中性,原子核的正电荷数与核外电子的负电荷数相等。

(5)原子核对核外电子有束缚作用。

2.电荷量与元电荷

概念	符号	单位	元电荷
电荷的多少叫电荷量	Q	库仑(C)	$e=1.6\times10^{-19}$ C

知识4 摩擦起电的原因和实质

1.摩擦起电的原因

(1)不同物质的原子核束缚电子的本领不同。

(2)两个物体互相摩擦时,哪个物体的原子核束缚电子的本领强,它就容易得到电子而带负电,另一个物体因失去电子而带等量的正电。

2.摩擦起电的实质

摩擦起电并不是创造了电荷,只是电子从一个物体转移到另一个物体,使正、负电荷分开,如图。同种物质摩擦不起电,原因是同种物质的原子核束缚电子的本领相同,摩擦时不会发生电荷的转移。

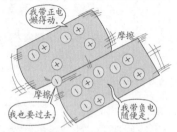

例 把餐巾纸摩擦过的塑料吸管放在支架上,吸管能在水平面自由转动。如图所示,手持带负电的橡胶棒,靠近吸管A端,A端会远离橡胶棒。实验中　　　　(　　)

A.吸管不带电

B.吸管带正电

C.摩擦时,吸管得到电子

D.与吸管摩擦的餐巾纸一直不带电

解析 吸管与橡胶棒相互排斥说明两者带同种电荷,橡胶棒带负电,所以吸管也带负电,A、B 两项错。摩擦起电的实质是电子的转移,吸管带负电说明其在摩擦时得到电子,C 项正确。摩擦时,电子从餐巾纸转移到吸管上,所以餐巾纸会带上等量正电荷,D 项错。

答案 C

知识 5 验电器

1.验电器是检验物体是否带电的仪器。它是由金属球、金属杆、金属箔等几部分组成的,如图。

2.它的原理是同种电荷相互排斥。当用带电体接触验电器的金属球时,就有一部分电荷转移到验电器的金属箔片上,这两片金属箔由于带同种电荷相互排斥而张开。

3.金属箔片张开的角度越大,说明带电体所带的电荷量越多。

知识 6 导体与绝缘体

1.导体与绝缘体的比较

	导体	绝缘体
导电能力	容易导电	不容易导电
原因	有大量的自由电荷	电荷几乎都被束缚在原子的范围内
常见材料	金属、人体、大地、石墨、酸碱盐的水溶液等	玻璃、橡胶、陶瓷、塑料、油等
用途	输电线等	电器外壳等

2.导体容易导电,绝缘体不容易导电的原因

(1)金属导体容易导电是因为导体中有大量的自由电子,它们受原子核的束缚力很小,能够从导体的一部分移到另一部分;(2)绝缘体中,电荷几乎都被束缚在原子

的范围内,不能从绝缘体的一部分移到另一部分。

3.导体和绝缘体之间没有绝对的界限,玻璃在常温下是绝缘体,而在高温下会变成导体。

知识 7 半导体

1.半导体材料的导电能力介于导体和绝缘体之间,比导体差、比绝缘体强,具有一些特殊的物理性质,温度、光照、杂质等因素都对它的性能有很大影响。常见的半导体材料有硅、锗和砷化镓等。

2.用半导体材料可以制造半导体二极管、三极管和集成电路等多种半导体元件。

(1)半导体二极管具有单向导电性,即只允许电流由一个方向通过元件(如图)。

半导体二极管

(2)半导体三极管可以用来放大电信号。

(3)应用

①太阳能电池:当光照到某些半导体时,在半导体内会产生电流。太阳能电池是一种不用燃料、不污染环境、对人类健康无害的电源。

②条形码扫描仪:条形码扫描仪由发光二极管、光敏二极管等元件构成。当发光二极管照射条形码时,光敏二极管便接收被条形码反射回来的光,并将光信号变为电信号,电脑则依据获取的电信号分析、检测物品。条形码扫描仪广泛应用于商业、邮政、交通等领域。如图所示。

利用条形码扫描仪,电脑就能识别所检测的物品

③微处理器:微处理器集成了成千上万个半导体元件。

④机器人:机器人内有由大量半导体元件构成的电路。智能机器人将成为工业生产活动的好帮手。

⑤LED灯:是一种新型的高效节能光源,它的核心元件是由半导体材料制成的发光二极管。

例 半导体在我们的生活中有着广泛应用,用它制成的半导体二极管具有_____性。

解析 半导体二极管只允许电流由一个方向通过元件,电流反向时,它的电阻很大,可视为断路。

答案 单向导电

知识 **8** 超导体

1.超导现象:某些物质在很低的温度下,电阻就变成了零,这就是超导现象。

2.应用

(1)利用超导体的零电阻特性可实现远距离大功率输电。超导输电线可以无损耗地输送较大的电流,这意味着用细电线就可以输送大电流。

(2)超导磁悬浮现象,使人们可以利用超导体来实现交通工具的"无摩擦"运行。

 超导材料通电时不发热,不能用来做保险丝。

 拓展知识

知识**1** 静电感应
知识**2** 电荷的中和

知识 **1** 静电感应

一个带电的物体与不带电的导体相互靠近时,由于电荷间的相互作用,会使导体内部的电荷重新分布:导体近端(距带电体近的一端)带有与带电体所带电荷电性相异的电荷,远端带有与带电体所带电荷电性相同的电荷,这种现象叫静电感应(如图)。

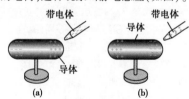

(a)　　　(b)

静电感应

例 一朵云飘到一个铁塔的上方,如图所示,如果云的下方带负电,根据_____,铁塔的尖端 A 带_____电。

(解析) 根据电荷间的相互作用规律可知,铁塔尖端 A 带正电。

(答案) 电荷间的相互作用规律　正

知识 **2** 电荷的中和

带等量异种电荷的物体相互接触,使两个物体都恢复到不带电的状态,叫做电荷的中和。

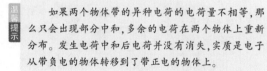 如果两个物体带的异种电荷的电荷量不相等,那么只会出现部分中和,多余的电荷在两个物体上重新分布。发生电荷中和后电荷并没有消失,实质是电子从带负电的物体转移到了带正电的物体上。

例 如图所示,甲、乙是两个相同的验电器,带有等量电荷,甲带正电,乙带负电,金属箔片都处于张开状态。下列说法正确的是_____(填写选项前的字母)。

甲　　　乙

A.若用橡胶棒连接甲、乙两验电器的金属球,则金属箔片的夹角不变

B.若用玻璃棒连接甲、乙两验电器的金属球,则金属箔片的夹角不变

C.若用金属棒连接甲、乙两验电器的金属球,则金属箔片的夹角不变

D.若用金属棒连接甲、乙两验电器的金属球,则金属箔片全都闭合

(解析) 因为橡胶和玻璃都属于绝缘体,因此若用橡胶棒或玻璃棒连接甲、乙两验电器的金属球,电子不发生转移,则金属箔片的夹角不变,故 A、B 正确;因为金属是导体,因此若用金属棒连接甲、乙两验电器的金属球,正负电荷中和,则金属箔片全部闭合,故 C 错误,D 正确。故选 A、B、D。

(答案) ABD

第⑤部分

方法 1 使物体带电的三种方法

类别	摩擦起电	接触起电	感应起电
起电实质	电子从一个物体转移到另一个物体	电子通过直接接触发生转移	物体中的电荷重新排列

例 雷电是"十大气象灾害"之一,虽然发生的时间极短,但它可在瞬间达到数十万伏高压,或使温度升至 600 ℃左右,所以可引发燃烧、爆炸,造成人畜伤亡,破坏力极大。

(1)雷电中的电是怎样形成的?

(2)打雷时,云层上的电荷发生了一种物理现象,这个现象是_____。

(3)打雷时为什么总是先看到闪电而后才听到雷声呢?

(解析) 由于两块云层相互摩擦,带上了异种电荷,异种电荷间发生电荷的中和。由于光速大于声速,所以总是先看到闪电,后听到雷声。

(答案) (1)云层之间相互摩擦。

(2)电荷的中和

(3)光速大于声速。

方法 2 判断物体是否带电的方法

判断物体是否带电可归纳为以下几种情况:

1.看物体能否吸引轻小物体。因为任何带电体都具有吸引轻小物体的性质。

2.看物体是否会跟其他带电体相互排斥。因为只有该物体带了电,它才有可能跟其他带电体相互排斥。若相互排斥,这时可以肯定该物体带有与其他带电体相同性质的电荷。

3.利用验电器。只要物体带电,则当它接触验电器的金属球时,验电器的金属箔都会张开一定的角度。同时,利用验电器还能大致比较带的电荷量的多少和检验带电体所带电荷的种类

例1 用丝绸摩擦玻璃棒,玻璃棒由于失去电子而带_____电。如图所示,用这个玻璃棒靠近悬挂的气球,气球被推开,则气球带_____电。

(解析) 原子核和核外电子带的电荷种类相反,数量相同,所以对外不显电性。当原子失去电子时,正电荷数量会大于负电荷数量,所以会对外显示带正电。同种电荷相互排斥,气球被推开说明和玻璃棒带同种电荷。

(答案) 正 正

例2 一个带电体跟一个带正电的验电器的金属球相接触,观察到验电器的金属箔先闭合后又张开,根据这一现象可以断定 ( )

A.带电体一定带有大量的负电

B.带电体一定带有大量的正电

C.带电体一定带有与验电器等量的正电

D.带电体一定带有与验电器等量的负电

(解析) 一个带电体跟一个带正电的验电器的金属球相接触,观察到验电器的金属箔先闭合,说明带电体带有负电;然后又张开,说明带电体所带的电荷量多于验电器所带的电荷量,故选 A。

(答案) A

第 2 节 电流和电路

知识清单

基础
知识

知识1 电流的形成及方向
知识2 电路及各元件作用
知识3 通路、开路和短路

知识 1 电流的形成及方向

1.电流形成的原因

电荷的定向移动形成电流。

温馨
提示

形成电流的电荷可以是正电荷,也可以是负电荷。在金属导体中能自由移动的电荷是带负电的电子,而在各种酸、碱、盐的水溶液中能自由移动的电荷是正、负离子。

2.电流的方向

(1)把正电荷定向移动的方向规定为电流的方向。

(2)正、负电荷的定向移动都可形成电流。金属

导线中的电流,主要是由自由电子(可以自由移动的电子)的定向移动形成的,由于电子带负电,所以金属导线中电流方向与自由电子定向移动的方向相反。

(3)在电源的外部,电流的方向是从电源正极出发,经用电器回到电源负极。

(4)在电源的内部,电流的方向是从电源负极流向正极。

知识 2 电路及各元件作用

1.电路

由电源、用电器、导线和开关组成的电流的路径叫做电路。

2.各元件作用

元件	作用	常见器件
电源	提供电能的装置,将其他形式的能量转化为电能	干电池、蓄电池和发电机等
用电器	用电来工作的设备,将电能转化为其他形式的能	电灯、电炉、电视机、电铃、电冰箱等
开关	用来接通或断开电路,起控制电路的作用	拉线开关、拨动开关、闸刀开关等
导线	将电源、用电器、开关连接起来,形成电流的通路	金属导线

例 在手电筒的完整电路中,干电池是_____,金属外壳是_____,金属外壳上的按钮是_____,小灯泡是_____。

(解析) 用导线把电源、用电器、开关连接起来,就组成了电路。电路由4个部分组成,手电筒的电路也不例外。观察手电筒,结合这4个组成部分,就可将它们一一对应起来。

(答案) 电源 导线 开关 用电器

知识 3 通路、开路和短路

电路状态	概念	特点
通路	处处接通的电路	电路中有电流通过,用电器能够工作(如图甲所示)
开路	又叫断路,是某处断开的电路	电路中无电流通过,用电器不能工作(如图乙、丙所示)
短路	将导线直接连接到电源两端的电路	电路中电流会很大,可能烧坏电源,这是绝对不允许的(如图丁所示)

甲　乙　丙　丁

温馨提示 得到持续电流的条件:①有电源;②电路为通路。

例 如图所示,当开关 S_1、S_2 都断开时,电路处于_____状态;当 S_1 闭合、S_2 断开时,电路处于_____状态;当开关 S_1、S_2 都闭合时,电路处于_____状态。

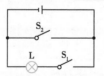

(解析) 由题图可知:S_1、S_2 都断开时,电路开路;S_1 闭合、S_2 断开时,灯 L、S_1、电源经导线连成通路;S_1、S_2 都闭合时,电源两端由导线直接连接,造成短路。

(答案) 开路 通路 短路

拓展知识 知识 电路图的画法

知识 电路图的画法

1.应完整地反映电路的组成,即有电源、用电器、开关和导线;

2.规范地使用电路元件符号,不能自选符号;

3.交叉相连的点要画粗黑圆点;

4.合理地安排电路元件符号的位置,尽可能让这些元件符号均匀地分布在电路中,使电路图清楚美观,并注意元件符号绝不能画在拐角处;

5.导线要横平竖直,转弯画成直角,电路图一般为长方形;

6.最好从电源的正极开始,沿着电流的方向依次画电路元件,且知道在电路图中导线无长短之分的原则。

如图甲所示电路的电路图如图乙所示。

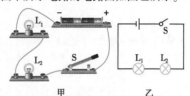

甲　　　　　乙

例 如图是手电筒结构剖面示意图,画出手电筒的电路图。

第⑤部分

解析 画电路图时,所画出的电路图中各元件的顺序应与实物图保持一致,应先弄清电流的路径,可从电源正极开始,沿着电流的方向逐个寻找,直到电源的负极。另外应注意图中各元件位置安排要适当,使图美观、匀称。手电筒的两节干电池是电源,小灯泡是用电器,按钮是开关,和灯泡接触处是电源的正极,和弹簧接触处是电源的负极,金属外壳是导线。

答案 如图所示

方法清单

方法 比较法识别开路和短路

方法 比较法识别开路和短路

常见的几种电路故障

电路状态	产生原因	结果
开路	开关未闭合、导线断裂、接头松动等	用电器不能工作
电源短路	电源短路——导线不经过用电器直接跟电源两极连接起来(如图)	轻则引起电路故障,重则烧毁电源,甚至引起火灾
局部短路	当电路中有多个用电器时,把其中部分用电器两端直接用导线连接起来(如图)	被短路的部分用电器不能工作

易混对比

短路必须避免吗?

短路分为电源短路和局部短路两类。一般说来,电源短路是必须避免的错误(特殊情况例外,如演示奥斯特实验)。局部短路可分为有意和无意两种。有意短路是一种知识在实际应用中的迁移(如一些电热器的保温电路等),而无意短路则是在操作中出现的错误或疏忽。短路未必会有严重的后果,有时也可以巧妙利用,但应视具体情况而定。

例1 如图所示电路中,当开关S闭合时灯 L_1、L_2 均不亮,某同学用一根导线去查找电路的故障,他将导线先并接在灯 L_1 两端,发现灯 L_2 亮,灯 L_1 不亮;然后并接在灯 L_2 两端,发现两灯均不亮。由此判断故障产生的原因是什么?

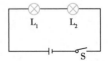

解析 由 S 闭合时 L_1、L_2 均不亮的现象可判断出此时无电流通过 L_1 和 L_2,电路开路。将导线并接在 L_1 两端,L_1 被短路,L_2 亮,说明 L_2 没有开路,也没有短路;将导线并接在 L_2 两端,L_2 被短路,L_1 不亮,说明 L_1 开路。

答案 见解析

例2 如图所示的电路,闭合开关 S_1 和 S_2 后,下列分析正确的是 ( )

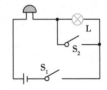

A.小灯泡亮、电铃响

B.小灯泡亮、电铃不响

C.小灯泡不亮、电铃响

D.小灯泡不亮、电铃不响

解析 由题中电路图可知,开关 S_2 与小灯泡并接,当闭合开关 S_1 和 S_2 后,S_2 将小灯泡短路,所以小灯泡不亮。电铃中有电流通过,所以电铃响。

答案 C

第3节 串联和并联

基础知识

知识**1** 串联电路及其特点
知识**2** 并联电路及其特点
知识**3** 串、并联电路的比较

知识 1 串联电路及其特点

1.定义:把电路元件逐个按顺序首尾连接起来,接入电路,这样连接成的电路叫做串联电路。如图所示,就是一个串联电路,其中 L_1、L_2 串联。

2.特点:(1)电流只有一条路径,无干路、支路之分。

(2)电流通过每一个用电器,各用电器的工作互相影响,一个用电器因开路停止工作,则所有用电器都不能工作。

(3)开关与用电器是串联的,一个开关控制所有用电器。

例 下列关于串联电路的说法中,错误的是

( )

A.各用电器是逐个顺次地连接起来的

B.若一个用电器的内部开路,其余用电器仍可通电工作

C.开关可使电路中的各灯泡同时发光或同时熄灭

D.连接电路时,开关可以从电池的正极或负极处接出,也可将开关接在用电器之间

解析 把电路元件逐个顺次连接起来接入电路,这样的电路叫串联电路,A 对;串联电路中一个用电器开路,所有用电器都不能工作,B 错;因串联电路中只有一条电流路径,一个开关可以控制所有用电器,开关可以接在电路中的任何地方,C、D 都正确。

答案 B

知识 2 并联电路及其特点

1.定义:两个或两个以上电路元件并列接在电路两点间,由这种方式连接成的电路叫并联电路。图中 L_1、L_2 并联。

2.特点:(1)电流有两条或两条以上的路径,有干路和支路之分。如图所示的电路,"+"→"a"与"b"→"-"部分是干路;支路有两条:一条是 L_1 所在的电路,由 S_1 控制,另一条是 L_2 所在的电路,由 S_2 控制。(a、b 是各支路两端的连接点,叫节点)

(2)干路电流在"节点"处分成两条或多条支路电流,每一支路都与电源形成一条通路。各支路中的用电器的工作互不影响,当某一支路开路时,其他支路仍可为通路。

(3)干路上的开关控制整个电路的用电器,支路上的开关只控制本支路上的用电器。

例 家庭厨房安装的油烟机都有照明灯和换气扇(电动机 M),使用时,有时需要它们各自独立工作,有时又需要它们同时工作。下列电路图中,符合上述要求的是

( )

　　　A　　　　　　B　　　　　　C　　　　　　D

解析 要求照明灯与换气扇(电动机 M)相互不影响,能独立工作,故应使照明灯与换气扇(电动机 M)并联,且各自的支路有一个开关控制,选 B。

答案 B

知识 3 串、并联电路的比较

	串联电路	并联电路
用电器连接特点	用电器逐个顺次连接,只有一条电流的路径,无分支	各用电器并列连接在电路的两个点之间,有干路与支路之分
工作特点	任意一个用电器断路,其他用电器均停止工作	某一支路断路时,其他支路上的用电器仍可工作
开关控制特点	电路中任意位置的一个开关即可控制整个电路的所有用电器	干路上的开关控制整个电路的所有用电器,支路上的开关只能控制所在支路上的用电器
连接的方法和技巧	逐个顺次,一一连接	"先串后并法"或"先并后串法"

第⑤部分

	串联电路	并联电路
电路图	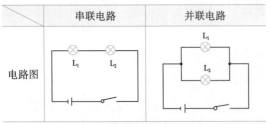	

方法	方法介绍
拆除法	拆除法的原理是:串联电路中各用电器互相影响,并联电路中各用电器互不影响。逐个拆除电路中的用电器,根据电路中其他用电器中有无电流通过来识别电路的连接方式
节点法	所谓"节点法"就是在识别不规范电路的过程中,不论导线有多长,只要中间没有电源、用电器,导线两端点均可以看成同一个点,从而简化电路,进而识别电路的连接方式

例 关于马路上路灯的连接,下列说法正确的是 ( )

A.一定是串联,否则不会同时亮同时灭

B.一定是并联,因为一盏灯坏了,其他灯不灭

C.用一个总开关控制这些灯,串、并联都可以

D.看不见电线,无法判断

解析 马路上的路灯是并联,所以一盏灯坏了,其他灯不灭。灯同时亮、灭是由一个总开关来控制。

答案 B

例 关于如图所示的电路,以下说法正确的是 ( )

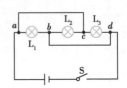

A.该电路属于串联电路

B.该电路属于并联电路

C.L_1 与 L_2 并联之后再与 L_3 串联

D.L_1 与 L_3 并联之后再与 L_2 串联

解析 该电路中 a、c 之间导线可缩为一个点 a,b、d 之间导线可缩为一个点 d,这样就可以看出这三盏灯是"首首相连,尾尾相连",其简化后的电路如图所示,故可知该电路属于并联电路,所以选 B。

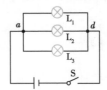

答案 B

 拓展知识 知识 串、并联电路的识别

知识 **串、并联电路的识别**

方法	方法介绍
定义法	若电路中各元件是逐个顺次首尾相连的,此电路就是串联电路;若各元件"首首相接,尾尾相接"并列地连在电路两点间,此电路就是并联电路
电流法	如果让电流从电源正极出发经过各用电器回到电源负极,途中不分流,始终是一条路径,则这些用电器的连接方式就是串联,此电路是串联电路;如果电流在某处分为几条支路,且每条支路上都有一个用电器,电流在电路中有分有合,则这些用电器之间的连接方式就是并联,此电路是并联电路

方法清单
- 方法1 串、并联电路的设计
- 方法2 电路设计中开关的用法

方法 1 串、并联电路的设计

设计电路就是运用电路连接的知识,根据具体要求,绘制电路图。一般电路设计步骤如下:(1)根据设计需要,弄清用电器、开关和电源的连接方式;(2)画出草图,之后根据设计要求验证设计的电路图与题目要求是否相符;(3)若符合题目要求,即可画出正规的电路图。

例1 将如图所示的方框内的符号连接起来,使其成为符合下列要求的电路图(设灯泡不会被烧坏):

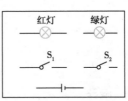

(1)只闭合开关S_1,红、绿灯都亮;

(2)只闭合开关S_2,红、绿灯都不亮;

(3)开关S_1 和S_2 都闭合,绿灯不亮,红灯亮。

解析 根据题意可知,红灯和绿灯一定是串联的。开关都闭合时,绿灯不亮,是因为此时开关S_2 把绿灯短路了。

答案 如图所示

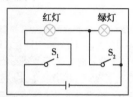

例2 教室里投影仪的光源是强光灯泡,发光时必须用风扇来降温。为了保证灯泡不被烧坏,要求:带动风扇的电动机启动后,灯泡才能发光;风扇不转,灯泡不能发光。则在如图所示的四个电路图中符合要求的是 ( )

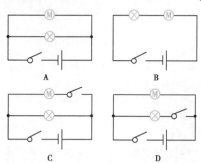

解析 由题述知电动机启动后,灯泡才能发光。根据分析可知,A、B两项中,电动机和灯泡同时工作;C项中,灯泡工作后,闭合支路开关电动机才能工作;D项中,电动机工作后,闭合支路开关,灯泡才可工作,因此选D。

答案 D

方法2 电路设计中开关的用法

1.用若干个开关控制同一个用电器:要求不管哪个开关闭合,用电器都能工作,那么这若干个开关一定是并联的,并且用电器在干路上。

2.开关的短路用法:要求当开关闭合时,一灯发光,开关断开时两灯都发光,就要把这两盏灯串联,把开关与其中一灯并联,在开关闭合时,这盏灯被短路,从而达到只有一盏灯发光的目的。

3.单刀双掷开关的应用:(1)改变电路的连接方式,使用电器由并联变为串联,或由串联变为并联。(2)方便控制一盏灯。把开关安装在两个不同的位置,随意拨动任何一个开关,都能使灯由亮变灭,由灭变亮;如图所示为床头开关的电路控制图,利用单刀双掷开关实现在卧室门边和床头都能控制顶灯的亮灭。

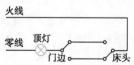

例 为了提醒司机关好车门,小轿车上一般都装有一个指示灯,四个车门中只要有一个车门没有关好(相当于有一个开关断开),该指示灯就会发光。如图所示的四个模拟电路图中符合要求的是 ( )

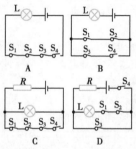

解析 分析题意可知,开关断开时指示灯发光,所以,该开关不应与指示灯串联,而应为并联,故选C项。

答案 C

第4节 电流的强弱

知识清单

知识1 电流
知识2 电流的三大效应
知识3 电流表及其使用方法

知识1 电流

1.定义:物理学中用每秒通过导体任一横截面的电荷量来表示电流。每秒内通过导体横截面的电荷量越多,电流就越大(强)。单位是安培(A),比安培小的单位还有毫安(mA)和微安(μA)。

2.公式:电流用符号"I"表示,若"Q"表示电荷量,"t"表示时间,则 $I=\dfrac{Q}{t}$,公式中三个量的单位分别为安(A)、库(C)、秒(s)。

3.方向:电路中的电流总是沿着电源正极→用电器→电源负极→电源正极的方向流动。

例 手电筒中的小灯泡工作时的电流为0.3 A，1 min内通过它的电荷量是 （ ）

A.0.36 C　　B.18 C　　C.3 C　　D.0.18 C

解析 由于电荷量的单位是库，因此公式中的电流、时间都必须用国际单位制中的单位。

$t = 1\ \text{min} = 60\ \text{s}$，由 $I = \dfrac{Q}{t}$，得 $Q = It = 0.3\ \text{A} \times 60\ \text{s} = 18\ \text{C}$。

答案 B

知识 2 电流的三大效应

1.电流的热效应:电流通过导体时,电能转化成内能。例如:电流通过灯泡内的钨丝,钨丝会发热,温度高达2 500 ℃,呈白炽状态而发光。

2.电流的磁效应:电流通过导体时,在导体周围产生磁场。例如:电流通过螺线管时周围的磁场分布与条形磁铁周围的磁场分布相似。

3.电流的化学效应:电流通过酸、碱、盐的水溶液时会发生化学反应。例如:电解、电镀就是利用了电流的化学效应。

例 随着我国人民生活水平不断提高,家庭中使用的电器越来越多,下列电器中主要利用电流的热效应工作的是 （ ）

A.电风扇　　B.电铃　　C.洗衣机　　D.电炉

解析 电风扇、电铃和洗衣机都是将电能转化为机械能,而电炉是将电能转化为内能,即电流流过电炉时,能使电炉的内能增加,温度升高。所以,电炉才是利用电流的热效应工作的。

答案 D

知识 3 电流表及其使用方法

作用	电流表是测量电路中电流的工具
实物图	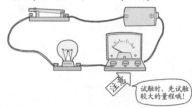 负接线柱　　　正接线柱
电路符号	Ⓐ
量程	电流表表盘上有两排示数,分别是0~0.6 A和0~3 A,有三个接线柱,分别是"-""0.6"和"3","-"表示负接线柱,"0.6"和"3"两个接线柱就是正接线柱(注意不是"+"极和"-"极),且使用"0.6"和"-"两个接线柱时,它的量程是0~0.6 A,最大可测量0.6 A的电流,使用"3"和"-"两个接线柱时,量程是0~3 A,最大可测量3 A的电流

使用注意事项	(1)电流表必须和被测用电器串联,不允许将电流表和用电器并联 (2)电流表接入电路中时,应使电流从"+"接线柱流进电流表,从"-"接线柱流出电流表 (3)注意观察所使用的电流表的量程,被测电流不能超过电流表的量程,无法估计待测电流时,可接大量程,用试触法来试一下(如图)  注意　试触时,先试触较大的量程哦! (4)绝对不允许不经用电器就把电流表直接接到电源的两极上 (5)使用电流表前,要看指针是否指零,若不指零,要先调零
读数方法	(1)分清所选电流表的量程,知道满刻度所表示的电流值,如量程是0~0.6 A时满刻度表示0.6 A,或量程是0~3 A时满刻度表示3 A (2)分清电流表的分度值,如0.02 A或0.1 A (3)看指针向右总共偏转了多少个小格,读出指针位置所示的电流值

温馨提示 电流表的内阻很小,可视为零,接入电路不会影响电路中电流的大小。所以在使用时,不允许把电流表直接接到电源的两极上,这样会造成电流过大,烧坏电流表。

例 1 如图所示电路,闭合开关,以下判断正确的是 （ ）

A.灯 L_1、L_2 串联
B.电流表测灯 L_1 的电流
C.电流表测灯 L_2 的电流
D.电流表测总电流

解析 分析题图可知,图中的 L_1 和 L_2 并联,电流表测量 L_1 的电流,故 B 正确,A、C、D 错误。

答案 B

例2 小红和小丽一起用电流表测量一电路中的电流,小红将电流表接入电路中,选用的量程是 0~0.6 A,而小丽却按照 0~3 A 的量程读得测量值为 2.4 A,则实际测得的电流应该是 ( )

A.1.2 A   B.4.8 A

C.0.12 A   D.0.48 A

解析 电流表的 0~0.6 A 和 0~3 A 两个量程之间是 5 倍的关系,解答此题时,要用 2.4 A 除以 5 得出电流为 0.48 A。

答案 D

拓展知识   知识 常见用电器的电流大小

知识 **常见用电器的电流大小**

计算器中电源的电流	约 100 μA
半导体收音机中电源的电流	约 50 mA
手电筒中的电流	约 200 mA
房间灯泡中的电流	约 0.2 A
家用电冰箱中的电流	约 1 A
家用空调器中的电流	约 5 A
雷电电流	可达 2×10^5 A

方法清单   **方法** 试触法选择电流表的量程

方法 **试触法选择电流表的量程**

在连接电流之前,为选择合适的量程有时要进行试触。试触时主要看指针的偏转情况。

(1)不偏转。一方面可能是电流表所在的电路断路,另一方面也可能是电流表已经损坏。

(2)反偏。即指针向反方向偏转,说明"+""−"接线柱接反了,造成通过表中电流的方向相反。这样不但无法读数,还会损坏电流表。

(3)满偏。即指针大幅度地向满刻度偏转,造成满偏的原因:一是待测电路可能发生了短路,电流过大;二是可能所选量程太小。短路和量程太小都会损坏电流表。

(4)偏转太小。偏转太小是由于电流表所选量程太大。一个电流表有 0~3 A 和 0~0.6 A 两个量程,用 0~3 A 量程时分度值为 0.1 A,用 0~0.6 A 量程时,分度值为 0.02 A,即 0~0.6 A 量程的精确度高些。所以用大量程测而偏角很小时,应该换用小量程。

例1 王红和小丽同学在学习电流表的使用时,连好电路图,闭合开关,试触时,发现电流表表盘上的指针位置分别如图中的甲、乙所示,请指出她们在连接电流表时各出了什么问题?

甲   乙

解析 使用电流表时应选择合适的量程,并使电流从"+"接线柱流入,从"−"接线柱流出。若所用量程太小,会使电流表指针偏转角度过大而烧坏电流表。若所用量程太大,则会使指针偏转角度太小,导致产生较大误差。若电流表的"+""−"接线柱接反,会使指针反向偏转,损坏电表。

答案 甲的电流表"+""−"接线柱接反了;乙的电流表错用了小量程。

例2 小红想测量手电筒灯泡中的电流,她准备使用有 0~0.6 A 和 0~3 A 两个量程的电流表,为了安全,她应先选用_____量程进行试触,发现电流表的指针偏转得很小,为了精确,她应该改用_____量程。

解析 为了安全,应选用电流表的大量程进行试触,根据指针的偏转情况确定合适的量程。若选用电流表的大量程试触时,发现电流表的指针偏转角度很小,为了精确,应该改用小量程。

答案 0~3 A   0~0.6 A

第⑤部分

第5节 探究串、并联电路中电流的规律

知识清单

知识 1 探究串、并联电路的电流规律

1.实验电路

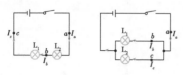

如图所示,两灯泡 L_1 和 L_2 组成的串、并联电路,流过 a、b、c 各点的电流分别用 I_a、I_b、I_c 表示。

2.实验步骤

(1)根据串、并联电路的电路图,组装好实验装置。

(2)选用合适量程的电流表,并把电流表接在电路中的 a 处。

(3)合上开关,测出 a 处的电流值。

(4)把电流表先后改接在电路中的 b、c 处,分别测出电流值,并分别对串、并联电路的 I_a、I_b、I_c 进行比较分析。

(5)改变两个小灯泡的规格,重做上述实验。这样实验的结论更具有普遍性。

3.结论

(1)串联电路:各处电流都相等,$I_a = I_b = I_c$。

(2)并联电路:干路电流等于各支路电流之和,$I_a = I_b + I_c$。

知识 2 串联电路中电流的特点

1.串联电路中各处电流均相等,即 $I_1 = I_2 = \cdots = I_n$。

2.在串联电路中只要测出任何一个位置的电流,就知道了其他位置的电流。

例 如图所示,A、B 是同种材料制成的电阻,它们的长度相等,A 的横截面积是 B 的两倍,将它们串联

在电路中,则通过 A、B 的电流 I_A、I_B 的关系正确的是

( )

A. $I_A = I_B$　　　　　　B. $I_A > I_B$

C. $I_A < I_B$　　　　　　D.无法确定

解析 串联电路中各处电流均相等。

答案 A

知识 3 并联电路中电流的特点

1.并联电路中的干路电流等于各支路电流之和,即 $I = I_1 + I_2 + \cdots + I_n$。

式中 I 表示干路中的电流,I_1 到 I_n 分别表示各支路中的电流。

2.并联电路中各支路的电流大小不一定相同,但所有支路电流之和等于干路中的总电流。

例 在研究并联电路的电流规律时,某次实验所用的实验器材如图甲所示,请根据要求完成下列任务:

(1)按照图乙所示的电路图,用笔画线代替导线,完成图甲的电路连接。

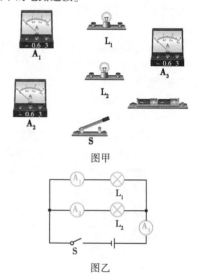

图甲

图乙

(2)实验时,电流表 A₁、A₂ 的示数如图丙所示,通过 L₁ 的电流为_____A;若不计实验误差,请在图丁中标出此时电流表 A₃ 的指针位置。

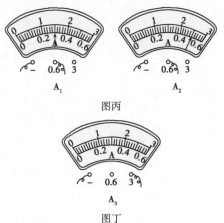

图丙

图丁

(解析) (1)先将电源、A₃、L₂、A₂ 和 S 串联,再将 L₁ 和 A₁ 串联为另一支路,并联在 L₂、A₂ 两端;(2)由题图可知,电流表 A₁ 测量通过 L₁ 的电流,读数为 0.30 A,A₂ 测量通过 L₂ 的电流,读数为 0.50 A,A₃ 测量干路中的电流,读数应为 0.30 A + 0.50 A = 0.80 A。指针位置见答案。

(答案) (1)电路连接如图所示

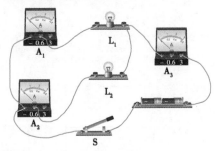

(2)0.30   指针位置如图所示

A₃

(点拨) 连接电路时,可用"节点法"帮助理解:只要导线之间无电源或用电器,可认为是同一点。本题中 A₃、L₁、L₂ 连线时,A₃ 负接线柱,L₁、L₂ 右接线柱为同一点,除答案中接法外也可采用图 1 或图 2 的连接方式;A₁、A₂、S 连线时,A₁、A₂ 的负接线柱和 S 的左接线柱为同一点,除答案中的接法外,也可采用图 3 或图 4 的连接方式。

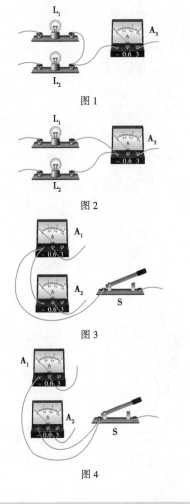

图 1

图 2

图 3

图 4

拓展知识   知识 并联电路中电流表的连接问题

知识 并联电路中电流表的连接问题

1.如图所示,要保证 L₁ 和 L₂ 并联,只要线头 *M* 接在从灯 L₂ 的左接线柱到电源负极的任一接线柱上都可以。

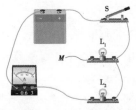

①当 *M* 接在灯 L₂ 的左接线柱上或电流表的"3"接线柱上时,电流表就测干路电流。

②当 *M* 接在电源负极或电流表的负接线柱上时,电流表测灯 L₂ 中的电流。

2.两种接法中电流表所处的位置不同,所测的电流也不同。

例 如图甲是小亮同学测量并联电路中的总电流时连接的电路。

(1)请你在 a、b 导线中撤掉一根多余的导线,使电路符合实验要求。你选择撤掉的是_____导线。

(2)撤掉多余的导线后,闭合开关,电流表的读数如图乙所示,其读数为_____A。

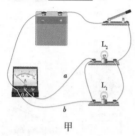

甲

乙

解析 (1)由图甲可以看出导线 b 是多余的,去掉 b 后,两灯泡并联,电流表测干路中的电流;(2)根据电流表的量程和指针偏转情况可以读出此时的示数为 0.34 A。

答案 (1)b (2)0.34

方法清单
方法1 比较法识别"探究串、并联电路的电流规律"实验中的电路故障
方法2 探究串、并联电路的电流规律时使结论更有普遍性的方法

方法1 比较法识别"探究串、并联电路的电流规律"实验中的电路故障

在做探究串、并联电路中电流的规律的实验时,可能会遇到各种各样的电路故障,一般可以根据故障的现象推断产生故障的原因。以下对此实验中可能出现故障的现象进行分析诊断。

1.串联电路中的故障

L_1 与 L_2 组成的串联电路如图所示:

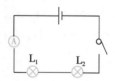

(1)只有一个灯泡亮,如 L_1 亮,说明问题出在不发光的灯泡 L_2 上,检查灯泡 L_2 和灯座是否有短路故障。

(2)两灯都不亮,电流表无示数,则电路中一定有断路,可以用一只好灯泡检测故障部位,将检验灯泡分别与灯泡 L_1、灯泡 L_2、电流表、开关、电源并联,或与多个元件并联,若观察到检验灯泡发光,说明与其并联的电路部分存在断路故障。例如:将检验灯泡 L 与

灯泡 L_1 并联(如图),如果 L 发光,说明灯泡 L_1 处断路。

2.并联电路中的故障

L_1 与 L_2 组成的并联电路如图所示:

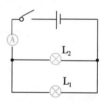

(1)只有一个灯泡亮,如 L_1 亮,只能是不发光的灯泡 L_2 所在支路上存在断路故障,检查灯丝是否烧断,灯座、导线是不是没有接好。

(2)两灯都不亮,电流表无示数,一般属于干路故障,检查电源、开关、电流表及干路导线中是否断路,也有可能是两条支路同时断路。

例 如图所示,两个小灯泡 L_1、L_2 串联,闭合开关 S,L_1 发光,L_2 不发光。发生这一现象的原因不可能是 ( )

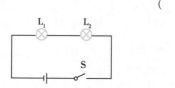

A.电源电压较低

B.L$_2$ 发生了断路

C.L$_2$ 发生了短路

D.L$_2$ 的实际功率很小

解析 L$_1$、L$_2$ 串联在电路中,由现象"闭合开关 S,L$_1$ 发光,L$_2$ 不发光"和"串联电路一处断则全断"的特点可知,发生这一现象的原因不可能是 L$_2$ 发生了断路,故选 B。

答案 B

方法 2 探究串、并联电路的电流规律时使结论更有普遍性的方法

1.探究串、并联电路的电流规律时,常用改变电源电压、换用不同规格灯泡等方法进行多次测量使结论更具普遍性。

2.利用如图所示电路探究并联电路的电流规律时,若两只灯泡 L$_1$ 与 L$_2$ 规格相同会得出结论:$I_b = I_c$,$I_a = I_b + I_c$,误认为各支路的电流相等;因为实验时使用了两只完全相同的灯泡,所以结论比较特殊,不具备普遍性,换用两只不同规格的灯泡重做实验,则 $I_b \neq I_c$,但仍有 $I_a = I_b + I_c$,所以两灯泡并联时,$I_a = I_b + I_c$ 才是正确结论。

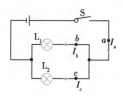

例 在"探究串联电路中的电流规律"实验中,某同学用电流表分别测出图中 a、b、c 三处的电流大小,并初步得到它们之间关系的结论。为了进一步确定它们之间的关系,他下一步的操作是 ( )

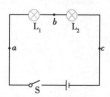

A.将电源两极对调,再次测量 a、b、c 三处的电流

B.改变开关 S 的位置,再次测量 a、b、c 三处的电流

C.将图中两只灯泡位置对调,再次测量 a、b、c 三处的电流

D.换用不同规格的灯泡,再次测量 a、b、c 三处的电流

解析 换用不同规格的灯泡,进行多次实验,可避免结果的偶然性。

答案 D

第15章 电压 电阻

知识梳理

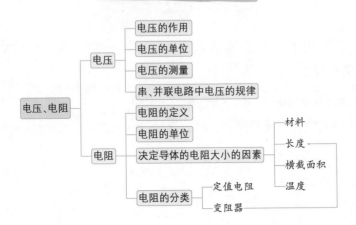

第1节 电压

知识清单

 基础知识

知识1 电压
知识2 电压表及其使用方法

知识 1 电压

作用		使电路中的自由电荷定向移动形成电流
单位	国际单位	伏特,简称伏,符号是 V
	常用单位	千伏(kV)、毫伏(mV)、微伏(μV)
	换算关系	1 kV = 10^3 V,1 V = 10^3 mV,1 mV = 10^3 μV

温馨提示 电源是提供电压的装置。

例 发生闪电的云层间的电压可达 10^6____,大型发电机的电压可达3.6 kV,合____V。

解析 1 kV = 1 000 V,1 V = 1 000 mV。发生雷电

时电压可达 1 000 kV,合 10^6 V。大型发电机的电压可达 3.6 kV,合 3 600 V。

答案 V 3 600

知识 2 电压表及其使用方法

作用	电压表是测量电路中电压的工具
实物图	
电路符号	Ⓥ
量程	电压表表盘上有两排示数,分别是 0~3 V 和 0~15 V;有三个接线柱,分别是"-""3"和"15","-"表示负接线柱,"3"和"15"两个接线柱是正接线柱(注意不是"+"极和"-"极)。使用"3"和"-"接线柱时,它的量程是0~3 V,最大可测量3 V的电压;使用"15"和"-"接线柱时,量程是 0~15 V,最大可测量15 V的电压

续表

使用方法	(1)电压表必须和被测用电器并联 (2)电压表接入电路中时,应使电流从"+"接线柱流入,从"-"接线柱流出 (3)注意观察所使用的电压表的量程,被测电压不能超过电压表的量程,若无法估计待测电压,可接大量程试触(如图) 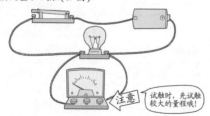 注意 试触时,先试触较大的量程哦!
读数方法	(1)分清所选电压表的量程,知道满刻度所表示的电压值,如:3 V或15 V (2)分清电压表的分度值,如:0.1 V或0.5 V (3)看指针向右总共偏转了多少个小格,根据分度值读出指针位置所表示的电压值

温馨提示 电压表可以直接接到电源两端测量电源电压。

例 1 如图所示的电压表,若选用"-"、"15"两个接线柱,它的量程是_____,指针所指示的电压值是_____;若选用"-"、"3"两个接线柱,它的量程是_____,电压表的示数应是_____。某同学使用这只电压表测量电压时记录的电压值为 2.4 V,可实际使用的接线柱是"-"、"15",则实际的电压是_____。

(解析) 指针在同一位置,不同的量程对应的电压值不同,它们之间是 5 倍的关系。因此,如果表盘上面的刻度线和数值看不清了,又用了 0~15 V 的量程,可以用下面的数值乘以 5,就得到测得的电压值。该同学是按 0~3 V 量程和 0.1 V 的分度值去读数,所以实际的电压应是所记录的电压值的 5 倍,即 12 V。

(答案) 0~15 V 8.5 V 0~3 V 1.70 V 12 V

例 2 小敬设计了如图所示的电路,用来测量灯泡两端的电压,他先将开关打到 1,用电压表测出了灯泡 L_1 两端的电压,然后他将开关打到 2,_____(选填"能"或"不能")测出灯泡 L_2 两端的电压,原因是_____。

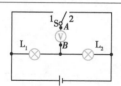

(解析) 电压表测电压时,要求电流"+"进"-"出,将开关打到 1 时,电压表测出灯 L_1 两端的电压,可知 A 点接"+"接线柱,B 点接"-"接线柱;将开关打到 2 时,虽然电压表并联到灯 L_2 两端,但电流不能"+"进"-"出,所以电压表不能测灯 L_2 两端的电压。

(答案) 不能 电压表的正、负接线柱接反了

拓展知识 知识1 电池的串、并联
知识2 分析电路时常见"电压表"的接法

知识 1 电池的串、并联

1.电池的串联:如图甲,把一节电池的负极和另一节电池的正极连在一起,一节电池的正极和另一节电池的负极就是这一电池组的正极和负极,电池的这种连接叫做电池的串联。电池串联后的总电压等于各节电池的电压之和。

2.电池的并联:如图乙,相同的电池并联后的总电压等于一节电池两端的电压。

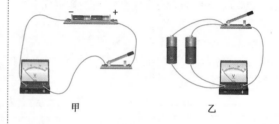

甲 乙

知识 2 分析电路时常见"电压表"的接法

用电压表测电源电压时,电路图如图 1 所示;在图 2 和图 3 中,灯泡(灯丝)相当于导线,电压表连在电源两端,测电源电压;图 4 中若灯 L_1 开路,则与图 2 等效,相当于电压表测电源电压,其示数接近电源电压,此问题在判断电路故障时经常遇见。

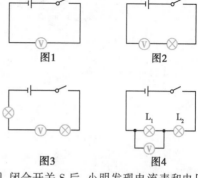

图1 图2
图3 图4

例 闭合开关 S 后,小明发现电流表和电压表的指针均不动。他断开开关 S,检查线路连接无误后,把电压表与 b 点相连的那根导线改接到 c 点,再次闭合开关 S 时,发现电流表的指针仍不动,但电压表的指

针有明显偏转。若电路中只有一处故障，则故障是___
___。

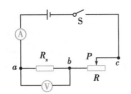

（解析） 开关闭合后电流表和电压表指针均不动，说明电路中出现了断路，且排除 a、b 间断路的可能；将电压表与 b 点相连的导线改接到 c 点时，电压表指针有了明显偏转，则能排除电源正、负极与 a、c 两点间相连的部分断路的可能，所以故障应是 b、c 间断路。

（答案） b、c 之间断路

方法清单

> 方法❶ 去源法判断电压表测哪部分电路的电压
> 方法❷ 由电压表示数判断电路故障

方法 1 去源法判断电压表测哪部分电路的电压

1.去源法是指在分析电路中电压表测的是哪个部分电路两端的电压时，可先将电源去掉，然后进行分析的方法。

2.使用去源法时应注意，在去掉电源（即电源处断开）后，电压表与哪部分电路组成回路，则电压表测的就是那部分电路两端的电压。

例 1 如图所示，当 S_1 断开、S_2 闭合时，电压表测的是___两端的电压；当 S_1 闭合、S_2 断开时，电压表测的是___两端的电压。

（解析） 当 S_1 断开、S_2 闭合时，电压表连到电源两端，测电源两端电压；当 S_1 闭合、S_2 断开时，用去源法

去掉电源后，电压表与灯 L_1 组成回路，电压表测灯 L_1 两端的电压。

（答案） 电源　灯 L_1

例 2 在如图所示的电路中，闭合开关 S，电压表是测量 L_1 两端电压的正确电路是　　　　（　　）

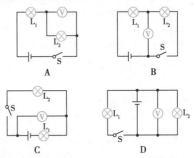

（解析） 去掉电源后，会发现 A、B、C 中电压表均与 L_2 构成回路；D 中电压表与 L_1、L_2 均构成回路。

（答案） D

方法 2 由电压表示数判断电路故障

电路出现故障，一般有两种情况：(1)发生短路；(2)发生断路。在两种情况下，电压表的示数都有可能是零或接近电源电压。具体分析如表：

故障	电压表示数	出现的故障及位置	出现故障的原因	用电器工作情况	电路图(以本图为例)
短路	零	与电压表并联的用电器发生短路	导线两端电压为零	部分用电器工作	
	接近电源电压	与电压表并联的用电器以外的用电器发生短路	电源电压全部加在与电压表并联的用电器两端	部分用电器工作	
断路	零	与电压表并联的用电器以外的用电器发生断路	电压表没有与电源接通	用电器不工作	
	接近电源电压	与电压表并联的用电器发生断路	电压表、用电器与电源直接构成了一个通路	用电器不工作	

例 在如图所示的电路中,闭合开关 S 后,两灯都不亮,电压表有示数,电流表无示数。则该电路故障可能是 ( )

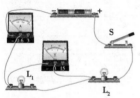

A.电流表短路　　　　B.灯泡 L_1 开路
C.灯泡 L_2 短路　　　　D.灯泡 L_2 开路

解析 闭合开关 S 后,两灯都不亮,电流表无示数,说明电路中发生了开路,又因为电压表有示数,说明电压表的两个接线柱与电源的两极连通,故该电路故障可能是灯泡 L_1 开路。

答案 B

第2节　探究串、并联电路电压的规律

知识清单

知识 1 探究串、并联电路电压的规律

1.实验器材:电源、导线、开关、灯座、几个规格不同的小灯泡、电压表。

2.实验电路图:如图甲、乙所示。

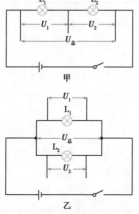

3.实验步骤:(1)按实验电路图连接好电路。连接电路过程中,开关应处于断开状态。

(2)将电压表并联在灯 L_1 两端,测出 L_1 两端电压 U_1。

(3)合上开关后,将电压表的示数记录在表中。

(4)再用电压表分别测出 L_2 两端电压 U_2、电路总电压 $U_总$,记下电压表示数,并填入表中。

	U_1/V	U_2/V	$U_总$/V
串联电路			
并联电路			

(5)换用规格不同的小灯泡,多测几组电压数据,分析得出结论。

知识 2 串、并联电路的电压特点

电路	电压关系
串联电路	串联电路两端的总电压等于各部分电路两端的电压之和,表达式:$U_总 = U_1 + U_2 + \cdots + U_n$
并联电路	并联电路各支路两端的电压都相等,表达式:$U_并 = U_1 = U_2 = \cdots = U_n$

例 图(a)所示电路,当闭合开关 S 后,两个电压表指针偏转均为图(b)所示,则电阻 R_1 和 R_2 两端的电压分别为 ( )

A.8 V　2 V
B.10 V　2 V
C.2 V　8 V
D.2 V　10 V

解析 由题图可知,电路为串联电路,电压表 V_1 测电源电压 U;电压表 V_2 测电阻 R_2 两端的电压 U_2。两个电压表指针偏转角度相同,根据串联电路的电压规律 $U = U_1 + U_2$ 可知,V_1 的量程是 0~15 V,读数为 10 V,即 $U = 10$ V;V_2 的量程是 0~3 V,读数为 2 V,即 $U_2 = 2$ V。故电阻 R_1 两端电压 $U_1 = U - U_2 = 10$ V -2 V $= 8$ V,电阻 R_1 和 R_2 两端的电压分别为 8 V 和 2 V,故 A 正确。

答案 A

拓展知识 | 知识 串、并联电路中电流和电压关系的比较

知识 串、并联电路中电流和电压关系的比较

	电流关系	电压关系
串联电路	串联电路中的电流处处都相等,表达式: $I=I_1=I_2=\cdots=I_n$	串联电路两端的总电压等于各部分电路两端电压之和,表达式: $U=U_1+U_2+\cdots+U_n$
并联电路	并联电路中干路电流等于各支路电流之和,表达式: $I=I_1+I_2+\cdots+I_n$	并联电路各支路两端电压都相等,表达式: $U=U_1=U_2=\cdots=U_n$

例 小明同学按如图所示的电路进行实验,实验中电阻 R_1 保持不变,三次调整滑动变阻器 R_2 的阻值,得到如表所示的实验数据:

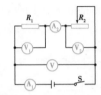

实验次数	A₁的示数 I_1/A	A₂的示数 I_2/A	V₁的示数 U_1/V	V₂的示数 U_2/V	V的示数 U/V
1	0.4	0.4	4	8	12
2	0.6	0.6	6	6	12
3	0.8	0.8	8	4	12

(1)分析电流表 A₁、A₂的示数,可得出＿＿＿＿＿＿＿＿＿＿。

(2)分析电压表 V₁、V₂、V的示数,可得出＿＿＿＿＿＿＿＿＿＿。

(解析) 由"去表法"判断此电路为串联电路,由表中电流表 A₁、A₂的示数可以看出:在串联电路中各处的电流都相等。由表中电压表 V₁、V₂、V的示数可以看出,V₁与V₂的示数之和等于V的示数,即串联电路中总电压等于各串联电阻两端电压之和。

(答案) (1)串联电路中,各处的电流都相等 (2)串联电路中,总电压等于各串联电阻两端电压之和

方法清单 | 方法① 电路中未知电表的判断方法
方法② 探究串、并联电路电压规律时常见问题的处理方法

方法 1 电路中未知电表的判断方法

对电路中未知电表的判定是个难点,下面介绍几种常用的方法。

1.短路法

电流表和电压表是测量仪表,将它们接入电路中对电路结构不产生影响。电流表内阻很小,相当于一根导线;电压表内阻很大,相当于开路。因此可将要填电表的地方换成一根导线,若电路出现短路,则所要填的电表应是电压表;若电路并未出现短路,则所要填的电表应是电流表。

2.去表法

假设把电表从电路中去除,分析电路是否因此而受到影响。若其他元件不能正常工作,则电表一定是串联在电路中,应是电压表;若其他元件不受影响,则电表一定是并联在电路中,应是电压表。

3.分析法

对于连接方式已确定的电路,可以先观察电路的连接情况,再考虑电表的连接规则,即电流表应串联在电路中,电压表应并联在电路中,最后进行综合判断。

例1 如图所示电路中,灯泡正常发光,a、b、c 是电压表或电流表,其中 （ ）

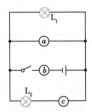

A.a、b 为电流表,c 为电压表
B.a 为电压表,b、c 为电流表
C.a 为电流表,b、c 为电压表
D.c 为电流表,a、b 为电压表

(解析) 短路法:将 a、b、c 三表分别换成一根导线,则灯泡 L_1 发生短路,所以 a 应为电压表,而 b、c 表所在处电路未出现短路,所以 b、c 应为电流表。故选B。

去表法:将 a 表去掉,其他元件正常工作,所以 a 为电压表;将 b 表去掉,电路断开,将 c 表去掉,灯 L_2 开路,所以 b、c 为电流表,故选B。

(答案) B

例2 如图所示的电路中,a、b、c是连接在电路中的电表,如果L_1和L_2为串联,则a表是_____,b表是_____,c表是_____。

（解析）分析法:如果L_1和L_2串联,则电表b相当于一根导线,使L_1和L_2顺次连接起来,所以电表b应为电流表,而这时另外两个电表a、c分别并联在L_1、L_2的两端,所以a、c应是电压表。

（答案）电压表　电流表　电压表

方法 2 探究串、并联电路电压规律时常见问题的处理方法

在用电压表探究串、并联电路电压规律时,常见问题主要涉及电路连接、电压表量程的选择、电路故障等,例如:①开关在连接电路的过程中是断开的,只有电路连接完毕且检查无误后,才闭合开关;②电压表的使用注意量程的选择和正负接线柱的接法要正确;③实验结论要具有普遍性,不能由一组数据得出结论。

例 小刚和小丽用如图所示的器材探究串联电路的电压关系,用三节干电池串联作电源,两只小灯泡的规格不同。

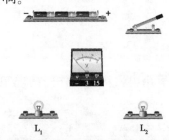

（1）请用笔画线代替导线,连接实验电路。要求:L_1和L_2串联,电压表测量两灯串联后的总电压。

（2）小刚用电压表测量L_1两端的电压时,直接选用0~3 V的量程,小丽说这样不行,规范的操作方法应该是_____。

（3）他们在测量L_2两端的电压时,两灯突然熄灭,电压表示数变为0。小刚用电压表检测L_1两端的电压,示数为电源电压,由此判断出L_1处的故障是_____；L_2是短路还是正常的? 小丽在原电路中又添加了一个电学器材,就检验出了结果,她的方法可能是_____。

（4）他们排除故障后继续实验,得出了如表所示的一组数据。为了得出串联电路电压关系的普遍规律,他们还应当_____。

L_1 两端 电压/V	L_2 两端 电压/V	串联总 电压/V
1.4	3.1	4.5

（解析）（1）可先把电源、开关、L_2、L_1连成一串联电路,再把电压表并接到L_1与L_2串联后的两端,3节干电池串联,电源电压为4.5 V,所以电压表要用大量程0~15 V。

（2）L_1两端电压若大于3 V,直接用0~3 V量程测量会损坏电压表,所以应先用0~15 V量程试触,若示数小于3 V,再换0~3 V量程测量。

（3）电压表与L_1并联,示数为电源电压,则相当于把电压表串联到电路当中了,所以L_1断路。判断L_2时可用其他电路元件(小灯泡或电阻)代替L_1,使电路为通路,若L_2短路则不亮,若正常则会亮。

（4）换用不同规格的器材测量使结论具有普遍性,多次测量得到多组数据可使结论更可靠,更有说服力。

（答案）（1）如图所示

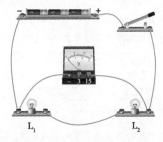

（2）先选用0~15 V量程试触,如果示数小于3 V,再改用0~3 V量程测量

（3）断路　用小灯泡(或定值电阻或滑动变阻器)与L_1并联(或替换L_1),若L_2发光,则L_2正常;若L_2不发光,则L_2短路

（4）换用不同规格的器材(灯泡、电源)或加滑动变阻器,多次测量

第3节 电阻

 知识清单

知识 **1** 电阻
知识 **2** 影响电阻大小的因素

知识 1 电阻

1.定义:导体对电流的阻碍作用叫做电阻。不同导体的导电能力是不同的,对电流的阻碍作用越大,导电能力越弱,电阻就越大(如图)。

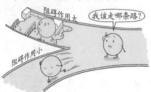

2.导体的电阻用字母 R 表示,在电路图中用符号 —▭— 表示。

3.单位:欧姆,符号是 Ω,还有千欧(kΩ),兆欧(MΩ)。它们之间的换算关系是:1 Ω = 10^{-3} kΩ = 10^{-6} MΩ。

知识 2 影响电阻大小的因素

1.电阻是导体的属性,它的大小只与材料、长度和横截面积有关,与导体两端的电压和通过导体的电流无关。在材料相同时,长度越长,横截面积越小,电阻越大。

2.导体的电阻还与温度有关。一般来说,导体的电阻随温度的升高而增大,如金属导体;也有少数导体的电阻随温度的升高而减小,如石墨。

温馨提示
①电阻是导体本身固有的一种属性,不同导体的导电能力是不同的。②绝缘体之所以能起到绝缘的作用,就是由于其电阻很大。

例1 白炽灯的灯丝断了一小段,若搭上仍能使用,则通过灯丝的电流将 ( )

A.变小 　B.变大 　C.不变 　D.无法确定

(解析) 灯丝搭接后,主要引起的变化是长度变短了,所以电阻变小,其对电流的阻碍作用变小,所以电流会变大。

(答案) B

例2 用灯泡、导线、开关和钨丝组成串联电路如图所示,闭合开关,灯泡发光。再用酒精灯对钨丝加热,会发现灯泡亮度变_____,由此你可以得出的结论是_____。

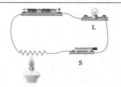

(解析) 金属导体的电阻随温度的升高而增大,故用酒精灯给钨丝加热时,钨丝电阻增大,对电流的阻碍作用增大,电路中电流变小,灯泡的亮度变暗。

(答案) 暗 钨丝温度升高时其电阻变大

知识 常见用电器正常工作时的电阻

知识 常见用电器正常工作时的电阻

常见用电器	电阻 R/Ω
白炽灯(15 W)	3 227
白炽灯(60 W)	807
电熨斗(600 W)	80.7
电烤箱(900 W)	54
电炉(1 000 W)	48.4

方法清单

 方法 控制变量法探究电阻大小与哪些因素有关

方法 控制变量法探究电阻大小与哪些因素有关

在"研究电阻的大小与什么因素有关"时,用到了控制变量法。因为影响电阻大小的因素有四个,即材料、长度、横截面积和温度。如要研究材料对电阻的影响,则需控制其他三个因素不变。

例 在研究性学习活动中,小美同学用如图所示的电路探究导体的电阻跟哪些因素有关。她选取了6根金属丝,其材料、规格和测得的电压、电流如下表所示,并计算出了每一根金属丝的电阻值。

金属丝代号	材料	长度L/m	横截面积S/mm²	电压U/V	电流I/A	电阻值R/Ω
①	镍铬合金	1.80	1.0	1.5	0.75	2.00
②	镍铬合金	0.90	1.0	1.5	1.50	1.00
③	镍铬合金	0.45	1.0	1.5	3.00	0.50
④	镍铬合金	0.90	2.0	1.5	3.00	0.50
⑤	镍铬合金	0.90	0.5	1.5	0.75	2.00
⑥	锰铜合金	0.90	0.5	1.5	1.90	0.79
⑦	镍铬合金	3.60	0.5	—	—	—

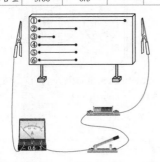

（1）请你利用代号为①②③的三组数据,在坐标中画出R-L图线。

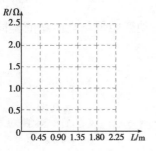

（2）代号为_____的3根金属丝,是用来探究导体电阻与横截面积的关系。代号为_____的2根金属丝,是用来探究导体电阻与材料的关系。

（3）根据表中数据所反映的规律,可推知代号为⑦的金属丝的电阻值,请将结果填在表中。

解析 （1）描点作图,材料和横截面积相等时,电阻R与长度L成正比。

（2）探究电阻与横截面积的关系,要控制材料和长度相同,改变横截面积。探究电阻与材料的关系,要控制长度和横截面积相同。

（3）⑦和⑤两组数据比较,可知$R_7 = 4R_5 = 8.0\ \Omega$。

答案 （1）如图所示

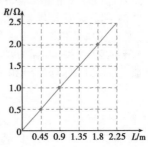

（2）②④⑤ ⑤⑥

（3）8.0

第4节 变阻器

知识清单

基础知识	知识**1** 电阻的分类
	知识**2** 滑动变阻器
	知识**3** 电阻箱

温馨提示 家用电器的挡位调节器是一种变阻器,它通过机械式旋钮调节阻值大小。可调亮度的电灯、可调温度的电热毯、电饭锅等都含有变阻器。

知识 **1** 电阻的分类

1.电阻分为定值电阻和可变电阻（阻值可调）。（1）定值电阻简称为电阻;（2）可变电阻,阻值大小可以调节,与之对应的是变阻器。

2.变阻器一般分为滑动变阻器、电阻箱和电位器三种,最常见的是滑动变阻器,学生实验中常采用滑动变阻器。

知识 **2** 滑动变阻器

1.构造:由线圈、瓷筒、滑片、金属杆等组成,如图所示。

(a)实物图

(b)结构示意图

说明:①金属杆;②金属滑片P;③电阻丝绕成的线圈;④瓷筒;⑤支架;A、B为电阻丝两端的接线柱;C、D是与滑片P连通的接线柱。

2.工作原理:通过改变接入电路中电阻丝的长度来改变电阻。

3.元件符号:——▭——。

4.作用:改变电流、调节电压和保护用电器。

5.使用方法:滑动变阻器一般串联在电路中。连接时应"一上一下"的把接线柱接入电路中。连接电路时应把滑动变阻器的滑片滑至阻值最大处。

6.铭牌:观察滑动变阻器的铭牌,能够了解它的最大阻值和允许通过的最大电流。例如铭牌上标有"20 Ω 1.5 A"的字样,说明该滑动变阻器的最大阻值是20 Ω,允许通过的最大电流是1.5 A。

7.优点:能连续地改变接入电路的电阻值。
缺点:不能直接读出接入电路的电阻值。

易混对比

滑片移动时滑动变阻器阻值大小的判断

(1)电路图中滑动变阻器的符号为 ——▭—— 时,实物图中滑动变阻器的连接方式为

；若滑片P向右移动,滑动变阻器的阻值变大;若滑片P向左移动,滑动变阻器的阻值变小。

(2)电路图中滑动变阻器的符号为 ——▭—— 时,实物图中滑动变阻器的连接方式为

；若滑片P向右移动,滑动变阻器的阻值变小;若滑片P向左移动,滑动变阻器的阻值变大。

例 若把两只标有"200 Ω 1.5 A"和"100 Ω 1 A"的滑动变阻器串联起来使用,则电路中允许通过的最大电流是 ( )

A.1.5 A   B.1 A
C.0.5 A   D.2.5 A

解析 若电路中的电流大于1 A,则"100 Ω 1 A"的变阻器将可能烧坏。

答案 B

知识 3 电阻箱

1.种类:分为旋盘式电阻箱和插塞式电阻箱。

2.元件符号:——▱——。

3.优点:能够直接读出接入电路的电阻值。
缺点:不能连续地改变接入电路的电阻值。

4.读数方法:旋盘下面"△"所对应的示数乘以相应的倍数之和。

例 如图所示的电阻箱的示数是_____Ω。

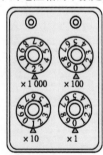

解析 按照电阻箱读数规则,其读数为(2×1 000+0×100+1×10+0×1)Ω=2 010 Ω。

答案 2 010

拓展知识
知识 滑动变阻器与电阻箱的异同

知识 滑动变阻器与电阻箱的异同

	不同点		相同点
	用法	优点与不足	
滑动变阻器	滑动滑片	能连续地改变电阻,但不能直接读数	①都能改变电阻 ②都有规定的最大电阻值和允许通过的最大电流值
电阻箱	调节旋钮	不能连续地改变电阻,但能直接读数	

例1 关于滑动变阻器,下列说法中错误的是 ( )

A.滑动变阻器上的电阻丝上面涂有绝缘漆

B.滑动变阻器串联在电路中可以改变小灯泡的亮度

C.滑动变阻器能改变连入电路中的电阻,但不能直接读出连入电路中的阻值

D.可以读出滑动变阻器连入电路中的阻值

解析 根据滑动变阻器的构造,可知A项正确;根据滑动变阻器的作用,可知B项也正确;滑动变阻器虽然能改变连入电路中电阻的大小,但不能显示出连入电路中的阻值,C项正确,D项错误。

答案 D

例2 如图所示是插塞式电阻箱接入电路的情况,则 （　）

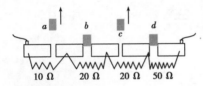

10 Ω　20 Ω　20 Ω　50 Ω

A.现在使用的电阻是 30 Ω
B.只将铜塞 d 插上,使用电阻为 80 Ω
C.将全部铜塞拔出,使用电阻为 0 Ω
D.将全部铜塞插上,使用电阻为 100 Ω

（解析）图中所示是将铜塞 a 和 c 拔出,是 10 Ω 和 20 Ω 的两个电阻串联,接入电路的电阻为 30 Ω;只将铜塞 d 插上,使用电阻为 50 Ω;将全部铜塞拔出,使用电阻为 100 Ω;将全部铜塞插上,使用电阻为 0 Ω。

（答案）A

方法清单 | 方法 电流流向法判断滑动变阻器的哪部分电阻接入电路

方法 电流流向法判断滑动变阻器的哪部分电阻接入电路

1.判断滑动变阻器哪部分电阻接入电路时,用到电流流向法:电流流经电阻丝的哪一段,哪段电阻接入电路。实际上是看接入电路的接线柱是滑动变阻器下端的哪一个,该接线柱和滑片之间的电阻即接入电路的电阻。

2.判断滑动变阻器的阻值变化时,滑片远离下面接入电路中的接线柱,变阻器接入电路中的电阻就变大,反之,接入电路中的电阻就变小。

例 在如图所示的电路中,闭合开关S,要使滑动变阻器的滑片 P 向右移动时,电流表的示数减小,则 M、N 应与滑动变阻器上的哪两个接线柱连接 （　）

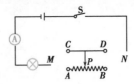

A.M 接 C、N 接 D
B.M 接 A、N 接 B
C.M 接 C、N 接 B
D.M 接 A、N 接 D

（解析）滑片 P 向右移动时,电流表的示数减小,滑动变阻器接入电路中的电阻变大,滑片应远离下接线柱,所以下接线柱选 A,上接线柱 C、D 任意选一个,本题选 D。

（答案）D

第16章 欧姆定律

知识梳理

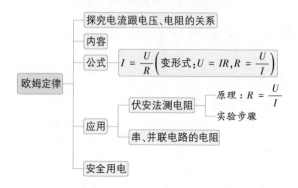

欧姆定律
- 探究电流跟电压、电阻的关系
- 内容
- 公式 $I = \dfrac{U}{R}$（变形式：$U = IR$，$R = \dfrac{U}{I}$）
- 应用
  - 伏安法测电阻 —— 原理：$R = \dfrac{U}{I}$；实验步骤
  - 串、并联电路的电阻
- 安全用电

第1节　探究电流与电压、电阻的关系

知识清单

基础知识
- 知识 **1** 电流与电压的关系
- 知识 **2** 电流与电阻的关系

知识 1　电流与电压的关系

1.实验目的

研究电路中的电流与电路两端的电压的关系。

2.实验器材

电源、开关、导线、电流表、电压表、定值电阻、滑动变阻器。

3.实验电路图

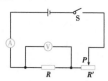

4.实验步骤

（1）按照电路图连接实物图；

（2）闭合开关 S 后，调节滑动变阻器的滑片 P，使定值电阻 R 两端的电压成整数倍地变化，如 2 V、4 V、

6 V 等；

（3）根据电压表和电流表的示数，读出每次 R 两端的电压值和通过 R 的电流值，并记录在数据表格中。

5.分析与论证

由实验数据可以看出电流和电压有关，电流随电压的增大而增大，将实验数据通过图像的形式表示出来，如图所示。

6.结论

在电阻一定的情况下，导体中的电流与该导体两端的电压成正比。

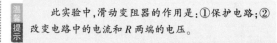

温馨提示　此实验中，滑动变阻器的作用是：①保护电路；②改变电路中的电流和 R 两端的电压。

例　小薇和小亮两位同学在"探究电流与电压的关系"的实验中，电源使用两节新干电池，滑动变阻器

R' 的规格是"20 Ω　2 A"。

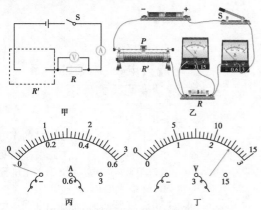

甲

丙　　丁

(1)如图甲所示是小薇画出的电路图,小亮进行实物连线如图乙所示,请你在虚线框内把电路图补画完整(要求所补画的元件与实物电路对应)。

(2)开关闭合前,小亮发现电流表的指针在零刻度线左端,如图丙所示,其原因是_____(选填"A"或"B")。

A.电流表没调零

B.电流表正负接线柱接反了

(3)确认电路无误后,闭合开关进行实验,第④次实验时电流表示数为 0.5 A,电压表示数如图丁所示,记为_____V;他们记录的数据如下表所示,老师指出其中一组数据有拼凑的嫌疑,你认为是第____组(填写实验序号),理由是_____。

实验序号	①	②	③	④
电压/V	0.5	1.2	1.8	
电流/A	0.10	0.24	0.34	0.5

(4)排除有拼凑嫌疑的数据后,分析数据可以得到的结论是:在_____不变时,通过导体的电流与导体两端的电压成_____比。

(5)小薇利用实验数据还计算出定值电阻 R 的阻值为_____Ω(结果保留一位小数)。

(6)以下实验与"探究电流与电压的关系"进行多次测量的目的不相同的是_____。

A.探究影响滑动摩擦力大小的因素

B.探究杠杆的平衡条件

C.刻度尺测物体的长度

〔解析〕(1)滑动变阻器的连接应与实物图对应。

(2)开关闭合前电路中无电流,指针在零刻度线左端说明电流表未调零。

(3)读数时要注意量程,示数为 2.5 V;第①组数据有拼凑的嫌疑,因为由表中数据知,电阻 R 的最大值为 $\dfrac{1.8\ V}{0.34\ A} \approx 5.3\ Ω$,所以电路中电流最小为 $I=$

$\dfrac{3\ V}{20\ Ω+5.3\ Ω} \approx 0.12\ A$,所以电流无法小到 0.10 A。

(4)根据控制变量法分析数据可知,在电阻不变时,I 与 U 成正比。

(5)$R_{②}=\dfrac{1.2\ V}{0.24\ A}=5\ Ω,R_{③}=\dfrac{1.8\ V}{0.34\ A}\approx5.3\ Ω,R_{④}=\dfrac{2.5\ V}{0.5\ A}=5\ Ω,$

则 $R=\dfrac{R_{②}+R_{③}+R_{④}}{3}=\dfrac{5\ Ω+5.3\ Ω+5\ Ω}{3}=5.1\ Ω。$

(6)本实验多次测量的目的是寻找普遍性规律,防止偶然性,而 C 选项多次测量的目的是求平均值,减小误差。

〔答案〕(1)如图所示

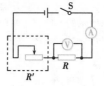

(2)A

(3)2.5　①　滑动变阻器的最大阻值偏小,无法使电流小到 0.10 A

(4)电阻　正　(5)5.1　(6)C

知识 **2** **电流与电阻的关系**

1.实验目的

研究电路中的电流与电阻的关系。

2.实验器材

电源、开关、导线、电流表、电压表、几个阻值不同的定值电阻、滑动变阻器。

3.实验电路图

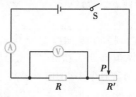

4.实验步骤

(1)按照电路图,连接实物图;

(2)闭合开关 S 后,换用不同的定值电阻 R,使电阻成整数倍地变化,如:5 Ω、10 Ω、15 Ω 等;

(3)调节滑动变阻器 R' 的滑片 P,保持每次定值电阻两端的电压不变;

(4)把对应着不同阻值的电流值记录在数据表格中。

5.分析与论证

由实验数据可以看出电流和电阻有关,电流随电阻的增大而减小。将实验数据通过图像的形式表示出来,如图所示。

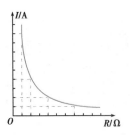

6.结论

在电压不变的情况下,导体中的电流跟导体的电阻成反比。

温馨提示

此实验中滑动变阻器的作用是:①保护电路;②控制电阻 R 两端的电压不变。

例 小亮同学想探究"导体中电流跟电阻的关系",设计了如图所示的电路图(电源电压恒定)。

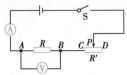

(1)小亮总共做了 2 次实验。他把第一次实验得到的数据填入表中;第二次实验,他将 A、B 两点间的定值电阻由24 Ω换成12 Ω,然后使滑动变阻器的滑片 P 向_____(选填"C"或"D")移动,使电压表的示数不变,则此时表格中空白处的电流为_____A。

实验序号	U/V	R/Ω	I/A
1	4.8	24	0.2
2	4.8	12	

(2)小亮根据实验数据得到如下结论:导体中的电流与其电阻成反比。请你对以上的探究过程进行评价,并写出两点评价意见:_____、_____。

解析 (1)将定值电阻由 24 Ω 换成 12 Ω,电路中的总电阻变小,电流变大,在滑动变阻器的滑片不移动的条件下,滑动变阻器两端的电压增大,由串联电路的特点知,定值电阻两端的电压变小,为使定值电阻两端的电压不变,须减小滑动变阻器接入电路的阻值,故应使滑片 P 向 C 移动;由欧姆定律可知,此时流过定值电阻的电流 $I = \dfrac{U}{R} = \dfrac{4.8\ \text{V}}{12\ \Omega} = 0.4\ \text{A}$。(2)为了避免偶然性,必须进行多次实验,该实验只有两组数据,不能避免偶然性,得出的结论可能会不准确;由于实验采用控制变量法,所以在得出结论时需要加上前提条件。

答案 (1)C 0.4 (2)实验次数少于 3 次,不能避免偶然性,结论可能不准确 结论缺少"电压一定"这个前提

拓展知识

知识 探究"电流与电压、电阻的关系"实验中滑动变阻器的作用

知识 探究"电流与电压、电阻的关系"实验中滑动变阻器的作用

1.滑动变阻器的作用

(1)探究电流与电压的关系时滑动变阻器的作用为:①保护电路,使电路中的电流不至于过大;②改变电路中的电流和定值电阻两端的电压,得到多组电流值和电压值,便于分析电流与电压的关系。

(2)探究电流与电阻的关系时滑动变阻器的作用为:①保护电路,使电路中的电流不至于过大;②通过移动滑片,使所替换的不同电阻两端的电压保持不变,便于分析电流与电阻的关系。

2.判断电路中滑动变阻器的阻值变化

(1)弄清滑动变阻器的哪部分连入电路(一般是滑片和下边所用接线柱之间的电阻丝);

(2)看滑动变阻器的滑片移动方向,远离下接线柱时变大,靠近下接线柱时变小。

3.注意事项

连接电路时开关应断开,在闭合开关前,应将滑动变阻器的滑片调到电阻值最大的位置,电压表和电流表应选用合适的量程。

例 在探究"电流与电压、电阻的关系"的过程中,两小组同学提出了以下猜想:

小组 1 猜想:电流可能跟电压成正比;

小组 2 猜想:电流可能跟电阻成反比。

(1)小组 1 的做法是:按图甲所示的电路图连接电路,此时开关应处于_____(选填"断开"或"闭合")状态。

甲

定值电阻 $R = 10\ \Omega$,闭合开关 S 后,调节滑动变阻器 R',得到多组数据。在分析数据的基础上得出结论。其中滑动变阻器 R' 的作用是_____。

(2)小组 2 连接了如图乙所示的电路。

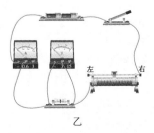

乙

实验步骤为:

①将 5 Ω 电阻接入电路,调节滑动变阻器,使电压表示数为 1.5 V,记下电流表示数;

②将 5 Ω 电阻换成 10 Ω 电阻,闭合开关后发现电压表示数大于 1.5 V,应将滑动变阻器的滑片向____(选填"左"或"右")移动,当观察到电压表示数为____V 时,记下电流表示数。

（解析）(1)连接电路时应当使开关处于断开状态,防止因发生短路而损坏电路中的元件。通过改变滑动变阻器接入电路中的阻值来改变电路中的电流,从而改变定值电阻 R 两端的电压。

(2)变阻器与定值电阻是串联关系,根据串联电路中电阻大则分压也大的关系可知,应将滑动变阻器滑片向右移动,增大连入电路中的电阻值,才能减小定值电阻两端的电压,直至电压表示数再次等于 1.5 V。

（答案）(1)断开　通过改变接入电路中的阻值来改变电路中的电流,从而改变电阻 R 两端的电压

(2)②右　1.5

方法
清单
　方法❶ 控制变量法探究电流与电压、电阻的关系
　方法❷ 图像法分析电流与电压、电阻的关系
　方法❸ 分析"电流与电压、电阻的关系"实验中电路故障的方法

方法 1　控制变量法探究电流与电压、电阻的关系

探究电流与电压、电阻的关系时用到了控制变量法:

(1)保持电阻不变。通过改变滑动变阻器的阻值,探究通过电阻的电流与电阻两端电压的关系。

(2)保持两点之间电压不变。在这两点之间换不同阻值的电阻后,调节滑动变阻器使这两点之间的电压不变,探究通过不同阻值的电流与电阻的关系。

例　某实验小组的同学在探究电流与电压、电阻的关系时,采用了如图甲所示的电路图,实验中他们选用的定值电阻分别是 5 Ω、8 Ω、10 Ω,电源电压是 3 V,滑动变阻器的阻值范围是 0~15 Ω。

甲

(1)他们在探究某一因素变化对电流的影响时,采用控制变量法。实验分两步进行:

①保持电阻不变,探究电流与_____的关系;

②保持电压不变,探究电流与_____的关系。

(2)实验中,电流表的量程应选_____A,电压表的量程应选_____V;某次实验中,若电流表的示数是 0.3 A,电压表的示数是 1.5 V,请根据你前面选择的量程,在图乙中分别画出两表指针的位置。

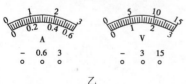

乙

(3)在研究电阻对电流的影响时,把定值电阻由 5 Ω 换成 10 Ω,闭合开关后,下一步的操作是:调节滑动变阻器的滑片,保持_____不变。

（解析）(1)影响电路中电流大小的因素有电压和电阻,因此实验采用控制变量的方法。实验分两步进行:一是保持定值电阻不变,改变定值电阻两端的电压,测量几次;二是保持定值电阻两端的电压不变,改变定值电阻的大小,测量几次。(2)实验器材中电源电压为 3 V,因此电压表量程选用 0~3 V 即可,所用定值电阻的最小阻值为 5 Ω,所以电路中最大电流为 $I=\dfrac{3\ \mathrm{V}}{5\ \Omega}=0.6\ \mathrm{A}$,电流表的量程选用 0~0.6 A。当电流值为 0.3 A,电压值为 1.5 V 时,指针均指在表盘的中央刻度。(3)改变定值电阻阻值是为了研究电流与电阻的关系,应控制电压不变,所以改变定值电阻后,应调节变阻器使定值电阻两端的电压与原来电阻两端的电压相同。

（答案）(1)①电压　②电阻　(2)0~0.6　0~3　指针位置如图所示　(3)定值电阻两端的电压(或电压表示数)

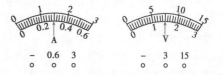

方法 2　图像法分析电流与电压、电阻的关系

1.在物理学中,经常利用图像表示一个物理量随另一个物理量的变化情况,它可以直观、形象地表示出物理量的变化规律,这种研究问题的方法称为图像法。

2.在探究电流跟电压、电阻的关系的实验中,对实验中得到的数据进行描点,分别画出电阻不变时电流随电压变化的图像和电压不变时电流随电阻(或电阻的倒数)变化的图像,分析图像,进而可得出电流跟电

第⑤部分

压、电阻的关系。

例1 某实验小组的同学"探究电流与电压的关系"时,用到如下器材:电源1个,电流表、电压表各1只,定值电阻(5 Ω、10 Ω、15 Ω各1只),滑动变阻器1只,开关1个,导线若干。设计的电路图如图甲所示。

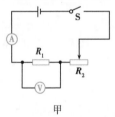

甲

(1)该实验中使用了控制变量的方法,其中被控制的变量是_____。

下面是他们获取的一组实验数据

电压 U/V	2	4	6	8	10
电流 I/A	0.39	0.79	1.20	1.58	2.00

(2)请在图乙的坐标系中画出电流随电压变化的图像。

(3)分析表中的数据或图像,你能得出的探究结论是:_____。

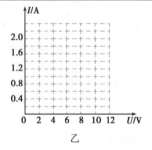

乙

(解析) 因为电流的大小是由电压和电阻两方面因素共同决定的,所以在探究电流与电压的关系时,必须控制电阻不变。数据处理用的是图像法,先根据数据描点,画出的图线是一条直线,则表明在电阻不变的情况下,电流与电压是成正比的。

(答案) (1)电阻 (2)如图所示 (3)电阻一定时,通过电阻的电流与加在电阻两端的电压成正比

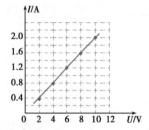

例2 图1是小强"探究通过导体的电流与电阻的关系"的实验电路(电源电压保持不变),图2是他依据测得的实验数据绘制的电流 I 随电阻 R 变化的图像。由图像可知 R 两端的电压为_____V;当 R 由

10 Ω更换为15 Ω时,闭合开关后,为使 R 两端的电压_____(选填"改变"或"不变"),滑动变阻器的滑片 P 应向_____(选填"a"或"b")端滑动。

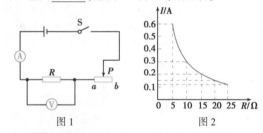

图1　　　　图2

(解析) 由题图2可知,图像上各点对应的 I 和 R 的乘积是3 V,因此可知,本实验控制的电压是3 V;要探究电流与电阻的关系,应控制电压不变,改变电阻;当电阻由10 Ω更换为15 Ω时,根据分压关系,电压表示数会大于3 V,故应将滑片 P 向 b 端滑动,使滑动变阻器分压增多,电压表示数才会减小到3 V。

(答案) 3　不变　b

方法3 分析"电流与电压、电阻的关系"实验中电路故障的方法

在本探究实验中,常会遇到电表无示数、示数偏低、实验数据或结论错误等问题,这都是电路中发生某种故障所致。准确地判断出电路故障的原因并予以解决,是中考经常考查的内容之一。

例 在探究"电流与电阻的关系"实验中。

(1)小新将实物连成如图所示电路,其中有一处连线错误,请你在连接错误的导线上画"×"并改正。

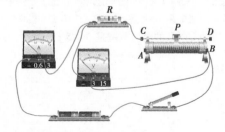

(2)纠正错误后,小新又练习一次电路连接,刚连完最后一根导线后就发现两个电表的指针发生偏转,并且指针总是晃动,造成上述现象的原因分别是_____、_____。

(3)将电路连接正确后,闭合开关,移动滑动变阻器滑片 P,使定值电阻 R 两端电压为2 V,电流表示数如图所示,为_____A,则 R 的阻值为_____Ω。

(4)换上10 Ω的电阻后,闭合开关,电压表示数

将_____(选填"变大"或"变小"),此时应将滑片P向_____(选填"A"或"B")端移动,使定值电阻两端电压为_____V。

(5)小芳同学正确连接电路后,闭合开关,移动滑动变阻器滑片,发现电流表无示数,电压表有示数,其原因可能是_____。

(6)将10 Ω电阻换成15 Ω电阻,闭合开关后发现,当滑动变阻器的滑片移到最左端时,电压表示数无法达到2 V,其原因可能是 (　　)
A.滑动变阻器最大阻值太大
B.滑动变阻器最大阻值太小
C.滑动变阻器断路
D.定值电阻短路

(解析)(1)电压表应与定值电阻并联,测定值电阻两端的电压,原图中电压表测滑动变阻器和定值电阻两端的总电压。

(2)最后一根导线连完,电表有示数,说明开关没有断开。示数不稳说明电路中某处接触不良。

(3)由题图可知,电流表示数为0.4 A,$R=\dfrac{U}{I}=\dfrac{2\ \text{V}}{0.4\ \text{A}}=5\ \Omega$。电流表读数时应先看量程和分度值,后看指针。

(4)探究"电流与电阻的关系"时,应控制电压不变。当换上10 Ω的电阻后,根据串联电路分压规律知R两端的电压变大,电压表示数变大,所以应调节滑片向A端移动,使R两端电压保持2 V不变。

(5)定值电阻断路时,电压表与电流表串联在电路中,由于电压表内阻很大,所以电路中电流很小,电流表指针几乎不偏转,电压表示数接近电源电压。

(6)滑动变阻器的最大阻值太小导致定值电阻两端电压无法达到2 V。

(答案)(1)如图所示

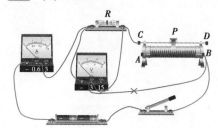

(2)连接电路时开关是闭合的　某处接触不良
(3)0.4　5　(4)变大　A　2
(5)定值电阻断路(答案科学合理即可)
(6)B

第2节　欧姆定律及其应用

知识清单

第⑤部分

基础知识
知识1 欧姆定律
知识2 电阻的串、并联
知识3 串联分压与并联分流
知识4 串、并联电路中电流、电压、电阻的规律

知识 1　欧姆定律

1.欧姆定律的内容:导体中的电流跟导体两端的电压成正比,跟导体的电阻成反比。

2.欧姆定律公式:$I=\dfrac{U}{R}$;变形式:$U=IR$,$R=\dfrac{U}{I}$。

3.单位:使用欧姆定律时各物理量的单位必须统一,I的单位用A,U的单位用V,R的单位用Ω。

易混对比

公式$I=\dfrac{U}{R}$与$R=\dfrac{U}{I}$中的正反比问题

①对于欧姆定律公式$I=\dfrac{U}{R}$,我们说I与U成正比的前提条件是R一定;I与R成反比的前提条件是U一定。只有符合前提条件,才能说成正比或成反比。

②对于变形式$R=\dfrac{U}{I}$,不能仅从形式上理解R与U成正比或R与I成反比,这种理解是错误的。对于某段导体,一般情况下(不受温度影响)其电阻的阻值为定值,其阻值只与导体的材料、长度、横截面积有关,与导体两端的电压和通过导体的电流无关。

例 从欧姆定律可以导出公式$R=\dfrac{U}{I}$。对电阻的理解,你认为正确的是 (　　)
A.当电压增大时,电阻也增大
B.当电流增大时,电阻减小

C.当电压为零时,电阻也为零

D.电阻由导体本身性质决定,与电流、电压无关

(解析) 电阻是导体本身的一种性质,电阻的大小与导体的材料、长度、横截面积和温度有关,与通过导体的电流和加在导体两端的电压无关。

(答案) D

知识 2 电阻的串、并联

1.串联电路中电阻的特点

(1)串联电路的总电阻与各分电阻的关系

如图,由欧姆定律得:

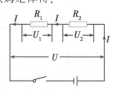

$U_1 = IR_1$,$U_2 = IR_2$

$U = IR$

由 $U = U_1 + U_2$ 得,$IR = IR_1 + IR_2$

即 $R = R_1 + R_2$

同理可得多个电阻串联时总电阻与各分电阻的关系:$R = R_1 + R_2 + \cdots + R_n$

即串联电路的总电阻等于各分电阻之和。

(2)理解:把 n 段导体串联起来,总电阻比任何一段导体的电阻都大,这相当于增加了导体的长度。

(3)n 个相同的电阻 R_0 串联,则总电阻 $R = nR_0$。

2.并联电路中电阻的特点

(1)并联电路的总电阻与各分电阻的关系

如图,由欧姆定律得:

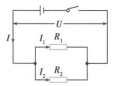

$I = \dfrac{U}{R}$,$I_1 = \dfrac{U}{R_1}$,$I_2 = \dfrac{U}{R_2}$

又因为 $I = I_1 + I_2$

得 $\dfrac{U}{R} = \dfrac{U}{R_1} + \dfrac{U}{R_2}$

即 $\dfrac{1}{R} = \dfrac{1}{R_1} + \dfrac{1}{R_2}$

结论:两个并联电阻的总电阻的倒数等于两分电阻的倒数之和。

同理可知当多个电阻并联时,并联电路的总电阻的倒数等于各个分电阻的倒数之和,即

$\dfrac{1}{R} = \dfrac{1}{R_1} + \dfrac{1}{R_2} + \cdots + \dfrac{1}{R_n}$

(2)理解:把 n 段导体并联起来,总电阻比任何一段导体的电阻都小,这相当于增大了导体的横截面积。

(3)n 个相同的电阻 R_0 并联,则总电阻 $R = \dfrac{R_0}{n}$;

两个电阻 R_1、R_2 并联的总电阻 $R = \dfrac{R_1 R_2}{R_1 + R_2}$。

例 在做物理实验时,需要阻值为 5 Ω、20 Ω 的电阻各一只,可手边只有一些 10 Ω 的电阻,以下做法可行的是   (   )

A.将两只 10 Ω 的电阻串联即可得到 5 Ω 的电阻

B.将两只 10 Ω 的电阻并联即可得到 5 Ω 的电阻

C.将两只 10 Ω 的电阻串联即可得到 20 Ω 的电阻

D.将两只 10 Ω 的电阻并联即可得到 20 Ω 的电阻

(解析) 将两只 10 Ω 的电阻串联,总电阻:$R = R_1 + R_2 = 10\ \Omega + 10\ \Omega = 20\ \Omega$。

将两只 10 Ω 的电阻并联,总电阻:$\dfrac{1}{R'} = \dfrac{1}{R_1} + \dfrac{1}{R_2}$

$\dfrac{1}{R'} = \dfrac{1}{10\ \Omega} + \dfrac{1}{10\ \Omega}$,

$R' = 5\ \Omega$。

(答案) BC

(点拨) 对于两个相同的电阻 R,串联后总电阻 $R_{总} = 2R$;并联后总电阻 $R_{总}' = \dfrac{R}{2}$。

知识 3 串联分压与并联分流

1.串联分压

(1)在串联电路中,导体两端的电压跟导体的电阻成正比,即 $\dfrac{U_1}{U_2} = \dfrac{R_1}{R_2}$。

(2)如图所示,在串联电路中,根据欧姆定律的变形公式 $U = IR$ 可得:电阻 R_1 两端的电压 $U_1 = IR_1$,电阻 R_2 两端的电压 $U_2 = IR_2$,所以 $\dfrac{U_1}{U_2} = \dfrac{IR_1}{IR_2}$,即 $\dfrac{U_1}{U_2} = \dfrac{R_1}{R_2}$,这便是分压原理。

2.并联分流

在并联电路中,导体中的电流跟导体的电阻成反比,即 $\dfrac{I_1}{I_2} = \dfrac{R_2}{R_1}$。

如图所示,在并联电路中,根据欧姆定律 $I = \dfrac{U}{R}$ 可得:通过电阻 R_1 的电流 $I_1 = \dfrac{U}{R_1}$,通过电阻 R_2 的电流 $I_2 = \dfrac{U}{R_2}$,因此 $\dfrac{I_1}{I_2} = \dfrac{U}{R_1} \times \dfrac{R_2}{U}$,即 $\dfrac{I_1}{I_2} = \dfrac{R_2}{R_1}$,这就是分流原理。

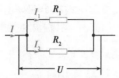

例 某兴趣小组的同学们想制作一个简易的台灯，所用小灯泡的额定电压为 27 V，正常发光时灯丝的电阻为 90 Ω。因身边只有电压为 36 V 的电源，为了保证小灯泡能正常发光，应将一个定值电阻与灯泡串联后接在电源上。请你帮他们求出该电阻的阻值。

(解析) $I_灯 = \dfrac{U_灯}{R_灯} = \dfrac{27 \text{ V}}{90 \text{ Ω}} = 0.3 \text{ A}$

$U_阻 = U - U_灯 = 36 \text{ V} - 27 \text{ V} = 9 \text{ V}$

由于定值电阻与灯泡串联，故 $I_阻 = I_灯 = 0.3 \text{ A}$

$R_阻 = \dfrac{U_阻}{I_阻} = \dfrac{9 \text{ V}}{0.3 \text{ A}} = 30 \text{ Ω}$

(答案) 30 Ω

知识 **4** 串、并联电路中电流、电压、电阻的规律

	串联电路	并联电路
电路图		
电流	$I_总 = I_1 = I_2$	$I_总 = I_1 + I_2$
电压	$U_总 = U_1 + U_2$	$U_总 = U_1 = U_2$
电阻	$R_总 = R_1 + R_2$（若 n 个相同的电阻 R 串联，则 $R_总 = nR$）	$\dfrac{1}{R_总} = \dfrac{1}{R_1} + \dfrac{1}{R_2}$，$R_总 = \dfrac{R_1 R_2}{R_1 + R_2}$（若 n 个相同的电阻 R 并联，则 $R_总 = \dfrac{R}{n}$）
比例分配	$\dfrac{U_1}{U_2} = \dfrac{R_1}{R_2}$	$\dfrac{I_1}{I_2} = \dfrac{R_2}{R_1}$

例 如图所示的电路中，已知电阻 $R_1 : R_2 = 1 : 3$。如果甲、乙两表均为电压表，当开关 S 闭合时，R_1 与 R_2 的连接方式是 _____ 联，此时，两表的示数之比 $U_甲 : U_乙 =$ _____；如果甲、乙两表均为电流表，当开关 S 断开时，两表的示数之比 $I_甲 : I_乙 =$ _____。

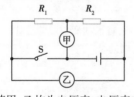

(解析) 若甲、乙均为电压表，电压表在电路中相当

于断路，当开关 S 闭合时，两电阻串联；根据串联电路中各部分电压之比等于电阻之比可知 $U_1 : U_2 = R_1 : R_2 = 1 : 3$，甲电压表测量 R_1 两端的电压，$U_甲 = U_1$，乙电压表测量电路总电压，$U_乙 = U_1 + U_2$，所以 $U_甲 : U_乙 = 1 : 4$。若甲、乙均为电流表，电流表在电路中相当于导线，所以当 S 断开时，两电阻并联；根据并联电路中各支路电流之比等于电阻的反比可知：$I_1 : I_2 = 3 : 1$，甲电流表测干路电流，则 $I_甲 = I_1 + I_2$，乙电流表测 R_1 中的电流，则 $I_乙 = I_1$，所以 $I_甲 : I_乙 = 4 : 3$。

(答案) 串 1 : 4 4 : 3

点拨 当甲、乙均为电压表时，可用去表法判断 R_1 与 R_2 串联；再用去源法判断甲电压表测 R_1 两端的电压。

拓展知识 **知识** 解析"欧姆定律"

知识 **解析"欧姆定律"**

欧姆定律是电学中的基本定律和核心内容，是贯穿整个电学的主线，下面我们从以下几个方面进行深入分析。

1. 要理解欧姆定律的内容

（1）欧姆定律中的关于成正比、成反比的结论是有条件的。如果说导体中的电流与导体两端的电压成正比，条件就是对于同一个电阻，也就是说在电阻不变的情况下；如果说导体中的电流与导体的电阻成反比，条件就是导体两端的电压不变。

（2）注意顺序，不能反过来说电阻一定时，电压跟电流成正比。这里存在一个逻辑关系，电压是原因，电流是结果。是因为导体两端加了电压，导体中才有电流，不是因为导体中通了电流才有了电压，因果关系不能颠倒。

同样也不能说导体的电阻与通过它的电流成反比。我们知道，电阻是导体本身的一种性质，即使导体中不通电流，它的电阻也不会改变，更不会因为导体中电流的增大或减小而使它的电阻发生改变。

2. 要知道欧姆定律的适用范围

欧姆定律只适用于纯电阻电路，如：电路中只接有电热器、白炽灯等用电器的电路。对于非纯电阻电路，如：接有电动机的电路、接有电风扇的电路等，则不能直接应用。

3. 要理解欧姆定律的注意事项

（1）物理量的同一性。在运用欧姆定律 $I = \dfrac{U}{R}$ 进行计算时，必须注意同一性，即 $I、R、U$ 必须是对应同一导体或同一段电路的物理量。在表示 $I、U、R$ 时，注

第⑤部分

意脚标的一一对应。

（2）物理量的同时性。由于电路的连接方式发生改变，开关的断开、闭合或滑动变阻器滑片的左右移动都可能使电路中总电阻发生变化，从而可能引起电路中电流和各部分电阻两端的电压发生变化。因此，必须注意在同一时刻、同一过程中的电压、电阻与电流的相互对应，不可将前后过程的 I、R、U 随意混用。

例 一个电阻两端的电压是 4 V 时，通过的电流是 0.2 A，电阻的阻值是 _____ Ω。如果电阻两端的电压变为 8 V 时，通过电阻的电流是 _____ A。当电阻两端电压为零时，电阻的阻值是 _____ Ω，通过导体的电流是 _____ A。

解析 解此类题关键在于明确电阻大小只是等于电压和电流的比值，和电流、电压无关，且能正确理解欧姆定律及其变形公式。$R = \dfrac{U}{I} = \dfrac{4 \text{ V}}{0.2 \text{ A}} = 20 \ \Omega$。因为导体的电阻跟材料、长度、横截面积、温度有关系，跟电流、电压无关，当电压变为 8 V 时，电阻仍为 20 Ω，此时电流 $I' = \dfrac{U'}{R} = \dfrac{8 \text{ V}}{20 \ \Omega} = 0.4 \text{ A}$。当电压为零时，电阻仍然是 20 Ω，此时电流 $I'' = \dfrac{U''}{R} = \dfrac{0 \text{ V}}{20 \ \Omega} = 0 \text{ A}$。

答案 20 0.4 20 0

方法清单

方法 1 利用欧姆定律进行计算
方法 2 判断电压表、电流表示数变化的方法
方法 3 求电表的示数变化范围

方法 1 利用欧姆定律进行计算

根据串、并联电路的特点和欧姆定律的公式可进行有关计算。解题的方法是：(1)根据题意画出电路图，看清电路的连接方式（串联还是并联）；(2)明确题目给出的已知条件与未知条件（可在电路图上标明）；(3)针对电路特点依据欧姆定律进行分析；(4)列式解答。

例 如图所示，$R_1 = 20 \ \Omega$，闭合开关，电压表和电流表的示数分别为 6 V 和 0.5 A。

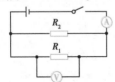

求：(1)通过电阻 R_1 的电流；
(2)电阻 R_2 的阻值。

解析 由图可知：R_1 与 R_2 并联，ⓥ 测 R_1 （R_2 或电源）两端电压，Ⓐ 测干路电流。

(1) $I_1 = \dfrac{U}{R_1} = \dfrac{6 \text{ V}}{20 \ \Omega} = 0.3 \text{ A}$

(2) 方法一：$I_2 = I - I_1 = 0.5 \text{ A} - 0.3 \text{ A} = 0.2 \text{ A}$

$R_2 = \dfrac{U}{I_2} = \dfrac{6 \text{ V}}{0.2 \text{ A}} = 30 \ \Omega$

方法二：$R_总 = \dfrac{U}{I} = \dfrac{6 \text{ V}}{0.5 \text{ A}} = 12 \ \Omega$

$\dfrac{1}{R_总} = \dfrac{1}{R_1} + \dfrac{1}{R_2}$

$\dfrac{1}{R_2} = \dfrac{1}{R_总} - \dfrac{1}{R_1} = \dfrac{1}{12 \ \Omega} - \dfrac{1}{20 \ \Omega}$

$R_2 = 30 \ \Omega$

答案 (1) 0.3 A (2) 30 Ω

方法 2 判断电压表、电流表示数变化的方法

1.明确电路的连接方式和各元件的作用

开关在电路中并不仅仅是起控制电路通断的作用，有时开关的断开和闭合会引起短路，或改变整个电路的连接方式，进而引起电路中电表示数发生变化。

2.认清滑动变阻器的连入阻值

如果在与变阻器的滑片 P 相连的导线上接有电压表，如图所示，则此变阻器的连入阻值就是它的最大阻值，并不随滑片 P 的滑动而改变；但滑片 P 移动时，电压表的示数会改变。

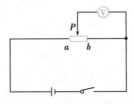

3.弄清电路图中电表测量的物理量

在分析电路前，必须通过观察弄清各电表分别测量哪部分电路的电流或电压，若发现电压表接在电源两极上，则该电压表的示数是不变的。

4.与变化前比较

分析电路的总电阻怎样变化和总电流的变化情况，综合得出电路中电表示数的变化情况。

例 1 如图所示的电路中，电源两端电压保持不变。闭合开关 S，将滑动变阻器的滑片 P 向右滑动，则下列说法中正确的是　　　　（　　）

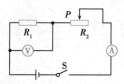

A.总电阻变小

B.电流表的示数变小

C.电压表的示数变大

D.滑动变阻器接入电路中的电阻变小

(解析) 将滑动变阻器的滑片 P 向右滑动,滑动变阻器连入电路中的电阻变大,总电阻变大,A、D 项错误;电源电压不变,由欧姆定律知电流变小,B 项正确;通过定值电阻的电流变小,它两端的电压变小,C 项错误。故选 B。

(答案) B

例 2 如图所示,电源电压恒定不变,闭合开关 S,滑片 P 向右移动,下列说法正确的是 (　　)

A.(A_1)示数变小,(V)示数变小

B.(A_1)示数不变,(V)示数变小

C.(A_1)示数不变,(V)示数不变

D.(A_1)示数变小,(V)示数不变

(解析) 分析题图可知,R_1 和 R_2 并联,由于电压表接在滑片上,所以滑片向右滑动时,R_2 连入电路的阻值不变,故两个电流表的示数不变,电压表并联部分的电阻变小,故电压表示数变小,本题应选择 B。

(答案) B

方法 3　求电表的示数变化范围

解决此类问题的关键是把变化问题变成不变问题,把问题简单化。根据开关的断开与闭合情况或滑动变阻器滑片的移动情况,画出等效电路图,然后应用欧姆定律,结合串、并联电路的特点进行有关计算。

例 1 如图所示电路中,电源电压为 3 V 且保持不变,$R=10$ Ω,滑动变阻器的最大阻值 $R'=20$ Ω。当开关 S 闭合后,在滑动变阻器的滑片由 B 端移动到 A 端的过程中,电流表示数的变化范围是 _____。

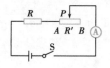

(解析) 把滑片在 A 点和 B 点时的电路图分别画出来,如图甲、乙所示,应用欧姆定律要注意 I、U、R 的同一性和同时性。滑片在 A 端时,$I_1=\dfrac{U}{R}=\dfrac{3\text{ V}}{10\text{ Ω}}=$ 0.3 A;滑片在 B 端时,$I_2=\dfrac{U}{R+R'}=\dfrac{3\text{ V}}{10\text{ Ω}+20\text{ Ω}}=0.1$ A。

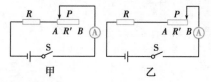

甲　　　　　乙

(答案) 0.1 A~0.3 A

例 2 如图所示,电阻 R_1 的阻值为 5 Ω。

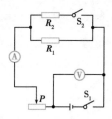

(1)当开关 S_1 闭合,S_2 断开,滑片 P 滑至最左端时,电压表示数为 6 V,电流表示数为 0.3 A,则滑动变阻器的最大阻值是多少?

(2)若 R_2 的阻值为 20 Ω,当开关 S_1、S_2 均闭合,滑片 P 滑至最右端时,电流表的示数是多少?

(解析) (1)当开关 S_1 闭合,S_2 断开,滑片 P 滑至最左端时等效电路图如图甲所示,R_1 与滑动变阻器串联,由欧姆定律 $I=\dfrac{U}{R}$ 得,电路中的总电阻 $R=\dfrac{6\text{ V}}{0.3\text{ A}}=$ 20 Ω。滑动变阻器的最大阻值 $R'=R-R_1=20$ Ω-5 Ω$=$ 15 Ω。

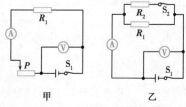

甲　　　　　乙

(2)当开关 S_1、S_2 均闭合,滑片 P 滑至最右端时等效电路图如图乙所示。R_1 与 R_2 并联,则 $U_1=U_2=$ U,$I_1=\dfrac{U}{R_1}=\dfrac{6\text{ V}}{5\text{ Ω}}=1.2$ A,$I_2=\dfrac{U}{R_2}=\dfrac{6\text{ V}}{20\text{ Ω}}=0.3$ A。$I=I_1+$ $I_2=1.2$ A$+0.3$ A$=1.5$ A,即电流表的示数是 1.5 A。

(答案) (1)15 Ω　(2)1.5 A

第⑤部分

第 3 节　伏安法测电阻

基础知识

知识 **1** 伏安法测导体电阻
知识 **2** 伏安法测小灯泡的电阻

知识 **1** 伏安法测导体电阻

1.实验原理:欧姆定律的变形公式 $R=\dfrac{U}{I}$。

2.实验器材:电源、开关、电压表、电流表、滑动变阻器、待测电阻、导线若干。

3.实验电路图:如图所示。

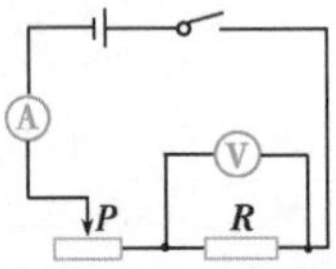

4.实验步骤:(1)按如图所示的电路图正确连接电路。

(2)检查电路无误后,闭合开关,调节滑动变阻器的滑片 P 的位置,使电阻两端的电压分别为 U_1、U_2、U_3,观察电流表对应的电流为 I_1、I_2、I_3,分别填入设计的表格中(如表)。

实验序号	电压 U/V	电流 I/A	电阻 R/Ω
1			
2			
3			

(3)根据记录的电压值和电流值求出对应的电阻值 R_1、R_2、R_3,求出它们的平均值 $R=\dfrac{R_1+R_2+R_3}{3}$。

5.滑动变阻器在本实验中的作用:(1)保护电路;(2)改变导体两端的电压。

> **温馨提示** 用电压表和电流表分别测出待测电阻两端的电压和通过其中的电流,就可以求出电阻的阻值,这种方法叫做伏安法。

例 在测量定值电阻的实验中,

(1)连接电路时开关应_____。

(2)请你用笔画线代替导线,将图中的实物电路连接完整。

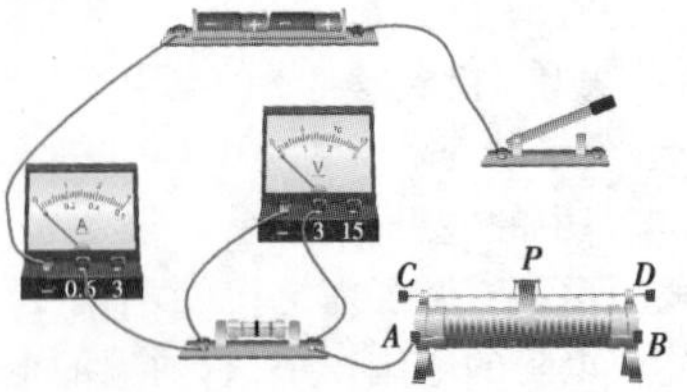

(3)闭合开关前,滑动变阻器的滑片 P 应移至_____(选填"A"或"B")端。小青闭合开关后,移动滑片 P 到某一点时,电流表示数为 0.2 A,电压表示数如图所示,为_____V,计算出的电阻值为_____Ω。

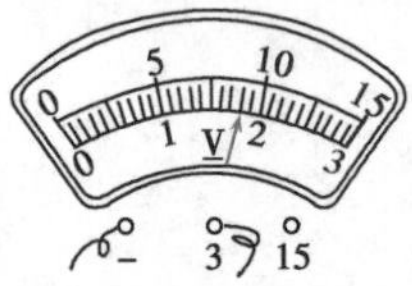

(4)小青把这一次实验测量所得的阻值作为最后的结果,你认为合适吗?_____,理由是_____。

(5)如图所示是其他两组同学根据测得数据作出的 I–U 图像,分析图像可知 R_a_____R_b(选填">"、"="或"<")。

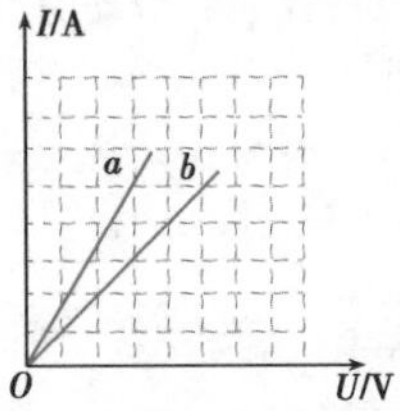

解析 (1)为保护电路元件和保证安全,连接电路时开关应断开。

(2)见答案

(3)闭合开关前滑片应置于阻值最大处,滑片应滑至 B 端。读数时应先看量程,再根据指针位置确定读数,这时电压为 1.8 V。电阻值 $R=\dfrac{U}{I}=\dfrac{1.8\text{ V}}{0.2\text{ A}}=9\ \Omega$。

(4)测量阻值时应注意多次测量取平均值以减小误差,所以把一次测量值作为最后结果是不合适的。

(5)由图像可知,在相同电压下,$I_a>I_b$。根据 $R=\dfrac{U}{I}$ 可知,$R_a<R_b$。

答案 (1)断开

(2)如图所示(滑动变阻器接上端接线柱 C 也可,图略)

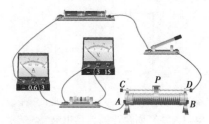

（3）B　1.8　9

（4）不合适　没有多次测量取平均值以减小误差

（5）<

知识 2　伏安法测小灯泡的电阻

1.原理:欧姆定律的变形公式 $R=\dfrac{U}{I}$。

2.实验电路图

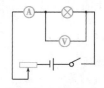

3.实验器材:电压表、电流表、电源、开关、滑动变阻器和导线。

4.注意事项

（1）在选取器材时,电流表所选用量程的最大值要大于电路中的最大电流;滑动变阻器的最大阻值应略大于或接近小灯泡的电阻。

（2）连接电路时要断开开关,并按照电压表、电流表、滑动变阻器的使用规则,将它们正确地接入电路。电压表与电流表要注意量程的选择、连接和读数,滑动变阻器也要注意规格的选择。

（3）进行实验时,在闭合开关前,要把滑动变阻器的滑片调到阻值最大处,使电路中的电流最小,目的是保证电路中的灯泡、滑动变阻器、电压表、电流表等仪器的安全。

（4）把每次测量的结果记录下来,以便最后分析、总结。

（5）分析处理数据,对于测得的各组电流和电压值,计算出相应的电阻,然后比较测得的电阻,找出其中的规律。

5.滑动变阻器的作用

①保护电路;②改变电路中的电流和小灯泡两端的电压。

例　在"伏安法测小灯泡电阻"的实验中,待测小灯泡的额定电压为 2.5 V。

（1）请用笔画线代替导线,将如图所示的实验电路中未连接部分连接好(连线不得交叉)。闭合开关前,滑动变阻器的滑片应置于_____(选填"a"或"b")端。

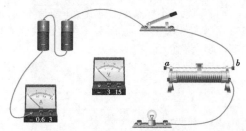

（2）闭合开关,移动滑动变阻器的滑片,记录下多组小灯泡两端不同的电压值及对应的通过小灯泡的电流值,根据这些数据在坐标纸上作出通过小灯泡的电流随其两端电压变化关系的图像(如图所示)。分析图像可知,小灯泡正常工作时的电阻为_____Ω。

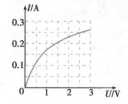

（3）从图像中还可以看出,小灯泡的电阻随电压的增大逐渐_____(选填"变大"或"变小"),从物理学角度分析,造成这一现象的原因是_____。

（4）实验中测出了小灯泡在不同电压下的电阻,有些同学认为可以进一步求出它们的平均值以减小误差。你是否同意他们的观点?请说明理由。

（5）该实验的整套装置还可以用于其他实验,请举出一例。

解析　（1）连接电路时,电流表要串联在电路中,电压表要与小灯泡并联。在闭合开关前,先要将滑动变阻器的滑片滑到阻值最大的位置,即滑到 a 端。（2）小灯泡额定电压为 2.5 V,所以小灯泡正常工作时的电阻即电压是 2.5 V 时的电阻,由题图知这时电流为 0.25 A,根据欧姆定律求出电阻为 10 Ω。（3）见答案。（4）在测电阻时,多次测量求平均值可以减小测量误差。但由于小灯泡的电阻大小与温度有关,所以小灯泡在不同工作状态下(温度不同)的电阻是不同的。因此如果要测量一个灯泡的电阻,不能用多次测量求平均值的办法。（5）见答案。

答案　（1）连线如图所示　a

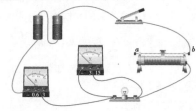

（2）10

（3）变大　电压增大时,小灯泡功率增大,灯丝温度升高

(4)不同意。小灯泡在不同温度下阻值不同,主要不是由实验误差造成的,而是其真实值发生了改变,所以取平均值无意义。

(5)测量小灯泡的电功率。

拓展知识 **知识** 特殊方法测量电阻

知识 特殊方法测量电阻

伏安法测电阻实验是初中物理最重要的实验之一,但除此方法外,还有几种测量电阻的特殊方法。

1.有电流表、无电压表的方案设计

由于不能利用电压表测出电压,所以可利用电流表多次测量电路中的电流,运用并联分流原理进行设计。

(1)利用一只电流表和一个已知阻值的定值电阻 R_0 测电阻 R_x。

①移动电表法

实验电路如图所示。

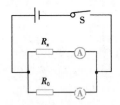

实验方法:将电流表串联在 R_x 支路上,闭合 S,读出电流表的示数 I_x;再将电流表串联在 R_0 支路上,闭合开关 S,读出电流表的示数 I_0。根据 $U_0 = U_x$,即 $I_0R_0 = I_xR_x$,得 $R_x = \dfrac{I_0R_0}{I_x}$。

②利用开关控制测量法

实验电路如图所示。

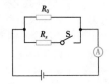

实验方法:先将开关断开,读出电流表的示数 I_0(通过 R_0 的电流);再将开关闭合读出电流表的示数 I(干路电流)。根据 $I_0R_0 = (I-I_0)R_x$,得 $R_x = \dfrac{I_0R_0}{I-I_0}$。

(2)利用一只电流表和一只已知最大阻值为 R_{max} 的滑动变阻器测电阻 R_x。

实验电路如图所示。

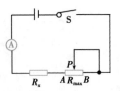

实验方法:将滑片 P 移到 A 端(此时变阻器连入电路的电阻为零),闭合开关 S,读出电流表的示数 I_1;再将滑片 P 移到 B 端(此时变阻器连入电路的电阻为 R_{max}),闭合开关 S,读出电流表的示数 I_2。

根据串联电路电压特点:$U = U_x + U_R$,即 $I_1R_x = I_2R_x + I_2R_{max}$,得 $R_x = \dfrac{I_2R_{max}}{I_1-I_2}$。

2.有电压表、无电流表的方案设计

由于不能利用电流表测出电流,所以可利用电压表多次测电压,运用串联分压原理进行设计。

(1)利用一只电压表和一个已知阻值的定值电阻 R_0 测电阻 R_x。

①移动电表法

实验电路如图所示。

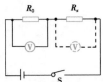

实验方法:先将电压表并联在 R_0 两端,闭合开关 S,测出 R_0 两端电压 U_0;再将电压表并联在 R_x 两端,闭合开关 S,测出 R_x 两端电压 U_x。根据串联电路的电流特点:$I_0 = I_x$,即 $\dfrac{U_0}{R_0} = \dfrac{U_x}{R_x}$,得 $R_x = \dfrac{U_x}{U_0}R_0$。

②利用开关控制测量法

实验电路如图所示。

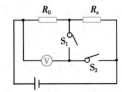

实验方法:闭合开关 S_1,断开 S_2,测得 R_0 两端的电压为 U_0;断开 S_1、闭合 S_2,测得 R_0 与 R_x 串联的总电压 U,$U_x = U - U_0$。根据 $\dfrac{U_0}{R_0} = \dfrac{U_x}{R_x} = \dfrac{U-U_0}{R_x}$,得 $R_x = \dfrac{U-U_0}{U_0}R_0$。

(2)利用一只电压表和一只已知最大阻值为 R_{max} 的滑动变阻器测电阻 R_x。

实验电路如图所示。

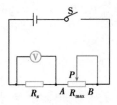

实验方法:将滑片 P 移到 A 端(此时变阻器连入电路的电阻为零),读出电压表的示数为 U(等于电源电压);再将滑片 P 移到 B 端(此时变阻器连入电路的电阻为 R_{max}),读出电压表的示数为 U_x,$U_{AB}=U-U_x$。根据 $\dfrac{U_x}{R_x}=\dfrac{U_{AB}}{R_{max}}=\dfrac{U-U_x}{R_{max}}$,得 $R_x=\dfrac{U_x}{U-U_x}R_{max}$。

例 某同学在没有电流表的情况下,利用电压表和已知阻值的定值电阻 R_0,测量未知电阻 R_x 的阻值,

图中可实现测量 R_x 阻值的正确电路图是 （　　）

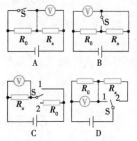

解析 B 选项中,若 S 闭合,R_x 被短路,电压表测电源电压;若 S 断开,电压表还是测量电源电压,故无法知道 R_0 和 R_x 在同一时刻的电压。A、C、D 选项则可以,故 A、C、D 都正确。

答案 ACD

方法清单　方法 伏安法测电阻实验中常见故障的排除法

方法 **伏安法测电阻实验中常见故障的排除法**

伏安法测电阻的原理如图所示。

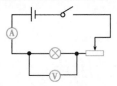

下面将可能出现的故障归纳如下:

故障一:闭合开关,灯泡不亮,电流表示数是零,电压表示数很大。

分析原因:电压表直接接在了电源两极上,小灯泡开路。

排除方法:更换好的小灯泡或检查灯泡与底座是否接触良好。

故障二:闭合开关后发现小灯泡不亮,电流表、压表都没有示数。

分析原因:电路中除小灯泡和电压表外的某处接触不良或者在此同时小灯泡的灯丝也断了。

排除方法:将连接各个电路元件的接线处重新连接,若同时小灯泡的灯丝断了则更换好的小灯泡。

故障三:闭合开关 S,发现小灯泡不亮,同时电流表和电压表有示数,但非常小。

分析原因:电流表和电压表有示数说明电路是通路,小灯泡不亮,是因为加在小灯泡两端的电压太小,导致通过小灯泡的电流太小而不亮,可能是电源电压太低或滑动变阻器接入电路中的阻值过大。

排除方法:可以适当提高电源电压或将滑动变阻器接入电路中的阻值调小。

故障四:闭合开关 S 后,小灯泡亮,发现电流表和电压表的指针向左偏转。

分析原因:指针向左偏转说明电流表和电压表的正负接线柱接反了。

排除方法:将接电流表和电压表的正负接线柱的接线端对调即可。

故障五:连接好实验电路后,闭合开关并移动滑动变阻器的滑片,发现小灯泡变亮,电流表示数变大时,电压表示数反而变小;小灯泡变暗,电流表示数变小时,电压表示数反而变大。

分析原因:电压表并联在滑动变阻器两端。

排除方法:只要将电压表改接到小灯泡的两端即可。

故障六:将实验电路连接好后,闭合开关 S,发现小灯泡特别亮,并且无论怎样移动滑动变阻器滑片,灯泡亮度不变。

分析原因:滑动变阻器接线有误。

排除方法:将滑动变阻器一个接线柱接法纠正即可。

例 图甲是小明在测定灯泡正常发光时灯丝电阻的实验电路图。已知电源电压恒为 6 V,灯泡额定电压为 3.6 V,正常发光时,通过灯泡的电流约为 0.32 A。

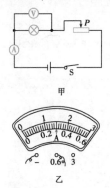

甲

乙

(1)小明选择电流表的量程为 0~0.6 A,电压表的量程应选_____V;

(2)当开关闭合后,发现小灯泡不亮,经过分析,有些同学猜想了一些可能的原因,如表所示。请根据猜想,在表中写出对应的电压表和电流表的示数情况。

猜想	电压表示数情况	电流表示数情况
灯泡断路		
灯泡短路		

(3)正确连接电路后,闭合开关,小明移动滑片 P,灯泡正常发光时,发现电压表指针偏转角度很小。根据测量时电表示数超过所用量程的一半可以减小误差的原则,小明在不增减实验器材的情况下,重新设计电路,顺利完成了实验。请在虚线框内画出他重新设计的电路图。

(4)正确连接新的电路后,移动滑片 P,当灯泡正常发光时,电流表的示数如图乙所示,是_____A,此时,灯丝的阻值是_____Ω。

解析 (1)灯泡的额定电压是 3.6 V,所以电压表的量程应选 0~15 V。(2)小灯泡断路时,电路中电流接近零,电压表示数接近 6 V;小灯泡短路时,与小灯泡并联的电压表也被短路,其示数为零,电流表有示数。(3)电源电压为 6 V。当灯泡正常发光时其两端的电压是 3.6 V,灯泡与变阻器串联,此时变阻器两端的电压为 6 V−3.6 V=2.4 V,可选用量程为 0~3 V 的电压表测量变阻器两端的电压,当变阻器两端电压达到 2.4 V 时说明灯泡正常发光,这样可以减小误差。(4)灯丝电阻 $R=U/I=3.6$ V/0.3 A $=12$ Ω。

答案 (1)0~15

(2)见表

猜想	电压表示数情况	电流表示数情况
灯泡断路	示数接近 6 V	示数接近零
灯泡短路	示数为零	有示数

(3)电路如图所示

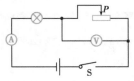

(4)0.3 12

第4节　欧姆定律和安全用电

知识清单

基础知识

知识 **1** 安全电压
知识 **2** 用欧姆定律分析短路现象
知识 **3** 注意防雷

知识 **1** 安全电压

1.加在人体上但不会对人体造成危害的电压,称为安全电压。**不高于 36 V 的电压对人体是安全的,是安全电压。**

温馨提示

不高于 36 V 是指低于或等于 36 V。

2.我国家庭电路的电压是 220 V,动力电路的电压为 380 V,高压输电线路的电压可以达到 10^5 V,都远远高于安全电压。

知识 **2** 用欧姆定律分析短路现象

1.短路分为电源短路和用电器短路两类

(1)电源短路:导线不通过用电器而直接连到电源两极上。

(2)用电器短路:如图所示,灯泡 L_1 的两端由一根导线直接连接而发生短路。

2.分析

(1)电源短路:导线电阻极小,可忽略不计,根据 $I=\dfrac{U}{R}$ 可知,电流 I 很大,会烧坏电源和导线。

(2)用电器短路:图中与 L_1 并联的这段导线通过

灯泡 L_2 接在电源上,这段导线中就有一定的电流 I,我们对这段导线应用欧姆定律,导线两端的电压 $U = IR$,由于 $R \to 0$,说明加在它两端的电压 $U \to 0$,那么与之并联的灯泡 L_1 两端的电压 $U_1 = U \to 0$,对 L_1 应用欧姆定律知,通过 L_1 的电流 $I_1 = \dfrac{U_1}{R_1} \to 0$,可见,电流几乎全部通过这段导线,而没有电流通过 L_1,因此 L_1 不会亮,这种情况我们称为灯泡 L_1 被短路。

如果我们在与 L_1 并联的导线中串联一只电流表,由于电流表的电阻也是很小的,结果与上述相同,那么电流表中虽然有电流,电流表有读数,但不是 L_1 中的电流,电路变成了电流表与 L_2 串联,电流表测过 L_2 的电流,L_1 被短路了。

例 物理知识的应用无处不在。如图所示,甲、乙两地相距 L,两地之间沿直线架设了两条输电线,输电线每千米的电阻是 R_0。现输电导线某处发生了短路,为了尽快确定短路位置,及时修复供电,机智的检修员在甲地利用实验室常用的电学仪器,根据伏安法进行了检测,并根据检测数据确定了短路位置距甲地的距离 s。

(1)请你在甲处的虚线框内把检测需要的仪器与两条输电线连接起来,组成检测电路。(所需仪器用元件符号表示)

(2)请根据学过的电学知识,推导求出短路位置距甲地的距离 $s =$ _____。(用已知量、检测量表示,检测电路导线的电阻忽略不计)

并写出推导过程。(检测量用字母表示,推导过程要有必要的文字说明)

解析 (1)如图所示(电路中无开关也可以,电压表、电流表、电源符合题意即可)

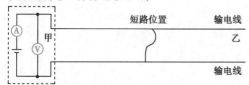

(2)推导过程:

假设电压表示数为 U,电流表示数为 I,

甲处到短路处输电线电阻为 $R = \dfrac{U}{I}$

甲处到短路处输电线的总长度 $L = \dfrac{R}{R_0} = \dfrac{\frac{U}{I}}{R_0} = \dfrac{U}{IR_0}$

甲处到短路位置的距离 $s = \dfrac{L}{2} = \dfrac{\frac{U}{IR_0}}{2} = \dfrac{U}{2IR_0}$

答案 (1)、(2)见解析

知识 3 注意防雷

1.雷电现象及破坏作用

雷电是大气中一种剧烈的放电现象。云层之间、云层和大地之间的电压可达几百万伏至几亿伏。根据 $I = \dfrac{U}{R}$,云层与大地之间的电压非常高,放电时会产生很大的电流,雷电通过树木、建筑物时,巨大的热量和空气的振动都会使它们受到严重的破坏。因此,我们应注意防雷。避雷针就可以起到防雷的作用。

2.避雷针

高大建筑物的顶端都有针状的金属物,通过很粗的金属线与大地相连,可以防雷,叫做避雷针。高压输电线最上面的两条导线也是用来防雷的。

拓展知识 **知识** 电流对人体的作用特征

知识 电流对人体的作用特征

电流 I/mA	作用特征	
	50~60 Hz 交变电流	恒定电流
0.6~1.5	开始有感觉——手轻微颤抖	无感觉
2~3	手指强烈颤抖	无感觉
5~7	手部痉挛	感觉痒和热
8~10	手已难于摆脱电极,但还能摆脱,手指尖到手腕剧痛	热感觉增强
20~25	手迅速麻痹,不能摆脱电极,剧痛,呼吸困难	热感觉大大增强,手部肌肉轻微收缩
50~80	呼吸麻痹,心房开始震颤	强烈的热感觉,手部肌肉收缩、痉挛,呼吸困难
90~100	呼吸麻痹,延续 3 s 就会造成心脏麻痹	呼吸麻痹
300 以上	作用 0.1 s 以上时,呼吸和心脏麻痹,机体组织遭到电流的热破坏	—

温馨提示 研究表明,电对人体造成的伤害程度与通过人体的电流的大小及持续时间有关。

第⑤部分

方法 利用欧姆定律解释生活中的触电现象

触电是电路中的电流过大造成的,根据欧姆定律 $I=\dfrac{U}{R}$ 可知:电阻一定时,电压越高,电流越大;或电压一定时,电阻越小,电流越大。生活中一般是由于电阻变小而造成触电事故。

例 现代家庭电气化程度越来越高,用电安全是一个十分突出的问题。如表提供一组部分人体电阻值:

测量项目	完全干燥时电阻/kΩ	出汗或潮湿时电阻/kΩ
手与手之间	3.6	0.9
手与脚之间	5.4	1.08
手与塑料鞋底之间	14.4	1.448

(1)分析表中数据可得到结论:_____
_____。

(2)若对人体安全的电流为 10 mA 以下,那么干燥人体的安全电压是_____,潮湿人体的安全电压是_____。

(3)从计算结果中可得出结论:_____
_____。

解析 (1)从表中可以看出,人体出汗或潮湿时,人的手与手、手与脚、手与塑料鞋底之间的电阻比干燥时的电阻都小得多,说明人体的电阻随人体皮肤湿度的增加而减小。

(2)对人体的安全电压要根据人体最小的电阻和安全电流求出,$I = 10$ mA $= 0.01$ A,人体干燥时的电阻选 $R = 3.6$ kΩ $= 3\,600$ Ω,安全电压 $U = IR = 0.01$ A × $3\,600$ Ω $= 36$ V,人体潮湿时的安全电压 $U' = 0.01$ A × 900 Ω $= 9$ V。

(3)根据上述数据可知,人体潮湿时的安全电压降低了(或人体潮湿时,原来的安全电压也不安全了)。

答案 (1)人体的电阻随人体皮肤湿度的增加而减小 (2)不高于 36 V 不高于 9 V (3)人体潮湿时,原来的安全电压也不安全了

第17章

电功率

知识梳理

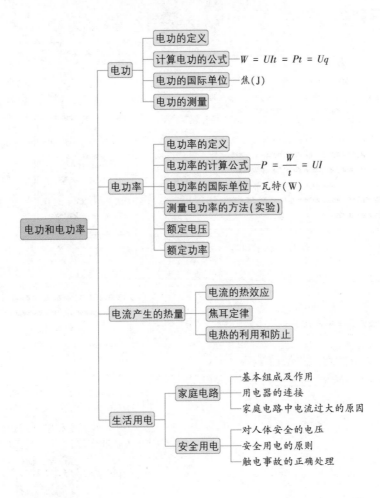

电功和电功率
- 电功
  - 电功的定义
  - 计算电功的公式 — $W = UIt = Pt = Uq$
  - 电功的国际单位 — 焦(J)
  - 电功的测量
- 电功率
  - 电功率的定义
  - 电功率的计算公式 — $P = \dfrac{W}{t} = UI$
  - 电功率的国际单位 — 瓦特(W)
  - 测量电功率的方法(实验)
  - 额定电压
  - 额定功率
- 电流产生的热量
  - 电流的热效应
  - 焦耳定律
  - 电热的利用和防止
- 生活用电
  - 家庭电路
    - 基本组成及作用
    - 用电器的连接
    - 家庭电路中电流过大的原因
  - 安全用电
    - 对人体安全的电压
    - 安全用电的原则
    - 触电事故的正确处理

第⑤部分

第1节　电能

基础知识

知识 **1** 电能与电功
知识 **2** 电能表

知识 1 电能与电功

知识点	内容
电能的转化	电能可以转化成其他形式的能。例如,点亮小灯泡,电能转化为光能;给电热器通电,电能转化为内能;给小电动机通电,电能转化为机械能;给电视通电,电能转化为声能和光能
电功	电能转化为其他形式的能的过程是电流做功的过程。电流做了多少功,就有多少电能转化为其他形式的能,或消耗了多少电能
电功的公式及推导公式	公式:$W=UIt$　电流所做的功跟电压、电流和通电时间成正比
	推导公式:$W=\dfrac{U^2}{R}t$,$W=I^2Rt$　适用范围:纯电阻电路
电功单位	国际单位:焦耳(J)
	常用单位:千瓦时(kW·h)
	关系:$1\ kW·h=3.6×10^6\ J$

例 如图所示电路,电源电压恒定不变,电阻$R_1=20\ \Omega$,$R_2=60\ \Omega$。当S断开时,电流表的示数为0.3 A;当S闭合时,电流表的示数为_____A,电路1分钟内总共产生的热量为_____J。

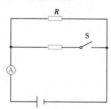

解析 S断开时,电源电压$U=I_1R_1=0.3\ A×20\ \Omega=6\ V$。

S闭合时,电路总电流$I=I_1+I_2=\dfrac{U}{R_1}+\dfrac{U}{R_2}=0.4\ A$,即电流表的示数。

产生热量$Q=W=UIt=6\ V×0.4\ A×60\ s=144\ J$。
或采用如下方法计算热量:

$Q=W_1+W_2=UI_1t+UI_2t$
$=6\ V×0.3\ A×60\ s+6\ V×0.1\ A×60\ s$
$=144\ J$。

答案 0.4　144

知识 2 电能表

作用	用来测量用电器在某一段时间内消耗的电能
铭牌及其意义	"220 V"是说这个电能表应该在220 V的电路中使用;"10(20)A"是说这个电能表的标定电流是10 A,额定最大电流为20 A,工作时电流不能超过20 A;"50 Hz"是说这个电能表在50 Hz的交流电路中使用;"600 revs/(kW·h)"是说电路中每消耗1 kW·h的电能,电能表上的转盘转过600转
读数方法	①电能表前后两次的示数之差就是用电器在对应的这段时间内消耗的电能;②最右边方框内数字为小数点后的位数;③上图中若月初的数字为3 567.3 kW·h,月末电能表数字如图中所示,则本月所耗电能$W=3\ 687.3\ kW·h-3\ 567.3\ kW·h=120\ kW·h$
种类	除了目前使用较普遍的机械式电能表之外,常用的还有IC卡电能表(读数是由液晶板显示的)

例 如图所示是单相电子式预付费电能表,关于它的技术参数和作用,下列叙述正确的是 (　　)

220 V 5(30) A 50 Hz
3 200 imp/(kW·h)
NO. 2005-263184

A.220 V 表示电能表适用的工作电压

B.5 A 表示允许通过电能表的最大电流

C.3 200 imp/(kW·h)表示电路中每消耗1 kW·h电能,电能表的表盘转3 200转

D.电能表是测量电功率的仪表

解析 5 A是电能表的标定电流,30 A才是允许通过的最大电流;3 200 imp/(kW·h)表示电路中用电器每消耗1 kW·h电能,电能表上指示灯闪3 200

次;电能表是测电功或电能的仪表,而不是测电功率的仪表。

（答案） A

拓展知识　知识 利用电能表计算电功

知识 利用电能表计算电功

根据电能表的转数或指示灯闪烁次数可以求出通过家用电器的电流在某段时间内做的功,或消耗的电能。在计算时通常有两种方法:

1.根据每千瓦时的转数和表盘在一段时间内的转数,或每千瓦时指示灯闪烁次数和表盘在一段时间内指示灯闪烁次数,求出这段时间内消耗的电能。

2.由于电能表的转盘的转数与电流做的功(或消耗的电能)成正比,因此可以先统一单位,然后列出比例式,再求解答案。

例 下课后王老师去关闭微机房的总电闸时,发现如图所示的电能表的转盘在缓慢地转动,他利用手表估测了一下,2 min 转盘转动了 5 转,那么 2 min 内消耗了_____J电能;经检查发现,原来机房内共有 20 台型号相同的电脑显示器处于待机状态,则一台电脑显示器的待机功率约为_____W。

（解析） 2 min 内消耗电能为 $\frac{5}{2\,500} \times 3.6 \times 10^6$ J $= 7.2 \times 10^3$ J;每台显示器的待机功率 $P = \frac{W}{20t} = \frac{7.2 \times 10^3 \text{ J}}{20 \times 120 \text{ s}} = 3$ W。

（答案） 7.2×10^3　3

方法清单　方法 控制变量法探究电流做功与哪些因素有关

方法 控制变量法探究电流做功与哪些因素有关

1.采用串联电路,控制通过两段电阻丝的电流相同,在通电时间相同的情况下,探究电流做功与电压大小之间的关系。

2.采用并联电路,使加在两段电阻丝上的电压相同,在通电时间相同的情况下,探究电流做功与电流大小之间的关系。

例1 对于"电流做功与哪些因素有关"的问题,刘星同学作了如下猜想:

猜想 A:电流做功可能与电压有关;

猜想 B:电流做功可能与电流有关;

猜想 C:电流做功可能与通电时间有关。

为了验证自己的猜想,他选择了如图甲所示的装置(除电阻丝阻值不同外,其余条件均相同)及电源、开关、电压表、导线若干。他将两电阻丝串联后接入电路,如图乙所示。

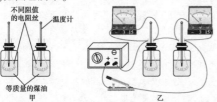

(1)将两电阻丝串联接入电路的目的是控制通过电阻丝的_____和通电时间相同,他采用的科学探究方法是_____。

(2)接通电路前,他想:通电一段时间后观察温度计示数的变化,若两支温度计示数变化不同,则说明电流做功与电阻丝两端的_____有关,这就验证了猜想_____。

（解析） 在通过实验探究电流做功与某个因素的关系时,应采用控制变量法。实验装置采用串联的目的是使通过两电阻丝的电流和通电时间相同(同时接通,同时断开),这是为了研究电流做功与电压的关系,阻值大的电阻两端电压大。电流做功时将电能转化为煤油的内能,因此电流做功的多少可以通过煤油温度的变化显示出来。若通电一段时间后,两瓶中煤油温度变化不同,则说明电流做功与电压有关。

（答案） (1)电流　控制变量法　(2)电压　A

点拨　电流做功的多少通过煤油的温度变化显示出来,这种方法为转换法。

例2 利用如图所示的电路可以验证电功与电流的关系。

(1)图中两只灯泡的连接方式是_____联,它们工作时的电阻要_____(选填"相同"或"不同")。

(2)小明正确操作,验证了实验的结论。支持该结论的实验现象是_____。

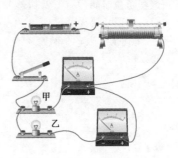

（解析）（1）由题图可知,两灯泡是并联的;探究电功与电流的关系时应控制电压和通电时间相同而电流不同,故两灯泡的电阻应该不同。

（2）在电压和通电时间相同时,电流越大,电流做的功越多,所以如果电流表示数较大的支路中灯泡较亮,则可以验证实验结论。

（答案）（1）并　不同　（2）电流表示数较大的支路中灯泡较亮

第2节　电功率

知识清单

基础知识
知识 1 电功率
知识 2 额定功率和实际功率
知识 3 串、并联电路的总功率

知识 1 电功率

1.定义

电流所做的功与所用时间之比叫做电功率。电功率是表示电流做功快慢的物理量。

2.电功率的计算公式

(1)定义式:$P=\dfrac{W}{t}$;

(2)常用公式:$P=\dfrac{W}{t}=\dfrac{UIt}{t}=UI$,即$P=UI$;

(3)推导公式:$P=I^2R=\dfrac{U^2}{R}$(只适用于纯电阻电路)。

3.电功率的单位

W 和 kW,1 W=1 V·A,1 kW=1 000 W。

例 关于电功和电功率,下列说法正确的是 （　）

A.电流通过用电器做功越多,其电功率越大

B.电功率越大的用电器,单位时间内电流做功越多

C.电功率是表示电流做功多少的物理量

D.千瓦时是电功率的单位,千瓦是电功的单位

（解析）电流通过用电器做功多,其电功率不一定大,还需要看做功的时间,A 错;根据 $W=Pt$ 可知:电功率越大的用电器单位时间内电流做功越多,B 正确;电功率是表示电流做功快慢的物理量,C 错;千瓦时是电功的单位,千瓦是电功率的单位,D 错。

（答案）B

知识 2 额定功率和实际功率

知识点	内容
额定功率	(1)用电器正常工作时的电压,即用电器上标明的电压值就是额定电压;(2)用电器在额定电压下正常工作时的电功率,即用电器上标明的电功率就是额定功率
实际功率	(1)用电器实际工作时的电压叫实际电压,它可能与额定电压相等,也可能比额定电压大或者小;(2)用电器在实际电压下的电功率叫做实际功率,它可能与额定功率相等,也可能比额定功率大或者小
灯泡亮暗的比较（实际功率越大,灯泡越亮）	若灯泡都能正常发光,则额定功率大的比较亮。因为实际功率等于额定功率。额定功率大的灯泡,实际功率就大,灯泡就亮
	若灯泡串联且不能正常发光,电阻大的灯泡较亮。在串联电路中,由于各处电流相等,根据 $P=I^2R$ 知灯泡的电阻越大,灯泡的实际功率越大
	若灯泡是并联的且不能正常发光,电阻小的灯泡较亮。在并联电路中,由于各支路两端的电压相等,根据 $P=\dfrac{U^2}{R}$,灯泡的电阻越小,灯泡的实际功率就越大,灯泡就越亮

温馨提示
（1）实际生活中的照明电路是并联电路,如果并联的用电器越多,并联部分的总电阻就越小。在总电压不变的条件下,电路中的总电流就越大,因此输电线上分担的电压就越大。这样,分给用电器的电压就越小,每个用电器消耗的功率也就越小。所以开的灯少时比开的灯多时要亮些。晚上七八点钟,大家都用电灯照明,所以电灯发的光就比深夜时暗。

（2）额定功率是用电器生产后就已经确定的,它是唯一的,是不可变的;而实际功率随着实际电压的变化而变化,是可变的,可以有很多个。

例 将正常工作的"200 V　25 W"白炽灯 L_1 和"36 V　25 W"白炽灯 L_2 相比较(设两灯丝长度、材料相同),下述说法正确的是　　　（　）

A.L_1 的灯丝细,但比 L_2 亮

B.L_1 的灯丝粗,但比 L_2 亮

C.L_1 的灯丝细,两灯一样亮

D.L_1 的灯丝粗,两灯一样亮

解析 灯泡亮度由灯的实际功率决定,因两灯正常工作,则两灯的实际功率均等于其额定功率,可排除 A、B 两选项。根据 $P_额=U_额^2/R$,$P_额$ 相同,$U_额$ 大的电阻大,因长度、材料相同,故额定电压大的灯丝细,C 正确,D 错误。

答案 C

知识 3 串、并联电路的总功率

1.串联电路的总功率

因为 $P_1=IU_1$,$P_2=IU_2$

$P=IU=I(U_1+U_2)=IU_1+IU_2$

所以 $P=P_1+P_2$

即串联电路总功率等于各串联用电器的电功率之和。

串联电路电功率的分配:

因为 $P_1=IU_1$,$P_2=IU_2$

所以 $\dfrac{P_1}{P_2}=\dfrac{IU_1}{IU_2}=\dfrac{U_1}{U_2}$

又因为 $\dfrac{U_1}{U_2}=\dfrac{R_1}{R_2}$,所以 $\dfrac{P_1}{P_2}=\dfrac{R_1}{R_2}$

即串联电路中,电功率的分配跟电阻成正比。

2.并联电路的总功率

因为 $P_1=I_1U$,$P_2=I_2U$

$P=IU=(I_1+I_2)U=I_1U+I_2U$

所以 $P=P_1+P_2$

即并联电路的总功率等于各并联用电器的电功率之和。

并联电路电功率的分配:

因为 $P_1=I_1U$,$P_2=I_2U$

所以 $\dfrac{P_1}{P_2}=\dfrac{I_1U}{I_2U}=\dfrac{I_1}{I_2}$

又因为 $\dfrac{I_1}{I_2}=\dfrac{R_2}{R_1}$,所以 $\dfrac{P_1}{P_2}=\dfrac{R_2}{R_1}$

即并联电路中,电功率的分配跟电阻成反比。

例1 如图所示,电源电压恒定,小灯泡 L_1、L_2 均标有"6 V　3 W"的字样(忽略温度对灯丝电阻的影响),当开关 S_1、S_2 都闭合时,灯泡 L_1 正常发光,则电源电压为　　　V;当开关 S_1 闭合,S_2 断开时,电路的总功率为　　　W。

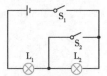

解析 L_1、L_2 均标有"6 V　3 W",阻值 $R_1=R_2=\dfrac{U^2}{P}=12\ \Omega$

S_1、S_2 都闭合时,L_2 被短路,L_1 正常发光,则 $U_总=6$ V

S_1 闭合、S_2 断开时,L_1 与 L_2 串联,则

$P_总=\dfrac{U_总^2}{R_1+R_2}=\dfrac{(6\ \text{V})^2}{12\ \Omega+12\ \Omega}=1.5$ W。

答案 6　1.5

例2 如图所示是电阻甲和乙的 I–U 图像。由图可知:电阻乙的阻值为　　　Ω。若将电阻甲和乙并联后接在电压为 6 V 的电源两端时,则干路的总电阻为　　　Ω,总电功率为　　　W。

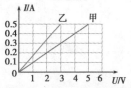

解析 根据欧姆定律由图像可知电阻乙的阻值 $R_乙=\dfrac{U}{I}=\dfrac{3\ \text{V}}{0.5\ \text{A}}=6\ \Omega$。甲、乙两定值电阻并联的总电阻在不同的电源电压下阻值都相同,由图像可知,3 V 的电源电压对应的干路电流是 0.5 A+0.3 A=0.8 A,$R_总=\dfrac{U_总}{I_总}=\dfrac{3\ \text{V}}{0.8\ \text{A}}=3.75\ \Omega$,当电源电压为 6 V 时,并联的总电阻不变,仍为 3.75 Ω(也可由图像计算出 $R_甲=10\ \Omega$,根据并联电阻的公式 $\dfrac{1}{R_总}=\dfrac{1}{R_甲}+\dfrac{1}{R_乙}$,计算出 $R_总=3.75\ \Omega$)。此时干路的总电流为 $I_总{}'=\dfrac{U_总{}'}{R_总}=\dfrac{6\ \text{V}}{3.75\ \Omega}=1.6$ A,$P_总=U_总{}'I_总{}'=6$ V×1.6 A=9.6 W。

答案 6　3.75　9.6

拓展知识

知识① 灯泡铭牌问题

知识② 灯丝通常在开灯瞬间被烧断的原因

知识 1 灯泡铭牌问题

"铭牌问题"是电功率知识与实际生活相结合的热点问题,做这类题目时,首先要读懂用电器的"铭牌"。

如图为某灯泡上的铭牌:"PZ"是"普通照明灯泡"中"普"和"照"的汉语拼音的第一个字母,表示灯

泡的型号;另外可知:$U_{\text{额}} = 220$ V,$P_{\text{额}} = 25$ W。

例 L_1 灯规格为"6 V　3 W",L_2 灯规格为"3 V　3 W",忽略灯丝电阻变化,则下列说法正确的是 (　　)

A.L_1 与 L_2 灯丝电阻之比为 2∶1

B.两灯串联,当电路中电流为 0.5 A 时,L_2 灯两端电压为 3 V

C.两灯并联,当一个灯正常发光时,通过另一个灯的电流为 1 A

D.两灯并联在 3 V 电压下,L_1 灯与 L_2 灯消耗的实际功率之比为 1∶4

解析 $R_1 = \dfrac{U_1^2}{P_1} = \dfrac{(6\text{ V})^2}{3\text{ W}} = 12$ Ω,$R_2 = \dfrac{U_2^2}{P_2} = \dfrac{(3\text{ V})^2}{3\text{ W}} = 3$ Ω,$\dfrac{R_1}{R_2} = \dfrac{4}{1}$,A 项错误。两灯串联时,$U_2 = IR_2 = 0.5$ A×3 Ω = 1.5 V,B 项错误。两灯并联,一个灯

正常发光,则电源电压应为 3 V,L_2 正常发光,则通过 L_1 的电流 $I_1' = \dfrac{U}{R_1} = \dfrac{3\text{ V}}{12\text{ Ω}} = 0.25$ A,C 项错误。两灯并联在 3 V 电压下时,$\dfrac{P_1}{P_2} = \dfrac{R_2}{R_1} = \dfrac{3\text{ Ω}}{12\text{ Ω}} = \dfrac{1}{4}$,D 正确。

答案 D

知识 2 灯丝通常在开灯瞬间被烧断的原因

1.导体的电阻随温度的变化而变化,金属导体的电阻随温度的升高而增大,一般金属导体温度变化几摄氏度或几十摄氏度,电阻变化不过百分之几欧,可忽略不计。

2.电灯的灯丝(钨丝)不发光时温度较低,电阻较小,正常发光时灯丝的温度较高,达2 000 ℃左右,电阻值就要增大许多倍。在刚接通电路的瞬间,灯丝的温度还没有升高,由于电阻还很小,通过灯丝的电流要比正常发光时大得多,根据 $P = U^2/R$,这时实际功率很大,远远超过正常工作时的功率,所以通常灯丝容易在开灯时的瞬间烧断。

方法清单

方法1 公式法计算电功率
方法2 巧用电阻不变求实际功率

方法 1 公式法计算电功率

1.$P = \dfrac{W}{t}$

这是电功率的定义式,此公式适用于各种用电器和电路。

2.$P = UI$

这是电功率的决定式,即电功率是由用电器两端的电压和通过它的电流之积来决定的。此公式适用于所有电路,它是"伏安法"测小灯泡电功率的理论依据。当然这个公式的最大用处还是用来计算各类用电器实际消耗的电功率或电路的总功率。

3.导出公式:$P = I^2R$,$P = \dfrac{U^2}{R}$

这两个公式是利用 $I = \dfrac{U}{R}$ 和 $P = UI$ 推导得出的,只适用于纯电阻电路(即用电器把消耗的电能全部转化成内能的电路)的电功率计算。

例 如图甲所示,电源电压保持不变,闭合开关 S,变阻器滑片 P 从 a 端滑到 b 端的整个过程中,电流表示数 I 与电压表示数 U 的关系图像如图乙所示。由

图像可知,R_1 的阻值为 _____ Ω;当电路中的电流为 0.2 A 时,R_1 与 R_2 消耗的电功率之比为 _____。

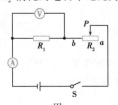

甲

乙

解析 由变阻器滑片 P 从 a 端滑到 b 端过程中,电流表与电压表示数关系的图像可知,电路中电源电压为 3 V,R_1 的阻值:$R_1 = \dfrac{U}{I} = \dfrac{3\text{ V}}{0.3\text{ A}} = 10$ Ω;由图像可知,当电路中电流为 0.2 A 时,R_1 两端电压为2 V,则 R_2 两端电压 $U_2 = U - U_1 = 3$ V − 2 V = 1 V,故 R_1 与 R_2 消耗的功率之比:$\dfrac{P_1}{P_2} = \dfrac{U_1 I}{U_2 I} = \dfrac{2\text{ V} \times 0.2\text{ A}}{1\text{ V} \times 0.2\text{ A}} = \dfrac{2}{1}$。

答案 10　2∶1

方法 2 巧用电阻不变求实际功率

由用电器铭牌上的 $U_额$、$P_额$，求出电阻，即由 $P = \dfrac{U^2}{R}$ 解出 $R = \dfrac{U_额^2}{P_额}$；电阻不变时，当求不同电压下的实际功率时，可依据 $P_实 = \dfrac{U_实^2}{R}$ 求得。

例 如图是某款有加热和保温功能的电热饮水机电路原理图，机内有温控开关 S_0。该饮水机的部分参数已知：额定电压为 220 V，加热时的总功率为880 W，保温时的功率为 40 W，R_1、R_2 为加热电阻丝（假设它们的阻值不变）。

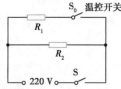

求：(计算结果若不能整除，保留一位小数)

(1)当 S 和 S_0 闭合时，饮水机处在什么状态？此时电路的总电流是多大？

(2)在加热状态下，电阻丝 R_1 的阻值为多少？

(3)傍晚用电高峰期，若实际电压只有 200 V 时，饮水机加热的实际总功率是多大？

解析 (1)当 S、S_0 同时闭合时电路消耗的功率最大，饮水机处于加热状态。

根据题目可知，总电压 $U_总$ 是 220 V，总功率 $P_总$ 是 880 W，总电流是：

$$I_总 = \frac{P_总}{U_总} = \frac{880\ \text{W}}{220\ \text{V}} = 4\ \text{A}$$

(2)保温时，S 闭合、S_0 断开，电路中只有 R_2 工作，其功率为 40 W。

在加热状态下，电阻 R_1 消耗的功率为

$$P_1 = P_总 - P_保温 = 880\ \text{W} - 40\ \text{W} = 840\ \text{W}$$

因为 R_1 和 R_2 并联，所以 $U_1 = 220$ V

$$R_1 = \frac{U_1^2}{P_1} = \frac{(220\ \text{V})^2}{840\ \text{W}} \approx 57.6\ \Omega$$

(3)由题目可知，$U_实 = 200$ V，$U_额 = 220$ V，$P_总 = 880$ W

因为饮水机总电阻不变，所以 $\dfrac{U_额^2}{P_总} = \dfrac{U_实^2}{P_{实总}}$

即：$\dfrac{P_{实总}}{P_总} = \left(\dfrac{U_实}{U_额}\right)^2$

$$P_{实总} = \left(\frac{U_实}{U_额}\right)^2 \times P_总 = \left(\frac{200\ \text{V}}{220\ \text{V}}\right)^2 \times 880\ \text{W} \approx 727.3\ \text{W}$$

答案 (1)加热 4 A (2)57.6 Ω (3)727.3 W

第 3 节　测量小灯泡的电功率

知识清单

基础知识　知识 1 伏安法测小灯泡的电功率
知识 2 伏安法测小灯泡电阻与测小灯泡电功率的异同点

知识 1 伏安法测小灯泡的电功率

实验原理	$P = UI$
实验电路图	
实验器材	电源、滑动变阻器、电压表、电流表、小灯泡、灯座、开关、导线若干

实验步骤	(1)按设计的电路图连接实物,并设计实验记录表格 (2)检查电路无误后,闭合开关S,移动滑动变阻器的滑片,观察电压表的示数。当电压表的示数等于小灯泡的额定电压时,停止滑动,并记下电流表的示数 (3)调节滑动变阻器,使小灯泡两端的电压为额定电压的1.2倍,观察小灯泡的发光情况,并记下电压表和电流表的示数 (4)调节滑动变阻器,使小灯泡两端的电压低于额定电压的1/5,观察小灯泡的发光情况,并记下电压表和电流表的示数 (5)整理实验器材

实验表格

	电压 $U(V)$	电流 $I(A)$	电功率 $P(W)$	灯泡亮度
$U_实 = U_额$				
$U_实 > U_额$				
$U_实 < U_额$				

实验结论	若 $U_实 > U_额$,则 $P_实 > P_额$,小灯泡很亮 若 $U_实 = U_额$,则 $P_实 = P_额$,小灯泡正常发光 若 $U_实 < U_额$,则 $P_实 < P_额$,小灯泡很暗
注意事项	(1)选择的器材规格要合适,例如滑动变阻器允许通过的最大电流要大于灯泡的额定电流;(2)连接电路时开关断开,滑动变阻器的滑片滑到阻值最大处;(3)使小灯泡的电压高于额定电压时,要注意观察电压表示数的变化,以免电压过高,烧坏小灯泡

温馨提示 伏安法测功率与伏安法测电阻以及欧姆定律实验中探究 I 与 U 和 I 与 R 关系时所用电路图相同;电路中都是一个电阻(或灯泡)与一个滑动变阻器串联,再用 Ⓐ测电流,Ⓥ测电阻(或灯泡)两端的电压。

例 在测量标有 2.5 V 小灯泡额定功率的实验中:

(1)请你用笔画线代替导线,将图甲中的电路连接完整。

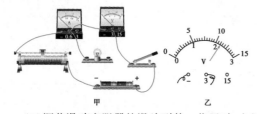

(2)调节滑动变阻器的滑片到某一位置时,电压表示数如图乙所示,为了测量小灯泡的额定功率,应将滑片向_____(填"左"或"右")端移动。当小灯泡正常发光时,电流表的示数是 0.28 A,则小灯泡的额定功率为_____ W。

(3)实验时若发现灯泡发光,电流表指示正常,电压表示数为 0,产生这种现象的原因可能是_____。

解析 (1)小灯泡串联在电路中,电压表与灯泡并联,电路连接见答案。

(2)由乙图可知:小灯泡两端的电压为 2.2 V,若使小灯泡两端电压增大到 2.5 V,滑动变阻器分担的电压应减小一些;根据串联分压可知,其电阻应减小一些。因此滑片 P 应向右移动,此时 $P = UI = 2.5 \text{ V} \times 0.28 \text{ A} = 0.7 \text{ W}$。

(3)电流表和灯泡正常工作,说明串联电路无故障,电压表示数为 0 的原因应是电压表断路。

答案 (1)如图所示

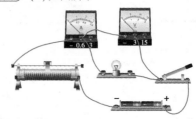

(2)右 0.7

(3)电压表断路

		测小灯泡的电功率	测电阻
相同点	所测物理量	灯泡两端的电压(U)和通过灯泡的电流(I)	
	实验器材	电源、滑动变阻器、电压表、电流表、小灯泡、灯座、开关,导线若干	
	电路图		
	连接电路时	开关断开,滑动变阻器的滑片滑到阻值最大处	
不同点	原理	$P=UI$	$R=\dfrac{U}{I}$
	计算公式	$P=UI$	$R=\dfrac{U}{I}$
	滑动变阻器的作用	保护电路,控制灯泡两端电压	保护电路,改变电路中的电流

易混对比

伏安法测功率与测电阻时滑动变阻器的作用

(1)伏安法测功率时,滑动变阻器的作用是保护电路和控制灯泡两端电压。多次测量的目的是测量不同电压下小灯泡的实际功率,不是为了多次测量求平均值。所以设计的表格中没有"平均功率"这一栏。

(2)伏安法测电阻时,滑动变阻器的作用是保护电路和改变电路中的电流和电阻两端电压,多次测量是为了多测几组对应的电压、电流值,求出电阻值,用多次测量求平均值来减小误差。

(3)伏安法测小灯泡电阻时,由于灯丝电阻大小与温度有关,在不同的电压下,小灯泡温度不同,灯丝电阻也不同。因此测小灯泡电阻时滑动变阻器的作用是保护电路和改变电路中的电流和灯泡两端的电压,不是多次测量求平均值。

例 "测量小灯泡的电功率"的电路如图甲所示,已知小灯泡的额定电压为3.8 V,电源为三节干电池。

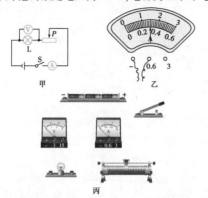

甲　乙
丙

(1)用笔画线表示导线,根据电路图(图甲)将实物图(图丙)连接起来。

(2)正确连好电路后,闭合开关 S,灯 L 不发光,

但电流表、电压表指针有偏转。原因可能是_____
_____。

(3)若闭合开关 S,发现灯泡 L 不亮,两电表均无示数。为了查找故障,小明将电压表拆下,在开关闭合状态下,分别将电压表接在电源、滑动变阻器及开关两端,结果只有接在滑动变阻器两端时,电压表无示数,则肯定出现故障的元件是_____。

(4)排除故障后进行实验,测得三组实验数据,请你分析实验记录数据和现象,回答问题。

物理量 \ 次数	1	2	3
电压 U	2.0	3.8	4.5
电流 I	0.26		0.32
亮度	逐渐增大		
电功率 P/W			

①当电压表示数为 3.8 V 时,电流表示数如图乙所示,此时通过小灯泡灯丝的电流为_____A,小灯泡消耗的电功率是_____W。

②请写出此实验记录表格设计存在的不足之处:
_____。

③经多次测量和计算比较,我们发现小灯泡两端的电压与对应电流的比值并不是一个定值,而是变化的,其可能的原因是_____。

解析 (1)根据电路图中各元件间连接方式对实物图连线。

(2)当滑动变阻器的阻值较大时,电路中有较小的电流,灯泡的实际功率比额定功率小得多,灯泡不发光,但电流表、电压表指针都有偏转。

(3)灯泡不亮,两电表无示数,说明电路断路。将电压表接在电源两端,有示数,说明电源能输出电能;将电压表接在开关两端,电压表有示数,说明开关以外电路都是通路;接在滑动变阻器两端,电压表无示数,说明滑动变阻器之外的电路有断路。综上所述,断路点应该在开关处。

(4)①根据电流表接入的量程和指针位置可知$I=0.3\ A$,则小灯泡电功率$P=UI=3.8\ V\times0.3\ A=1.14\ W$。②记录数据时必须标注物理量的单位。没有单位的数字没有物理意义。③根据表格中U、I数值及$R=\dfrac{U}{I}$,计算出 1、2、3 次电阻值分别约为 7.69 Ω、12.67 Ω、14.06 Ω,则可知小灯泡的灯丝电阻随温度的升高而增大。

(答案)(1)如图所示

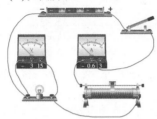

(2)滑动变阻器阻值较大(或:灯泡的实际功率比额定功率小得多)

(3)开关

(4)①0.3 1.14

②物理量没带单位(或电压、电流没带单位)

③小灯泡的灯丝电阻随温度的升高而增大(小灯泡的灯丝电阻随温度的改变而改变)

拓展知识 **知识** 利用电能表和停表测家用电器的功率

知识 利用电能表和停表测家用电器的功率

1.实验原理:$P=\dfrac{W}{t}$。

方法清单 **方法** "伏安法测功率"实验中常见故障的排除方法

方法 "伏安法测功率"实验中常见故障的排除方法

"伏安法测功率"是电学中的重要实验。在实验

2.实验设计思路

在家庭电路中,家用电器消耗的电能可以由电能表进行测量。例如,一只电能表标着3 000 r/(kW·h),这表示每消耗 1 kW·h 的电能,电能表的转盘转3 000转。利用盘面上的这个参数可以测定家用电器的功率。

3.实验步骤

要测量某家用电器的功率,可只让它在电路中工作,将其他用电器关掉。观察电能表的转盘转过的转数 N,同时用停表测出所用的时间 $t(s)$,若以上述电能表为例,则该电器的功率大小为 $P=\dfrac{W}{t}=\dfrac{\dfrac{N}{3\ 000}\times3.6\times10^{6}\ J}{t}$。

还有一种电子式电能表,其表盘上"$n\ \text{imp}/(kW\cdot h)$"的含义是每消耗 1 kW·h 的电能,指示灯闪烁 n 次。若测得某用电器工作时间 $t(s)$内指示灯闪烁了 N 次,则该用电器的功率为 $P=\dfrac{W}{t}=\dfrac{\dfrac{N}{n}\times3.6\times10^{6}\ J}{t}$。

例 如图所示是现在家庭常用的电子式电能表表盘,表盘上标有 3 200 imp/(kW·h),表示每消耗 1 kW·h 的电能,指示灯闪烁 3 200 次。小明将某家用电器单独接在该电能表上正常工作6 min,电能表指示灯闪烁了 320 次。该家用电器的额定电功率是_____W,则这个家用电器可能是_____(选填"电热水壶"、"台灯"或"电视机")。

(解析)指示灯闪烁 320 次,故消耗电能 0.1 kW·h,$P=\dfrac{W}{t}=\dfrac{0.1\ kW\cdot h}{0.1\ h}=1\ kW=1\ 000\ W$,电视机和台灯的功率均小于这个值,电热水壶的功率可以达到1 000 W。

(答案)1 000 电热水壶

过程中,容易出现一些实验故障,下面就在实验中易出现的故障从以下几方面进行分析。

1.器材选择不当导致故障

故障一:电流表、电压表指针偏转的角度小。

[分析原因]①电压表、电流表量程选择过大;②电源电压不高。

[排除方法]选择小量程,如果故障还存在,只有

调高电源电压。实验中若电表指针偏转的角度太小，估读电流或电压时产生的误差将增大。为了减小实验误差,选择量程时既不能使电表指针超过最大刻度,又要考虑到每次测量时应该使电表指针偏过刻度盘的$\frac{1}{3}$。

2.器材连接过程中存在故障

故障二:电压表、电流表指针反向偏转。

[分析原因]电表的"+""-"接线柱接反了,当电流从"-"接线柱流入时,指针反向偏转,甚至出现指针打弯、损坏电表的情况。

[排除方法]将接电表的"+""-"接线柱的接线对调。

故障三:滑动变阻器的滑片滑动时,电表示数及灯泡亮度无变化。

[分析原因]滑动变阻器连接有误,没有遵循"一上一下"的接线原则,把滑动变阻器接成了定值电阻。

[排除方法]遵循"一上一下"原则正确连接滑动变阻器。

故障四:滑动变阻器的滑片滑动时,电表示数都不变,灯泡极亮且亮度无变化。

[分析原因]滑动变阻器的连接有误,没有遵循"一上一下"的接线原则,且滑动变阻器在电路中的阻值为零。

[排除方法]遵循"一上一下"的原则正确连接滑动变阻器。

故障五:刚接好最后一根导线,灯泡立即亮了。

[分析原因]连接电路的过程中,开关没有断开。

[排除方法]连接电路前注意断开关,保护电路。

3.元件损坏导致故障

故障六:闭合开关后,灯不亮,电流表、电压表都没有示数。

[分析原因]电路中存在断路:①接线柱接触不良;②电路中电源、电流表、开关或变阻器可能损坏;③连接导线可能断开。

[排除方法]可先把各接线柱拧紧,若还不行,用一根导线让各元件依次短路,找出故障位置。

故障七:闭合开关,灯不亮,电流表几乎没有示数,电压表指针明显偏转。

[分析原因]可能是灯泡灯丝断了或灯座与灯泡接触不良。

[排除方法]更换灯泡或使灯座与灯泡接触良好。

例 某小组做"测定小灯泡功率"的实验,小灯泡标有"3.8 V 1.5 W",电源电压6 V,其他器材正常。

(1)甲同学连接好电路后,闭合开关,发现灯泡发光较暗,电流表有示数,任意移动滑动变阻器的滑片,电压表示数不变(示数不为零)且小于6 V。具体原因是_____。

(2)乙同学连接电路时,电流表、电压表、滑动变阻器接法均正确,连接完最后一根导线时,灯泡发出很强的光,电流表超量程;丙同学接成如图所示

实物图。

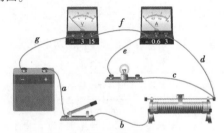

请根据以上信息填写下表:

	存在的问题	导致的结果	解决的方法
乙			
丙			

(3)丁同学合理地连接好电路,闭合开关,无论怎样调节滑动变阻器灯泡都不亮。他分析产生故障的原因可能是:a.小灯泡灯丝断了;b.小灯泡短路;c.滑动变阻器断路。电流表、电压表均无故障,请你根据下表中电流表、电压表示数可能出现的几种情况,帮助判断故障原因,并将其序号填写在表对应的空格里。

电流表	电压表	故障原因
示数不为0	示数为0	
示数为0	示数不为0	

(4)电路连接正确后重新实验,电流表、电压表示数如图所示,电流表示数为_____A,电压表示数为_____V,小灯泡功率为_____W,灯泡发光2 min消耗电能为_____J。

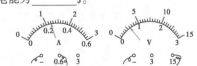

解析 (1)由题中现象可知滑动变阻器接了下面两个接线柱。

(2)乙同学连接电路时灯泡发光很强,电流表超量程,说明滑动变阻器连入电阻太小,电路中电流超过灯泡的正常工作电流,可能会烧坏灯泡、电流表,解决方法是调节滑片,使滑动变阻器连入电路的电阻变大;连接完电路后,灯泡即亮,说明开关已闭合,导致的结果是开关未起作用,解决方法是在连接电路前断开开关。丙同学将电流表与灯泡并联,会使灯泡不发光;电压表没有并联在灯泡的两端,电压表无法测出灯泡电压,解决方法是使电流表与灯泡串联,电压表并联在灯泡的两端。

(3)灯泡不亮有两方面可能,即断路或短路,断路时电路中无电流但灯泡两端有电压,短路时电路中有电流但灯泡两端电压为零,所以上空填b,下空填a。

(4)电流表所选量程为0~0.6 A,分度值为0.02 A,读数为0.24 A。

电压表所选量程为 0~15 V,分度值为 0.5 V,读数为 3 V。

$P = UI = 3 \text{ V} \times 0.24 \text{ A} = 0.72 \text{ W}$。

$W = Pt = 0.72 \text{ W} \times 2 \times 60 \text{ s} = 86.4 \text{ J}$。

(答案)(1)滑动变阻器接了下面两个接线柱

(2)如下表所示

	存在的问题	导致的结果	解决的方法
乙	连接电路时,开关没断开(或已闭合)	开关没有起到控制电路的作用	断开开关
	连接电路时,滑片的位置不对(或没有滑到阻值最大位置处)	电路中电流过大,可能烧坏灯泡、电流表	滑片滑到滑动变阻器的阻值最大位置

续表

	存在的问题	导致的结果	解决的方法
丙	电流表与灯泡并联	灯泡不发光(或灯泡短路或电流表无法测出灯泡的电流)	将电流表、电压表交换位置
	电压表与电流表串联,没有并联在灯泡的两端	电压表示数不变(或电流表几乎无示数或电压表无法测出灯泡两端的电压)	将电流表、电压表交换位置

(3)b a

(4)0.24 3 0.72 86.4

第4节 电与热

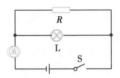

知识清单

基础知识

知识 1 电与热

知识 2 电热和电功

知识 3 电热的利用和防止

知识 1 电与热

焦耳定律	内容:电流通过导体时产生的热量与电流的平方成正比,与导体的电阻成正比,与通电时间成正比
	公式:$Q = I^2Rt$;适用范围:任何电路
	推导公式:$Q = \dfrac{U^2}{R}t$,$Q = UIt$;适用范围:纯电阻电路
串、并联电路电热关系	串联电路中,电热之比等于电阻之比,即 $\dfrac{Q_1}{Q_2} = \dfrac{R_1}{R_2}$(根据:$Q = I^2Rt$)
	并联电路中,电热之比等于电阻的反比,即 $\dfrac{Q_1}{Q_2} = \dfrac{R_2}{R_1}$(根据:$Q = \dfrac{U^2}{R}t$)

例 图中电源电压保持不变,灯泡标有"6 V 3 W"字样,当开关 S 闭合时,灯泡 L 正常发光,电流表的示数为 0.8 A,则电阻 $R = $ _____ Ω,通电 10 s,R 产生的热量为 _____ J。

(解析)灯泡正常发光时电流 $I_L = \dfrac{P}{U} = \dfrac{3 \text{ W}}{6 \text{ V}} = 0.5$ A。图中灯泡和电阻并联,电流表测干路电流,则电阻 R 中的电流 $I_R = I - I_L = 0.8 \text{ A} - 0.5 \text{ A} = 0.3$ A,电阻 R 两端的电压 $U_R = U = 6 \text{ V}$,$R = \dfrac{U_R}{I_R} = \dfrac{6 \text{ V}}{0.3 \text{ A}} = 20$ Ω,电热 $Q = I_R^2Rt = 0.3^2 \times 20 \times 10 \text{ J} = 18$ J。

(答案)20 18

知识 2 电热和电功

1.电热和电功是两个完全不同的概念。只有在纯电阻电路中(如电炉、电烙铁、电熨斗等),电流做功消耗的电能全部转化成内能时,电热在数值上才与电功相等,即 $Q = I^2Rt = W = UIt = Pt = U^2t/R$。

2.对于非纯电阻电路(如电动机、电视机、电冰箱等)。$W = UIt = Pt > Q = I^2Rt$,电功中只有一部分转化为内能,还有一部分转化为其他形式的能量。

电动机消耗的电功率用 $P=UI$ 还是 $P=I^2R$ 计算？

含有电动机的电路是非纯电阻电路,消耗的电能(电流做的功 $W=UIt$)主要转化为机械能,只有少部分转化为内能($Q=I^2Rt$),因此 $W>Q$,即 $UIt>I^2Rt$,所以计算电动机消耗的电功率可以用 $P=\dfrac{W}{t}$ 或 $P=UI$ 计算,不能用 $P=I^2R$ 或 $P=\dfrac{U^2}{R}$ 计算。

例 一台直流电动机,线圈电阻为 $R=0.5\ \Omega$,接在 $U=12\ V$ 电源上时,通过的电流为 $I=2\ A$。这台电动机工作 $t=10\ min$,电流做了多少功？产生多少热量？

解析 $W=UIt=12\times2\times600\ J=14\ 400\ J$,$Q=I^2Rt=2^2\times0.5\times600\ J=1\ 200\ J$。

这台电动机消耗的电能为 14 400 J,其中产生了 1 200 J 热量,剩下的 13 200 J 转化为机械能。

答案 14 400 J　1 200 J

知识 3 电热的利用和防止

1.电热的利用

用来焊接　用来熨衣服

电热

用来煮饭　用来烘烤食品

如图所示是电热在日常生活中的应用,它们的共同点是:

(1)它们都是用电器,都是用电来加热的设备,都有发热体。

(2)它们的原理都是利用电流的热效应。

(3)它们都是把电能转化为内能。

2.电热的防止

电热会使用电器温度过高,影响用电器的工作,缩短使用寿命,甚至损坏用电器。在用电器上装有散热窗、金属片外壳、散热风扇等,可用来防止用电器温度过高。如电视机的后盖有很多孔,就是为了通风散热,使用时一定要把防尘的布罩拿开。电动机的外壳有很多翼状散热片,使用时与轴相连的扇叶还向散热片吹风,也是为了降温。计算机内也装有散热风扇降温。

知识 1 为什么电炉工作时"电炉丝热得发红而导线却不怎么热"

电炉丝和导线串联在电路中,通过它们的电流相等。

电炉丝的电阻比导线的电阻大得多,根据 $Q=I^2Rt$ 可知,在通电时间相同时,电流通过电炉丝产生的热量比电流通过导线产生的热量要多很多。所以电炉丝热得发红,而导线却不怎么热。

知识 2 电热器的"双挡"问题

1."双挡"中的电阻:电热器通常设计有"高温挡"和"低温挡"。根据 $P=\dfrac{U^2}{R}$ 可知,当 U 一定时,电阻越大,电功率越小;电阻越小,电功率越大。所以高温挡总电阻最小,低温挡总电阻最大。

2."双挡"的控制开关

(1)短路式

两个电阻串联,把开关与其中一个电阻并联,如图所示。

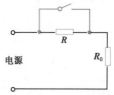

当闭合开关时,有一个电阻短路,只有一个电阻工作,此时为高温挡;当断开开关时,两电阻串联,电阻大一些,电热器的功率小一些,此时为低温挡。

(2)单刀双掷式

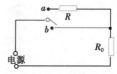

当开关掷向 a 时,两电阻串联,为低温挡;当开关掷向 b 时,只有电阻 R_0 工作,此时为高温挡。

例 如图甲所示为一款利用高温水蒸气熨烫衣服的便携式挂烫机,它的正常工作电压为 220 V,水箱装水最多 0.3 kg,加热功率有大、小两个挡位。设计师最初设计的内部电路有如图乙、丙两种接法,其中电热丝 $R_1=56\ \Omega$,$R_2=44\ \Omega$。

甲

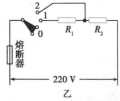
乙

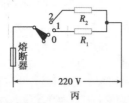
丙

（1）高温水蒸气熨烫衣服时，水蒸气遇到衣服迅速_____成小水珠，放出热量，将衣服熨平(填物态变化名称)。

（2）如果选择乙电路，电路中最大电流为_____A；如果选择丙电路，电路中最大电流为_____A，由于两个电路中所选熔断器里的熔丝允许通过的最大电流为 8.2 A，故设计师最终选择了乙电路。(计算结果保留一位小数)

（3）若选用乙电路，请分别计算这款挂烫机两个挡位的额定功率。

（4）若将水箱中 0.22 kg 的水从 25 ℃加热到 100 ℃，挂烫机至少需要加热多长时间？[水的比热容 $c = 4.2 \times 10^3$ J/(kg·℃)]

解析 （1）水蒸气变为小水珠是由气态变为液态，属于液化。

（2）如果选择乙电路，则只把 R_2 接入电路时，电路中电阻最小，电流最大，$I_{大} = \dfrac{U}{R_2} = \dfrac{220\ V}{44\ \Omega} = 5\ A$；如果选择乙电路，则 R_1 和 R_2 并联时，电路中电阻最小，电流最大，$I_{大}' = \dfrac{U}{R_1} + \dfrac{U}{R_2} = \dfrac{220\ V}{56\ \Omega} + 5\ A \approx 8.9\ A$。

（3）挂烫机大功率挡工作时，电路中电流为 5 A，此时功率

$P_{大} = UI_{大} = 220\ V \times 5\ A = 1\ 100\ W$

挂烫机小功率挡工作时，R_1、R_2 串联，电路中电流

$I_{总} = \dfrac{U}{R_{总}} = \dfrac{U}{R_1 + R_2} = \dfrac{220\ V}{56\ \Omega + 44\ \Omega} = \dfrac{220\ V}{100\ \Omega} = 2.2\ A$

小功率挡的功率

$P_{小} = UI_{总} = 220\ V \times 2.2\ A = 484\ W$

（4）水吸收的热量

$$Q_{吸} = cm(t - t_0)$$
$$= 4.2 \times 10^3\ \text{J/(kg·℃)} \times 0.22\ \text{kg} \times (100\ ℃ - 25\ ℃)$$
$$= 6.93 \times 10^4\ \text{J}$$

要使加热时间最短，应选用大功率挡，且电流产生的热量全部被水吸收。

由 $P = \dfrac{W}{t}$ 得，加热时间

$$t = \dfrac{W}{P_{大}} = \dfrac{Q_{吸}}{P_{大}} = \dfrac{6.93 \times 10^4\ \text{J}}{1\ 100\ \text{W}} = 63\ \text{s}$$

答案 （1）液化 （2）5 8.9 （3）1 100 W 484 W （4）63 s

方法
清单

方法 控制变量法探究焦耳定律

方法 控制变量法探究焦耳定律

研究焦耳定律的实验运用了控制变量法。

1.控制电流和电阻不变，改变通电时间的长短，研究电热与通电时间的关系。

2.控制通电时间和电阻不变，改变电流的大小，研究电热与电流的关系。

3.控制通电时间和电流不变，改变电阻的大小，研究电热与电阻的关系。

例 如图甲和乙是研究"电热大小与哪些因素有关"的实验装置。通电后，若要比较电阻丝产生热量的多与少，只需比较与之相连的 U 形管中_____。甲是探究电热与_____的关系的实验装置，乙是探究电热与_____的关系的实验装置。

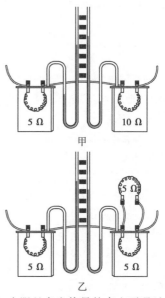
甲

乙

解析 电阻丝产生热量的多少可通过 U 形管中液面高度变化显示出来；甲图中不同阻值的两电阻串

联,控制电流 I 和通电时间 t 相同,根据 $Q=I^2Rt$ 可知探究的是 Q 与 R 的关系;乙图中控制 R 与 t 相同,左边电阻在干路,右边电阻在支路,通过左、右两边电阻的电流不同,故探究的是 Q 与 I 的关系。

（答案）液面高度变化　电阻　电流

第5节　电功率和安全用电、生活用电常识

知识清单

基础知识

知识 **1** 家庭电路的组成及各部分作用
知识 **2** 试电笔
知识 **3** 插座和电灯的接法
知识 **4** 触电及触电事故的处理
知识 **5** 安全用电常识

知识 1 家庭电路的组成及各部分作用

1.主要组成部分有:进户线、电能表、闸刀开关、保险盒、用电器、插座、开关等,如图。

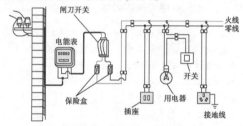

2.家庭电路各部分的作用及连接方法

（1）进户线:一根叫火线,另一根叫零线,火线和零线之间有 220 V 电压,它们构成家庭电路的电源（火线和大地间有 220 V 电压,零线和大地间没有电压）。

（2）电能表:其作用是测量用户在一定时间内消耗的电能,装在干路上。电能表的铭牌有额定电压 $U_{额}$ 和额定电流 $I_{额}$,电路可使用的功率 $P \leqslant U_{额}I_{额}$。

（3）闸刀开关:其作用是控制整个家庭电路的通断,装在干路上,安装闸刀开关时,上端为静触头,接输入导线,切不可倒装。

（4）保险丝:①由电阻率大、熔点低的铅锑合金制成,当电路中的电流过大时能自动熔断而切断电路,起保险作用;②保险丝应串联在电路中,绝对不允许用铁丝、铜丝代替保险丝;③选择原则是保险丝的额定电流等于或稍大于电路中正常工作电流。

（5）插座:给可移动的家用电器供电,插座应并联在电路中,三孔插座中一个孔应接地（如图）。

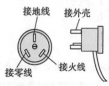

（6）开关:可以控制本支路的通断,开关应和被控制的用电器串联。

（7）用电器:直接利用电能工作的器件,各个用电器应并联接入电路。

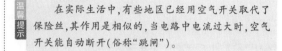

温馨提示　在实际生活中,有些地区已经用空气开关取代了保险丝,其作用是相似的,当电路中电流过大时,空气开关能自动断开(俗称"跳闸")。

知识 2 试电笔

1.试电笔是用来辨别火线和零线的工具。构造:由笔尖金属体、大电阻、氖管、弹簧和笔尾金属体等组成。（如图甲所示）

2.使用时,用手捏住笔尾金属体,用笔尖接触进户线,若碰到的是火线,则氖管发光;若笔尖接触的是零线,氖管就不会发光。（如图乙、丙所示）

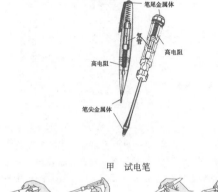

甲　试电笔

乙　试电笔的使用方法

氖管发光,这是火线　　　氖管不亮,这是零线

丙　用试电笔辨别火线与零线

3.使用试电笔时,切不可用手直接接触笔尖金属体,这样人会触电。

4.检查电路故障时,用笔尖接触导线,若两根导线都不发光,表明火线断路;若两根导线都发光,表明零线断路。

知识 3　插座和电灯的接法

1.插座:插座可分为两孔插座和三孔插座。如图甲所示。

两孔插座:左孔接零线,右孔接火线。

三孔插座:左孔接零线,右孔接火线,中间上端的孔接地线。 这样用电器的金属外壳即便带电,电流也会流入大地,不致对人造成伤害。国家规定:带有金属外壳的家用电器,其金属外壳必须接地,也就是必须使用三孔插座和三脚插头,如图乙所示。

2.用电器:以电灯为例,如图丙所示,电灯接入电路时,灯座上两个接线柱,一个接火线,一个接零线,**控制电灯的开关一定要安装在火线上,这样做是为了**安全。螺口灯座的螺旋套与零线相连,绝不许接在火线上。

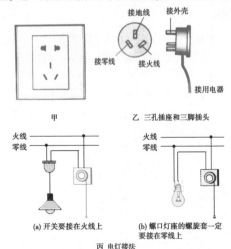

甲　　　乙　三孔插座和三脚插头

(a) 开关要接在火线上　(b) 螺口灯座的螺旋套一定要接在零线上

丙　电灯接法

温馨提示　①三脚插头上端接外壳的插头较长,是为了使用时先将用电器外壳接地,用电更安全。②控制开关或保险丝一定要安装在火线上是指把开关接在灯与火线相连的那段导线上;把保险丝接在插座与火线相连的那段导线上。

知识 4　触电及触电事故的处理

通常所讲的"触电"是指一定大小的电流通过人体所引起的伤害事故。

1.低压触电:一般分为单线触电和双线触电,如图所示。单线触电是人体直接触摸电源、火线或漏电的用电器等,使人体、导线、大地和电网中的供电设备形成回路。双线触电是人体的两部分(如两只手)分别接触到火线和零线,使人体、导线和电网中的供电设备形成回路。

(a) 单线触电　　(b) 双线触电

2.高压触电:最常见的是高压电弧触电和跨步电压触电。

(1)高压电弧触电:当人体靠近高压带电体到一定距离时,高压带电体和人体间发生放电现象,电流通过人体,造成高压电弧触电。

(2)跨步电压触电:高压输电线落在地上,地面上与电线断头距离不同的各点存在电压,当人走近断头时,两脚位于离断头远近不同的位置上,因而两脚之间有了电压,这时电流通过人体,造成跨步电压触电。

温馨提示　小鸟站在高压线上时,由于空气绝缘,小鸟体积较小,且不与大地相连,在它接近电线时,电弧放电量极小;又由于两脚间距离很短,分得的电压相对很少;另外,双脚站立时,相对于电线,小鸟身体电阻要大得多,尤其爪子上面有角质层,电阻很大,相当于电线在小鸟两脚间形成短路,所以通过小鸟的电流很小;如果小鸟双脚站在两根电线上,相当于电源短路,有很大的电流通过小鸟身体,造成触电事故;下图中裸露电线上的两只小鸟,闭合开关后,流过左边小鸟的电流很小,而右边小鸟有较大的电流流过。

快飞,你会触电的!　你怎么不怕?

3.触电事故的处理

具体做法:一是切断电源,或者用一根绝缘棒将电线挑开,尽快使触电者脱离电源;二是尽力抢救;三是发生电火灾务必在切断电源后,才能泼水救火。在整个救护过程中,必须随时注意自身保护,防止自己也触电。

知识 5　安全用电常识

1.了解几个电压值:安全电压不高于 36 V;家庭

电路电压为 220 V;动力电压是 380 V。家庭电路电压和动力电压都远远高于安全电压,所以禁止靠近或接触。

2.安全用电原则:对于安全用电必须做到"四不",即不接触低压带电体,不靠近高压带电体,不弄湿用电器,不损坏绝缘层。例如,在日常生活中,首先不要私拉乱接电线,私拉乱接是违反用电制度的,在安装电路上是不符合要求的,是容易引发事故的;另外,在日常生活中换灯泡、擦灯泡的时候,应先将电源断开,不要用湿手、湿布擦灯泡,不要站在地上去擦,要站在木凳或桌子上去擦,防止万一开关失灵漏电造成触电事故,要特别注意安全。

例 如图所示的做法中,符合安全用电原则的是 (   )

雷雨天站在
大树下避雨
A

用手指触碰
插座的插孔
B

用湿抹布擦
发光的灯泡
C

将冰箱的金
属外壳接地
D

(解析) A、B、C 三项容易发生触电事故;将冰箱的金属外壳接地后,若外壳带电,可及时导入大地,防止触电事故的发生,所以选 D。

(答案) D

拓展
知识
知识**1** 家庭电路中电流过大的原因
知识**2** 地线、火线和零线的区分

知识 1 家庭电路中电流过大的原因

1.发生短路情况:装修电路时不细心,使火线和零线直接连通;电线绝缘皮被刮破,或者电线和用电器使用时间过久,绝缘皮破损或老化,使火线和零线直接连通,都会发生短路现象。发生短路现象时,有很大的电流通过导线和用电器,会造成导线和用电器烧毁,这是必须要避免的。

2.用电器总功率过大情况:当电路中同时使用的用电器过多,或使用的用电器功率过大,都会造成整个电路中的总功率过大,当总功率过大时,根据公式

$P=UI$,也会导致电路中电流过大(如图)。例如,居民楼里电炉子、电暖气、微波炉、电熨斗等大功率的用电器同时工作,会导致电流过大烧毁保险丝或造成跳闸。所以不能同时使用大量大功率的用电器,这是很危险的。

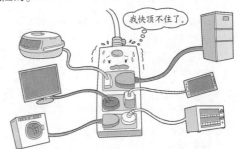

我快顶不住了。

例 小明家新买了一个电热水器,刚接入电路,家里的空气开关就断开了。他猜想造成空气开关断开的原因是:①连入电路中的用电器总功率过大;②电热水器或插头处短路。于是他请电工师傅检修后,将空气开关复位,只让电热水器单独工作,家里标有"2 000 r/(kW·h)"电能表的转盘 3 min 内转了 100 转,电热水器的功率为_____W。小明猜想_____(选填序号)是正确的。(已知电热水器接入电路前,小明家正在使用的用电器的总功率约为 3 200 W,空气开关允许通过的最大电流为 40 A)

(解析) 电热水器 3 min 内消耗的电能 $W=\dfrac{3.6\times10^6 \text{ J}}{2\ 000\ \text{r}}\times100\ \text{r}=1.8\times10^5\text{ J}$,电热水器的功率 $P=\dfrac{W}{t}=\dfrac{1.8\times10^5\text{ J}}{180\text{ s}}=1\ 000$ W;电热水器接入电路后的总功率为 4 200 W,而由题意可知电路中允许消耗的最大功率为 $P=UI=220\text{ V}\times40\text{ A}=8\ 800$ W,故空气开关跳闸的原因不是电路中的用电器总功率过大,而是电热水器或插头处短路。

(答案) 1 000 ②

知识 2 地线、火线和零线的区分

1.低压供电线路由两根电线(火线和零线)与家庭电路相连。火线和零线之间有 220 V 电压,火线与大地之间也有 220 V 电压。在三孔插座中有一根电线将家用电器外壳与大地相连,这根线称为地线,虽然在正常情况下地线和零线之间没有电压,但绝不能将地线和零线接通,否则容易造成触电事故。

2.用试电笔接触火线时,试电笔的氖管发光。接触零线和地线时,正常情况下氖管不发光;如果发光了,说明零线断路或有用电器的外壳带了电。

第
⑤
部
分

方法清单

方法❶ 判断家庭电路故障的方法
方法❷ 家庭电路安装图的画法

方法 1 判断家庭电路故障的方法

家庭电路故障主要是由于断路、短路、总功率过大等引起的。(1)若是短路或用电器总功率过大,保险丝会熔断;(2)若是进户火线断路,试电笔不会发光;(3)若试电笔接触零线氖管发光,说明进户线零线断路。如图所示,闭合开关 S 后,灯泡都不亮,保险丝完好,在闭合开关 S 的情况下用试电笔接触插座的两个孔,发现氖管都发光,说明零线 EF 段断路。

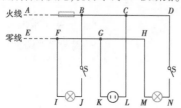

例 1 如图所示为居民家中某房间的电路,电灯 L 与电热壶均正常工作,在三孔插座上接入电饭煲后,电热壶突然停止工作,灯 L 仍正常发光,拔了电饭煲的插头,用测电笔分别测试三孔插座的左、右两孔,氖管均发光,此时电路故障可能是 ( )

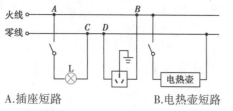

A.插座短路　　　　　　B.电热壶短路
C.AB 间断路　　　　　　D.CD 间断路

（解析）灯 L 正常发光,电热壶停止工作,说明电路某处断开;测电笔测试插座左、右两孔氖管均发光,说明零线断路,灯 L 正常发光,说明是 CD 间断路。

（答案）**D**

例 2 如图是一条刚装好的家庭电路,在未装保险丝之前,先把灯泡 L_0 接在装保险丝的两个接线柱上,当只闭合 S_1 时,L_0 和 L_1 发光都偏暗;当只闭合 S_2 时,L_0 正常发光;当只闭合 S_3 时,L_0 不发光。则下列判断正确的是(四只灯泡的额定电压均为 220 V) ( )

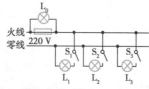

A.灯泡 L_1 所在支路正常
B.灯泡 L_2 所在支路断路
C.灯泡 L_3 所在支路短路
D.装好保险丝,合上所有开关后,灯泡都能正常发光

（解析）当只闭合 S_1 时,L_0 和 L_1 发光都偏暗,说明两灯泡两端的电压均小于 220 V,两灯串联,灯泡 L_1 所在支路正常,A 项正确;当只闭合 S_2 时,L_0 正常发光,说明 L_0 两端的电压为 220 V,L_2 被短路,灯泡 L_2 所在支路短路,B 项错误;当只闭合 S_3 时,L_0 不发光,说明灯泡 L_3 所在支路是断开的,C 项错误;综上所述,装好保险丝,合上所有开关后,电路会发生短路,灯泡都不能工作,D 项错误。

（答案）**A**

方法 2 家庭电路安装图的画法

1.家庭电路中有火线、零线和地线,单根保险丝接在火线上,开关接在火线上。

2.电灯安装时,零线、火线并排走,零线直接进灯座。火线通过开关进灯座。如果灯泡是螺丝口的,尾部中心接火线,螺旋套接零线。

3.插座安装时,两孔插座左孔接零线,右孔接火线;三孔插座的左边的孔接零线,右边的孔接火线,中间的孔接地线,所以称为"左零右火中接地"。如果在插座上接保险丝,保险丝应接在火线上。

4.插座与插座之间是并联的,插座与电灯之间是并联的,各种用电器之间是并联的。

例 居民楼的楼道里,夜间楼道灯一直亮着会造成浪费,科研人员用"光敏"材料制成"光控开关",它能在天黑时自动闭合,天亮时自动断开。利用"声敏"材料制成"声控开关",它能在有人走动发出声音时闭合,无人走动时自动断开。请将如图所示的"光控开关"、"声控开关"、灯泡用笔画线代替导线正确连入电路,设计出只有在夜晚且有声音时灯才亮的楼道灯自动控制电路,同时安装一个不受开关控制的三孔插座。

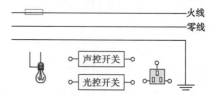

（解析）天黑时,光控开关闭合,有人走动发出声音时声控开关闭合,因此,光控开关和声控开关应串联;开关应接在火线上,灯泡螺旋套应与零线相连;三孔插座应左零右火中接地。

（答案）如图所示

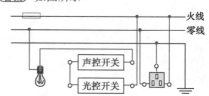

电与磁、信息的传递

知识梳理

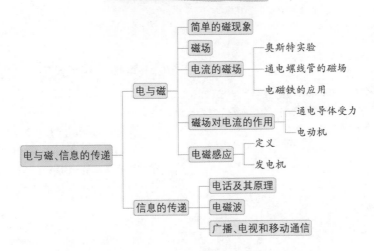

第1节 磁现象和磁场

知识清单

基础知识	知识1 磁性、磁体、磁极和磁化 知识2 磁场

知识 1 磁性、磁体、磁极和磁化

磁性	能够吸引铁、钴、镍等物质,这种性质叫磁性
磁体	具有磁性的物体叫磁体
磁极	(1)磁体上磁性最强的部分叫做磁极。自由转动的磁体静止下来时,指南的那一端叫磁体的南极,用符号 S 表示,指北的那一端叫磁体的北极,用符号 N 表示 (2)磁极间的相互作用规律:同名磁极互相排斥,异名磁极互相吸引(如图) 
磁化	使原来没有磁性的物体获得磁性的过程叫磁化

例 一根条形磁体的一端吸起两枚大头针,小华说两枚大头针会保持平行,如图甲所示;小红说两枚大头针会张开,如图丙所示;小明说两枚大头针会靠近,如图乙所示。你认为说法正确的是_____,因为_____。

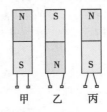

甲　乙　丙

解析 条形磁体的一端吸起大头针后,大头针就被磁化。以图甲为例,被吸引的两枚大头针靠近磁体 S 极的那一端被磁化后都为 N 极,两枚大头针的下端都为 S 极,根据磁极间的相互作用规律可知,两枚大头针下端因是同名磁极互相排斥而分开。

答案 小红　两枚大头针被磁化后下端是同名磁极而互相排斥

知识 2 磁场

概念	磁体的周围存在磁场,磁场是看不见摸不着的,但它是确实存在着的,是一种物质
性质	磁场的基本性质是对放入其中的磁体能够产生力的作用,也就是说,磁极间的相互作用力是通过磁场来发生的。小磁针静止后一端指南,另一端指北,当把条形磁体放在小磁针附近时,会看到小磁针发生了偏转,这是因为小磁针受到了条形磁体磁场的作用
方向	规定:在磁场中的某一点,小磁针静止时北极(N极)所指的方向就是该点的磁场方向
磁感线	磁场可借助磁感线来描述,磁感线上任何一点的切线方向就是该点的磁场方向,磁感线的疏密还可以表示磁场的强弱。磁感线在磁体外总是从N极发出,最后回到S极。几种常见磁场的磁感线如图所示 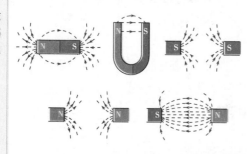

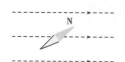

磁场与磁感线

①磁场是真实存在的,人们为了形象地描述磁场,参照铁屑落在磁体周围所呈现的形状绘制了磁感线;②在磁体外部,规定磁感线的方向是从N极到S极;磁体周围某点小磁针静止时N极所指的方向为该点磁场方向;③磁感线的疏密程度可表示磁场的强弱。

例 一个能绕中心转动的小磁针在图示位置保持静止。某时刻开始小磁针所在区域出现水平向右的磁场,磁感线如图所示,则小磁针在磁场出现后 (　　)

A.两极所受的力是平衡力,所以不会发生转动

B.两极所受的力方向相反,所以会持续转动

C.只有N极受力,会发生转动,最终静止时N极所指方向水平向右

D.两极所受的力方向相反,会发生转动,最终静止时N极所指方向水平向右

解析 小磁针所在区域出现水平向右的磁场时,小磁针两极所受的力方向相反,但不在同一直线上,故小磁针受非平衡力作用,会发生转动;当小磁针转到水平位置时,两极所受的力大小相等,方向相反,在同一直线上,小磁针最终在此位置静止,此时小磁针N极所指方向水平向右。故A、B、C错误,D正确。

答案 D

拓展知识 知识 地磁场和磁偏角

知识 地磁场和磁偏角

1.地磁场

(1)地球是一个巨大的磁体,在地球周围的空间里存在着磁场,叫做地磁场。

(2)地磁北极在地理南极附近,地磁南极在地理北极附近,地磁场的磁感线从地磁北极出发到地磁南极,能自由转动的小磁针静止时指南北,就是因为受到地磁场的作用。

2.磁偏角

地磁的两极跟地理的两极并不重合,小磁针所指的南北方向与地理的南北方向略有偏离。我国宋代学者沈括(1031年~1095年)是世界上最早记述这一现象的人,比西方早了400年。

例 若假想地磁场是由地球内部一块大磁铁产生的,如图所示的四个示意图中,能合理描述这块大磁铁的是 (　　)

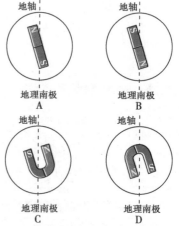

解析 地磁场的北极在地理南极附近,而地磁场的南极在地理北极附近。题图中只有B图符合实际,故应该选B。

答案 B

242 初中物理知识清单

方法清单

方法①　转换法探究磁场的存在
方法②　理想模型法描述磁场
方法③　判断物体是否有磁性的方法

方法 1　转换法探究磁场的存在

1.对于不易研究或不好直接研究的物理问题,通过研究其表现出来的现象、效应、作用效果来间接研究物理问题的方法,叫转换法。

2.对于磁场,既看不见又摸不着,无法直接感知它,我们可以通过磁场对磁体的作用来证明磁场的存在。在磁体周围放入小磁针,小磁针方向发生了偏转,这说明磁体的周围存在磁场;又如电磁铁磁性的强弱可以通过吸引大头针的多少来判断,吸引的大头针越多,磁性越强。

3.用铁屑显示永磁体的磁场分布,如图所示。通过铁屑的分布显示出磁场的存在及磁场的强弱。

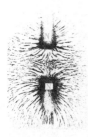

例 磁场是一种看不见的特殊物质,我们可以通过磁场对小磁针作用的效果来认识它。这是科学研究的一种常用方法。下列研究实例中不是采用这种研究方法的是　　　　　　　　　(　　)

A.比较温度的高低,我们可以通过液体受热后体积的变化来认识它

B.学习电压,我们可以通过对比水压来认识它

C.了解电磁铁磁性的强弱,我们可以通过观察它吸引大头针的多少来认识

D.电路中是否有电流,我们可以通过观察电路中电流表的指针是否偏转来认识

解析　已知题中叙述的方法是转换法。B中的方法是类比法,其他都属于转换法,故选B。

答案　B

方法 2　理想模型法描述磁场

1.研究物理问题时,需要把复杂的问题简单化,构建理想化的物理模型,有时为了形象地描述某种物理现象,需要引入一些模型,这种方法称为“理想模型法”。用磁感线描述磁场用的就是这种方法。

2.磁感线上某一点的切线方向代表该点的磁场方向,磁感线密的地方表示磁场强,磁感线疏的地方表

示磁场弱。

例 人类在探索自然规律的过程中,总结出了许多科学研究方法,如:“控制变量法”、“等效替代法”、“类比法”、“理想模型法”等。下面是初中物理中的几个研究实例:

①研究电流时,把电流比作水流;

②研究磁场时,引入“磁感线”;

③研究动能与速度的关系时,让物体的质量保持不变;

④研究光的传播时,引入“光线”。

其中,采用了相同研究方法的是　　　　　(　　)

A.①和②　　　　　　　　　B.②和③

C.②和④　　　　　　　　　D.③和④

解析　①采用了类比法,②采用了理想模型法,③采用了控制变量法,④采用了理想模型法。因此,采用了相同研究方法的是②和④。

答案　C

方法 3　判断物体是否有磁性的方法

1.磁体磁性判断

磁体有四种特性:一是吸铁性,二是指向性,三是磁极磁性最强,四是磁极间的相互作用。在判断一个物体是否有磁性时,可以利用上面的任何一个特性。但要判断一个磁体的N、S极时,只能利用“指向性”和“磁极间的相互作用”。

2.钢棒磁性的判断

图例	判断方法
A B　B A　1　2	如两次都不吸引,则A、B都没有磁性
	如两次都吸引,则A、B都有磁性
	如只有1吸引,则B有磁性,A没有
	如只有2吸引,则A有磁性,B没有
A　→向右平移　B	如始终没有相互作用,则A、B都没有磁性
	如吸引力保持不变,则A没有磁性,B有磁性
	如吸引力由强→弱→强,则A有磁性,B没有磁性
	如先吸引后排斥,或先排斥后吸引,则A、B都有磁性

例 如图所示,甲、乙均为外形相同的钢棒,当乙从图的左端沿水平方向向右移动时,若吸引力的大小不变,则_____棒有磁性;若吸引力先由大变小,然后由小变大,则_____棒有磁性。

解析 条形磁体两端的磁性最强,中间最弱,而普通钢棒无磁性。若用条形磁体的一端去靠近钢棒的任何部位都具有一定的大小不变的吸引力。若用钢棒一端去靠近条形磁体,则条形磁体两端附近吸引力较大,在条形磁体中部时几乎没有磁性,因此它们之间的吸引力很小。

答案 乙　甲

第2节　电生磁、电磁铁、电磁继电器和扬声器

知识清单

基础知识
知识**1** 奥斯特实验　　知识**2** 通电螺线管
知识**3** 电磁铁　　　　知识**4** 电磁继电器
知识**5** 扬声器

知识 **1** 奥斯特实验

1.实验过程:如图所示,将一根导线平行地拿到静止小磁针上方,观察导线通电时小磁针是否偏转,改变电流方向,再观察一次。

甲:通电　　乙:断电　　丙:改变电流方向

2.实验现象:导线通电时小磁针发生偏转,切断电流时小磁针又回到原来位置,当电流方向改变时,磁针的偏转方向也相反。

3.结论:(1)比较甲、乙两图说明通电导体周围存在着磁场。

(2)比较甲、丙两图说明磁场方向与电流方向有关。

知识 **2** 通电螺线管

1.通电螺线管周围的铁屑分布情况与条形磁体的一样,因此,其周围的磁场与条形磁体的磁场相同。

2.通电螺线管的磁极不仅和电流的方向有关,还和线圈的绕向有关。

3.通电螺线管的磁极极性可用安培定则(右手螺旋定则)来判定:

用右手握螺线管,让四指弯向螺线管中电流的方向,则大拇指所指的那端就是螺线管的N极,如图所示。

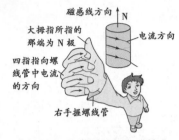

4.通电螺线管的磁性强弱与有无铁芯(有铁芯称为电磁铁)、电流的大小、线圈匝数的多少有关。

温馨提示 通电螺线管内部磁场的方向是:S极→N极,螺线管内部小磁针静止时的指向如图所示。

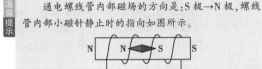

例 小磁针可以在水平面内自由转动,当闭合开关后,小磁针的指向如图所示,由此可知电源的正极在_____端(选填"左"或"右")。

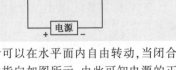

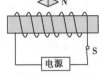

解析 小磁针右端是N极,根据异名磁极相互吸引可知螺线管右端为S极,利用安培定则可判断电源右端是正极。

答案 右

知识 3 电磁铁

知识点	内容
电磁铁	内有铁芯的螺线管
影响电磁铁磁性强弱的因素	电流的大小、线圈匝数的多少(如图)。 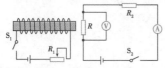
电磁铁的优点	磁性的有无由电流通断来控制;磁性的强弱可以由电流的大小来改变;磁性由变换电流的方向来改变
电磁铁的用途	电磁起重机、电铃、电磁继电器、听筒等

例 1 在如图所示的电路中,磁敏电阻 R 的阻值随磁场的增强而明显减小。将螺线管一端靠近磁敏电阻 R,闭合开关 S_1、S_2,下列说法正确的是 （　　）

A.螺线管左端为 S 极,右端为 N 极
B.当 R_1 的滑片向左滑动时,电压表示数减小
C.当 R_1 的滑片向右滑动时,电流表示数增大
D.在螺线管中插入铁芯,电压表示数减小

(解析) 根据安培定则判断通电螺线管的左端为 N 极,A 项错。分析右侧电路图可知:电阻 R 与 R_2 串联,电压表测 R 两端的电压。左侧电路中变阻器 R_1 的滑片向左滑动时,滑动变阻器接入电路中的电阻变小,则通电螺线管中的电流变大,磁场增强;在螺线管中插入铁芯,磁场也会增强;又知磁敏电阻阻值随磁场增强而变小,根据串联分压原则,当磁场增强时磁敏电阻两端的电压随阻值变小而变小,所以电压表示数减小,B、D 两项正确。反之,R_1 的滑片向右移动,磁敏电阻阻值变大,右侧串联电路中的电流变小,所以 C 项错误。

(答案) BD

例 2 如图所示,电源电压不变,R 为定值电阻,弹簧测力计下端挂一条形磁铁,且与螺线管 B 在同一竖直线上,将开关 S 闭合,条形磁铁静止时,测力计的示数为 F_0,则 （　　）

A.在螺线管中插入铜棒后,测力计的示数增大
B.在螺线管中插入铁棒后,测力计的示数减小
C.只改变电流的方向,测力计的示数增大
D.只减小线圈的匝数,测力计的示数减小

(解析) 当 S 闭合后,由电流的磁效应可知,通电螺线管将有磁性,根据安培定则可知,通电螺线管的上端是 N 极,因为同名磁极相互排斥,所以当通电螺线管产生磁性时,会与条形磁铁相互排斥,在螺线管中插入铜棒后,铜不能被磁化,所以不能使磁性增强,则不能使斥力增大,故测力计的示数不变,A 错误;在螺线管中插入铁棒后,铁棒被磁化,磁性增强,斥力增大,故测力计的示数变小,B 正确;只改变电流的方向,螺线管的磁极对调,与磁体之间由斥力变为引力,所以测力计的示数增大,C 正确;减小线圈匝数,螺线管的磁性减弱,斥力减小,测力计的示数增大,D 错误。选 B、C。

(答案) BC

知识 4 电磁继电器

知识点	内容
电磁继电器	电磁继电器是通过电磁铁,利用低电压、弱电流的通断,来控制高电压、强电流电路的装置
电磁继电器工作原理	电磁铁通电时,把衔铁吸下来,使动触点和静触点接触,工作电路闭合;电磁铁断电时,电磁铁失去磁性,弹簧把衔铁拉起来,切断工作电路
电磁继电器的实质	一个由电磁铁控制的开关

例 在昼夜明灯的地下停车场,驾驶员根据车位入口上方的红绿灯停车。如图是小吴设计的自动控制电路图,将光控开关(遮光时开关闭合)装在每个车位地面中央,红绿灯装在车位入口上方。当车位未停车时绿灯亮,当车位已停车时红灯亮,则图中 L_1、L_2 （　　）

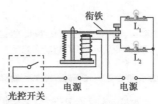

A.都是红灯　　　　　B.都是绿灯
C.分别是红灯、绿灯　　D.分别是绿灯、红灯

(解析) 题图为电磁继电器的应用原理图,当车位停车即遮光时红灯亮,此时光控开关闭合,电磁铁吸

第⑤部分

引衔铁，L_2 接入电路，故 L_2 为红灯；当车位未停车时绿灯亮，此时光控开关断开，电磁铁失去磁性，衔铁弹起，L_1 接入电路，故 L_1 为绿灯。故本题选 D。

（答案）D

知识 5 扬声器

1.作用：扬声器是把电信号转换成声音信号的一种装置。

2.构造：由永久磁体、线圈、锥形纸盆构成，如图所示。

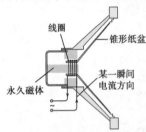

3.原理：线圈通电产生磁性后与永久磁体发生作用，当电流方向如图所示时，两者相吸，通电线圈带动纸盆向左运动；当电流方向改变时，通电线圈带动纸盆向右运动；电流的大小影响纸盆振动的幅度，于是扬声器就发出了随电流变化的声音。

4.应用：收音机、电视机、音箱中都有扬声器。

温馨提示 扬声器与电动机的工作原理相同：都是通电线圈在磁场中受力运动。

拓展知识 **知识** 通电螺线管绕线方法及其画法

知识 通电螺线管绕线方法及其画法

要画通电螺线管的绕线，需要抓住两点：

第一点：找准起点。

起点非常重要，如果第一根线画错了，那么答案正好相反。在绕制时，可按"正上左 N，正下右 N"的

原则，意思是如果向上的电流在螺线管正面，那么左边是 N 极；如果向下的电流在螺线管正面，那么右边是 N 极。

第二点：抓住终点。

最后一根线是从正面绕过去接导线，还是从反面绕过去接导线，如果画错了，会导致导线衔接不上，出现错误。

解决结尾问题，可采用"二一、一二"原则。

①意思是出线和入线在螺线管的两侧（即螺线管上下都有导线），则出线和入线会分布在螺线管同一面上（同正面或同反面），如甲图所示。

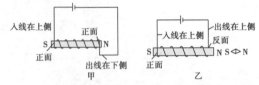

②如乙图所示，出线和入线在螺线管的一个侧面上（都在上面或都在下面），则出线和入线会分布在螺线管两个面上（一个正面，一个反面）。

例 试根据如图所示的电池极性和螺线管的 N、S 极，画出螺线管的绕法。

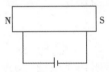

（解析）先根据螺线管的磁极，用安培定则确定螺线管中的电流方向（可用铅笔在图上轻轻画出），然后按"正上左 N"的原则从电源正极流出电流的那端画起，看线是从正面绕到背面符合要求，还是从背面绕到正面符合要求。使正面电流方向向上，先画出第一匝，再依次画出其余线圈使电流流回电源的负极，最后可用安培定则检查一遍。

（答案）如图所示

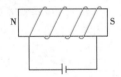

方法清单 **方法** 控制变量法探究电磁铁的磁性强弱与哪些因素有关

方法 控制变量法探究电磁铁的磁性强弱与哪些因素有关

由于电磁铁的磁性强弱与电流的大小、线圈的匝数多少有关。因此，在探究电磁铁磁性强弱与其中某

一因素的关系时，必须同时控制其他因素不变来进行分析比较。

例 为了探究电磁铁的磁性强弱跟哪些因素有关，小琴同学用漆包线（表面涂有绝缘漆的导线）在大铁钉上绕若干匝，制成简单的电磁铁，图甲、乙、丙、丁为实验中观察到的四种情况。

（1）当开关闭合后，请在甲图中标出磁体的 N 极；

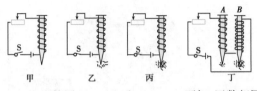

(2)比较图_____和_____可知:匝数相同时,电流越大磁性越强;

(3)由图_____可知:当电流一定时,匝数越多,磁性越强。

解析 由题中乙、丙两图可看出,电磁铁外形和匝数相同,当接入电路的电阻减小,即电流增大时,吸引大头针越多,表明电磁铁磁性越强。由丁图可看出两外形相同的电磁铁是串联,故通过它们的电流相等,匝数越多的吸引大头针越多,其磁性越强。

答案 (1)如图所示 (2)乙 丙 (3)丁

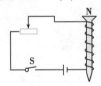

第3节 电动机

基础知识	知识 **1** 探究"磁场对通电导体的作用"
	知识 **2** 电动机的原理

知识 **1** 探究"磁场对通电导体的作用"

提出问题	通电导体在磁场中是否受力的作用
设计实验	将金属轨道放在磁场中,再取一轻质金属杆,放在金属轨道上,将金属轨道连入电路中
实验器材	电源、开关、导线、金属轨道、金属杆、蹄形磁铁、滑动变阻器
实验步骤	(1)将所需器材按如图所示的电路连接好; (2)将金属杆横放在金属轨道上,观察金属杆是否运动; (3)闭合开关,观察金属杆是否运动,运动方向如何? (4)改变电流的方向,观察金属杆是否运动,运动方向如何? (5)保持电流方向不变,改变磁场的方向,观察金属杆的运动情况; (6)同时改变电流方向和磁场方向,观察金属杆的运动情况

实验记录	电流方向	无	$A→B$	$B→A$	$A→B$	$B→A$
	磁场方向	上→下	上→下	上→下	下→上	下→上
	金属杆运动情况	不动	向左移动	向右移动	向右移动	向左移动

实验结论	通电导体在磁场中受到力的作用,力的方向跟导体中的电流方向和磁场方向有关,当电流方向或磁场方向与原来相反时,力的方向也与原来相反;当电流方向和磁场方向同时改变时,力的方向不变

如图所示,把导体 AB 放在蹄形磁铁的磁场里。接通电源,让电流通过原来静止的导体 AB,可以看到 AB 向右滑动,这个现象说明了_____,若保持磁铁的位置不变,改变 AB 中的电流方向,则 AB 向_____滑动;若保持 AB 中的电流方向不变,而对调磁极,则 AB 向_____滑动,这

说明通电导体在磁场中受力的方向跟_____和_____方向有关;这个现象里_____能转化为_____能。

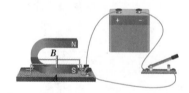

(解析) AB向右滑动,说明通电导体在磁场里受到力的作用。若保持磁铁位置不变即磁场方向不变,而改变AB中的电流方向,则AB受力方向改变,向左滑动;若保持AB中电流方向不变,改变磁极位置即改变磁场方向,则AB向左滑动,这说明通电导体在磁场中受力的方向跟电流方向和磁场方向有关。在此过程中电能转化为机械能。

(答案) 通电导体在磁场中受力的作用　左　左　电流方向　磁场　电　机械

知识2 电动机的原理

工作原理	直流电动机是根据通电线圈在磁场中受力的作用而发生转动的原理制成的
基本构造	直流电动机主要由两部分组成,即能够转动的线圈和固定不动的磁体。在电动机里,能够转动的部分叫转子,固定不动的部分叫定子,电动机工作时,转子在定子中飞快地转动。如图所示
能量转化	电能转化为机械能
换向器	(1)构造:由两个铜半环构成 (2)作用:能自动地改变线圈中的电流方向,使线圈能连续转动
优点	构造简单、控制方便、体积小、效率高、功率可大可小、价格低、无污染

(例) 如图所示,线圈abcd位于磁场中。K与1接通时,ab段导线受磁场力F的方向向上;当K改为与2接通时,ab段导线受磁场力　　　　　(　　)

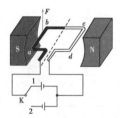

A.方向向下
B.方向向上
C.为零,因为电源反接
D.为零,因为电路一定是断路

(解析) 题图是电动机的模型,其工作原理是通电导体在磁场中受到力的作用而转动,影响导体受力方向的因素是磁场方向和导体中电流的方向。当K由与1接通改为与2接通时,在同一磁场中导线ab中的电流方向与之前相反,所以其受力方向与之前相反,所以A项正确,B、C、D三项错误。

(答案) A

拓展知识　知识 直流电动机不转或转速过小的原因

知识 直流电动机不转或转速过小的原因

安装直流电动机模型时,线圈不转的原因主要有电路断路、磁铁无磁性和线圈处于平衡位置等几种情况。转速过小是因为电流小或磁性弱。

例1 正确连接好直流电动机模型的电路后,合上开关,电动机不转,试列出可能产生故障的原因及相应排除故障的方法。
(1)_____,排除故障的办法_____;
(2)_____,排除故障的办法_____;
(3)_____,排除故障的办法_____。

(解析) 通电线圈在磁场作用下才能运动,如果磁铁失去磁性,电动机就不会转动。电动机靠换向器改变线圈中电流方向,使线圈连续转动,但若换向器接触不良,则不能使线圈转动。线圈通过平衡位置时靠的是惯性,但线圈如果原来是静止在平衡位置上的,那么线圈将保持静止的状态。

(答案) (1)磁铁无磁性　更换磁铁　(2)电刷与换向器接触不良　可压紧电刷与换向器　(3)线圈处于平衡位置　让线圈转过平衡位置

例2 小明同学想使一台直流电动机模型的转速增大,他采用的方法正确的是　　　　(　　)
A.增大电流　　　　B.改变电流方向
C.减小电流　　　　D.把磁铁两极对调

(解析) 根据直流电动机的原理,要想增大直流电

动机模型的转速,可增大其线圈所受的磁场力,而要增大磁场力可采用增大通过线圈的电流或增大磁体

的磁性的办法。

答案 A

方法 控制变量法探究通电导体在磁场中的受力方向与哪些因素有关

1.通电导体在磁场中受力情况的判定常与电动机原理相结合;通电导体在磁场中受力方向与磁场方向和电流方向有关。

2.探究受力方向与电流方向的关系时,需控制磁场方向相同;探究受力方向与磁场方向的关系时,需控制电流方向相同。

例 如图所示,导体放入(a)图磁场中的受力方向已经标出,请在(b)图、(c)图上标出它的受力方向。

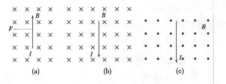

(a)　　　(b)　　　(c)

解析 通电导体在磁场中的受力方向与电流方向和磁场方向都有关系。运用控制变量法:在磁场方向相同时,根据电流方向判断磁场力方向;在电流方向相同时,根据磁场方向判断磁场力方向。

比较图(a)、(b):磁场方向相同,都是垂直纸面向里,电流方向相反,受磁场力方向也应相反,(a)图中磁场力的方向水平向左,则(b)图中磁场力的方向水平向右。

比较图(b)、(c):电流方向相同而磁场方向相反,受到磁场力的方向也应该相反,因(b)图中磁场力的方向水平向右,所以(c)图中磁场力的方向应水平向左。

答案 如图甲、乙

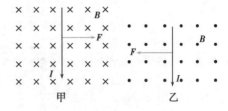

甲　　　　　　乙

第4节　磁生电

知识清单

基础知识 知识① 电磁感应　知识② 发电机原理
知识③ 麦克风(话筒)　知识④ 变压器与高压输电

知识 1 电磁感应

电磁感应的定义	闭合电路的一部分导体在磁场中做切割磁感线运动时产生电流的现象称为电磁感应,电磁感应中产生的电流称为感应电流
产生感应电流的条件	一是"闭合电路的一部分导体",这句话包括两层意思:①电路应该是闭合的,而不是断开的,即组成电路的各元件连接成一个电流的通路;②导体一定是闭合电路的一部分。二是"做切割磁感线运动",所谓切割磁感线,可以是垂直切割,也可以是斜着切割,但导体运动方向不能与磁场方向平行,可能是导体运动,也可能是磁场运动

续表

与感应电流方向有关的因素	在电磁感应现象中,感应电流的方向跟导体切割磁感线运动的方向和磁场方向有关,若将导体运动方向改为与原运动方向相反,或将磁场方向改为与原方向相反,则感应电流方向将与原方向相反;若导体运动方向和磁场方向都变为与原来相反,则感应电流的方向不变
能量转化	机械能转化为电能
应用	发电机、动圈式话筒、变压器等

例 小黄利用如图所示装置探究产生感应电流的条件。

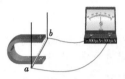

（1）当导体棒 ab 在磁铁内沿竖直方向上下运动时，电流计指针_____（填"不动"或"动"），表明_____电流产生；

（2）当导体棒 ab 在磁铁内沿左右方向运动时，电流计指针_____（填"不动"或"动"）；

（3）当导体棒 ab 在磁铁内沿前后方向运动时，电流计指针_____（填"不动"或"动"）。

（4）通过对比可知，产生感应电流的条件是闭合电路的一部分导体在磁场中做_____运动。

解析 导体棒 ab 上下或前后运动时，不切割磁感线，电路中没有感应电流产生，电流计指针不动；导体棒 ab 左右运动时，闭合电路的一部分导体切割磁感线，电路中有感应电流产生，电流计指针会发生偏转。

答案 （1）不动 没有 （2）动 （3）不动 （4）切割磁感线

点拨 导体切割磁感线有两种方式：一种是磁场不动导体动（如本题中磁铁静止，ab 棒运动）；另一种是导体不动磁场动（题中也可采用 ab 棒静止，磁体左右运动）。

知识 2 发电机原理

1.工作原理：如图所示，交流发电机中的闭合线圈在磁场中转动，切割磁感线，产生感应电流，故发电机的原理是电磁感应。

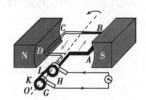

2.能量转化：在发电过程中，发电机把机械能转化为电能。

例 如图所示，是一个磁信息阅读器。只要将磁卡刷过，检测头中就会产生感应电流，便能得到相应的信息。以下电器件中工作原理与此相同的是（　）

A.扬声器　　　　　B.发电机
C.电磁继电器　　　D.电铃

解析 由题中提供的信息：将磁卡刷过，检测头中就会产生感应电流，可得其应用的是电磁感应原理，故与此工作原理相同的是发电机，本题应选择 B。

答案 B

知识 3 麦克风(话筒)

（1）麦克风也叫话筒，它是一种将振动转换成变化电流的装置。

（2）声音是由物体振动产生的，当对着话筒说话时，声音的振动使膜片发生振动，与膜片相连的线圈也跟着一起振动，线圈在磁场中能产生感应电流，即通过电磁感应将声音变成电流。

（3）由于声音的大小变化，线圈的振动也是强弱不同的，产生的感应电流也会随着变化。

（4）变化的电流由扬声器还原为声音。

例 动圈式话筒的结构如图，它工作时：①线圈振动能产生随着声音变化而变化的电流；②与膜片相连的线圈随之一起振动；③人唱歌或说话产生的声音使膜片振动；④变化的电流经过放大后，由扬声器还原为声音。关于它的原理，排序正确的是（　）

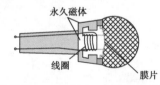

A.①②③④　　　　B.②①④③
C.③①④②　　　　D.③②①④

解析 有声音时先使膜片振动，线圈与膜片是相连的，会引起线圈的振动，线圈振动会切割磁感线，产生感应电流，电流放大后，由扬声器还原为声音就把声音放大了。

答案 D

知识 4 变压器与高压输电

1.变压器的工作原理是电磁感应，它能将输入变压器的交流电压升高(升压变压器)，也可以降低(降压变压器)。变压器不能改变直流电压。

2.从发电厂输出的交流电先经过变压器把电压升高,然后将高压电输送到远方的用户附近,再经过变压器把电压降低,供用户使用。

3.由于输电线有电阻,因而在电能输送的过程中,电能损失是不可避免的。在输送功率一定的情况下,由$I=P/U$可知,提高输电电压能够减小输电电流,又由$Q=I^2Rt$可知在输电线上的损失减少。所以为了减少电能损耗,远距离输电要用高电压。

温馨提示 因为高压输电输送功率一定,计算时首先根据$P_输=U_输I$求出输电线中的电流I,再根据$P_线=I^2R_线$求出输电线损失的功率。

例 一座水电站输送的电功率是 4 800 kW,输电线电压是 220 kV,若输电线总电阻为 0.5 Ω,那么输电线路损失的电功率是多少?如果改用 10 kV 的电压输电,输电线路上损失的电功率是多少?

解析 $I_1=\dfrac{P_1}{U_1}=\dfrac{4\ 800\ \text{kW}}{220\ \text{kV}}=\dfrac{240}{11}\ \text{A}$

$P_{损失1}=I_1^2R=\left(\dfrac{240}{11}\ \text{A}\right)^2\times0.5\ \Omega\approx238.02\ \text{W}$

$I_2=\dfrac{P_2}{U_2}=\dfrac{4\ 800\ \text{kW}}{10\ \text{kV}}=480\ \text{A}$

$P_{损失2}=I_2^2R=(480\ \text{A})^2\times0.5\ \Omega=1.152\times10^5\ \text{W}$

答案 238.02 W　1.152×10⁵ W

拓展知识 　知识❶ 直流电动机与交流发电机的比较
知识❷ 交流电特征

知识 1 直流电动机与交流发电机的比较

		直流电动机	交流发电机
构造	相同	均由磁体、线圈组成	
	不同	需要换向器(两个铜半环),外电路上有电源	用两个铜环和电刷连接电路,外电路上无电源
原理	不同	磁场对通电线圈的作用	电磁感应现象
用途	相同	两者一起帮助人类利用水能、内能、核能等	
	不同	电能转化为机械能	机械能转化为电能

易混对比 　电动机与发电机的识别
区别电动机与发电机,要分清是通电后运动,还是运动产生电,从而确定电能与机械能的转化;装置方面一个有电源,一个没有电源,电动机是通电产生运动,所以有电源的是电动机,没电源的是发电机。

例 如图所示的是直流发电机的工作原理图,关于直流发电机下列说法中正确的是 （　　）

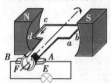

A.直流发电机线圈内产生的是交流电,供给外部电路的是直流电

B.直流发电机线圈内产生的是直流电,供给外部电路的也是直流电

C.它是利用通电线圈在磁场中受到力的作用而

转动的原理工作的

D.图中的 E、F 称为换向器,它的作用是改变线圈中的电流方向

解析 线圈的 ab、cd 两边在转动时切割磁感线的方向会发生改变,因此产生的感应电流的方向会发生变化,产生的是交流电。外电路中有两个铜半环,能保证电流流出时从一个方向经过灯泡,是直流电。

答案 A

点拨 任何发电机线圈中产生的电流都是交流电,方向都是周期性变化的。如果外接换向器则输出的是直流电;如果不接换向器,则输出的是交流电。

知识 2 交流电特征

1.发电机输出的这种周期性地改变方向的电流,叫交变电流,简称交流。

2.在交变电流中,电流在每秒内周期性变化的次数叫做频率,频率的单位是赫兹,符号 Hz,我国的交流频率是 50 Hz。

例 电流方向_____的电流叫交流,我国生产和生活中的交流的频率是_____,电流方向每秒钟改变_____次。

解析 解答本题时要注意:(1)是周期性改变,不

是随便地改变;(2)每秒内有一个周期对应 1 Hz,一个周期内电流方向改变 2 次,50 Hz 就是每秒内有 50 个周期,电流方向改变 100 次。

答案 周期性改变 50 Hz 100

方法
清单
方法1 控制变量法探究电磁感应现象
方法2 逆向思维法区分电动机和发电机

方法 1 控制变量法探究电磁感应现象

感应电流的产生及方向不只与一个因素有关,在研究感应电流的产生及方向与哪些因素有关时,我们用到了控制变量法。

例 某实验小组利用如图所示的实验装置探究电磁感应现象:

(1)小黄探究感应电流方向与哪些因素有关时,猜想金属棒在磁场中运动产生的感应电流的方向可能与磁场的方向有关,也可能与金属棒的运动方向有关。他进行了如下实验操作:

①使金属棒向右运动,看到灵敏电流计指针向左偏。

②把磁铁南、北极上下对调,金属棒变为向左运动,看到灵敏电流计指针仍向左偏。

根据以上现象,小黄得出感应电流的方向与磁场的方向、金属棒的运动方向无关的结论。

你认为小黄的结论正确吗? 若认为正确,请说明理由;若认为错误,请分析小黄得出错误结论的原因。

(2)小李所在实验小组想进一步探究感应电流的大小跟哪些因素有关,小李猜想:可能跟导体切割磁感线运动的快慢有关。

请你根据图示的实验装置,帮助小李设计实验来验证她的猜想,你设计的实验做法是:_____。

解析 (1)小黄的结论错误,他在实验过程中没有控制变量。要研究感应电流方向和磁场方向的关系,应该控制运动方向不变,改变磁场方向,观察灵敏

电流计指针偏转方向;要研究感应电流方向与金属棒的运动方向的关系,应该控制磁场方向不变,改变金属棒的运动方向,观察电流表指针偏转方向。

(2)本实验要应用控制变量法。在其他条件不变的情况下,只改变导体切割磁感线运动的速度,然后观察灵敏电流计指针的偏转程度。

答案 见解析

方法 2 逆向思维法区分电动机和发电机

从问题反方向的角度进行研究,即逆向思维法,它是科学研究的重要方法。电动机和发电机都是由线圈和磁体构成的,研究问题时注意认清是通电线圈在磁场中受力转动,还是线圈在磁场中做切割磁感线运动。

例 小明将微风电风扇与小灯泡按如图所示的电路连接并进行实验。用手快速拨动风扇叶片,这时发现小灯泡发光,微风电风扇居然变成了"发电机"。关于该实验,下列说法正确的是 ( )

A.电风扇发电的原理是电磁感应

B.电风扇发电的原理是通电导线在磁场中受到力的作用

C.电风扇发电过程是把电能转化为机械能

D.小灯泡发光是把光能转化为电能

解析 电动机的基本构造与发电机相同,都是由线圈和磁体组成的。当旋转风扇叶片时,会带动里面的线圈转动,切割磁感线,从而产生电流,将机械能转化为电能。小灯泡发光是把电能转化为光能。电风扇发电的原理是电磁感应。

答案 A

第5节 信息的传递

知识清单

> **基础知识**
> 知识**1** 话筒、听筒的构造及电话的工作原理
> 知识**2** 电磁波
> 知识**3** 电磁波与现代信息传递
> 知识**4** 广播、电视和移动通信
> 知识**5** 光纤通信、卫星通信与网络通信

知识 1 话筒、听筒的构造及电话的工作原理

1.话筒、听筒的构造

(1)话筒基本构造:老式话筒中有一个装着炭粒的小盒子,上面盖有膜片,如图甲所示。

(2)听筒基本构造:听筒内有一个永磁铁,永磁铁上绕着线圈,永磁铁前面有一个薄铁膜片,如图乙所示。

 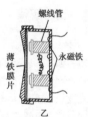

2.电话的工作原理

$$\boxed{声音(振动)} \xrightarrow{话筒} \boxed{变化的电流} \xrightarrow{听筒} \boxed{振动(声音)}$$

(1)话筒中有能振动的膜片和随话音跳动的炭粒。人们对着话筒说话时,膜片便随着声音的强弱而发生振动,从而压缩炭粒一紧一松,这样就把强度不同的声音变成了相应大小的电信号。

(2)听筒里有电磁铁和膜片。通话时,一方的话筒和另一方听筒是串联的。当对方强弱不同的电信号传到听筒后,电磁铁便将电信号变成膜片的强弱不同的振动,把声音还原出来。

例 下列叙述正确的是 （ ）

A.话筒的作用是把声音直接传递到对方的听筒

B.话筒的作用是把忽大忽小的电流转化为声音

C.话筒的作用是把声音的振动转化成大小变化的电流

D.话筒的作用是把电流直接传递到对方的听筒

(解析) 话筒把声音信号转化为电信号,传到对方的听筒中,通过听筒还原成声音。

(答案) C

知识 2 电磁波

1.电磁波的产生

迅速变化的电流能在周围的空间中产生电磁波。

2.电磁波的传播

电磁波的传播不需要介质,因而电磁波可以在真空中传播(如图),其速度与光速相同,为 $3×10^8$ m/s。

3.电磁波的特征

频率和波长是描述电磁波特征的物理量。电磁波频率的单位是赫兹(Hz)、千赫(kHz)、兆赫(MHz),它们之间的换算关系是 1 kHz = 10^3 Hz, 1 MHz = 10^6 Hz。电磁波波长的单位是米(m)。

4.电磁波的波速、波长和频率的关系

波速=波长×频率,即 $c = \lambda f$。

> **温馨提示** 不同频率(或波长)的电磁波在真空中的波速相同。

例 我国自行研制的北斗卫星导航系统具有定位、导航和通信等功能,它传递信息是利用 （ ）

A.超声波　　　　　　　B.次声波

C.微波　　　　　　　　D.激光

(解析) 超声波和次声波都不能在真空中传播,激光是一种波长很短的电磁波,它的能量较强,可以穿透物体,北斗卫星导航系统传递信息利用的是另一种电磁波——微波,因此答案为C。

(答案) C

知识 3 电磁波与现代信息传递

1.电磁波是现代社会最主要的信息载体。正是因为有了电磁波,我们才能在任何地方都能收看电视,

收听广播,接收到手机信号;正是因为有了电磁波,我们才能在汪洋大海中、在太空中建立广泛联系。

2.电磁波的频率越高,所能传输的信息量越大。

3.电磁波传递信息的方式有两类:一是以模拟信号传播(分为调频和调幅两种方式);二是以数字信号传播[主要用于电脑、数字电视、数字通信(如图)等]。

例 3G时代的到来,将使我们可以使用3G手机随时随地进行无线网络登录。对于手机无线上网,下列说法正确的是 ( )

A.使用电磁波传输数字信号

B.使用电磁波传输模拟信号

C.使用超声波传输数字信号

D.使用红外线传输模拟信号

(解析) 手机是利用电磁波来传递信息的,它的无线上网功能使用的是数字信号。

(答案) A

知识 4 广播、电视和移动通信

1.无线电广播和电视都是将要传递的信息(声音、图像)转变为电信号,加载到高频电流上,然后通过天线将电磁波发射到空中,人们再利用收音机、电视机的天线将这样的高频信号接收下来,再经过专门的装置将电信号还原成声音信号和图像信号。

2.手机(移动电话)既是无线电发射装置,又是无线电接收装置,手机之间通话时,将要传递的信息加载到电磁波上发射出去,同时接收对方手机加载到电磁波上的信息。手机之间的通话要靠基地台转接。

温馨提示 收音机只接收电磁波,而手机可以发射和接收电磁波。

知识 5 光纤通信、卫星通信与网络通信

1.光可以沿着弯曲的水流和玻璃丝传播。

为了减少传输损耗,我们现在用高纯度的石英玻璃制成光导纤维来传递光信号。光纤也可以像电缆一样做成多芯的光缆。

光在光导纤维中传输损耗小,可长距离传输,光纤通信容量极大,不怕雷击,不受电磁干扰,通信质量高,保密性好。

2.卫星通信是用通信卫星作为微波通信的中继

站。用通信卫星作为中继站,可以使它转发的信号跨越大陆和海洋,覆盖地球上的很大范围。现在我们看到的很多电视节目都是通过卫星传送的。

通信卫星大多是相对地球"静止"的同步卫星,在地球周围均匀配置三颗通信卫星就可以几乎实现全球通信。

3.计算机网络,是指将地理位置不同的具有独立功能的多台计算机及其外部设备,通过通信线路连接起来,在网络操作系统、网络管理软件及网络通信协议的管理和协调下,实现资源共享和信息传递的计算机系统。利用计算机网络进行的通信叫做网络通信。

例 在光纤通信中,用来传递信息的光是 ( )

A.普通光源发出的光　　　B.激光

C.太阳光　　　　　　　　D.以上都可以

(解析) 普通光源发出的光和太阳光太分散,在光纤通信中,用来传递信息的光是激光。

(答案) B

拓展知识 知识 电磁波谱

知识 电磁波谱

1.电磁波谱

(1)电磁波包括的范围很广,无线电波、红外线、可见光、紫外线、X射线、γ射线都是电磁波。它们在频率或波长上有很大差别。

(2)光波的频率比无线电波的频率要高很多,光波的波长比无线电波的波长短很多;而X射线和γ射线的频率则更高,波长则更短。

(3)为了对各种电磁波有个全面的了解,人们按照波长或频率的顺序把这些电磁波排列起来,这就是电磁波谱(如图)。

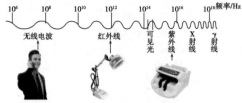

2.微波

微波通常有穿透、反射、吸收三个特性。遇到玻璃、塑料和瓷器,微波几乎是穿透而不被吸收;遇到水和食物,微波被吸收,从而使食物自身发热;遇到金属类物品,微波会被反射。

例 举出以下四种电磁波在人们生活、生产中应用的事例(每种电磁波各举一例)。

(1)无线电波:_____;

（2）微波：＿＿＿＿＿＿＿＿＿＿＿；
（3）紫外线：＿＿＿＿＿＿＿＿＿＿＿；
（4）X 射线：＿＿＿＿＿＿＿＿＿＿＿。

解析 短波、中波、长波称为无线电波，可利用到通信广播事业上，广播电台就是利用无线电波广播。因为微波具有反射、吸收、穿透三种特性，应用于通

信、微波炉。紫外线有杀菌的作用，所以医院利用紫外线杀菌。X 射线用于拍摄医学 X 光片。

答案 （1）广播电台利用无线电波广播 （2）微波炉利用微波加热 （3）医院利用紫外线杀菌
（4）医院利用 X 射线对人体透视

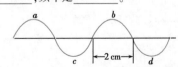

方法 公式法计算电磁波的波长和频率

方法 公式法计算电磁波的波长和频率

电磁波的波速（c）、波长（λ）、频率（f）三者的关系是 $c=\lambda f$。只要知道其中任意两个，就可用此公式计算出第三个。

例1 兰州人民广播电台现办有三套节目，第一套为新闻综合广播，发射频率为 AM954 kHz、FM97.3 MHz，其中 AM 表示＿＿＿＿＿；发射频率为 AM954 kHz 的电磁波波长为＿＿＿＿＿m（计算结果保留一位小数）。

解析 发射频率为 AM954 kHz、FM97.3 MHz，其中 AM 表示调幅，FM 表示调频；电磁波在真空中的波速都是 3×10^8 m/s，发射频率为 AM954 kHz 的电磁波的波长 $\lambda=\dfrac{c}{f}=\dfrac{3\times10^8\ \text{m/s}}{9.54\times10^5\ \text{Hz}}\approx314.5$ m。

答案 调幅 314.5

例2 某电磁波的波形如图所示，则该电磁波的波长是＿＿＿＿＿，频率是＿＿＿＿＿。

解析 相邻两个波峰（或波谷）之间的距离叫做波长。观察图像可知，波长为 4 cm＝0.04 m。根据波速＝波长×频率，电磁波的频率 $f=\dfrac{c}{\lambda}=\dfrac{3\times10^8\ \text{m/s}}{0.04\ \text{m}}=7.5\times10^9$ Hz。

答案 0.04 m 7.5×10⁹ Hz

附录

附录 1　常用的研究方法及其应用

名称	简介	应用举例
等效替代法	在物理学中,在保证某种效果相同的前提下,将一个物理量、物理状态或过程用另一个物理量、物理状态或过程来替代,得到同样的结论,这种研究问题的方法叫做等效替代法。运用这种方法可以使所要研究的问题简单化、直观化	(1)在"曹冲称象"中,用石块等效替代大象,效果相同 (2)在力的合成中,用一个合力可以等效替代几个力的共同作用的效果 (3)在电路中,若干个电阻对电流的阻碍作用可以等效为一个电阻 (4)在分析电路时,可以将一个复杂的电路等效为一个简单的电路
理想模型法	把复杂的问题简单化,摒弃次要因素,抓住主要因素,对实际问题进行理想化处理,构建理想化的物理模型,这是一种重要的物理思想。有时为了更加形象地描述所要研究的物理现象、物理问题,还需要引入一些模型	(1)研究原子结构时,将肉眼观察不到的原子结构设想为原子核式结构模型(行星模型) (2)匀速直线运动就是一种理想模型。在生活实际中,严格的匀速直线运动并不存在,但有很多运动情形都近似于匀速直线运动,按匀速直线运动来处理,大大降低了难度 (3)在研究连通器的原理时,理想液片是一种理想模型 (4)光线、磁感线都是引入的模型,它们直观、形象地描述了物理情境与事实。通过磁感线可以研究磁场的分布,通过光线可以研究光的传播路径和方向 (5)电路图是实际电路的模型,可以简单明了地反映实际电路的连接情况
控制变量法	在研究物理问题时,某一物理量往往受几个不同因素的影响,为了确定该物理量与各个不同因素之间的关系,就需要控制某些因素,使其固定不变,只研究其中一个因素,看所研究的因素与该物理量之间的关系,这种研究问题的方法叫做控制变量法。这种研究方法是物理探究实验中最常用的一种研究方法	(1)研究弦乐器的音调与弦的材料、长度和横截面积的关系 (2)研究蒸发快慢与液体温度、表面积和空气流速的关系 (3)研究力的作用效果与力的大小、方向和作用点的关系 (4)研究滑动摩擦力与物体间的压力和接触面粗糙程度的关系 (5)研究压力的作用效果与压力和受力面积的关系 (6)研究液体压强与液体的密度和深度的关系 (7)研究浮力与液体密度和物体排开液体体积的关系 (8)研究物体的动能与物体质量、速度的关系 (9)研究物体的重力势能与物体质量、被举高度的关系 (10)研究导体的电阻与导体的材料、长度和横截面积的关系 (11)研究电流与电压、电阻的关系 (12)研究电功率与电压、电流的关系 (13)研究电流产生的热量与导体的电阻、电流和通电时间的关系 (14)研究电磁铁的磁性强弱与线圈的匝数、电流的大小的关系 (15)研究感应电流的方向与磁场方向、导体运动方向的关系
理想实验法	理想实验法是以大量可靠的事实为基础,以真实的实验为原型,通过合理的推理得出结论,深刻地揭示出物理规律的本质,是物理学研究问题的一种重要的思想方法	(1)研究力与运动的关系,推理出牛顿第一定律 (2)将闹钟放在钟罩内,不断抽去罩内空气,听到的铃声越来越弱,由此推理出真空不能传声

名称	简介	应用举例
转换法	在物理学中,对于一些看不见、摸不着的现象或不易直接测量的物理量,通常用一些非常直观的现象去认识或用易测量的物理量间接测量,这种研究方法称为转换法	(1)音叉的振动幅度很微小,不容易直接观察到。研究声音是由振动产生时,用乒乓球的可视的振动认识音叉的振动 (2)压力的作用效果不好理解,研究压力的作用效果时,用海绵的凹陷程度来表示 (3)电流的有无与大小不能直接观察。往往根据灯泡是否发光及发光程度、电流表指针是否发生偏转及示数的大小来判断电流的有无和大小 (4)磁场看不见、摸不到,不好研究。在判断磁场是否存在时,将小磁针放在其中,看是否转动来确定 (5)电磁铁的磁性强弱不能直接观察到。在实验时,用吸引大头针个数多少观察电磁铁磁性强弱
类比法	所谓类比法,就是把在某些方面相同或相似的对象或事物进行对比的一种思维方法。类比可以帮助我们从较复杂的事物或现象中,提取出有用的信息或答案,合理类比,还可以降低知识的认知难度,从而对知识透彻理解。通过类比,可以把抽象的、无形的、陌生的事物用直观的、有形的、熟悉的事物来说明,并且找出类似的规律	(1)研究声波、电磁波时,将声波、电磁波与水波进行类比,理解其产生和传播 (2)研究电流时,用水流来类比电流 (3)研究电压时,用水压来类比电压 (4)研究电路时,用水路来类比电路:用抽水机类比电源,用水轮机类比用电器,用阀门类比开关,用水管类比导线等
归纳法	在大量经验材料的基础上,从具体事物中抽象出共同本质,从特殊实例中概括出一般规律的推理方法。在所有的科学实验和原理的得出中,我们几乎都用到了这种研究方法	通过声带振动发声、尺子振动发声、拨动张紧的橡皮筋、敲响音叉等实例,总结出物体发声时的共同特征是:声是由物体的振动产生的
比较法	当要寻找两件事物的相同和不同之处,就需要用到比较法,对不同或有联系的两个对象进行比较,我们主要从中寻找它们的不同点和相同点,从而进一步揭示事物的本质属性。利用比较法可加深对它们的理解,利于区别记忆	(1)比较蒸发和沸腾的异同点 (2)比较汽油机和柴油机的异同点 (3)比较电压表和电流表的使用方法的异同点 (4)比较电与磁的异同点 (5)比较电动机和热机的异同点 (6)比较发电机和电动机的异同点

附录

附录2 一些常见的物理量及其单位

物理量		单位①		单位换算	计算公式
名称	符号	名称	符号		
摄氏温度	t	摄氏度	℃	0 ℃ = 273.15 K	—
长度(路程)	$l(s)$	米	m	1 km = 10^3 m 1 m = 10 dm = 100 cm = 10^3 mm = 10^6 μm = 10^9 nm	—
时间	t	秒	s	1 h = 3 600 s	—
速度	v	米每秒	m/s	1 m/s = 3.6 km/h	$v = \dfrac{s}{t}$
面积	S	平方米	m^2	1 m^2 = 10^2 dm^2 = 10^4 cm^2 = 10^6 mm^2	—
体积	V	立方米	m^3	1 m^3 = 10^3 dm^3 = 10^6 cm^3 = 10^9 mm^3 1 L = 10^3 mL 1 L = 1 dm^3 1 mL = 1 cm^3	—
质量	m	千克	kg	1 t = 10^3 kg 1 kg = 10^3 g = 10^6 mg	—
密度	ρ	千克每立方米	kg/m^3	1 g/cm^3 = 10^3 kg/m^3	$\rho = \dfrac{m}{V}$
力(重力)	$F(G)$	牛顿(牛)	N	—	$G = mg$
压强	p	帕斯卡(帕)	Pa	1 Pa = 1 N/m^2	$p = \dfrac{F}{S}$
功	W	焦耳(焦)	J	1 J = 1 N · m	$W = Fs$
功率	P	瓦特(瓦)	W	1 W = 1 J/s	$P = \dfrac{W}{t}$
能量(内能)	E	焦耳(焦)	J	—	—
热值	q	焦每千克	J/kg	—	—
热量	Q	焦耳(焦)	J	—	$Q = mq$ $Q_{吸} = cm(t-t_0)$ $Q_{放} = cm(t_0-t)$
比热容	c	焦每千克摄氏度	J/(kg · ℃)	—	—
电压	U	伏特(伏)	V	1 kV = 10^3 V 1 V = 10^3 mV	—
电流	I	安培(安)	A	1 A = 10^3 mA = 10^6 μA	—
电阻	R	欧姆(欧)	Ω	1 MΩ = 10^3 kΩ = 10^6 Ω	—
电功	W	焦耳(焦)	J	1 kW · h = 3.6×10^6 J 1 J = 1 V · A · s	$W = UIt$
电功率	P	瓦特(瓦)	W	1 W = 1 J/s = 1 V · A	$P = \dfrac{W}{t} = UI$

①"单位"是国际单位制的主单位,括号内为该单位的中文简称。(温度除外,温度的国际单位是"开尔文",简称"开",用符号"K"表示)

附录3　一些重要的物理观点、现象或史实与相应的科学家

物理观点、现象或事实	发现者	发现时间	备注
小孔成像	墨子(中国)	两千多年前	记载于《墨经》一书
日光色散实验	牛顿(英国)	1666 年	说明太阳光是由各种色光混合而成的
力是维持物体运动状态的原因	亚里士多德(古希腊)	两千多年前	—
理想斜面实验	伽利略(意大利)	300 多年前	力是改变物体运动状态的原因
牛顿第一定律	牛顿(英国)	—	揭示了力和运动的关系
帕斯卡定律	帕斯卡(法国)	1653 年	液压机的原理
马德堡半球实验	奥托·格里克(德国)	1654 年	证明了大气压的存在
托里拆利实验	托里拆利(意大利)	1644 年	测出大气压的数值
伯努利原理	伯努利(瑞士)	1738 年	流体流速越大,压强越小
阿基米德原理(浮力原理)	阿基米德(古希腊)	两千多年前	物体所受浮力等于它排开的液体所受的重力,$F_{浮} = G_{排}$
杠杆平衡条件	阿基米德(古希腊)	两千多年前	—
欧姆定律	欧姆(德国)	19 世纪初	电流跟电压、电阻的关系
焦耳定律	焦耳(英国)	1840 年	电热与电流、电阻和通电时间的关系
磁偏角的发现	沈括(中国)	宋代	比西方早 400 多年
电流的磁效应	奥斯特(丹麦)	1820 年	电流周围存在磁场
电磁感应现象	法拉第(英国)	1831 年	发电机的原理
发明了电话	贝尔(美国)	1876 年	—
电子的发现	汤姆生(英国)	1897 年	—
α 粒子散射实验	卢瑟福(英籍)	1919 年	提出原子核式结构(行星模型)

光(电磁波)在真空中的传播速度	3.0×10^8 m/s
声音在空气中的传播速度(15 ℃)	340 m/s
冰的熔点	0 ℃
水的沸点(标准大气压下)	100 ℃
水的比热容	4.2×10^3 J/(kg·℃)
水的密度	1.0×10^3 kg/m^3
冰的密度	0.9×10^3 kg/m^3
酒精的密度	0.8×10^3 kg/m^3
铁的密度	7.9×10^3 kg/m^3
铜的密度	8.9×10^3 kg/m^3
g 的数值	9.8 N/kg
1 标准大气压的数值	1.01×10^5 Pa、760 毫米汞柱
1 节干电池的电压	1.5 V
1 节铅蓄电池的电压	2 V
对人体安全的电压	不高于 36 V
我国照明电压	220 V
我国交流电的频率	50 Hz
我国交流电的周期	0.02 s

附录5　一些常用的生活中的数据

1 张纸厚度约 10^{-4} m

邮票质量 50 mg 左右,15 根火柴质量 1 g 左右

人步行正常速度为 1 m/s~1.5 m/s;骑自行车的正常速度为 3 m/s~5 m/s

一个鸡蛋的质量约为 50 g,举起两个鸡蛋用力约为 1 N

物理课本的质量约为 300 g,长约 25.5 cm,宽约 19 cm,面积约 5 dm^2

普通鸡蛋、人体的平均密度约为 1 g/cm^3,合 1.0×10^3 kg/m^3

报纸平时对桌面的压强约 0.5 Pa,砖块平放时对地面的压强约为 10^3 Pa

一名中学生的质量约为 40 kg,每只脚与地面的接触面积约为 150 cm^2,中学生对水平面的压强约为 10^4 Pa

普通墨水瓶的高度约为 6 cm,容积约为 60 mL

普通照明灯泡正常工作时的电流约为 0.2 A,功率约为 40~100 W

在正常工作时,冰箱的功率约为 120 W,电热水器的功率约为 800 W,微波炉的功率约为 1 100 W

彩电的功率约为 70~150 W,电脑的功率约为 200 W,人骑车的功率约为 80 W

一起找茬 有理有礼

图书纠错 意见反馈 真伪查询 举报盗版

扫描二维码进入平台

嗨，同学：

小曲为你刨出一块"自留地"——图书反馈平台，来这里找"茬"，一起赢话费。

来找茬儿

发现图书错误，及时在平台上反馈，每处错误第一位反馈者将获得20元话费奖励。

给我们好点子

对图书有什么好建议、好想法，通过平台告诉我们，只要意见被采纳，就会获得50元话费奖励。

担心买到的是假书怎么办？

刮开图书防伪标识涂层，输入防伪码即可查询真伪（温馨提示：防伪码只能输入一次，第二次输入会提示盗版）。一旦发现盗版，请立即向我们举报，你我携手让盗版无所遁形。

联系方式

- ☑ 盗版举报电话：010-87606918
- ☑ 邮购热线：400 898 5353（免长途费）、13311185353
- ☑ 客服热线：010-63735353

声明

本书所选用的部分资料，因各种原因而未能及时联系到的作者，查询稿酬及其他有关稿酬的未明事宜，请与曲一线联系（010-87605580）。

图书在版编目(CIP)数据

初中物理知识清单/曲一线主编.—北京:首都
师范大学出版社,2011.5(2018.4 重印)
ISBN 978-7-5656-0374-7

Ⅰ.①初… Ⅱ.①曲… Ⅲ.①中学物理课—初中
—教学参考资料 Ⅳ.①G634.73

中国版本图书馆 CIP 数据核字(2011)第 081957 号

CHUZHONG WULI ZHISHI QINGDAN
初中物理知识清单
主 编 曲一线

责任编辑 张 轩　　　　　　　　　责任录排 王 慧

出版发行 首都师范大学出版社
　　　　 北京西三环北路 105 号　　100048

教育科学出版社
　　　　 北京·朝阳区安慧北里安园甲 9 号　　100101

电　话 68418523(总编室) 68982468(发行部)
网　址 http://cnupn.cnu.edu.cn
北京盛通印刷股份有限公司印刷
全国新华书店发行
版　次 2013 年 4 月第 3 版
印　次 2018 年 4 月第 6 次印刷
开　本 787 毫米×1092 毫米　1/16
印　张 17
字　数 680 千
定　价 39.80 元